AGARDograph Number

One Hundred and Thirty

Measurement Techniques
in Heat Transfer

The Advisory Group for

Aerospace Research and

Development of NATO

Editors

ERNST R.G. ECKERT

RICHARD J. GOLDSTEIN

School of Mechanical and Aerospace Engineering, University of Minnesota,
Minneapolis, Minnesota, U.S.A.

Printed and published by

Technivision Services
Slough, England
A Division of Engelhard Hanovia International Ltd.

International Standard Book No. 0.85102.026.7
Library of Congress Catalog Card No. 78-82419

Contents

Foreword

Textbooks on heat transfer usually concentrate on the analysis of heat transfer processes and either devote only a small amount of space to the discussion of measurement techniques or exclude this subject completely. On the other hand, special problems are encountered in heat transfer measurements and experience is required when accurate results are desired. For this reason, a special summer course on "Measurement Techniques in Heat Transfer" was held in June, 1968, at the University of Minnesota, organized by its Extension Division with lectures presented by the staff of the Thermodynamics and Heat Transfer Division of the School of Mechanical and Aerospace Engineering at the University of Minnesota, and by speakers from other organizations who are specialists in the subjects of their lectures. Papers based on these lectures have been collected at the suggestion of the Advisory Group for Aerospace Research and Development and form the content of this book.

Temperature measurements in a heat transfer situation should not be considered without a check on possible systematic errors caused by conduction, radiation or, in an unsteady situation, heat capacity effects. Section 1 discusses these errors and the means to calculate them. Section 2 discusses resistance thermometers, thermocouples, and pyrometers, their calibration and use for temperature measurements. The corresponding lecture at the summer course was given by G. W. Burns of the Heat Division, Institute of Basic Standards, National Bureau of Standards. Experimentation of heat transfer processes under cryogenic conditions requires special techniques for temperature measurements which are discussed in Section 3.

Optical techniques have the advantage that they do not disturb the temperature field in which the measurements are to be made. Optical systems based on variations in index of refraction are reviewed in Section 4. At high temperatures spectroscopy can be used as a diagnostic tool and this technique is discussed in Section 5. A very useful tool for the measurement of the enthalpy in a high temperature gas stream is the enthalpy probe discussed in Section 6.

The measurement of heat flux poses special difficulties as illustrated by the techniques described in Section 7. The close analogy between heat transfer, on the one hand, and mass transfer, on the other, makes it possible to obtain information on a heat transfer process by measurements in an analagous mass transfer situation. This offers an advantage where mass transfer experiments are simpler to perform or where clearly defined boundary conditions are required. The electrochemical method offers, in addition, the advantage that it requires only electrical measurements and that local and instantaneous measurements can be performed. Section 8 discusses such analogy measurements. Thermal radiation as a means of heat transfer has increased in importance in recent years because of the trend in engineering systems towards higher temperatures and because it is the only mechanism for heat transfer from vehicles moving through space outside the atmosphere. Techniques used for the investigation of thermal radiation are discussed in Section 9.

Knowledge of thermodynamic and transfer properties is required to calculate heat transfer in specific engineering problems as well as to generalize the results of heat transfer measurements with the use of dimensionless parameters. Measurements of such properties are often performed concurrently with heat transfer investigations and the techniques used for such measurements are discussed in Sections 10 and 11.

The measurement of fluid velocity is often fundamental to measurements of convective heat transfer. The laser-Doppler method described in Section 12 permits velocities to be inferred from the frequency shift of a scattered laser beam. The light beam, unlike a normal velocity probe, does not affect the flow field. Velocity measurements which are usually performed by hot wires at low temperatures require special instruments when they are to be performed at higher temperature levels. Such instruments are discussed in Section 13.

The authors wish to acknowledge the assistance of W.T. Pennell in the preparation of the manuscript for publication and of D.R. Pedersen in the preparation of the index.

We hope that this volume will be useful for those in the various branches of science and engineering who have to perform heat transfer measurements.

E. R. G. Eckert and R. J. Goldstein

Minneapolis, Minnesota
November, 1968

1

Error Estimates in Temperature Measurement

E. M.. SPARROW
Heat Transfer Laboratory, University of Minnesota, Minneapolis.

Summary

Section one describes computational models for estimating errors in temperature measurements in fluids and in solids. Consideration is given to measurements performed with thermocouples and similar probes. The various analytical models include heat transfer by conduction, convection, radiation, and viscous dissipation effects. Both transient and steady-state error estimates are made.

Introduction

It is widely recognized that the output of a sensor such as a thermocouple or a thermometer represents an approximation to the temperature at some location in a fluid or a solid. There are a variety of factors which can cause deviations between the probe output and the actual temperature at the point of interest, in the absence of the probe. First of all, the presence of the probe itself may modify the thermal conditions at the point and in its surroundings, thereby altering the temperature distribution. This happens, for instance, when heat is conducted to or away from a thermocouple junction through the lead wires. A second major factor is that the sensor may communicate with other environments beside the one whose temperature is being measured. For example, a thermocouple whose function is to measure the temperature in a flowing gas may exchange heat by conduction and radiation with the duct walls.

In addition, certain basic characteristics of the energy transfer and energy storage processes tend to favor the occurrence of errors in temperature measurement. One such characteristic is that convective heat exchange cannot take place without a temperature difference (i. e., the heat transfer coefficient is not infinite). Another is that viscous dissipation (aerodynamic heating) occurs in the boundary layer adjacent to a body situated in a high speed flow. In addition, in transient processes, the heat capacity of the sensor brings about a temperature difference between sensor and fluid.

The task of designing low-error temperature sensors is aggravated by the fact that near-perfect thermal insulators do not exist. This is in contrast to the situation in electrical measurements, where essentially perfect insulators are readily available.

By careful design, it is possible to reduce the measurement errors that result from one or more of the aforementioned causes. For instance, convective heat transfer coefficients can be increased by locally increasing the fluid velocity adjacent to the sensor. Similar desirable effects can be achieved by manipulating the size and the shape of the sensor, and radiative exchange with the surroundings

VISIBLE SURFACES

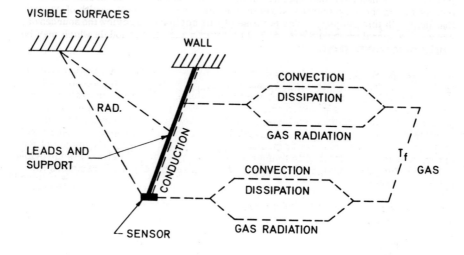

Fig. 1-1 Illustrative heat transfer paths for a temperature sensor in a gas flow

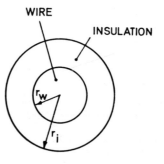

Fig. 1-2 Lead wire schematic

Fig. 1-3 Cross section of single insulated wire

can be diminished by shielding the sensor.   Design considerations are treated at length in the published literature, for instance, (1 - 4).

It will be assumed here that specific information related to probe design can be obtained from the aforementioned references and from the great wealth of papers that deal with this subject.   The purpose of this section is to review the sources of error in temperature measurement and to discuss analytical models which may be employed in the estimation of such errors.

A seemingly natural goal of analysis would be to furnish more or less precise correction formulas which would be used to adjust the output of the sensor and thereby provide accurate values for the temperature.   However, in practice the heat transfer problems involved with temperature probes are so complex as to defy precise analysis.   Even when large electronic computers are employed to facilitate the solution, relatively simple analytical models are still appropriate.   At present, a realistic goal of analysis is to furnish estimates of the order of magnitude of the errors that may be expected in temperature measurement.   Analysis also provides guidelines for probe design and suggests appropriate correlation parameters for calibration tests.

To illustrate the nature of the heat transfer problems that are encountered in analyzing temperature measurement errors, consider a sensor situated in a flowing gas stream such as that pictured schematically in Fig.1-1.   The sensor is positioned by some sort of support structure or by its own lead wires.   The dashed lines in the figure are intended to represent paths for energy transfer.   The sensor itself is shown to communicate by various paths to several environments which may in general have different temperatures.   By conduction through the support and/or its leads, the sensor communicates with the wall temperature at the point of attachment.   Radiation provides paths which connect the sensor to one or more visible surfaces (i. e., the wall or other structural elements) and to the gas stream (provided that the gas is radiatively participating).   In general, neither the visible surfaces nor the gas have temperatures which are spatially uniform.   Heat also passes between the sensor and the gas by convection.   In the presence of a high-speed flow, the convective transfer is modified by viscous dissipation in the boundary layer.

The support structure and/or the leads also exchange heat by radiation and convection with the walls and with the gas, and such exchanges may have a significant influence on the conduction heat transfer between the sensor and the wall.   Furthermore, the sensor itself may be a fairly complex unit with radiation shields, velocity shroud, etc.   Even if the sensor is a bare thermocouple junction, it represents a non-elementary geometrical configuration for each one of the transport mechanisms, conduction, convection, and radiation.

The foregoing discussion points up the great difficulty in making precise analytical corrections for temperature measurement errors and reaffirms that the essential role of analysis is to provide order of magnitude estimates.   This is the spirit that will be adopted in the forthcoming portions of the paper.

The quality of the error estimates furnished by analysis will depend on the faithfulness of the analytical model to the actual physical situation and the next few parts of this section will discuss illustrative analytical models relevant to temperature measurements of solids and of fluids.   In most cases, the discussion will be concerned with thermocouples; however, the basic ideas are applicable to other types of sensors.   Common to the analysis of both solid and fluid temperature measurements is the need for models of heat transfer in lead wires, and this is the next subject to be discussed.

Lead Wire Models

For the simplest viewpoint, lead wires may be envisioned as providing a heat conduction path between the temperature sensor and an isothermal zone located at the other extremity of the leads (Fig. 1-2). If the lead wires pass through a fluid, there will be heat transfer from the surface of the leads to the fluid by convection and perhaps by radiation. If the fluid is radiatively transmittant, heat is also exchanged by radiation between the leads and the surrounding visible surfaces.

The simplest lead is a single uninsulated wire. In view of the small diameter and relatively high thermal conductivity of such a wire, it is reasonable to neglect variations of temperature in the wire cross section. That is, the temperature may be regarded as a function of the axial coordinate x. The heat transfer in the lead wire may then be analyzed in a manner identical to that used for fins (5).

More commonly, the wire may be covered by an annular layer of insulation as pictured in Fig.1-3. With such a configuration, some alternatives present themselves for modeling the axial and the transverse heat transfer. For the wire itself, it is reasonable to assume that the temperature does not vary in the cross section, so, $T = T(x)$ alone. On the other hand, for the insulation, the temperature varies both radially and axially. An exact solution of such a heat conduction problem, with a convection and/or radiation boundary condition, is quite involved. Furthermore, such a solution probably is not justified by various other uncertainties (e.g., contact resistance).

A simple model, sufficient for most purposes, is to assume that all of the axial heat flow is confined to the wire, while the heat flow through the insulation is purely radial. Thus, if k_w and A_w respectively denote the thermal conductivity and cross sectional area of the wire and $T(x)$ is its local temperature, then the axial heat flow may be represented as:

$$Q_x = - k_w A_w \, dT/dx \qquad \text{(Eq. 1-1)}$$

On the other hand, the radial heat flow per unit length, dQ_r/dx, is given by:

$$dQ_r/dx = \frac{2\pi k_i (T - T_{surf})}{\ln (r_i/r_w)} \qquad \text{(Eq. 1-2)}$$

in which k_i is the thermal conductivity of the insulation and T_{surf} is the temperature on the outer surface of the insulation.

Under steady-state conditions, the dQ_r given by equation (1-2) is equal to the convective and/or radiative heat transfer at the surface; for instance, for convection:

$$dQ_r = h(2\pi r_i dx)(T_{surf} - T_f) \qquad \text{(Eq. 1-3)}$$

where T_f is the temperature of the fluid. By bringing together equations (1-2) and (1-3), one finds:

$$dQ_r/dx = (T - T_f)/R \qquad \text{(Eq. 1-4)}$$

$$R = \frac{1}{h \, 2\pi r_i} + \frac{\ln(r_i/r_w)}{2\pi k_i} \qquad \text{(Eq. 1-5)}$$

The symbol R denotes the thermal resistance, while $T - T_f$ is the temperature difference between the wire and the fluid.

By employing equations (1-1), (1-4), and (1-5), the insulated wire can be solved like a fin problem. It may be noted, in passing, that equation 1-1 may somewhat underestimate the axial conduction. An alternative representation, which overestimates Q_x, is obtained by replacing $k_w A_w$ by the quantity $\widetilde{kA}$, which is defined as:

$$\widetilde{kA} = k_w A_w + k_i A_i \qquad \qquad (\text{Eq. 1-6})$$

In thermocouple practice, a common lead configuration involves two wires and appropriate insulation as shown schematically in Fig.1-4. The wires have identical radii r_w, but different thermal conductivities k_{w1} and k_{w2}. Under the assumption that the wires have the same temperature at a given x, the axial conduction of heat may be represented as:

$$Q_x = - \widetilde{kA} \ dT/dx \qquad \qquad (\text{Eq. 1-7})$$

in which:

$$\widetilde{kA} = (k_{w1} + k_{w2}) \ A_w \qquad \qquad (\text{Eq. 1-8})$$

wherein axial conduction through the insulation is neglected. Adding terms $k_i A_i$ for the various layers of insulation to equation 1-8 overestimates the axial conduction.

To model the transverse conduction from the wires to the outer surface of the insulation, consider an equivalent composite cylinder consisting of a central wire and an annular layer of insulation. Let the outer and inner radii, r_2 and r_1, respectively, be defined as:

$$r_2 = (L_1 + L_2)/4 \ , \qquad \qquad (\text{Eq. 1-9})$$
$$r_1 = \sqrt{2} \ r_w$$

The radial heat flux through the insulation is given by equation 1-2, with r_i and r_w respectively replaced by r_2 and r_1. For convective heat exchange at the surface of the insulation, the radial heat flow dQ_r continues to be represented by equations 1-4 and 1-5, provided that the just-mentioned substitutions are made.

The foregoing computational models are representative of those that are employed to characterize the axial and radial heat conduction in lead wires.

Temperature Measurements in Solids

Attention will now be given to computational models for estimating errors in the measurement of steady-state temperatures of solids. Three illustrative situations will be discussed: (a) surface temperature of a relatively massive solid, (b) imbedded thermocouple in a relatively massive solid, and (c) measurement of the temperature of a thin plate. Errors in the measurement of time-dependent temperatures in solids will be considered in the last part of this section.

Surface temperature of a relatively massive solid

The physical situation under consideration is pictured schematically in Fig.1-5. A thermocouple is affixed to the surface of a relatively massive solid, well-bonded to the surface so that the thermal contact resistance is negligible. Alternatively, the thermocouple may be seated in a small hole drilled into the surface. The

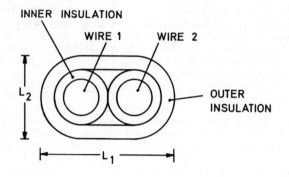

INNER INSULATION

WIRE 1   WIRE 2

L_2

OUTER
INSULATION

L_1

Fig. 1-4   Double wire configuration

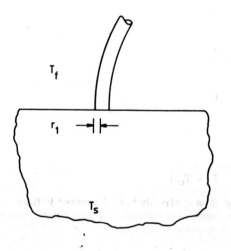

T_f

r_1

T_s

Fig. 1-5   Surface temperature measurement of a massive solid

thermocouple lead wires pass through a fluid whose temperature is T_f. The leads are sufficiently long so that, at some distance from the junction, they take on the fluid temperature T_f. It should be noted this arrangement, although common, is by no means optimum.

If the fluid temperature is lower than that of the solid, the thermocouple conducts heat away from the surface. Normally, the rate of heat loss due to the presence of the thermocouple is substantially greater than the convective heat transfer from the surfaces to the fluid. As a consequence, the temperature of the solid in the neighborhood of the thermocouple is depressed relative to that which would exist in the absence of the thermocouple. Thus, the thermocouple output is in error. If the fluid temperature exceeds that of the solid, then the thermocouple functions as an efficient pipeline through which heat flows into the surface, thereby causing a local increase in the temperature of the solid. Correspondingly, the thermo-couple reads high.

A simple model for estimating the temperature disturbance caused by the presence of the thermocouple will now be discussed. An upper bound on the temperature disturbance can be obtained by considering the problem wherein the interface between the solid and the fluid is perfectly insulated, so that in the absence of the thermocouple, the solid has a uniform temperature T_s. When the thermocouple is present, the temperatures at the junction and in the adjacent portions of the solid are altered. The departure of the junction temperature from T_s can be taken as an estimate of the measurement error.

Suppose that the thermocouple wires have an effective circular cross section of radius r_1. If there is one wire whose radius is r_w, then $r_1 = r_w$. When there are two wires, each of radius r_w, then r_1 is given by equation 1-9. It is assumed that the temperature at the circular area of contact between the thermocouple junction and the surface is uniform and is equal to T_{tc}.

Heat conduction theory (6) provides an expression for the rate of heat flow passing through an isothermal circular area situated on the otherwise insulated surface of a semi-infinite solid. If T_{tc} is the temperature of the circular area and T_s is the temperature of the solid at infinity, this heat transfer rate is:

$$Q = 4 \, r_1 k_s \, (T_{tc} - T_s) \qquad\qquad \text{(Eq. 1-10)}$$

where k_s is the thermal conductivity of the solid. Under steady state conditions, the heat transfer rate expressed by equation 1-10 must be equal to that conducted into the surface by the thermocouple leads which, from fin theory (5 and 7), is:

$$Q = \sqrt{kA/R} \, (T_f - T_{tc}) \qquad\qquad \text{(Eq. 1-11)}$$

The quantities $\widetilde{kA}$ and R have already been discussed in the preceding section for several types of thermocouple leads.

Upon eliminating Q from equations 1-10 and 1-11, one finds, after re-arrangement:

$$\frac{T_{tc} - T_s}{T_f - T_s} = \frac{1}{1 + 4r_1 k_s / \sqrt{\widetilde{kA}/R}} \qquad\qquad \text{(Eq. 1-12)}$$

in which $T_{tc} - T_s$ is the temperature measurement error. For a given value of $T_f - T_s$, the error is aggravated when k_s is small, $\widetilde{kA}$ is large, and R is small. These findings are in accordance with physical reasoning.

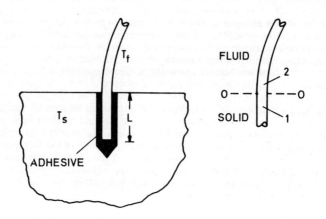

Fig. 1-6   Imbedded thermocouple in a massive solid

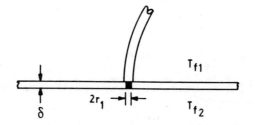

Fig. 1-7   Measurement of temperature of a thin plate

Imbedded thermocouple in a relatively massive solid

A schematic diagram of the problem being studied is shown in Fig. 1-6. A thermo-couple is situated in a hole drilled into the surface, with bonding being provided by some sort of adhesive (indicated as blackened in the figure), for example, epoxy. Upon emerging from the solid, the thermocouple leads pass through a fluid whose temperature is T_f. The leads are long enough to ultimately take on the fluid temperature T_f.

The thermocouple serves as a channel through which heat can flow into (or out of) the solid. Such heat flow gives rise to two sources of temperature measurement error. First, there is a raising (or lowering) of the temperature of the solid. Second, owing to the presence of the adhesive, there will be an additional temp-erature difference between the solid and the thermocouple junction. If the solid is a metal, then the second of these mechanisms is dominant. That is, as a first approximation, the temperature of the solid is assumed to be uninfluenced by the presence of the thermocouple. This is the case which will be considered here.

The analytical model and the resulting temperature error expression are due to Moffat (8). He envisions the thermocouple leads to be made up of two sections: (a) the segment that is imbedded in the solid, and (b) the segment that passes through the fluid. This is shown schematically at the right of Fig.1-6, o-o rep-resenting the dashed line location of the surface. Moffat begins by separately solving the heat conduction problems for regions 1 and 2 (see Fig.1-6), involving the temperature T_{oo} at the interface between the two regions. Then, the con-dition of heat flux continuity at o-o is imposed and by this T_{oo} is determined. Once T_{oo} is known, the temperature error at the junction is readily calculated. In region 1, the thermocouple leads behave like a fin situated in a uniform temp-erature environment (i.e., the solid at temperature T_s). The adhesive gives rise to a thermal resistance:

$$\ln(r_3/r_2)/2\pi k_a \qquad\qquad\qquad\qquad \text{(Eq. 1-13)}$$

in which k_a is the thermal conductivity of the adhesive, while r_2 and r_3 are, respectively, the outer radii of the thermocouple leads and of the adhesive. Then, the overall resistance R_1 for radial heat flow dQ_r/dx from the thermocouple wire (or wires) to the solid is:

$$R_1 = \frac{\ln(r_2/r_1)}{2\pi k_i} + \frac{\ln(r_3/r_2)}{2\pi k_a} \qquad\qquad\qquad \text{(Eq. 1-14)}$$

where r_2 and r_1 may represent equivalent radii when the thermocouple is com-posed of two wires and several layers of insulation (see earlier discussion).

If T_{oo} is the temperature at the plane o-o, then fin theory gives the following expression for the rate of heat flow across plane o-o into region 1.

$$Q_1 = \sqrt{\widetilde{kA}/R_1}\ (T_{oo} - T_s)\ \tanh(\widetilde{kA}R_1)^{-1/2}L \qquad\qquad \text{(Eq. 1-15)}$$

The quantity $\widetilde{kA}$ is the conductivity-area product for axial conduction through the thermocouple wires, and L is the length of the leads in region 1. Equation 1-15 neglects the axial heat transfer at the junction itself, but this can be included by employing an alternate expression from fin theory.

Region 2 has, in effect, already been considered in the already completed analysis of the surface-mounted thermocouple. By a modification of nomenclature in equation 1-11, the heat transfer passing across the plane o-o from region 2 is:

$$\frac{1}{\sqrt{\widetilde{kA}R_1}} \qquad\qquad \times L \qquad\qquad \tanh(mL) \qquad\qquad m = \sqrt{\frac{hP}{kA}}$$

$$Q_2 = \sqrt{\widetilde{kA}/R_2}\ (T_f - T_{oo}) \tag{Eq. 1-16}$$

The expressions for Q_1 and Q_2 must be equal, from which it follows:

$$T_{oo} - T_s = \frac{T_f - T_s}{1 + \sqrt{R_2/R_1}\ \tanh{(\widetilde{kA}R_1)^{-1/2}L}} \tag{Eq. 1-17}$$

Now, returning to region 1 and once again using fin theory, the temperature T_{tc} at the thermocouple junction can be expressed in terms of T_{oo} as follows:

$$\frac{T_{tc} - T_s}{T_{oo} - T_s} = \frac{1}{\cosh{(\widetilde{kA}R_1)^{-1/2}L}} \tag{Eq. 1-18}$$

Upon combining equations 1-17 and 1-18, one obtains an equation for the temperature error $T_{tc} - T_s$:

$$\frac{T_{tc} - T_s}{T_f - T_s} = \frac{1}{\cosh{(\widetilde{kA}R_1)^{-1/2}L}}\left[\frac{1}{1 + \sqrt{R_2/R_1}\ \tanh{(\widetilde{kA}R_1)^{-1/2}L}}\right] \tag{Eq. 1-19}$$

For a given value of $T_f - T_s$, the temperature error is accentuated by small imbedding depths L, large values of $\widetilde{kA}$, large values of the thermal resistance R_1, and small values of the thermal resistance R_2. These qualitative rules are physically reasonable.

Measurement of the temperature of a thin plate

Consider next a thin plate (thickness δ) situated between two flows, respectively having temperatures T_{f1} and T_{f2} (Fig.1-7). The corresponding convective heat transfer coefficients are h_1 and h_2. In the absence of the thermocouple, and assuming that the variation of the temperature across its thickness is negligible, the equilibrium temperature T^* of the plate is:

$$T^* = \frac{h_1 T_{f1} + h_2 T_{f2}}{h_1 + h_2} \tag{Eq. 1-20}$$

The effect of the thermocouple is to channel heat into (or out of) the plate, with the consequence that the temperature of the thermocouple junction and the adjacent portion of the plate is increased (or decreased). The corresponding temperature error has been calculated in (7, pp 173-9). If T_{tc} is the temperature indicated by the thermocouple and T^* is the plate temperature in the absence of the thermocouple, the error $T_{tc} - T^*$ is expressible as:

$$\frac{T_{tc} - T^*}{T_{f1} - T^*} = \left\{1 + 2\pi k_s \delta \epsilon\, r_1 \left[\frac{K_1(\epsilon r_1)}{K_0(\epsilon r_1)}\right]\frac{\sqrt{R/\widetilde{kA}}}{\tanh{(\widetilde{kA}R)^{-1/2}L}}\right\}^{-1} \tag{Eq. 1-21}$$

in which:

$$\epsilon = \sqrt{\frac{(h_1 + h_2)}{k_s\,\delta}} \tag{Eq. 1-21a}$$

The symbols K_1 and K_2 denote modified Bessel functions of the second kind. Numerical values of these quantities are listed in standard tables.

In deriving equation 1-21, it was assumed that only the actual thermocouple wire (or wires) is imbedded within the plate, that is, the insulation has been removed. Thus, for a single wire of radius r_w, $r_1 = r_w$, and for two wires, each of radius r_w, then $r_1 = \sqrt{2}\, r_w$. The quantity kA is the conductivity-area product for axial conduction in the thermocouple leads, while R is the thermal resistance for radial heat flow in the leads, both of which having already been discussed in detail. L is the length of the thermocouple leads, and k_s is the thermal conductivity of the solid. The relative temperature error (left-hand side of equation 1-21) is plotted in Figure 8-5 of (7). The figure shows that the error is accentuated at small values of both ϵr_1 and $k_s \delta \sqrt{R/kA}/\tanh(kAR)^{-1/2}L$.

Errors in measurements of unsteady temperatures

The estimation of errors in the measurement of unsteady temperatures in solids is a much more difficult task than is the estimation of steady-state temperature errors. A survey of published literature indicates that even a simple physical model leads to a formidable mathematical problem. The heart of the difficulty is that one must deal with partial differential equations even in cases where the spatial dependence is one-dimensional. Furthermore, owing to the thermal interaction between the sensor (e.g., thermocouple) and the solid, coupled pairs of partial differential equations are encountered. An analytical solution of such mathematical systems is possible only for the simplest conditions and even then, non-elementary mathematical methods are necessary. A published analysis for a semi-infinite body, subjected to a step change in its internal temperature distribution, and fitted with a surface-mounted thermocouple, typifies the mathematical task (9). Numerical solutions, carried out with the aid of a digital computer, appear to be more or less mandatory for time-dependent situations. Representative numerical solutions for temperature errors associated with imbedded thermocouples are reported in (10), (11) and (12).

It may be noted that the estimation of measurement errors for transient problems is by no means a casual undertaking, regardless of whether analytical or numerical solutions are contemplated. Each problem must be modeled more or less individually in order to justify the substantial solution effort that is required.

Temperature Measurements in Fluids

Consideration is now given to estimates of errors in temperature measurements in fluids, both under steady state and transient operating conditions. For the present, radiative exchange will be set aside. The role of radiation will be discussed subsequently.

Steady-state temperature measurements

The usual computational model employed to estimate the error in steady-state fluid temperature measurements envisions the thermocouple or other sensors to behave, in essence, like a fin. Although there are many variants depending on the specific application, the general nature of the problem can be illustrated by a diagram such as Fig. 1-8. The thermocouple leads (and/or support) are attached to a wall whose temperature is T_w. The fluid temperature is T_f. Owing to heat conduction in the leads, the temperature at the thermocouple junction will be between T_w and T_f, provided that the viscous dissipation is negligible (low Mach number).

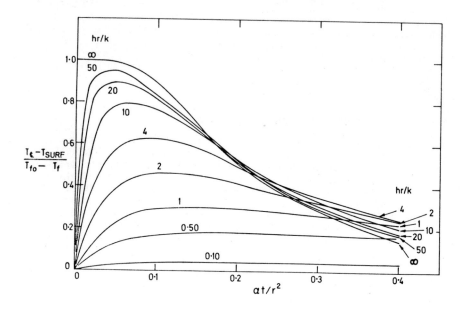

Fig. 1-8.   Schematic of fluid temperature measurement

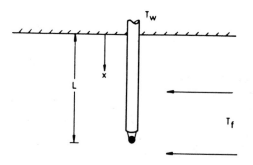

Fig. 1-9   Transient temperature difference between centerline and surface for a cylinder

For high-speed gas flows viscous dissipation plays an important role, such that in the absence of heat conduction in the leads, the thermocouple would read the recovery temperature T_r defined by:

$$T_r = T_f \left[1 + \mathcal{R} \frac{\gamma - 1}{2} M^2 \right] \qquad \text{(Eq. 1-22)}$$

where $\mathcal{R}$ is the recovery factor (a number on the order of unity), γ is the ratio of specific heats c_p/c_v, and M is the Mach number. In such a flow, the temperature sensed by the thermocouple junction lies somewhere between T_w and T_r.

The error analysis typically ignores possible variations of the heat transfer coefficient, recovery factor, and fluid temperature along the length of the leads. By applying fin theory and taking account of the viscous dissipation effects, the temperature at the thermocouple junction is expressible as:

$$\frac{T_{tc} - T_r}{T_w - T_r} = \frac{1}{\cosh(\widetilde{kA}R)^{-1/2}L} \qquad \text{(Eq. 1-23)}$$

in which the quantities $\widetilde{kA}$ and R have already been discussed in prior parts of the paper. Equation 1-23 also ignores axial conduction at the thermocouple junction itself, but this is probably a lesser cause for uncertainty than is the irregular geometry of the junction and the doubtful accuracy of the heat transfer coefficient in the junction region. Equation 1-23 can be employed for estimating the temperature error.

In the case of a non-dissipating flow (that is, $T_r \approx T_f$), it is evident that the temperature error can be minimized by making $L/(\widetilde{kA}R)^{\frac{1}{2}}$ as large as possible. There are, of course, certain natural limitations in such an undertaking. The wires must have a certain minimum cross section for strength; the insulation cannot be so thick as to provide a flow blockage; and the length is limited by a variety of considerations. One approach to increasing the length is to position the thermocouple leads axially in part of their passage through the fluid.

In a high-speed gas flow, dissipative effects more or less preclude the possibility of designing for equality of T_{tc} and T_f. Instead, one may attempt to design so as to minimize ($T_{tc} - T_r$) and then to apply equation 1-22 to determine T_f from T_r. To perform the latter calculation, it is necessary to know the recovery factor $\mathcal{R}$. Moffat (1, p. 555) has surveyed available experimental information and gives:

$$\mathcal{R} = 0.68 \pm 0.07, \text{ wires normal to flow} \qquad \text{(Eq. 1-24a)}$$

$$\mathcal{R} = 0.86 \pm 0.09, \text{ wires parallel to flow} \qquad \text{(Eq. 1-24b)}$$

These results are for gases whose Prandtl numbers are approximately 0.7.

In principle, the just-discussed error estimation could be improved by taking account of factors such as variations of fluid temperature, velocity and heat transfer coefficient along the length of the leads. However, in practice, this information is usually not known or is at best uncertain. As a consequence, such refinements are rarely incorporated into the error estimation calculations. Radiation effects are frequently accounted, as will be discussed later.

Unsteady temperature measurements

The traditional model for estimating errors in the measurement of unsteady fluid temperatures assumes negligible spatial temperature variations within the sensor and neglects lead wire conduction to or from the sensor. Thus, if M, c, and A_s are the mass, specific heat, and surface area of the sensor, the basic energy balance is (not including viscous dissipation effects):

$$Mc(dT_{tc}/dt) = hA_s (T_f - T_{tc}) \qquad \text{(Eq. 1-25)}$$

The temperature error $T_f - T_{tc}$ at any time is then equal to $(Mc/hA_s) (dT_{tc}/dt)$ and so, in principle, the error can be estimated from measured values of the temperature derivative dT_{tc}/dt.

For given time-variations $T_f(t)$ in the fluid temperature, the error in the thermo-couple output can be calculated by integrating equation 1-25. Some representative cases will now be discussed. Consider first a very rapid change (i.e., step change) in fluid temperature from T_{fo} to T_f. If the initial temperature of the sensor is also T_{fo}, then its response to the step change in fluid temperature is given by:

$$\frac{T_{tc} - T_f}{T_{fo} - T_f} = e^{-(hA_s/Mc)t} \qquad \text{(Eq. 1-26)}$$

It is customary to define the time constant τ of the sensor such that:

$$(T_{tc} - T_f)/(T_{fo} - T_f) = 0.5. \quad \text{Thus,}$$

$$\tau = 0.693 \, \frac{Mc}{hA_s} \qquad \text{(Eq. 1-27)}$$

For instance, for a cylindrical copper sensor of radius 0.508 mm and with h = 142W/m^2 °K, $\tau \approx 6$ seconds.

Although the time constant provides a convenient index of the response character-istics of a sensor, it may be necessary to make t considerably larger than τ to achieve the desired accuracy in the measurement of T_f. Thus, if it is desired that $(T_{tc} - T_f)/(T_{fo} - T_f) = 0.10$. then $t \approx 3.3 \, \tau$.

A second interesting case of potential practical interest is that in which the fluid temperature increases linearly with time, that is:

$$T_f - T_{fo} = \beta t \qquad \text{(Eq. 1-28)}$$

The thermocouple response to this imposed time-variation is obtained by solving equation 1-25, which gives, for times subsequent to an initial transient period:

$$T_{tc} - T_f = \beta \, \frac{Mc}{hA_s} \qquad \text{(Eq. 1-29)}$$

Thus, there will be a constant temperature error equal to $\beta(Mc/hA_s)$. Alter-natively, the quantity $\beta(Mc/hA_s)$ may be interpreted as the amount by which the thermocouple temperature lags behind the fluid temperature. Note also that $dT_{tc}/dt = \beta$, so that the temperature-time output of the thermocouple can in principle be employed to facilitate the estimation of the temperature error. For a given variation in fluid temperature, the error is diminished when M and c are as small as possible, and when h and A_s are as large as possible.

Periodic timewise variations of the fluid temperature are also of practical inter-est. Since any periodic function can be expanded in a Fourier series, it is natural to consider:

$$T_f = \overline{T}_f + \lambda \sin \omega t \qquad \text{(Eq. 1-30)}$$

By seeking a steady periodic solution of equation 1-25, one finds:

$$T_{tc} - T_f = \frac{-\lambda}{\sqrt{1 + (hA_s/Mc\omega)^2}} \sin \left[\omega t + \tan^{-1}(hA_s/Mc\omega) \right] \qquad \text{(Eq. 1-31)}$$

Evidently, only when $hA_s/Mc\omega$ is large will the measurement error $T_{tc} - T_f$ be small. On the other hand, when $hA_s/Mc\omega$ is small the sensor records the mean value of the fluid temperature, that is $T_{tc} \approx \overline{T}_f$.

The foregoing treatment of unsteady temperature measurements is based on the postulates that spatial temperature variations within the sensor are negligible, and that heat conduction to or from the sensor (through lead wires or supports) is very small. The validity of these assumptions will now be examined.

Consider first the question of spatial temperature uniformity. Suppose, for concreteness, that the sensor is a cylinder of radius r having thermal conductivity k and thermal diffusivity α. Initially, the sensor and the fluid are at the same uniform temperature T_{fo}. Then, at t = 0, the fluid temperature is step-changed to T_f and maintained uniform thereafter. If the possibility of radial temperature variations is admitted, the heat transfer process is governed by a partial differential equation in which the temperature is a function of the radial position and of time. This equation is to be solved subject to a convective boundary condition at the surface of the cylinder and to the above-mentioned thermal conditions at t = 0.

A solution of this mathematical system, given by Jakob (13, pp. 275-278), has been adapted to the problem of the temperature sensor by Clark (14). To characterize the extent of the spatial non-uniformity, he employs the quantity:

$$\frac{T_\ell - T_{surf}}{T_{fo} - T_f} \qquad \text{(Eq. 1-32)}$$

where T_ℓ and T_{surf} are, respectively, the temperatures at the centerline and the surface of the cylinder. A plot of this temperature ratio, taken from (14), is given in Fig. 1-8. For values of $\alpha t/r^2 > 0.4$, the curves can be extended by evaluating the equation:

$$\frac{T_\ell - T_{surf}}{T_{fo} - T_f} = \frac{2}{\chi_1} \frac{J_1(\chi_1)[1 - J_0(\chi_1)]}{J_0^2(\chi_1) + J_1^2(\chi_1)} e^{-\chi_1^2(\alpha t/r^2)} \qquad \text{(Eq. 1-33)}$$

where J_0 and J_1 are Bessel functions and χ_1 are constants, dependent on hr/k(bs), which are listed in Jakob's Table 13-9 (13). In the table bs is equivalent to hr/k.

With information such as Fig. 1-9 at hand, a judgment can be made about the correctness of neglecting spatial variations. In particular, if the magnitude of $(T_o - T_{surf})$ ⧸ $(T_{fo} - T_f)$ is much less than the magnitude of $(T_{tc} - T_f)/(T_{fo}-T_f)$ given by equation 1-26, then the neglect of spatial variations is justified. For instance, if the sensor is a copper wire of radius 0.508 mm and h = 142 watts/m²°K the aforementioned criterion is met.

Although the just-concluded examination provides information for the specific case of a step-change in fluid temperature, the same approach can be employed for the ramp and sinusoidal variations that were considered earlier. Having considered spatial temperature variations within the sensor, attention may now be directed to the matter of conduction to or from the sensor, through leads or supporting structure. To examine this point, a simple physical situation will be studied: a thermocouple such as that shown in **Fig. 1-8**. Initially the thermocouple, the fluid, and the wall are all at a common temperature T_{fo}. At $t = 0$, the fluid temperature is step-changed to T_f, while the wall temperature is maintained at its initial value. The temperature is assumed to be a function of axial position along the leads and of time (no spatial variations in the wire cross section).

A solution for the variation of the temperature at the thermocouple junction with time is (15):

$$\frac{T_{tc} - T_f}{T_{fo} - T_f} = \psi + (1-\psi)\, e^{-\frac{hA_s}{Mc(1 - \psi)} t} \qquad \text{(Eq. 1-34)}$$

where ψ is the steady-state temperature solution, an expression for which is given by the right-hand side of equation 1-23. By comparing equation 1-34, which includes conduction effects, with equation 1-26, which neglects conduction effects, it is seen that the omission of conduction is justified when $\psi << 1$, that is, when:

$$\cosh (kAR)^{-1/2} L >> 1$$

A more quantitative estimate of the influence of conduction can be obtained by numerically evaluating equation 1-34.

The Role of Radiation in Error Estimates

Up to this point, only heat transfer by conduction and convection have been included in the computational models employed for estimating temperature measurement errors. Now, consideration will be given to the contribution of thermal radiation. Although radiative transfer is more commonly encountered in situations in which the sensor and/or lead wires pass through a gas, there are also technically interesting applications involving partially transparent solids. It is widely recognized that, qualitatively speaking, the role of radiation will be small at moderate temperature levels and will become more important as the temperatures increase.

To provide some approximate quantitative guidelines, it is useful to estimate the magnitudes of the radiation heat transfer coefficient. Consider an enclosure whose walls have arbitrary radiation properties. If the walls are isothermal (temperature T_w) the thermal radiation within such an enclosure corresponds to black-body radiation at temperature T_w. The radiation heat loss per unit time and area of a small body situated within the enclosure is:

$$q_{rad} = \epsilon \sigma (T^4 - T_w^4) \qquad \text{(Eq. 1-35)}$$

in which ϵ and T denote the emittance and temperature of the small body. In computing radiation fluxes, all temperatures must be absolute temperatures . Equation 1-35 is based on the assumption that the small body has grey radiation characteristics.

An alternate form of equation 1-35 can be written in terms of the radiation heat transfer coefficient h_{rad}:

At top (handwritten annotations):

$$T = T_w + \text{...}$$

29

$$\frac{(T - T_w)(T + T_w)(T^2 + T_w^2)}{T - T_w}$$

$$(T^2 - T_w^2)(T^2 + T_w^2)$$

$$q_{rad} = h_{rad}(T - T_w) \qquad (Eq.\ 1\text{-}36)$$

where:

$$h_{rad} = \frac{\epsilon\,\sigma(T^4 - T_w^4)}{T - T_w} \qquad (Eq.\ 1\text{-}37)$$

If the temperature difference $T - T_w$ is substantially smaller than T_w, then h_{rad} becomes:

$$h_{rad} \approx 4\,\epsilon\,\sigma\,T_w^3 \qquad (Eq.\ 1\text{-}38)$$

5 °C

At any T_w, the largest value of h_{rad} is achieved when $\epsilon = 1$. At 278°K, $h_{rad} = 4.83$ watts/m²°K. This value of h_{rad} is comparable to heat transfer coefficients for natural convection in gases. It is, however, much lower than the heat transfer coefficients for most forced convection gas flows. Therefore, at this temperature level, radiation may be neglected except where natural convection processes are taking place.

The radiation coefficient h_{rad} increases markedly with increasing T_w, for instance, when $T_w = 555$°K, $h_{rad} \approx 39$ watts/m²°K. However, this is still well below forced convection coefficient for airflow across wires. When $T_w = 1110$°K, $h_{rad} \approx 310$ watts/m²°K, which is definitely competitive with coefficients for forced convection.

Radiation arriving at the sensor and/or its leads may originate at solid surfaces (e.g., duct walls) or in the adjacent gas. Many common gases such as air, nitrogen, oxygen, etc. are virtually radiatively non-participating except at very high temperature levels while others such as water vapor and carbon dioxide participate at intermediate temperature levels. Combustion gases and gas flows containing solid particles also may be radiatively active.

With respect to temperature measurement in gases, radiant energy arriving at the sensor and/or leads from solid surfaces tends to increase the error (if the temperature of such surfaces differs from the gas temperatures), while gas radiation tends to decrease the error. The role of these processes may be reversed in the case of surface-mounted or imbedded thermocouples for temperature measurement of solids. In cases where radiation is expected to cause a significant error in gas temperature measurements, it is common to shield the sensor so that its view of the error-inducing radiating solid surface is obstructed. In some temperature sensors, several such shields are employed.

Simple computational models for estimating temperature measurement errors in the presence of thermal radiation will now be discussed. For this purpose, consider an unshielded thermocouple immersed in a gas flow as illustrated in Fig. 1-8. Suppose first that the gas is radiatively nonparticipating. If the duct walls are isothermal at temperature T_w, then the thermocouple can be assumed to behave like a small body in a large isothermal enclosure, and the local radiative loss per unit area is given by equations 1-35 or 1-36. To facilitate the analysis, it is convenient to employ the radiation heat transfer coefficient and to neglect its variation along the length of the leads.

At any location x (see Fig. 1-8), the surface heat loss from the leads by convection and radiation is given by:

$$h2\pi r_2(T_{surf} - T_f) + h_{rad}\,2\pi r_2(T_{surf} - T_w) \qquad (Eq.\ 1\text{-}39)$$

where r_2 is the effective outer radius of the insulation and T_{surf} is the surface temperature of the insulation (T_{surf} is a function of x). It is convenient to re-phase the surface heat loss in terms of an effective heat transfer coefficient $\tilde{h}$ and effective environment temperature $\tilde{T}$. To this end, the surface heat loss may be represented as:

$$\tilde{h}2\pi r_2 (T_{surf} - \tilde{T})$$ (Eq. 1-40)

where:

$$\tilde{h} = h + h_{rad}$$ (Eq. 1-40a)

and:

$$\tilde{T} = (hT_f + h_{rad} T_w)/(h + h_{rad})$$ (Eq. 1-40b)

In terms of these variables, the radial heat transfer from the thermocouple wires, dQ_r/dx of equation 1-4, can be re-expressed as:

$$\frac{dQ_r}{dx} = \frac{(T - \tilde{T})}{R}$$ (Eq. 1-41)

in which:

$$R = \frac{1}{\tilde{h}2\pi r_2} + \frac{\ln(r_2/r_1)}{2\pi k_i}$$ (Eq. 1-42)

The foregoing formulation facilitates the direct application of fin theory, which yields the following expression for the temperature at the thermocouple junction:

$$\frac{T_{tc} - \tilde{T}}{T_w - \tilde{T}} = \frac{1}{\cosh(\tilde{k}AR)^{-1/2}L}$$ (Eq. 1-43)

from which the temperature error can be evaluated. If the conduction heat transfer at the thermocouple junction is negligible, i.e., if $\cosh(\tilde{k}AR)^{-1/2}L \gg 1$, then:

$$T_{tc} = \tilde{T} = (hT_f + h_{rad} T_w)/(h + h_{rad})$$ (Eq. 1-44)

The application of the foregoing error estimates requires that the numerical values of h_{rad} be known. In this connection, it is recommended that some reasonable initial guess be made for h_{rad}, and that this guess be refined using equation 1-37 in conjunction with the solution for the temperature distribution along the leads, that is:

$$\frac{T(x) - \tilde{T}}{T_w - \tilde{T}} = \frac{\cosh(\tilde{k}AR)^{-1/2}(L - x)}{\cosh(\tilde{k}AR)^{-1/2}L}$$ (Eq. 1-45)

The h_{rad} thus evaluated from equation 1-37 are a function of x and must, therefore, be averaged before being introduced into equations 1-40a and 1-40b.

The accounting of gas radiation introduces further uncertainties into the analysis because the radiative properties of gas bodies are not known to high accuracy. It is believed sufficient to treat the radiative interchange between the thermo-couple and the gas by employing a radiation heat transfer coefficient similar to that used for radiation between the duct surface and the thermocouple.

References

1.   Dahl, A.I., Editor, 'Temperature, its measurement and control in science and technology', Volume 3, Part 2, Section 4, Reinhold, New York (1962).

2.   Baker, H.D., Ryder, E.A., and Baker, N.H., 'Temperature measurement in engineering', Volume 1, John Wiley, New York (1953).

3.   Baker, H.D., Ryder, E.A., and Baker, N.H., 'Temperature measurement in engineering', Volume 2, John Wiley, New York (1961).

4.   Dean, R.C., Jr., Editor, 'Aerodynamic measurements', Chapter 2, MIT Press (1953).

5.   Eckert, E.R.G., and Drake, R.M. Jr., 'Heat and mass transfer', Chapter 3, McGraw-Hill, New York (1959).

6.   Gröber, H., Erk, S., and Grigull, U., 'Fundamentals of heat transfer', McGraw-Hill, New York, pp. 115-119 (1961).

7.   Schneider, P.J., 'Conduction heat transfer', Addison-Wesley, Reading, Massachusetts (1955).

8.   Moffat, R.J., 'Temperature measurement in solids: errors due to thermal resistance between the thermocouple and the specimen', personal communication, February 1968.

9.   Henning, C.D., and Parker, R., 'Transient response of an intrinsic thermocouple', Journal of Heat Transfer, C89, pp. 146-154 (1967).

10.   Beck, J.V., and Hurwicz, H., 'Effect of thermocouple cavity on heat sink temperature', Journal of Heat Transfer, C82, pp. 27-36 (1960).

11.   Beck, J.V., 'Thermocouple temperature disturbances in low conductivity materials', Journal of Heat Transfer, C84, pp. 124-132 (1962).

12.   Pfahl, R.C. Jr., and Dropkin, D., 'Thermocouple temperature perturbations in low conductivity materials', Paper 66-WA/HT-8, The American Society of Mechanical Engineers (1966).

13.   Jakob, M., 'Heat transfer', Volume 1, John Wiley, New York (1949).

14.   Clark, J.A., 'Transient temperature distribution within thermal sensing elements', personal communication, March 1967.

15.   Scadron, M.D., and Warshawsky, I., 'Experimental determination of time constants and Nusselt numbers for bare-wire thermocouples in high-velocity air streams and analytic approximation of conduction and radiation errors', NACA Technical Note 2599, January 1952.

Nomenclature

A   cross sectional area

A_s surface area

c   specific heat

h   convective heat transfer coefficient

h_{rad} radiative heat transfer coefficient

$\tilde{h}$ convective-radiative coefficient, eq. 1-40a

L   length

k   thermal conductivity

$\widetilde{kA}$ conductivity-area product for axial conduction

M   Mach number

M   mass of sensor

Q   heat transfer rate

Q_r radial heat transfer rate

Q_x axial heat transfer rate

q   heat transfer rate per unit area

R   thermal resistance based on dQ_r/dx, eq. 1-4

$\mathscr{R}$ recovery factor

r   radius

r_1 outer radius of an equivalent single thermouple wire

r_2 outer radius of an equivalent annulus of insulation

T   temperature

$\tilde{T}$ effective environment temperature, eq. 1-40

t   time

x   axial coordinate

α thermal diffusivity

γ ratio of specific heats

ϵ emittance

σ Stefan-Boltzmann constant

τ time constant

Subscripts

f   fluid

f o   initial fluid temperature

i   insulation

r   recovery

s   solid

surf   surface

t c   thermocouple

w   wire

w   wall

oo   interface

2A

Precision Resistance Thermometry and Fixed Points

H. F. STIMSON
Natural Bureau of Standards, Washington, D.C.

Introduction

The definition of the International Temperature Scale (1) gives the interpolation formulas relating temperature to the resistance of a standard resistance thermometer. The standard resistance thermometer and formula together provide the means for determining an unknown temperature relative to the ice point temperature from a determination of the ratio of two resistances of the thermometer, one at the unknown temperature and the other at the ice point. Precision resistance thermometry with a standard resistance thermometer, therefore, depends upon the precision and accuracy with which these ratios can be determined.

The standard resistance thermometer is calibrated at the ice, steam, and sulphur points for determinations of temperatures from the ice point to 630°C, and further calibrated at the oxygen point for determinations of temperatures between the oxygen and ice points. The accuracy of resistance thermometry depends fundamentally upon the accuracy with which the fixed-point temperatures can be realized. Precision resistance thermometry therefore requires not only precision measurements of resistances but also accurate realizations of the fixed points when the standard resistance thermometers are being calibrated.

The paper, "Precision Resistance Thermometry," at the temperature symposium held in New York in 1939, was contributed by E. F. Mueller (2). He mentioned the beginning of precision resistance thermometry in 1887, when Callendar's paper on resistance thermometry was published. He then described the procedures of precision resistance thermometry that were the best practice a half century later. The present paper describes some of the techniques which have been developed in the years since Mueller's paper was written.

At the time of the earlier symposium there had been some studies at the Massachusetts Institute of Technology (3), (11) on the reproducibility of the steam, sulphur and ice points which are the fixed points for the first resistance-thermometry part of the International Temperature Scale. Recognizing the importance of this work, the National Bureau of Standards began in 1942 to develop apparatus and techniques to improve the accuracy of the realization of all four fixed points which are the basis of both of the resistance-thermometry parts of the scale. The aim was to make the accuracy of realization of these fixed points comparable with the precision of measurement.

Recent Developments in Technique for Precision Determinations of Thermometer Resistances

Measurements of the resistances of platinum resistance thermometers are made with a small electric current flowing in the coils of the thermometers. This small current heats the platinum and raises its temperature above that of the

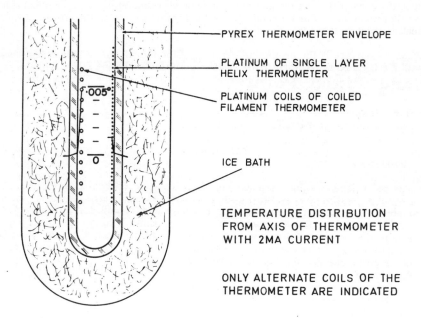

PYREX THERMOMETER ENVELOPE

PLATINUM OF SINGLE LAYER
HELIX THERMOMETER

PLATINUM COILS OF COILED
FILAMENT THERMOMETER

ICE BATH

TEMPERATURE DISTRIBUTION
FROM AXIS OF THERMOMETER
WITH 2MA CURRENT

ONLY ALTERNATE COILS OF THE
THERMOMETER ARE INDICATED

Fig. 2-A-1   Thermometers in ice bath

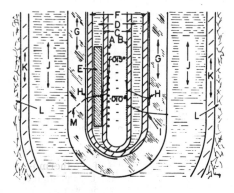

A = COILED FILAMENT
B = SINGLE LAYER
C = PYREX THERMOMETER
    ENVELOPE
D = WATER
E = METAL BUSHING
F = PYREX THERMOMETER WELL
G = ICE MANTLE
H = INNER MELTING
I = NO INNER MELTING
J = WATER IN CELL
K = CELL WALL
L = OUTSIDE ICE BATH
M = TEMPERATURE GRADIENT
    THROUGH MANTLE

TEMPERATURE DISTRIBUTION FROM AXIS OF THERMOMETER WITH 2MA
CURRENT

Fig. 2-A-2   Thermometers in triple point cell

surroundings.   The amount which the temperature of the platinum is raised depends upon the construction of the platinum thermometer and often on the environment of the thermometer.   For thermometry of the highest precision the effects of this heating must be taken into account.

When the surface of the protecting envelope of the thermometer is in direct contact with a substance which absorbs the heat of the measuring current, the platinum is heated only the amount of the temperature drop to the outside of the envelope itself. This condition might exist when the thermometer is directly in an ice bath or a stirred liquid bath.   (Fig. 2-A-1).   There are times, however, when this heat flows beyond the outside surface of the protecting envelope before it is absorbed. At these times there is a further temperature drop outside the envelope.   This condition exists, for example, when the thermometer is being calibrated in a triple point cell (described later. Fig. 2-A-2).   In this instance there is a temperature drop from the envelope to the inside wall of the triple-point-cell well through the fluid in the well, usually water.   There is a further drop in temperature through the glass of the well to the outside of the well and then another small drop through the film of water outside the well before the heat reaches the water-ice surface where the fixed point temperature is maintained by the liquid-solid equilibrium.

Sometimes the temperature drop from the outside of the thermometer envelope to the temperature of interest may be made smaller by the use of liquids or solids which improve the thermal contact.   In the triple point cell, for example, it is convenient to use water in the well of the cell.   Water is a much better thermal conductor than air but a free fitting metal bushing occupying most of the space in the water outside the thermometer coil helps a good deal more.   In the triple point cell, when 2 milliamperes are flowing in the thermometer coils, an aluminium bushing has reduced the temperature drop outside the thermometer envelope from about $0.0008°C$ to about $0.0002°C$.   In the benzoic acid cell (4) at about $122.36°C$ one cannot use water, so bushings are of great help (Fig. 2-A-3).   In the benzoic acid cells especially, it is wise not to use a bushing much longer than the coils because the upper parts of the cells cool much sooner than the lower parts. Glycerine or oil have been used in the wells of benzoic acid cells to improve the thermal contact, but care must be taken lest these conducting fluids undergo a chemical reaction when they are at these temperatures, and thus produce an independent source of energy to cause an erroneous determination of temperature. Obviously a thicker film of a given conducting medium will maintain a greater temperature difference across it.

Inasmuch as the platinum is heated by the measuring current it is necessary to wait till a sufficiently steady state of heat flow is established so that the resistance of the thermometer is constant enough for precision measurements.   The time that it is necessary to wait depends upon the temperature rise of the platinum, plus the various heat capacities and thermal conductivities of the parts of the thermometer and the surroundings that intervene between the platinum and the substance whose temperature is being measured.   The approach of the thermometer resistance to the steady state value, therefore, is not a simple exponential function of time.   For precision measurements it is necessary to have a continuous current flowing in the thermometer coil and to wait until the resistance of the coil has reached its final value within the desired precision of measurement.   Under different conditions this time has been found to range from a half to five minutes.

When the thermometer is to be used for precision measurements of temperature in places where the temperature is maintained beyond the outside boundary of the protecting envelope, the reliable way to make resistance determinations is to measure the resistance at two different currents and extrapolate to the resistance which the thermometer would have if no current were flowing.   In instances where the highest precision is not demanded the temperature drop outside the thermometer

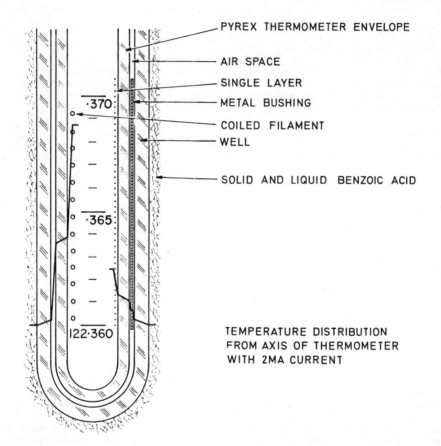

PYREX THERMOMETER ENVELOPE

AIR SPACE

SINGLE LAYER

METAL BUSHING

COILED FILAMENT

WELL

SOLID AND LIQUID BENZOIC ACID

·370

·365

122·360

TEMPERATURE DISTRIBUTION
FROM AXIS OF THERMOMETER
WITH 2MA CURRENT

Fig. 2-A-3   Thermometers in benzoic-acid cell

envelope may be small enough to be neglected. For these, the thermometer coefficients obtained with 2 milliamperes in the coils may be used. In the Callendar formula the alpha coefficient for the 2 milliampere current, however, will probably differ from the calibration at zero milliamperes by several units in the sixth significant figure. The delta coefficients will not differ significantly. During the past few years, certificates from the National Bureau of Standards have stated: "The following values were found for the constants in the formula:

$$t = \frac{R_t - R_o}{\alpha R_o} + \delta \left(\frac{t}{100} - 1 \right) \frac{t}{100},$$

in which t is the temperature at the outside surface of the tube protecting the platinum resistor - and R_t and R_o are the resistances of the platinum resistor at $t°$ and $0°C$ respectively, measured with a continuous current of 2.0 milliamperes."
In some instances, where the user needed to make measurements with higher precision, the alpha coefficients have been determined for the current extrapolated to zero. It is possible, however, as we shall see presently, to compute the difference in the alpha coefficient to a satisfactory approximation from a determination which one can make of the heating effect in an ice bath.

The alpha coefficient is defined by the equation $\alpha = (R_{100} - R_o)/100 R_o$. When a measuring current (for example 2 ma) is flowing in the coil the resistances R_o and R_{100} will be increased to $R_o + \Delta R_o$ and $R_{100} + \Delta R_{100}$. If we now call α_Δ the apparent alpha coefficient, at this measuring current, then:

$$\alpha_\Delta = \frac{(R_{100} + \Delta R_{100}) - (R_o + \Delta R_o)}{100(R_o + \Delta R_o)}$$

Performing the division indicated by the fraction we can write the equation in the form:

$$\alpha_\Delta = \frac{R_{100} - R_o}{100 R_o} + \frac{R_{100} - (R_{100}/R_o)\Delta R_o}{100(R_o + \Delta R_o)} = \alpha + \frac{\Delta R_{100} - (R_{100}/R_o)\Delta R_o}{100(R_o + \Delta R_o)}$$

With any given measuring current, the power dissipated in a coil is proportional to its resistance, so at $100°$ the power dissipated is greater than the power dissipated at $0°$ by the ratio R_{100}/R_o. At $100°$, however, the thermal conductivity of air is 30% greater than at $0°$ and the thermal conductivity of Pyrex glass is 13.5% greater. In thermometers of widely different construction the part of the temperature drop through glass from the platinum to the outside of the protecting envelope tube may range from 5% to 15% of the total drop. Although radiation from the platinum is a few times greater at $100°$ than at $0°$ it probably accounts for less than 1% of the heat transfer. The temperature drop from the platinum to the thermometer envelope tube, therefore, is predominantly through air so if we select the value 1.29 for the ratio of the average coefficient of heat transfer at $100°$ to that at $0°$ our computations probably will not be in error by more than one or two percent. We can, therefore, take $\Delta R_{100} = \Delta R_o (R_{100}/R_o)/1.29$. Since the value R_{100}/R_o is about 1.392 we can write:

$$\alpha_\Delta = \alpha + \frac{1.392 \Delta R_o (1/1.29 - 1)}{100(R_o + \Delta R_o)} = \alpha - \frac{0.313 \Delta R_o}{100 R_o} \quad \text{approximately.}$$

For two milliamperes current the values of ΔR_o for two widely different thermometers were found to be 460 microhms and 125 microhms respectively. The corresponding values for $-_\Delta$ are 53×10^{-9} and 15×10^{-9} respectively. We can get the significance of these values when we consider that 39×10^{-9} for $-_\Delta$ is equivalent to $0.001°$ in $100°$, hence for these thermometers the values for $-_\Delta$ are equivalent to about $0.0014°$ and $0.000°$ in $100°$ respectively. For one milli-ampere these values would be reduced by a factor of four.

In striving for a precision of a few microhms in the determination of the resistance extrapolated to zero current, it is necessary to control carefully the ratio of the currents used for the measurements and to consider the variance of the measure-ments at each of these currents. Thermometers having larger heating of the platinum at a given current require greater precision in the determination of the ratio of the two currents. Ordinary milliammeters are not sufficient for the high-est precision and an auxiliary potentiometer for setting the current is desirable. When using these measurements for extrapolation to zero-current determinations, it will be shown that precision in the resistance measurements at the lower current is more important than precision in the measurements at the higher current. Statistical theory shows that:

$$s_Y^2 = \left(\frac{x_2}{x_2 - x_1}\right)^2 s_{\bar{y}_1}^2 + \left(\frac{x_1}{x_2 - x_1}\right)^2 s_{\bar{y}_2}^2$$

where s_y^2 is the estimate of the variance of the zero-current resistance, $s_{\bar{y}_1}^2$ and $s_{\bar{y}_2}^2$ are the estimates of the variance of the means of the lower and the higher-current resistances respectively, and x_1 and x_2 are proportional to the power (current squared) put into the thermometer coils at the lower and higher currents respectively. The values of $s_{\bar{y}_1}^2$ and $s_{\bar{y}_2}^2$ can be determined by experiment.

It sometimes happens that $s_{\bar{y}_1}^2$ is greater than the $s_{\bar{y}_2}^2$ because the lower current is so small that the deflections of the balancing instruments are more difficult to detect. At different periods in the past we have used currents ranging from 1 and 1.41 ma to 2 and 7.5 ma but with the instrumentation used at the National Bureau of Standards it was found that the optimum value of $s_{\bar{y}_1}^2$ was for currents of about 2ma. With higher currents the amount of extrapolation to the zero-current resis-tance is greater and the determination of the ratio of the high to the low current is more important. A potentiometer of moderate precision should be sufficient, but the higher the current the more attention has to be given to the control of this current.

Let us assume that n observations are to be made to determine the resistance at zero current and of these n_1 are at the lower current and n_2 are at the higher. Having determined the estimates $s_{\bar{y}_1}^2$ and $s_{\bar{y}_2}^2$ by experiment we can choose the proportion of the observations that should be made at the two currents in order to get the smallest value for s_Y^2. Again using statistical theory, we find:

$$\frac{n_1}{n_2} = \frac{x_2 s_{\bar{y}_1}}{x_1 s_{\bar{y}_2}}$$

approximately. As an example let us assume that the currents are 2 ma and 5 ma. Then if we take, for simplicity, $s_{\bar{y}_1} = s_{\bar{y}_2}$ we have $n_1/n_2 = 25/4$ which is the ratio of the number of observations which must be made at x_1 to those at x_2 in order to get the best results. As another example let us assume with these same currents that $s_{\bar{y}_1} = 3s_{\bar{y}_2}/2$. We then have $n_1/n_2 = 25/4 \times 3/2 = 75/8$. In both of these examples it is evident that many more observations should be made at the lower current that at the higher in order to obtain the best precision with a given time spent in observing.

Thermometer Developments

In his symposium paper in 1939, Mueller mentioned the coiled filament thermometer construction described by C.H. Meyers (5). The purpose of this construction was to confine the resistor of the thermometer to a shorter length and a smaller diameter than had been throught practical for standard thermometers before. About 25.5 ohms at 0°C of 0.087 mm wire arc wound in a helix about 0.4 mm in diameter. This helix, in turn, is bifilar wound in a larger helix about 20 mm long which is supported on a mica cross within a Pyrex protecting tube, ranging from 7 to 7.5 mm outside diameter. Gold leads extend up the protecting tube about 43 cm to a head where the leads pass through a hermetic seal to copper leads.

In 1943 there came to the author's attention some other small thermometers which were made in Russia. These thermometers were intended for measurements of temperature in a range extending up to temperatures which are to high for mica to be used for supporting the coils. The resistor has a resistance of about 10 ohms at 0°C and is wound in a helix of about 0.6 mm in diameter. This helix is supported bifilarly on opposite sides of a twisted silica ribbon and the coils extend about 40 mm. The coils are enclosed in a fused silica protecting envelope of about 6 mm outside diameter. Platinum leads extend up to a head corresponding to that of the Meyers-type thermometers.

A platinum thermometer of small dimensions was described by C. R. Barber (6) of the National Physical Laboratory in 1950. Some of these thermometers had a resistance of about 28 ohms at 0°C. They were made of 0.05 mm wire wound, while hard drawn, on a 1 mm mandrel and supported inside a fine Pyrex tube of 1.5 mm inside diameter and 0.2 mm wall thickness. The fine tube is bent into the form of a U, the helix is held in place by fusing at the bottom of the U and 0.2 mm platinum extensions of the helix are sealed into the top of the U. The coils are in a space over 30 mm long. At the top of the U the platinum leads are fused to 0.5 mm gold leads which extend up to a head as in the other small thermometers. A 6 mm outside diameter Pyrex protecting envelope enclosed the leads and the U with the enclosed coils.

These three small thermometers, developed within the last 25 years, have proved their superiority for measuring temperatures in smaller diameter spaces than was heretofore possible. This superiority over the older type has been somewhat offset in some of these small thermometers by the disadvantage that the platinum temperature is not as near the temperature of the outside of the protecting envelope. To be sure, the resistance at any temperature can be extrapolated to that at zero current, as we have seen; but the precision does depend upon the amount to be extrapolated. In using these small coils some of the parts of the helices are several diameters of the wire away from the wall of the protecting envelopes, and furthermore the area through which heat flows to the protecting envelope is smaller in this type than it was in the older types. Meyers recognized this disadvantage in his coiled filament type of thermometer and developed another type to correct it. About 1943 he began making thermometers of this new design using 0.077-mm wire wound in a single-layer bifilar helix 22 mm long with the wire only 0.03 or 0.04 mm away from the inside wall of the protecting envelope. The helix is supported on a mica cross in U-shaped notches spaced about 0.25 mm on centers. The notches are about 1.5 diameters of the wire deep and just wide enough to allow freedom for the wire to adjust itself with a minimum of constraint. Gold leads 0.2 mm in diameter extend up the envelope to the head. In this type of construction the thermal contact of the wire with the envelope is so good that, when a current of 2 ma is in the coils, the temperature rise of the wire above the outside of the protecting envelope is less than 0.002°. In the other types of small thermometers, described above, the temperature rise ranges from 2 to 4 times as great.

One effect which must be guarded against in precision thermometry is the effect on the resistance of the thermometer coil caused by heat conduction along the leads. This effect is easily determined by experiment. One method is to pack the thermometer in a slush of ice and water till the ice is just above the coil of the thermometer. The resistance of the coil is then measured. Packing more ice up around the stem of the thermometer to increase the depth of immersion will change the resistance of the coil. This process is continued till further packing does not change the resistance by a significant amount. A plot of these data on semi-log paper shows the immersion necessary for the precision desired.

Thermometers with heavy gold leads in poor thermal contact with the envelope obviously will require greater immersion than those with light platinum leads near the envelope wall. The immersion necessary to reduce the effect to within the equivalent of $0.0001°$ on some of the small thermometers described above ranged from 11 cm to 26 cm from the ends of the protecting envelopes. Usually there is provision for sufficient immersion so that the lead conduction will produce no significant error in the determination of temperature, but this effect must be kept in mind for precision temperature determinations. Some special thermometers have been constructed where special attention was paid to thermal contact of the leads with the envelope wall in order to make the necessary immersion very small. Ordinarily this precaution is not demanded.

Thermometers for calorimetry at temperatures below the oxygen point are made of the coiled filament type and enclosed in platinum capsules, 5.5 mm in diameter and 48 mm long. When in use, these thermometers are usually soldered into the calorimeters with low melting solder so heat conduction outside the protecting envelopes is seldom a problem. Platinum leads are sealed through glass which covers the end of the platinum capsule. At the sulphur point, however, the glass seals become conducting and increase the difficulty and uncertainty of the calibrations at that temperature. The electrical conduction in the glass insulation of these resistance thermometers has been discussed by H. J. Hoge (7). In order to have thermal contact of the platinum wire with the envelopes of these thermometers at temperatures ranging down to near $10°K$ these capsules are filled with hydrogen-free helium containing some oxygen.

In Mueller's paper in 1939 (2) there was a speculation about changes in coefficients of a thermometer accompanying progressive changes in ice-point resistances. He stated "The changes of resistance which occur in the resistor of the thermometer are likely to be additive. Changes which affect the resistance of the thermometer at all temperatures in the same proportion are less likely to occur." This is to say $R_{100} - R_o$ was expected to be more constant than R_{100}/R_o. Since that time we have some evidence, with thermometers made of high purity platinum, that the ratio R_{100}/R_o remains constant within our precision of measurement even when the resistance of the thermometer at $0°C$ does increase by significant amounts. There is also come confirming evidence of this from other national laboratories. It appears, therefore, that changes affect the resistance of thermometers proportionally at all temperatures when the thermometers are of high purity platinum and well annealed.

R. J. Corruccini (8) on the other hand, has shown that rapid chilling of platinum does cause changes which are more nearly additive. He attributes these changes to strains set up by chilling because reannealing restores the platinum to the old condition. In general, however, it seems unlikely that standard resistance thermometers in protecting envelopes could be subjected to such drastic chillings as he was able to give to his platinum. We conclude, therefore, that additive changes are not likely in standard thermometers.

Bridge Developments

Since Mueller's paper (2) in 1939 two new bridges have been designed and constructed, and are being used for precision resistance thermometry. One is an improved Smith Bridge that is in use at the National Physical Laboratory and is described elsewhere (9). The other is a bridge which Mueller, using his many years of experience, designed after his retirement from the National Bureau of Standards. Prototypes of this design were delivered to the Bureau in 1949. Since an extensive description of this bridge is not in prospect in the near future a brief description will be given here.

The intention of the design was to make measurements possible within an uncertainty not exceeding two or three microhms. The bridge has a seventh decade which makes one step in the last decade the equivalent of ten microhms. One uncertainty was that of the contact resistance in the dial switches of the decades. Experience shows that with care this uncertainty can be kept down to the order of 0.0001 ohm. Switches made with well-planed copper links bridging well-planed copper posts and making contact with an excess of mercury have uncertainties of contact resistance of considerably less than one microhm.

In Mueller's design the ends of the equal-resistance ratio arms are at the dial-switch contacts on the one ohm and tenth ohm decades. He has made the resistances of the ratio arms 3000 ohms so that the uncertainty of contact resistance, 0.0001 ohm, produces an uncertainty of only one part in 30,000,000. For example, with 30 ohms, in each of the other arms of the bridge these two ratio-arm contacts should produce an uncertainty of resistance measurement of 1.41 microhms. The next largest uncertainty would appear to be in the hundredth ohm decade which has the largest steps of four Waidner-Wolff elements. In the zero position of this decade the 0.0001 ohm uncertainty in contact resistance is part of a shunt of over 20 ohms and produces an uncertainty of 0.4 microhm.

The 10 ohm decade has mercury contacts and the commutator switch has large mercury contacts. One new feature in the commutator switch is the addition of an extra pair of mercury-contact links which serve to reverse the ratio coils simultaneously with the thermometer leads; a feature suggested by Hoge, who was then at the National Bureau of Standards. This automatically makes the combined error of the normal and reverse readings only one in a million, for example, when the ratio arms are unequal by as much as a part in a thousand, and thus practically eliminates an error from lack of balance in the ratio-arms. It does not eliminate any systematic error in contact resistance at the end of the ratio arms on the decades, however, because the mercury reversing switch has to be in the arms.

The commutators on these bridges are made so as to open the battery circuit before breaking contacts in the resistance leads to the thermometer. This makes it possible to lift the commutator, rotate it, and set it down in the reversed position in less than a second and thus not disturb the galvanometer or the steady heating of the resistor by a very significant amount. In balancing the bridge, snap switches are used to reverse the current so the heating is interrupted only a small fraction of a second. This practice of reversing the current has proven very valuable. It not only keeps the current flowing almost continuously in the resistor but also gives double the signal of the bridge unbalances.

In striving for greater precision in resistance thermometry we may ask what our limit is. One limit which we cannot exceed is that imposed by the Johnson noise which exists in all resistors. The random voltage in resistors at 300°K is given by the formula $\delta V = 1.12 \times 10^{-10} \sqrt{R/\tau}$ where R is the resistance in ohms and τ is the time in seconds over which the voltage is averaged. The quantity, τ,

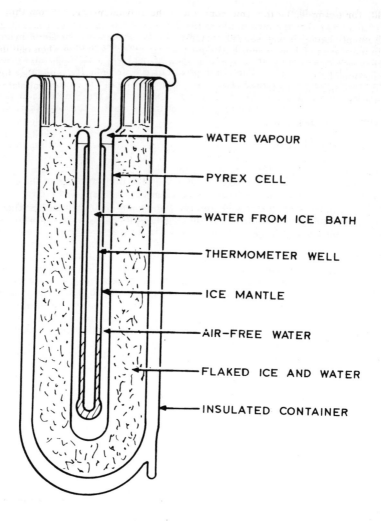

WATER VAPOUR

PYREX CELL

WATER FROM ICE BATH

THERMOMETER WELL

ICE MANTLE

AIR-FREE WATER

FLAKED ICE AND WATER

INSULATED CONTAINER

Fig. 2-A-4   Triple point cell

could, for example, be the time constant of the galvanometer. From this formula it would appear that the magnitude of the Johnson noise in a circuit including an instrument having a one-second period would be of the same order of magnitude as an unbalance of 1 microhm in the measuring arm of a bridge when one milliampere was flowing in a 25-ohm thermometer.   In practice there seems to be a discrepancy between this limit and what we realize.   We have found that for a net time of over a minute for observations at 1.5 and 2.5 ma to extrapolate to zero current, the determinations of the resistance of thermometers in triple point cells have a standard deviation of about 8 microhms in a single determination. We have not yet been able to attribute this discrepancy either to the bridge, the thermometer, the galvanometer, the triple point cell, or the observer and it remains one of the unsolved problems of precision resistance thermometry.

Fixed Points

For the calibration of platinum resistance thermometers on the International Temperature Scale four equilibrium fixed points are defined, one of which is a freezing point and the others boiling points.   For fixed points it is assumed that it is better to strive for realizations of the definitions rather than to follow recommended procedures which were set up as standard practice in the past.   At the National Bureau of Standards the triple point of water sealed in cells is used exclusively to derive the ice point.   The boiling points of sulphur and water are realized by active ebullition in boilers connected to a pressure-controlled reservoir of helium.   The pressure of the helium is controlled manually by means of a precision manometer, to give one atmosphere pressure at the level of the thermometer coils.   The boiling point of oxygen is realized in an apparatus which contains saturated liquid oxygen and its vapor at one atmosphere pressure.   The oxygen is separated from the helium of the reservoir by a thin metal diaphragm which indicates the balance between the oxygen and helium pressures.

Triple Point of Water

At the General Conference on Weights and Measures in 1948 the following resolution was adopted:

"With the present-day technique, the triple point of water is susceptible of being a more precise thermometric reference point than the 'melting point of ice.'

"The Advisory Committee considers, therefore, that the zero of the thermodynamic centrigrade scale should be defined as being the temperature 0.0100 degree below that of the triple point of pure water."

The triple point of water has been realized for the past several years in glass cells of about 5 cm in diameter with reentrant coaxial walls for the thermometers about 39 cm long and 1.3 cm in inside diameter.   Figure 2-A-4 shows a sectioned drawing of a triple point cell in an ice bath.   Extending up from the cell is a tube which is sealed off above the cell after filling with gas-free distilled water.   Below the sealing-off point is a side tube, extending horizontally which serves as a handle for lifting and turning the cell and also for supporting the cell when it is packed in a bath of flaked ice and water.

After the cells are blown and annealed they are cleaned with acid and distilled water and then steamed for several days until the condensed steam on the walls runs down in a continuous film over the entire inner surface.   They are then connected to a still which removes 99.9 per cent of dissolved gases from distilled water. They are evacuated and filled with water to within about 2 cm of the top and sealed off.

To prepare the cell for measurements it is first immersed into an ordinary ice bath for several minutes to cool the cell and its contents. A mantle of ice from 3 to 10 mm thick is then frozen onto the outside of the well. One procedure for freezing the ice mantle is to dry the well and keep it filled with crushed dry ice (solid CO_2) until the ice mantle is thick enough. This takes about thirty minutes. When the cooling with dry ice is first started it may take a minute or two to init-iate freezing, crystals first appear as fine needles along the outside of the well. As cooling is continued these initial crystals disappear and a clear glass-like mantle builds up. When sufficient ice has been frozen on the well, the dry ice is withdrawn and the cell immersed below the water level in the ice bath so that ice-cold water fills the well in order to improve the thermal contact of the thermometer with the water-ice interface.

The process of freezing purifies the water and concentrates the impurities in the water ahead of the ice as it forms on the outside surface of the ice mantle. These concentrated impurities lower the temperature on the outside mantle surface by a significant amount unless the water was very pure before freezing. If, now, a warm tube is immersed into the well for a few seconds, enough of the pure ice next to the well will be melted to free the mantle and provide a new water-ice interface. It is easy to see when the ice mantle is free by giving the cell a quick rotation about the axis of the well and noting whether or not the mantle rotates with the cell. This new water-ice surface provides the temperature for calibrating thermometers. (Fig. 2-A-4).

Inner melting is believed to be very valuable for obtaining reproducibility of temperature as freezing purifies the sample from the well outward and inner melt-ing produces liquid from ice which is much purer than the water outside the mantle. This means that less effort has to be expended in preparing and filling the cells than would be necessary if other procedures for freezing were used. Experience shows that the inner melting procedure, in the cells at the National Bureau of Standards, provides temperatures which are as identical to each other and as reproducible as we are now able to differentiate temperatures, namely, within about $0.00008°C$.

Temperatures at the outside of thick mantles in some cells about two years old were found to be about $0.002°$ low, when first determined within a half hour of freezing, but were rising for several hours thereafter. These low temperatures are believed to be caused by impurities (including dissolved glass) and the rising temperatures by diffusion of the concentrated impurities away from the outside surface of the mantle into the water. The lower temperature at the outside of the mantle causes no error when the inner melting technique is used as small transfers of heat caused by radial temperature gradients merely cause freezing or melting at the water-ice interfaces and do not change the temperature by sig-nificant amounts.

Previous investigators have frozen the water in their triple point cells by super-cooling until spontaneous freezing fills the cells with mush ice. When the water in these same NBS cells was spontaneously frozen, the temperatures were a few ten-thousandths of a degree low, presumably due to impurities. This result again emphasizes the value of the simple inner-melting technique for obtaining reproducible temperatures.

Precision Manometer

The precision manometer at the National Bureau of Standards was designed for precision gas-thermometer measurements. The apparatus consists of two large cells for mercury surfaces connected by an articulate tube and supported on a base

by long and short columns of end standards.   The aim in the design was to make
this manometer capable of determining pressure to an accuracy of one part in a
million but this accuracy is not demanded by present-day precision thermometry.
Figure 2-A-5 shows a diagram of the manometer at the left connected to the steam
point boiler, the oxygen point apparatus, and the sulphur point boiler.

The pressure which is measured with this manometer is balanced by a column of
mercury.   Pressure is the product of the height of the column multiplied by the
density of the mercury and by the gravitational acceleration.   It is believed that
the height of the column can be determined with this apparatus to the accuracy of
calibration of the end standards, which heretofore has been about two parts in a
million.   The value of the density of mercury at $0°C$, according to recent reports,
may be uncertain to one or two parts in 100, 000 but it is the opinion at the National
Bureau of Standards that differences of more than about four parts in a million
are not to be expected between different samples of virgin mercury, gathered
anywhere on the earth.   The value for the gravitational acceleration may be
uncertain by nearly one part in 100, 000 but values relative to the value determined
at Potsdam are known with high precision.   For these reasons it is believed that
the reproducibility of the steam point in different laboratories could be in the order
of $0.0001°C$, inasmuch as this corresponds to about four parts per million in
pressure.

The principal features of this manometer, which make such precision possible, are
the large cells for the mercury surfaces to eliminate the uncertainties of capillary
depression, an electrostatic capacitance scheme for determining the height of the
mercury surface, and the use of end-standards 2.4 cm square for supporting
these cells.

The mercury cells (B) (Fig. 2-A-5) are about 7.3 cm in inside diameter, and are
made of steel with the tops and bottoms about 2 cm thick, thick enough to prevent a
significant flexure by a change of pressure of one atmosphere.   A steel tube (D)
about 3 mm inside diameter permits mercury to flow from one cell to the other,
having three joints with horizontal axes, the "shoulder," "elbow," and "wrist"
joints, to permit raising the upper cell to the desired height.

Both cells are supported on a cast iron base by Hoke gage blocks (A) which are
end-standards as precise as the better-known Johansson blocks, but being square,
are more suitable as columns for supporting the cells.   The ends of these blocks
are accurately parallel.   The columns of blocks are 18 cm apart at the base.
One block is fastened securely to the bottom of each cell and another block is
fastened securely to the base at the bottom of each column.   The two blocks
under the lower cell are seldom moved but the intermediate blocks in the column
supporting the upper cell are changed every time the length of the column is
changed.   The top surface of the supporting block for the upper cell was carefully
leveled and the set has enough blocks to permit a column of blocks to be selected
having a nominal height of any desired ten-thousandth of an inch.   Blocks of this
type can be wrung together with a separation of less than a hundredth of a micron.
In 14 years the blocks have been calibrated a few times at the National Bureau of
Standards and none has changed for more than four parts in a million.

Above the mercury there is an electrically insulated steel plate (E) 3.5 cm in
diameter for determining the height of the mercury in the cells.   The electrostatic capacitance between the plate and the mercury is part of the capacitance in
one of the two circuits of a beat frequency oscillator.   In a shielded chamber
above the cell is a reference capacitor, (F) adjusted so that its capacitance is
equal to the capacitance between the plate and the mercury for the desired height
of the mercury.   A pneumatic mercury switch (G) permits the interchange of

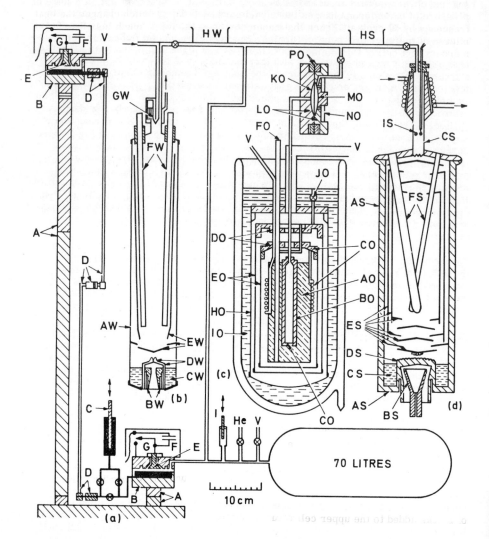

Fig. 2-A-5 Standard oxygen point, steam point and sulphur point apparatus

(a) Manometer (b) Steam point boiler (c) Oxygen point apparatus
(d) Sulphur point boiler.

C. Mercury pump I. Helium pump V. Vacuum line
For other annotations see text

these two capacitors in a few seconds. It has been found convenient to have the spacing of the mercury from the plate about 0.15 mm. At that height, a change of pressure of one micron changes the capacitance by 0.2 $\mu\mu$f which changes the beat frequency by 60 cycles; hence the manometer is sensitive to much less than 0.1 micron of mercury pressure. Ripples are always present on the surface of the mercury in a cell of this diameter (7.3 cm) at any place within the National Bureau of Standards. Their wavelength is small in comparison with the radius of the plate and the effect of the crests of ripples compensates for that of the troughs. No effect on the capacitance is noticeable until the mercury approaches to within 0.1 mm of the plate.

It is obvious that temperature control is important not only for the length of the steel blocks but especially for the density of mercury. The combined effect is such that a change in pressure of one part in a million is produced by a change in temperature of about 0.006°C. To provide for temperature control the mano-meter is mounted on a low pier in a cellar below the basement floor where temp-. erature fluctuations are minimized. It is about 4.5 meters deep, 4.3 meters long and 2.1 meters wide and the manometer is operated by remote control. The air is circulated in the cellar and the relative humidity reduced below 50 per cent by passing it over refrigerated coils and reheating it.

At the base of the manometer a platinum resistance thermometer is placed in a copper block. On the surface of this block are placed reference junctions of three sets of multiple-junction thermocouples for determining the mean temp-erature of three different parts of the mercury column. There are twelve measuring junctions in series on the manometer arm from the shoulder to the wrist joint, six junctions on the tube from the lower cell down to the shoulder joint, and three junctions from the wrist joint up to the upper cell. These pro-visions make it possible to determine the mean temperature of the mercury itself, and, should the temperature not be the same on the tubes to the upper and lower cells, the difference in density can be accounted for. The temperature of the manometer ordinarily drifts only a few hundredths of a degree per day, a rate is so small that occasional measurements taken during the day are sufficient for corrections. The temperature of the blocks is assumed the same as the mean temperature of the mercury.

The procedure for obtaining the desired pressure by means of the height of mercury column is, first, to determine the zero level, and then to increase the height of the upper cell by the height of the desired column. For the zero level, the proper blocks can be found and the reference capacitance made equal to the mercury capacitance on each cell with both cells evacuated. When this equality of capa- . citances is again realized, with pressure in the lower cell but with the upper cell still evacuated, the height of the mercury column is the same as the extra height of blocks added to the upper cell column.

Since the two columns of gage blocks are spaced 18 cm apart it is important to know whether they maintain their relative heights. For this reason the zero level of the manometer has been followed for several days before and after the time when the manometer is used at one atmosphere. Experience shows that the drift in zero level is less than one micron. The effect of the change of level caused by the extra weight of 30 inches of gage blocks (about 3.4 kg) was deter-mined experimentally and found to be about 0.2 micron. The compression of the 30 inches of gage blocks by half the weight of these blocks and by the weight of the cell with its mercury contents was found to be about 0.3 micron. These effects are small but are accounted for.

To control the pressure of the helium there are needle valves for admitting or removing helium from the lines. Small changes in the helium pressure are controlled by a piston about 0.75 cm² cross section area which can be moved in or out of a small chamber in the helium line at the control bench, 4.5 meters above the manometer. The piston is moved by a screw of such pitch that one turn changes the volume connected to the helium line by about one part in a million. The helium pressure may be affected by small drifts in the temperature of the 70-litre reservoir or by larger and more rapid changes in the temperature of the tubes above the floor. The pressure changes are indicated by the beat frequency oscillator and usually are so small they can be compensated for by a fraction of a turn of the piston screw. Such sensitive control of pressure enables the operator to keep the pressure controlled to within a part in a million for as long a time as is needed for thermometer calibrations.

Steam Point Boiler

The steam point apparatus is a closed system with helium gas transmitting the water vapor pressure to the precision manometer (Fig. 2-A-5). The boiler (AW) is made of copper heavily tinned on the inside to prevent contamination of the water and is a tube 8.7 cm in diameter and 46 cm long, closed at the ends. There are six reentrant thermometer wells (FW) 35 cm long extending from the top cap down into the vapor space. These wells are of various diameters of thin-wall copper-nickel tubing which is also tinned on the surface exposed to the water. They are separated where they extend through the top but at the bottom they are as close together as is convenient without touching. Surrounding the wells is a conical radiation shield of tinned copper, sufficiently open at the top and bottom for free passage of vapor.

At the bottom of the boiler there is a reentrant copper-nickel heater dome with a shallow conical cap at the top. Inside the dome is a heater (BW) wound on mica over a copper spool which is enlarged at the top for a short length for soldering. By this construction most of the heating power is supplied in a zone just below the surface of the water (CW) in the annular space at the bottom of the boiler surrounding the dome. On the outside of the dome is a single layer of closely spaced vertical silver wires (DW) about 0.4 mm in diameter bound to the surface with three horizontal hoops of silver wire. The wires extend from the bottom to about 2 cm above the top of the dome and there the ends are brought together in a bundle around the axis. This construction was adopted for the purpose of holding a small residue of vapor in the cusp-shaped spaces between the dome and the wires, to avoid explosive vaporization. It has proved most effective.

Below the radiation shield around the thermometer wells are two shallow conical shields (EW) which serve to prevent direct radiation from the walls to the outside walls of the boiler and also serve to drain condensed water from the boiler wall to the axis where it drips onto the bundle of silver wires at the top of the dome. By this construction it is believed that these wires are kept wet continually during operation and there are no exposed surfaces at temperatures above the saturation temperature.

Since the temperature of the boiler is about 75° above that of the room, considerable heat flows out through the boiler wall. This heat is supplied on the inside of the boiler by condensation of the water vapor to liquid which flows down the wall in a film computed to be 0.05 mm thick. Assuming the liquid-vapor surface to be at the saturation temperature there is a temperature gradient through the liquid film so that the inside wall of the boiler is probably less than 0.1 degree below. Since the boiler is a little below the saturation temperature, the radiation shield radiates a small amount of energy mostly received by condensation of vapor on both its inner and outer wall surfaces. The radiation shield, is therefore nearer to the saturation temperature than the wall of the boiler is by a factor of several hundred. The wells, (FW) in turn, radiate heat to the radiation shield; but, since the temperature of the radiation shield itself is very near the saturation temperature, the wells certainly should be at the saturation temperature within our precision of temperature measurements. Indeed, computations indicate that there might have been sufficient attenuation by the wells alone but the radiation shields provide enough extra attenuation to give little chance that the thermometer wells are at a significantly low temperature.

From the top of the boiler the excess vapor flows up through a short tube, about 1.8 cm inside diameter, to a condenser (GW) which starts above the boiler and is cooled by ice-cold water first flowing in a core on the axis and then in a water jacket on the outside of the 1.8 cm tube. The inner and outer water-cooled surfaces are about 3.7 cm long. This construction provides an annular space with a radial separation of about 0.4 cm for the vapor to flow through on its way to the cold walls where it is condensed to liquid. In this space the water vapor meets helium from above. The level of this interface depends on the amount of excess water vapor that must be condensed and the area over which condensation is taking place is determined by the temperature of the metal, the thickness and thermal conductivity of the liquid film, and the power flowing through this film. The liquid-vapor surface may be assumed to be at the saturation temperature.

Above the condenser, the helium extends up in a tube which is soldered to the incoming cold water tube where there is a shut-off valve. It then extends in a 0.5 cm horizontal tube that is soldered to a copper tray for dry ice (solid CO_2) (HW) and down to the manometer and a 70 litre helium reservoir on the pier in the cellar.

The radiation shields and wells in the boiler provide such effective protection against a low temperature that the question arose whether or not the wells might be superheated by the measuring current in the thermometers and the temperature be above the saturation temperature. To test this, two strips of silver gauze were placed so that one drains the liquid from the axial condenser surface to the surface of one well and the other drains the liquid from the outer condenser surface to another well. Thermometers interchanged from these wells to wells without draining have, so far, failed to indicate any difference in temperature depending on the wells. This indicates not only that the liquid film running down the wells has approached the saturation temperature but also that no superheating exists on the other wells.

On the outside the boiler is insulated by two coaxial radiation shields made of aluminium-coated paper and these are enclosed in a metal cover. This construction gives thermal insulation so that only about 70 watts of power are necessary to maintain the boiler at 100°C. The excess power goes to maintaining a flow of vapor into the condenser to meet the helium. It is common practice to use 125 watts in the boiler at the steam point.

Since the steam point is defined as the temperature of equilibrium between liquid and its vapor at 1 atmosphere pressure it is necessary to determine this pressure at the height of the center of the thermometer coils. The accounting for pressure considers the fluid heads of columns of water vapor, helium, and liquid mercury at their respective temperatures and the saturation pressure of mercury vapor at the upper cell temperature. Increasing the power input to the boiler increases the flow of water vapor into the condenser and raises the helium because more surface is required for condensation of the water vapor. This increases the pressure a little because the head of water vapor is greater than that of helium. The more noticeable change, however, is the volume of helium which must be withdrawn from the system to maintain the pressure constant.

Some flow into the condenser is necessary to oppose diffusion of helium down to the level of the thermometer coils.   Helijm near the thermometer wells would decrease the water-vapor partial pressure and hence the temperature and for this reason the tube to the condenser is not large.   The fact that helium is lighter than water vapor is favorable for avoiding convective instability.   Too great an excess of power can be undesirable, because it increases both the length and the velocity of the stream of vapor ascending into the condenser, increasing the head loss due to viscous or turbulent flow.   Experience shows, however, that the excess power can be increased by·100 watts without producing any significant error in the determination of temperature near 100°C, although these effects become significant at measurements in the neighborhood of 30°C.

Sulphur Point Boiler

In the text of the 1927 International Temperature Scale (10) the recommended experimental procedure for the sulphur point was specified in considerable detail. At that time the precision of temperature realization at the sulphur point was considered good when it was in the order of 0.01°.   Since that time it has been demonstrated that a greater precision is attainable when the sulphur boiler is connected to a closed system.   This led in 1948 to the definition of the sulphur point temperature as 444.600°C, (1) where the last figure only represents the degree of reproducibility of that fixed point.   A temperature change of 0.001° at this point corresponds to a change of pressure of about 10 microns of mercury.

In 1951 a closed-system sulphur boiler (AS) was completed at the National Bureau of Standards and connected to the precision manometer.   In the design of this boiler the same principles were used that proved successful in the steam boiler. The liquid and vapor sulphur are exposed only to 2S aluminium (the purest commercial grade).   The boiler was constructed from sheet nearly 1 cm thick, is 45 cm tall and 13 cm in inside diameter.   The entire apparatus was welded together by means of an inert-gas arc using welding rolds of the same 2S aluminium.

At the bottom is a heater dome analogous to that in the steam boiler.   It is surrounded by a single layer of closely spaced vertical aluminium wires (DS) 1.5 mm in diameter, analogous to the silver wires in the steam boiler and also effective for avoiding explosive vaporization.   Heat for boiling is supplied by a radiant heater (BS) and about 420 watts are normally used.   On the boiler itself is wound an additional heater with a capacity of about 1000 watts which aids in raising the temperature of the boiler and contents from room temperature to near the sulphur temperature in about an hour.   As this is approached the power in this heater is reduced until the whole load can be taken on the radiant heater.   The heat conducted away from the boiler itself is about 380 watts when the steady date has been established.   (CS) is liquid sulphur.

Ten thermometer wells (FS) of various sizes extend down from the top into the vapor space.   The axes of these wells approach each other as they extend down into the vapor space so they are closest together at the level of the centres of the thermometer coils.   Stainless steel liners 0.25 mm thick were drawn with the aluminium tubing for the thermometer wells.   These liners serve not only to stiffen the wells but also to prevent the aluminium from rubbing off onto the protecting tubes of the thermometers when they are hot.

Between these wells and the walls of the boiler are two cylindrical radiation shields (ES), at the top there are four, and at the bottom six conical radiation shields (ES) alternately diverting the fluid flow to and away from the axis yet preventing direct radiation away from the wells.   These shields are spaced not less than 9 mm apart which should be ample to avoid any significant drop in pressure of the vapor as it enters these spaces. As it was found for the steam boiler, computations indicate that one less shield might have been sufficient, so with the present number of radiation shields, there is little chance that the wells containing the thermometers are at a temperature significantly lower than saturation temperature.

On the axis above the top of the boiler is a stack, (GS) 1.9 cm inside diameter, for condensing the excess of sulphur vapor. In all, the stack extends up with this diameter nearly 18 cm above the body of the boiler. For about 9 cm above the top of the boiler the stack has a wall thickness of only about 1 mm. Above this thin section is welded a thick section on which is turned a cone about 5.3 cm long with a taper of 1 in 10 from the axis. On this cone there rests a sleeve of brass to which are soldered several turns of copper tubing for cooling water. Above the cooling section is a cap, sealed with a Teflon gasket, from which a tube leads away to the manometer through a dry ice trap (HS). Down through this cap there also extends an aluminium tube, about 4 mm in diameter, carrying a pair of thermoelement wires (IS) to a ring of aluminium within the thin section of the stack. This is a feeler thermoelement which serves to indicate the height at which the helium meets the hot sulphur vapor during the operation of the boiler. Its height is adjustable but it is usually kept about 3 cm below the thick section of the stack.

It may seem paradoxical that water cooling is used for sulphur which freezes at about 119°C. The hot saturated sulphur vapor at 1 atmosphere pressure, however, does not reach the thick section of the stack which is water cooled but stops at the level where the heat of vaporization has all been given up to the thin wall of the stack at temperatures well above the freezing point. At this level the stack temperature differs most from that of the saturated vapor so the rate of heat flow to the stack is a maximum as is also the temperature gradient in the stack. Above this level there is little condensation and the gradient decrease slightly owing to the loss of heat from the side of the stack.

Experiments were made changing the power input into the boiler to change the height of the hot saturated vapor in the stack. Temperature gradients along the stack were determined by means of ten thermocouples spaced uniformly. From these experiments it was concluded that the height of the top of the hot vapor was about at that level of where the thermocouple electromotive force increases most rapidly with an increase in vapor height. From these experiments it also was concluded that viscous flow of vapor in the stack caused an insignificant loss of head, as was found for the steam boiler.

It is important to know the height of the saturated vapor at one atmosphere, because, according to the values used at the Massachusetts Institute of Technology (11) its density is such that 4.0 cm of vapor head corresponds to a change of saturation temperature of 0.001°. Having determined the height of the hot saturated vapor with the feeler thermocouple, a better accounting can be made of the pressure of the vapor at the height of the thermometer coils. In the helium above the top of the hot vapor the stack temperature is so much lower than the sulphur point that the cooler saturated sulphur vapor at these temperatures contributes very little partial pressure head.

The stability of this boiler has brought to light a phenomenon which heretofore had escaped attention. When the sulphur is started to boil after a period of rest, the temperature is observed to fall for a period of about a day. The temperature then approaches constancy at about a hundredth of a degree below the initial temperature and has been found to remain there for periods lasting over a week. On account of this phenomenon the practice is to delay calibrations in the sulphur boiler until at least a day after the boiling is begun.

An analysis was made of the purity of the sulphur which had been used for sulphur boilers. It was found to contain less than a part in a million each of selenium, arsenic, and tellurium. Mueller (12) reported that one part in a thousand of selenium and arsenic added to the sulphur gave a combined raising in boiling temperature of less than 0.1°. After having been boiled the sulphur did, however, contain about 140 parts per million of carbon, 76 parts per million of nonvolatile matter, and about 8 parts per million of iron. Sulphur was purified by T. J. Murphy in the NBS Chemistry Division and was found to contain 2 parts per million of carbon, 3 parts per million of nonvolatile matter, and less than 1 part per million of iron. When this purified sulphur was used in the boiler no changes were found either in the final boiling temperature or the phenomenon of falling temperature. The practice in the use of the sulphur boiler has been to boil a new batch of sulphur for several hours to drive off gases and then to cool it in order to evacuate these gases before starting the boiling for calibration work. During use a small amount of helium is in the boiler stack for transmitting the pressure out to the manometer. Between runs this helium is left in the boiler. Our present conclusion is that the phenomenon of falling temperature is not a result of impurities in the sulphur, but is another unsolved problem concerning precision thermometry.

Oxygen Point Apparatus

A new oxygen boiling point apparatus is now in operation, also connected to the precision manometer. It uses the stable equilibrium between liquid oxygen and its vapor rather than active boiling as in the steam and sulphur boilers. The essential part of this apparatus is a copper block (AO) which contains an oxygen vapor-pressure bulb (BO) and eight wells (FO) for resistance thermometers. In operation the oxygen bulb contains a few drops of liquid oxygen (CO) in equilibrium with vapor near the position of the resistors of the thermometers being calibrated. Superheated oxygen vapor extends from the saturated oxygen in the bulb out to a diaphragm cell (LO) which is at about room temperature. The diaphragm (KO) transmits the pressure from the oxygen to the helium of the precision manometer.

The copper block is a cylinder about 7 cm in diameter and 18 cm tall. The eight wells of the thermometers extending up from the copper block are of thin copper-nickel tubing which has a low thermal conductivity. These wells lead up through liquid nitrogen to the outside of the apparatus near room temperature. Above the copper block are two heat interceptors (DO) soldered to the wells. In thermal contact with these heat interceptors are copper shields (EO) which surround the entire copper block.

Outside the shields is a brass envelope placed in a bath of liquid nitrogen (IO) which boils at about 13° below the oxygen point. The brass envelope is evacuated in order to eliminate heat transfer by gaseous conduction from the copper block and the surrounding shields. The heat interceptors are heated electrically and controlled to temperature close to that of the copper block. These interceptors serve to isolate the block so completely that temperature variations do not exceed 0.001° in the block near the thermometer resistors. For the initial cooling of the block and interceptors, tubes are soldered to them so that liquid nitrogen from the bath can be admitted through a valve (JO) above the envelope. The vaporization and heating of the nitrogen remove energy at a rate which makes it possible to cool the apparatus to a temperature below the oxygen point in about 2 hours.

In the helium line from the precision manometer to the steam and sulphur bath it is a simple matter to prevent either the steam or sulphur vapor from reaching the manometer by the use of dry ice to cool a horizontal portion of the transmitting line. For the oxygen point apparatus, however, it is not so simple. The method chosen is to use a plane metal diaphragm (KO) about 60 microns thick which separates the oxygen from the helium yet is so sensitive and so reproducible that it will permit the determination of the oxygen pressure within the equivalent of 0.0001° in its saturation temperature. The diaphragm is held in a cell (LO) with walls so close that the diaphragm is supported after it has been displaced a small amount by pressure, preventing the diaphragm from being strained beyond its elastic limit.

The diaphragm cell is made of stainless steel and has an over-all diameter of about 13 cm. This diameter is for flanges, which extend out from each of two central supporting walls which are about 10.2 cm in diameter. The diaphragm is held between these supports on plane areas about 6 mm wide near the 5-cm radius. Inside this supporting surface the wall is ground, lapped, and polished to a spherical concave surface having a radius of curvature of about 15 meters. On the helium side of the diaphragm the cell wall has a central electrically insulated island (MO) about 4.5 cm in diameter which is used for determining the null position of the diaphragm. This island is spaced about 0.15 mm from the main wall. The insulation (NO) is an annular sheet of Pyrex glass about 8 mm thick which is clamped both to the island and to the body of the cell. The insulator was used to hold the island in place when the cell body wall was being made spherical. Subsequently the island was removed for cleaning and replaced so the spherical surface of the island was continuous with that of the body wall within a fringe of light. Between the flanges there is a recessed space for a pair of clamping rings (PO) each about 13 cm in diameter and 1 cm thick, which clamp the diaphragm at a diameter of about 11 cm. When the diaphragm is clamped in its rings, it is laid on the island side of the cell and drawn axially toward the flange by means of screws. This stretches the diaphragm to a plane in a manner analogous to the tuning of a kettle drum.

The center of the diaphragm is about 70 microns from the island surface when the diaphragm is in equilibrium. The difference in electrostatic capacitance between that of a reference capacitor and that of the island to the diaphragm indicates the displacement of the diaphragm away from its equilibrium position. A beat frequency oscillator is used in a manner analogous to that for the precision manometer.

An excess of pressure on one side forces the diaphragm against the wall on the other side of the cell and further excess pressure makes little change. When the excess pressure is removed the diaphragm returns nearly to its original position. To be effective for a precision of 0.0001°, the diaphragm must return to its original position within the equivalent of 10 microns of mercury pressure. This has been done to within the equivalent of a few microns pressure so the reproducibility appears adequate, as the cell has been found to be somewhat sensitive to temperature changes, so it is enclosed inside a pair of thick-walled aluminium boxes with the outside box thermostatted at 28°C.

The diameters of the protecting envelopes of the thermometers which must be calibrated in this apparatus differ so much that various diameters of wells are provided, ranging from 7.5 to 13 mm in diameter. The length of the wells is a compromise at about 41 cm long. This provides sufficient immersion for most thermometers but may be too long for a few special thermometers with short stems. Since the boiling point of oxygen is below that of some of the gases in air, such as carbon dioxide and water vapor, it is desirable to avoid these gases in the wells. Provision is made, therefore, for sealing the thermometers in the wells by means of rubber sleeves at the top, evacuating the air, and introducing dry helium in the wells. This has the added advantage that helium has a greater thermal conductivity than air and hence improves the thermal contact of the well with the thermometer envelope.

Conclusion

In conclusion we may ask how far we have come in precision resistance thermometry and how much farther we may expect to go with the experimental possibilities that are known to us now. The precision of resistance thermometry has been increased by the attention to some details in the technique of measurement and by improved designs of instruments. It has been seen that the present triple point cells and the boilers for realizing the steam, sulphur and oxygen points make it possible to attain an accuracy that is comparable to that indicated in the text of the International Temperature Scale. These accomplishments, however, yield results which fall short of the precision in resistance thermometry which appears to be possible before it is limited by Johnson noise.

References

1. Stimson, H. F., 'The International Temperature Scale of 1918,' J. Research NBS Vol. 12, pp. 209 (1949).

2. Mueller, E. F., 'Precision Resistance Thermometry,' in 'Temperature, Its Measurement and Control in Science and Industry,' Reinhold, (1911)

3. Beattie, J. A., and Blaisdell, B. E., 'The Reproducibility of the Steam Point. The Effect of Pressure on the Steam Point,' Proc. Am. Acad. Arts Sci, Vol. 71, pp. 361 (1937).

   Beattie, J. A., Tzu-Ching Huang, and Benedict, M., 'The Reproducibility of the Ice Point and the Triple Point of Water. The Temperature of the Triple-Point of Water,' Proc. Am. Acad. Arts Sci. Vol. 72, pp. 137 (1938).

4. Schwab, F. W., and Wichers, E., 'Freezing Temperature of Benzoic Acid as a Fixed Point in Thermometry,' J. Research NBS Vol. 31, pp. 333 (1945).

5. Meyers, C. H., 'Coiled Filament Resistance Thermometers,' BS J. Research, Vol. 9, pp. 807 (1932).

6. Barber, C. R., 'Platinum Resistance Thermometers of Small Dimensions,' J. Sci. Instruments, Vol. 27, pp. 47 (1950).

7. Hoge, H. J., 'Electrical Conduction of Glass Insulation of Resistance Thermometers,' J. Research NBS Vol. 28, pp. 489 (1942).

8. Corruccini, R. J., 'Annealing of Platinum Thermometers,' J. Research NBS, Vol. 47, pp. 94 (1951).

9. Barber, C. R., Gridley, A., and Hall, J. A., 'An improved construction of the Smith bridge, type 3,' J. Sci. Instruments, Vol. 32, pp. 213 (1955).

10. Burgess, G. K., 'The International Temperature Scale,' BS J. Research, Vol. 1, pp. 635 (1928).

11. Beattie, J. A., Benedict, M., and Blaisdell, B. E., 'The Reproducibility of the Sulphur Point. The Effects of Pressure on the Sulphur Point,' Proc. Am. Acad. Arts Sci, Vol. 71, pp. 327 (1937).

12.   Mueller, E. F., and Burgess, H. A., 'The Standardization of the Sulphur Boiling Point,' J. Am. Chem. Soc., Vol. 41, pp. 745 (1919).

2-A (APPENDIX)

Notes To Supplement Resistance Thermometer Reports

The practical value of a standard resistance thermometer depends upon the precision and convenience with which it can be used to determine temperatures on a definite temperature scale. In view of the increasing use of platinum resistance thermometers and the increased precision sought with them, these notes have been prepared to supplement the calibration reports.

Temperature Scale

The International Practical Temperature Scale is based upon six defining fixed points to which numerical values have been assigned. Values between these fixed points are defined by the indications of specified measuring instruments and the use of specified interpolation formulas to relate these indications to temperature. Between -182.97 °C and 630.5 °C the instruments are platinum resistance thermometers which have been calibrated at specified defining fixed points to determine the constants in the interpolation formula may be put in the form,

$$t = \frac{R_t - R_o}{\alpha \, R_o} + \delta \, (\frac{t}{100} - 1) \frac{t}{100} , \qquad \text{Eq. 2-A-1}$$

devised by Callendar and commonly used in this country for hand computation of values of t. In this formula, t is the temperature in °C, R_t is the resistance at the temperature t, and R_o is the resistance at 0 °C. The constants, α and δ, have values which are characteristic of the individual thermometer. The constant α,

which is equivalent to $\dfrac{R_{100} - R_o}{100 \, R_o}$, is determined from measurements of thermo-

meter resistor at the triple point of water (0.01 °C) and the steam point. The value of α must be greater than 0.003920 to satisfy one of the international requirements for a standard thermometer. The constant δ is determined from measurements at an additional fixed point, either the boiling point of sulphur, a defining fixed point, or the freezing point of zinc, which is recommended in the text of the International Practical Temperature Scale as an alternative.

Tables having entries at given values of t are more easily computed from the equivalent formula which is given in the text of International Practical Temperature Scale:

$$R_t = R_o \, (1 + At + Bt^2). \qquad \text{Eq. 2-A-2}$$

R_t is the resistance of the resistor of the thermometer at temperature t, and R_o is the resistance at 0 °C. A and B are constants which are related to α and δ of the Callendar formula by the identities:

$$A \equiv \alpha \, (1 + \frac{\delta}{100}) \text{ and } B \equiv -\frac{\alpha\delta}{100^2}. \qquad \text{Eq. 2-A-3}$$

Over the range $0°$ to $-182.97°$ C, the interpolation formula may be put in the modi-fied Callendar form:

$$t = \frac{R_t - R_o}{\alpha\, R_o} + \delta\left(\frac{t}{100} - 1\right)\frac{t}{100} + \beta\left(\frac{t}{100} - 1\right)\left(\frac{t}{100}\right)^3,$$

Eq. 2-A-4

devised by Van Dusen. The constant β is also characteristic of the individual thermometer and is determined from an additional measurement at the boiling point of oxygen.

The equivalent international formula for this part of the scale is:

$$R_t = R_o\left[1 + At + Bt^2 + C(t - 100)t^3\right],$$

Eq. 2-A-5

where R_t, R_o, A and B are as stated in the previous paragraph. The constant C is related to the constants in the Callendar formula by the identity:

$$C = -\frac{\alpha\beta}{100^4}.$$

Eq. 2-A-6

Measurement for the Determination of Temperature

A standard platinum resistance thermometer is constructed so that precise measurements may be made of the resistance of its platinum resistor. The resistor is made of very pure platinum wire, is compact in form, and is contained in a protecting tube. At each end of it is a branch point to which are joined two leads, commonly called current and potential leads. This construction makes it possible to measure the resistance of the resistor alone (i.e. between the branch points), independent of the resistance of the leads.

The resistance of the thermometer may be measured in various ways. The Wheatstone bridge and commutator of Mueller's design are commonly used in this country. The function of the commutator is to interchange the thermometer leads in such a way that the average of the resistances measured with the commutator in the N (normal) position and in the R (reverse) position is the resistance of the resistor of the thermometer. The resistance of the leads is completely eliminated by this technique only if the difference in the resistance of the two leads appearing in the arms of the bridge is the same when measurements are made in the N as when measurements are made in the R position. By making a series of four meas-urements at equal time intervals in the order N R R N, any charge of the difference of the lead resistance is computable and the average value of the four meaurements is independent of any linear drift in this difference. The resistance may also be measured with a potentiometer and a stable reference resistor or with a Kelvin-type double bridge.

The calibration report for a resistance thermometer gives the values of α and δ which were found to apply to the resistor of that particular thermometer. If the thermometer were calibrated at the oxygen point, the value β which was found is given for calculating temperatures below 0 °C. The constants are characteristic of the material in the particular resistor but do not depend on the magnitude of its resistance. This is not to say that changes in the magnitude of a given resistor at some reference point are not accompanied by a change in the constants. It is to say that the constants are independent of the unit of resistance. For accurate determinations of temperature with a platinum thermometer it is necessary to refer to some known and reproducible temperature (fixed point) which should be readily available whenever it is needed. This fixed temperature is most commonly either the ice point or the triple point of water (0.01 °C). Measurement of the resistance of the thermometer in a suitable ice bath will give R_o directly, while a small correction, very nearly equivalent to 0.01 degree C, is necessary if a triple point cell is used (See Section 2A). The choice between these two fixed points is largely on the basis of the accuracy required as the triple point may be realized within ±0.0002 degrees C while the accuracy of realizing the ice point is typically five to ten times worse. The value of R_o is given in the report primarily to enable the determination of any change occurring in R_o between the time of calibration and the time that R_o is measured in the user's laboratory. In addition to the errors of realizing the ice point or triple point, the accuracy of such a check is limited by the uncertainty of the difference in the resistance units used.

The accuracy of temperature determined from values of R_t/R_o obviously is not limited by the uncertainty of the resistance units if the values of R_t and R_o are determined in the same units. Hence, precision temperature determinations with any thermometer should be based upon a value of R_o determined from measurements with the bridge which is to be used. Since temperature determinations depend directly upon R_o, it should be redetermined frequently enough to assure the user that he has a sufficiently reliable value when measurements are made.

Since only ratios of resistances are required to determine temperature, the units may be absolute ohms, international ohms or any arbitary unit; but the calibrated bridge (or potentiometer) must be self-consistent. A bridge that is self-consistent may be used for precision temperature determinations using the constants reported for the thermometer, or using the table of R_t/R_o values which has been derived from the reported constants. It is advisable to calibrate the bridge often enough to assure the user that the calibrations are reliable within the accuracy necessary for his work. They are not difficult and may be made in the same place and under the same laboratory conditions as the measurements for temperature determinations. A method of calibrating the bridge is described in the last part of this Appendix.

Certain precautions must be observed if reliable temperature determinations are to be made with a resistance thermometer. The thermometer coil must be immersed to a depth sufficient to prevent a significant error from transfer of heat along the thermometer leads and protecting tube. A check of the adequacy of the immersion in each uniform constant-temperature bath may be made by varying the depth of immersion of the thermometer and noting whether there is a change in resistance. When a measuring current flows in the thermometer, some heating of the resistor results; consequently the same current should be used in making measurements as was used in the calibration.

Sufficient time must be allowed after the current is turned on for equilibrium to be established. The characteristic constants of a thermometer may change as a result of changes in the dimensions of the wire, strains in the wire, or the subjection of the thermometer to excessive temperatures. It is particularly important that care be taken to protect the thermometer from small mechanical shocks, each of which strain the wire slightly to produce small changes in the characteristics of the wire in the platinum resistor. If the measured resistance at a reliable fixed point is found to have changed by a significant amount, and the change cannot be attributed to the bridge, recalibration of the thermometer is advisable. The maximum change of the calibration indicated by a change in R_o may be estimated using the following expression:

$$\text{(Maximum Error at temperature } t) = t(\frac{Bt}{A} - 1)\frac{\Delta}{R_o}, \qquad \text{Eq. 2-A-7}$$

where Δ is the change in R_o since calibration. This assumes that temperatures are computed from values R_t/R_o using a current value of R_o. The value for the maximum error is based on experience with standard platinum thermometers. It is not likely to be valid for others.

Tables

The labor involved in computing temperatures can be greatly reduced by making use of the table which is computed for each thermometer. The table relates resistance ratios to temperature over that part of the temperature range appropriate to both the thermometer and the calibration, or over the range requested. The table gives the resistance ratios at intervals of one degree; a linear interpolation will not introduce an additional error greater than the equivalent of 0.0001 degree at any point on the scale.

The table is calculated for each degree in the range by a direct machine computation using the calibration constants of the Callendar formula in the form:

$$\frac{R_t}{R_o} = [1 + \alpha t - \alpha\delta \left(\frac{t}{100} - 1\right)\frac{t}{100}], \qquad \text{Eq. 2-A-8}$$

for temperatures above 0 °C, and in the modified Callendar formula in the form:

$$\frac{R_o}{R_o} = [1 + \alpha t - \alpha\delta \left(\frac{t}{100} - 1\right) \frac{t}{100} - \alpha\beta \left(\frac{t}{100} - 1\right)\left(\frac{t}{100}\right)^3], \qquad \text{Eq. 2-A-9}$$

for temperatures below 0 °C. It will be noted that these forms resemble those of the international formulas; and, indeed, the substitution of the relations given in equations 2-A-2, 2-A-3, 2-A-5 and 2-A-6 shows the equivalence.

Calibration of a Mueller-Type Bridge

The bridge may be calibrated in terms of any convenient unit of resistance, such as a bridge unit which may be established by arbitrarily defining the sum of the resistance of the ten 1 ohm resistors in the 1 ohm decade to be equal to 10 bridge units. However, it is decidedly preferable for the bridge to be calibrated in terms of absolute ohms by means of a suitable standardized resistor because one may then make checks on the stability of the thermometer. In any case it is essential that the calibrated bridge be self-consistent, meaning that the resistance change corresponding to each deacde step be expressed in terms of a single unit of resistance. The resistance of a decade step is the change in the effective resistance of the variable arm of the bridge when that step is added to or taken from the bridge setting. The method of calibration is to compare the resistance of each decade step with the resistance of the X (sum of all ten steps) of the next lower decade. This comparison is made by alternately including in the variable arm of the bridge either the step being calibrated or the X of the next lower decade. The lower decades are used to make the variable arm balance an external resistance. From these alternate balances, a relation between the step being calibrated and the X of the next lower decade is obtained and the complete calibration consists of repeating this process for each decade step.

The comparisons require external resistors connected in such a manner that the resistance of the external circuit including all contacts will remain adequately constant during the short time required for each comparison. The external resistance may be a series circuit consisting of a resistance box, variable in 0.1 ohm steps up to 100 ohms, and a slide wire shunted to have a resistance slightly greater than 0.1 ohm. The shunted slide wire is convenient for getting the necessary external resistances for calibration of the 0.01 ohm and lower decades, and it is useful for the calibration of the 0.1 ohm and higher decades. When both the slide wire and the resistance box are connected to the bridge, the movable contact of the slide wire is connected to the c post of the bridge, one end of the slide wire to the C post; and the resistance box between the other end of the slide wire and the T post of the bridge. If the resistance box is used alone, one terminal of the box is connected to both the C and c posts on the bridge and the other to the T post. The resistance of the individual steps of a decade will be designated by means of subscripts, for example, the successive steps of the 10 ohm decade will be designated as 10_1, 10_2, ---- 10_9, 10_x. The sum of the steps which are included in any setting will be designated without a subscript, for example, in the 10 ohm decade, as 10, 20, ---- 90, X0.

Before beginning the bridge calibration the ratio arms should be adjusted to equality. This is necessary because the 0.1 ohm decade is not in the same arm of the bridge as the other decades. The bridge zero is not used in calibration; but if it is observed and found to have its usual value, there is added confidence in the calibration. The current may be increased to obtain greater sensitivity, and also, if the external circuit is connected as indicated above then the commutator must be set in the N (normal) position and not in the R (reverse) position while calibrating.

The steps in the calibration are than as follows:

(a) Set 10 on the 10 ohm decade of the bridge and 0 on the 1 ohm decade and use the lower decades to balance an appropriate resistance in the external circuit. It is good practice to interpolate with galvanometer deflections to one tenth of a step on the lowest decade.

(b) Without disturbing the external circuit, change the bridge setting to 0 on the 10 ohm decade and X. on the 1 ohm decade and again use the lower decades to balance. It is convenient to adjust the slide wire in the external circuit so that the lower decade balances are near zero for the lesser of (a) or (b).

(c) Repeat (b) and then (a).

(d) Set 20 on the 10 ohm decade of the bridge and 0 on the 1 ohm decade and balance with a corresponding resistance in the external circuit, as in (a).

(e) Change the bridge setting to 10 in the 10 ohm decade and X. in the 1 ohm decade and proceed as in (b) and (c).

(f) Continue this process until each of the 10 ohm steps has been compared with the sum of the ten 1 ohm steps. The observations under (a) (b) and (c) yield the relation $10_1 + a_1 = X + b_1$ where a_1 and b_1 are the corrected averages of the respective lower decade readings, including galvanometer interpolations, which were obtained in the balancing of the bridge.

Similar equations are obtained from (d) and (e) leading to the complete set:

$$10_1 + a_1 = X. + b_1 \qquad \text{Eq. 2-A-10}$$

$$10_2 + a_2 = X. + b_2 \qquad \text{Eq. 2-A-11}$$
$$\vdots$$

$$10_9 + a_9 = X. + b_9 \qquad\qquad \text{Eq. 2-A-12}$$

$$10_x + a_x = X. + b_x \qquad\qquad \text{Eq. 2-A-13}$$

It is convenient to define the bridge unit by means of the relation,

$$X. = 10 \text{ bridge units} = 10 \text{ ohms (approximately).} \qquad \text{Eq. 2-A-14}$$

The above relations will then yield the resistance of 10_1, 10_2, 10_3, etc. and by adding these successively the resistances of 10, 20, 30 etc. will be obtained. For the 1 ohm decade, the procedure is similar and leads to similar equations. However, the resistance of 0.X must be determined. To do this the equations are added to obtain their sum:

$$X. + \sum a = 10(0.X) + \sum b, \text{ so that:}$$

$$0.X = \frac{X. + \sum(a - b)}{10}. \qquad\qquad \text{Eq. 2-A-15}$$

This value for the resistance of 0.X is then substituted in the original equations and the rest of the procedure is the same as for the 10 ohms decade. The calibration of the 0.1 ohm decade proceeds similarly.

So far the procedure has yielded calibration data for the 10, 1 and 0.1 ohm decades, and also the resistance of 0.0X of the 0.01 ohm decade. A comparison of the value obtained for the resistance of 0.0X with that of a previous calibration will indicate whether recalibration of the lower decades is advisable. Calibration of the 0.01 ohm and lower decades is done in a similar manner by using the slide wire alone. The .0001 ohm steps, which ordinarily are the lowest, may be calibrated by comparing galvanometer deflections for each successive step.

If it is desired to calibrate the bridge in terms of absolute ohms or other units represented by a calibrated resistance standard, this standard, preferably one of 10 ohms, may be connected to the bridge, just as a four lead thermometer, and measured in terms of the X. of the 1 ohm decade. The result of this measurement (bridge zero to be taken into account) leads to a relation between the bridge unit and the unit of the standard. The corrections previously obtained may be modified so that resistances are expressed in terms of the unit represented by the standard.

The use of a reliable resistance standard has the advantage of holding the bridge unit as constant as the resistance standard and thus it may enable one to determine whether apparent drifts in R_0 are due to the thermometer or to the bridge. Another advantage in this is that a thermometer may be used interchangeably on these bridges with the precision to which the bridge units agree. For work of the highest precision however, it is considered better practice when using any thermometer to determine R_0 at the time measurements are made and to be sure that the bridge is self-consistent. The art of standard platinum resistance thermometer construction and stablization has now developed to such an extent that the resistance of a well-treated thermometer at a reliable fixed point may have a constancy comparable with that of resistance standards.

2B

A Study of Stability of High Temperature Platinum Resistance Thermometers

J. P. EVANS AND G. W. BURNS
National Bureau of Standards, Washington, D.C.

Below 630.5°C the most precise and accurate temperature measurements are made with platinum resistance thermometers. Present-day science and technology is experiencing an increasing need for more precise and accurate measurements at higher temperatures. Consequently, the NBS is studying the performance of platinum resistance thermometers at temperatures up to the gold point, 1063°C.

The International Practical Temperature Scale of 1948 (1) is defined in the region 630.5° to 1063°C by a platinum versus platinum-10% rhodium thermocouple calibrated at 630.5°C and the silver and gold points. The precision of such a thermocouple is about 0.1 degree, and its absolute accuracy with respect to the International Practical Temperature Scale is about 0.2°C. "Accuracy here means estimated standard deviation of the mean of determinations from each laboratory in which which attempts have been made to realize either the international or the thermodynamic temperature scales about the mean of all laboratories. Precision of a thermometer means the estimated standard deviation of the determinations of any laboratory about the mean of the determinations in the same laboratory." Experiments by other investigators have indicated that it is possible to determine values of temperature in this range more precisely and reliably with platinum resistance thermometers than with thermocouples.

Waidner and Burgess first investigated the use of platinum resistance thermometers up to 1100°C at the NBS in 1909 (3). They found that temperatures determined with their thermometers agreed with thermocuple determinations within about 1 degree. Their thermometers changed considerably with use; this may now be attributed, for the most part, to the relatively low purity of the platinum available at that time. In 1930 Moser made a similar study and found that temperature determinations with his thermometers were reproducible to about 0.1 degree (4). His thermometers were made of a higher purity platinum and they were significantly more stable than those of Waidner and Burgess.

It is evident from the earlier work that if a platinum resistance thermometer is to be stable at high temperatures, its temperature sensing resistor must be made from very pure platinum wire supported in a strain-free manner. Furthermore, the materials used for support and protection must not contaminate the resistor during use. Materials suitable for support become poorer electrical insulators at high temperatures, hence the resistance of the thermometer should be kept low to minimize the effect of electrical leakage.

Figure 2-B-1 is a photograph of one type of temperature sensing resistor. It consists of 8 straight lengths of platinum wire 0.4 or 0.5 millimeters in diameter threaded through holes in synthetic sapphire discs. These wires are welded together in series. A central platinum rod serves to support and position the discs. The assembled resistor has become known as a "bird cage resistor" because of its shape. It is 5 millimeters in diameter, 35 to 40 millimeters long, and has a nominal resistance at 0°C of 0.25 ohm. It is nearly noninductive.

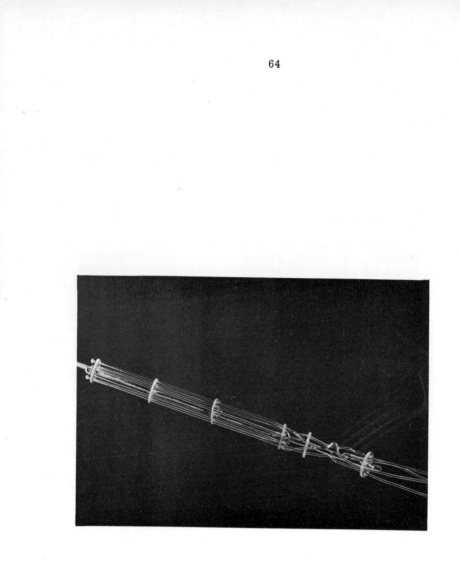

Fig. 2-B-1   Bird cage resistor

Four platinum leads are welded to the resistor. The leads are separated by four-hole sapphire discs, and between the discs are sapphire rod spacers 12.7mm long. The resistor and lead assembly is placed in a closed end protecting tube about 450 millimeters long, which has been cleaned with acid and fired in oxygen at 1100°C. The four platinum leads extend to within a few millimeters of the open end of the tube where they are butt welded to bare copper wires of the same diameter. The copper to platinum junctions are located side by side in a small piece of four-hole porcelain tubing which is surrounded by a close-fitting copper sleeve. In this manner the junctions are kept at nearly the same temperature, thereby reducing thermal emf in the thermometer. For sealed thermometers, the open end of the protecting tube is fitted with a hermetic seal header through which the bare copper wires are sealed. The copper wires are then soldered to insulated thermometer lead wires. An aluminium head attached to the end of the thermometer completes the construction.

Many resistance thermometers have been found to suffer an increase in resistance at 0°C when mistreated by tapping. This increase in resistance is believed to be the result of work hardening of the platinum. The bird cage resistors, however, have proven to be very rugged mechanically. Although one thermometer with this type resistor was tapped on a solid object 5000 times, this treatment resulted only in a barely detectable change in the resistance of the thermometer at 0°C.

Resistance measurements are made with a resistance thermometer bridge of the type designed by Mueller (5). A recent version of this bridge has a range 0 to 422 ohms in 1 microhm steps (6). This instrument may also be used as a decade resistor in a potentiometer circuit similar to that described by Dauphinee (7). It should be pointed out that the resistance of the platinum leads of these thermometers exceeds that of the temperature sensing resistor. Temperature changes along the leads thus cause resistance changes which can be very disturbing when using a Mueller bridge. A potentiometric method of resistance determination would eliminate this difficulty.

The stability of the thermometers at high temperatures was tested by heating the thermometers for long times in a tube furnace. Periodically the thermometers were removed from the furnace for determination of their resistance at 0 and 100°C. The resistance at 100°C was determined by placing the thermometer under test, together with a calibrated resistance thermometer, in a copper block bathed in steam at atmospheric pressure. Simultaneous measurements of the resistance of both thermometers were made. The resistance at 0°C was determined by measuring the resistance of the test thermometer at the triple point of water, 0.01°C. Simple corrections were applied to obtain the resistances at 0 and 100°C. The constancy of the ratio R_{100}/R_o, where R_{100} is the resistance of the thermometer at 100°C and R_o is the resistance at 0°C, is taken as an indicator of thermometer stability.

The ratio R_{100}/R_o was chosen to indicate thermometer stability for several reasons. First, it is relatively easy to obtain R_{100} and R_o with sufficient precision. Second, it is believed that 100°C is not a high enough temperature to cause changes in a thermometer during the time it takes to make a resistance measurement. Third, the ratio R_{100}/R_o is independent of purely dimensional changes in the platinum wire.

A number of thermometers have been constructed and heated in a furnace at various temperatures between 500 and 1100°C for periods up to 500 hours. The data shown in Figures 2-B-2 and 2-B-3 are representative of results obtained for thermometers employing different resistor designs, various protecting tube materials, and two types of platinum wire. From time to time the thermometers were removed from the furnace for determination of R_{100} and R_o.

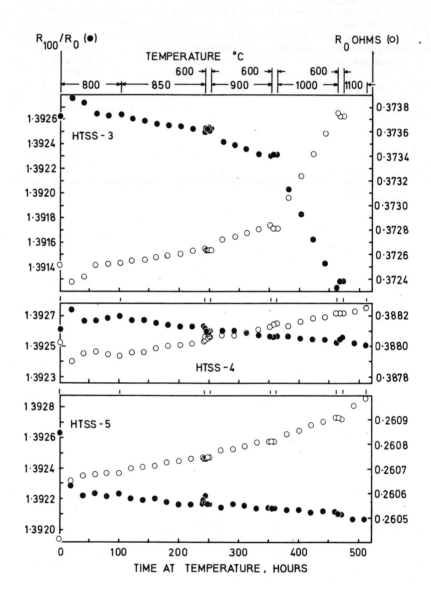

Fig. 2-B-2 Change in R_{100}/R_0, and R_0, with time for three resistance
thermometers heated to various temperatures.

The upper set of curves in Figure 2-B-2 shows the results of heating a thermometer designated HTSS-3. This was a bifilar helix resistor encased in a porcelain protecting tube. Heating at 850°C produced a definite change in the thermometer, and at 1000°C the change became so rapid as to make the thermometer virtually useless. The rapid decrease in R_{100}/R_o with heating at high temperatures was probably due to contamination of the platinum with metals or metal oxides from the porcelain. It thus appears that porcelain is not a suitable protecting tube material. The lower two sets of curves in Figure 2-B-2 present data obtained with thermometers HTSS-4 and HTSS-5, both of which were encased in pure alumina tubes. During the 500-hour heating period, the average change in R_{100}/R_o for these thermometers was equivalent to a drift in thermometer calibration of about 0.001 degree per hour at 1000°C, indicating that pure alimina is more suitable than porcelain as a protecting tube material.

The resistor in thermometer HTSS-4 was in the form of a bilifar helix wound on a synthetic sapphire cross, while a bird-cage resistor was used in thermometer HTSS-5. Comparison of the curves in Figure 2-B-2 indicates that thermometer stablility is not significantly dependent on resistor configuration. Other experiments tend to confirm this.

Figure 2-B-3 presents another comparison of various protecting tube materials. Thermometer HTSS-11 was encased in alumina, thermometer HTSS-13 in silica, and thermometer HTSS-14 in pure platinum, all bird-cage resistors. The silica tube thermometer appears relatively stable below 1000°C, but above that temperature R_{100}/R_o begins to decrease, probably because of silicon contamination. No clear-cut superiority of platinum over alumina as a protecting tube material is shown by the curves in Figure 2-B-3.

Recently a new material called Fibro platinum has come on the market (8). Wires made of Fibro platinum have a fibrous structure which is asserted to prevent excessively large grain growth upon recrystallization at high temperatures. Two of the thermometers for which data are shown in Figure 2-B-3 (HTSS-11 and HTSS-14) were made with this wire.

Thermometers made with platinum tubes could be hermetically sealed, while thermometers made with alumina tubes were left open to the air since it was questionable whether the alumina tubes were gas tight. The platinum tube thermometer HTSS-14 was sealed in an argon atmosphere. In general, platinum tube thermometers sealed in argon and alumina tube thermometers open to the air exhibited no significant difference in stability which could be attributed to the surrounding atmosphere. Other investigators working at higher and lower temperatures, however, have found that various gases have considerable effect on the resistance characteristics of platinum (9-11). The situation concerning gaseous atmospheres, as it relates to thermometer stability, is not clear at this time, but thermometers made with metal oxide protecting tubes should probably be filled with a gas containing some oxygen. The oxygen would tend to inhibit the formation of free metal atoms which alloy with the platinum.

It appears desirable that the thermometers be sealed to keep out contaminants and water vapor, but this has not always been done, Barber, (12), for example, has allowed the thermometer free access to the air but has incorporated a drying agent in the thermometer head. Only by carefully removing water vapor and carbonaceous material from the thermometers constructed for the present study has it been possible to maintain consistently an insulation resistance across the thermometers greater than 1 megohm at 1100°C. Although the error in resistance determinations due to electrical leakage is negligible at low temperatures, it becomes significant at high temperatures. At 1000°C, where the thermometer resistance may exceed 1 ohm, a shunting resistance of 1 megohm introduces an error greater than a part

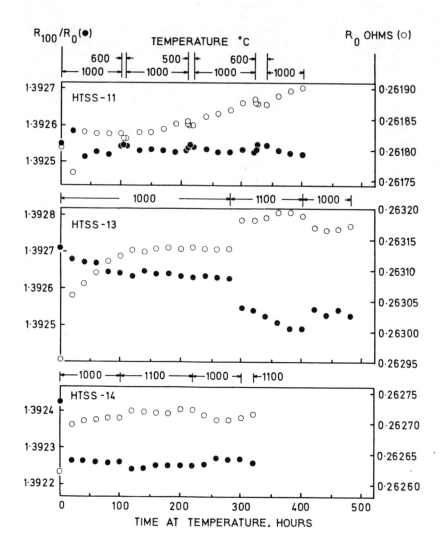

Fig. 2-B-3   Change in R_{100}/R_0, and R_0, with time for three resistance thermometers heated to various temperatures.

per million in the resistance determination. This corresponds to an uncertainty in temperature determination of more than 0.001 degree.

Two interesting aspects of the curves in Figures 2-B-2 and 2-B-3 for thermometers encased in alumina and platinum should be noted. First, it is seen that after initial annealing, these thermometers, in general, exhibit a slow decrease in R_{100}/R_o with heating which is not strongly dependent on the heating temperature. The cause of this slow decrease is not known. There are possibly several contributing factors; among these are: the effect of recrystallization and grain growth at high temperatures, a slow diffusion of surface impurities into the platinum, contamination of the platinum by the protecting tube material, and the taking into solution by the platinum of gases surrounding it. In any case, the decrease apparently can be made small by suitable construction. For example, the thermometer sealed in argon in a platinum tube changed, on the average, by less than the equivalent of 0.05 degree at 1063°C when heated for 300 hours at 1000°C or higher.

The second interesting aspect is that heating a thermometer for a period at a temperature lower than previously produces a "recovery" in R_{100}/R_o. Upon further heating at the higher temperature, R_{100}/R_o returns to its lower value. This reversibility in the value of R_{100}/R_o dependent on heating temperature was observed by Moser, and also by Meyers in an unpublished work at the NBS. Corruccini, in his investigations on the annealing of platinum for thermometery, (13) recognized that the effect could be caused by a comparatively rapid cooling from high temperatures and would be dependent on the cooling rate. He found that the effect was reversible; R_{100}/R_o could be restored to its initial value by subsequent annealing. He also found that the quantity $R_{100} - R_o$ remained essentially unchanged during the course of the experiments.

Some of Corruccini's results are represented by the solid curve in Figure 2-B-4, which gives the change in R_{100}/R_o from its value in the well-annealed state, as a function of cooling time. $((R_{100}/R_o)^*$ is the value of the ratio after an anneal at 500 or 600°C followed by a slow cool.) Bare wires were heated at 1450°C by passing an electric current through them. The estimated time for incandescence to disappear after the removal or reduction of current was taken as the comparative index of the cooling rate.

The dashed curves in Figure 2-B-4 show results of experiments performed with a silica tube thermometer and a platinum tube thermometer. The thermometers were heated in a furnace at 1100°C. The resistance as a thermometer was withdrawn from the furnace was followed with a recorder. In this experiment, the comparative index is based on the estimated average time of cooling from 1100 to 600°C. If the three curves in Figure 2-B-4 are adjusted to have the same starting point, they appear to be closely similar for cooling times greater than about 50 seconds. No serious attempt has been made to explain the slight divergence of the curves for shorter cooling times. If the change in R_{100}/R_o is strongly dependent on the cooling rate during the first part of a cooling period, some divergence could be expected.

Throughout these experiments the quantity $R_{100} - R_o$ remained considerably more stable than the quantity R_{100}/R_o. In fact, the platinum tube thermometer sealed in argon exhibited no significant change in $R_{100} - R_o$ during the 300-hour heating period and during the cooling rate experiments.

An explanation of these results can be found in recent work on quenched-in point defects in platinum (14-16). The procedure in these quenching experiments was to cool a sample of platinum wire from temperatures in the range 1000 to 1600°C to room temperature. The cooling rates were such that the temperature of the sample was within a few degrees of its final value in less than a second. Ascoli *et al* found that when the quenching time was less than 0.1 second, the increase in

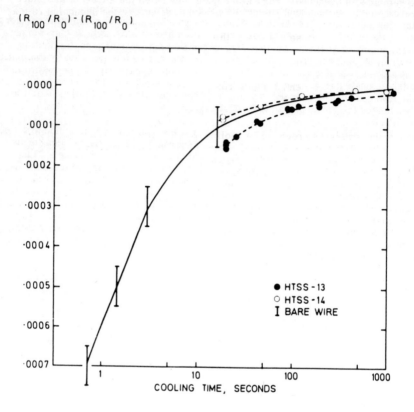

Fig. 2-B-4   Decrease in R_{100}/R_0 with cooling times from high temperatures.

resistivity $\Delta\rho$ of platinum at 15°C due to quenching could be represented by:

$$\Delta\rho = 1.3 \times 10^{-4} \exp(-1.23/kT) \text{ ohm cm}$$

where kT is expressed in electron volts, and T is the temperature in °K from which the sample was quenched. For slower quenching rates the situation was more complicated, and the added resistivity tended to depend on the quenching rate as well. It never exceeded the value given by the above equation, however. The explanation given by these authors is that a temperature-dependent equilibrium concentration of lattice-site vacancies is produced at the quenching temperature T, and that for quenching times of less than 0.1 second practically all of the vacancies are frozen in the platinum crystals. It is assumes that the added resistivity is proportional to the concentration of frozen-in vacancies.

It was stated that for a least one of the thermometers the quantity $R_{100} - R_o$ remained unchanged during the cooling rate experiments. This fact suggests that the changes in resistance produced by cooling obey Matthiessen's rule. Further, added resistivity measured at a low temperature (15°C in the experiments described above) when all the vacancies are quenched in would equal that part of the total resistivity at temperature T contributed by the vacancies. If the equation above is applied to resistance thermometers in their range of interest, it is found that vacancies contribute to thermometer resistance an amount which is equivalent to a temperature increment of the order of 0.3 degree at 1063°C and 0.001 degree at 600°C. One can also deduce that, since the equation gives the maximum added resistivity that can be quenched in from temperature T, cooling the thermometers at any rate from temperatures below 600°C would produce insignificant changes due to quenched-in vacancies.

The assumptions and conclusions of the preceding paragraph may or may not be generally valid. Certainly the situation would be confused if the platinum wire in a thermometer were constrained in any way during the cooling process, or if quenching were to produce point defects other than vacancies. Suffice it to say that no thermometer changes attributable to quenched-in point defects have been observed upon cooling from 600°C and below.

Ascoli *et al* found that more than 90% of the quenched-in resistivity could be removed upon annealing for about one minute at 700°C. The kinetics of annealing may not be simple. Annealing behaviour may depend on vacancy concentrations and quenching rate (15). In any case, Corruccini found that he could reestablish the initial values of R_{100}/R_0 with two hours annealing at 500°C. The thermometers described here were restored to their highest values of R_{100}/R_0 in an annealing period of from one to two hours at 600°C.

It is clear that the presence of vacancies and the fact that vacancies can be quenched in upon cooling must be taken into account in considering thermometer stability. If a temperature determination is to be based on a resistance measurement made at a reference temperature that is low, say 0°C, as well as a resistance measurement made at the temperature to be determined, then something must be known about the vacancy concentration at the low temperature. For example, at the low temperature the platinum might be required to contain all the vacancies that were present at the high temperature. Conversely, one might require the platinum to contain at every temperature a vacancy concentration differing insignificantly if at all from its equilibrium concentration. Since it seems improbable that practical thermometers can be cooled rapidly enough to quench in all vacancies, the alternative requirement, which can be met by proper annealing prior to a low-temperature determination, appears preferable.

These studies at the NBS have shown that stable high-temperature platinum resistance thermometers can be made. Thermometers have been developed which drifted the equivalent of only a few hundredths of a degree at 1000°C when heated for several hundred hours at 1000°C or higher. Synthetic sapphire has been found suitable for the support of the resistor wires, and both pure platinum and pure alumina have been used successfully as protecting tube materials. An easily constructed, mechanically rugged resistor, the bird-cage resistor, has been built and tested.

These studies have also shown that themometer stability is dependent on the rate at which thermometers are cooled from temperatures above 600°C. This cooling rate effect has been explained by the quenching-in of point defects, probably lattice site vacancies, in the platinum. It has been found that the effect is reversible; the thermometers can be restored to the condition existing before a rapid cooling by annealing at 600°C and lower. Consequently, the cooling rate effect must be taken into account when calibrating and using high-temperature platinum resistance thermometers.

References

1.   Stimson, H. F., 'The International Practical Temperature Scale of 1948,' J. Research Natl. Bur. Standards Vol 65A, pp. 139 (1961).

2.   Kostowski, H. J., 'Proceedings of an International Symposium on High Temperature Technology.' 'The Accuracy and Precision of Measuring Temperatures above 1000°K,' McGraw-Hill, New York,(1960.)

3.   Waidner, C. W. and Burgess, G. K., 'Platinum resistance thermometry at high temperatures,' Bull. Standards Vol 6, pp. 149 (1909).

4.   Moser,Helmut., 'Temperature measurement with platinum resistance thermometers up to 1100°C, Ann. Physik (5) Vol 6, pp. 852 (1930).

5.   Mueller, E. F.,'Temperature, Its Measurement and Control in Science and Industry., 'Precision Resistance Thermometry,' Reinhold, New York, 1941, Vol. 1, pp. 162.

6.   Evans, J. P.,'Temperature, Its Measurement and Control in Science and Industry. 'An Improved Resistance Thermometer Bridge,' Reinhold, New York, 1962, Vol. 3.

7.   Dauphinee, T. M., 'Potentiometric Methods of Resistance Measurement,' 'Temperature, Its Measurement and Control in Science and Industry', 'An isolating potential comparator', Can. J. Phys, Vol. 31, pp. 577 (1953). Reinhold, New York, Vol. 3. (1962).

8.   Hill, J.S., Temperature, Its Measurement and Control in Science and Industry, 'Fibro Pt for Thermal Elements,' Reinhold, New York, 1962, Vol. 3.

9.   Comité International des Poids et Mesures, 'Procès-Verbaux des Seances de 1954,' Vol 24, T166 (1955).

10.   Berry, R.J.,'Temperature, Its Measurement and Control in Science and Industry,' 'Stability of Platinum Resistance Thermometers at Temperatures up to +630°C, Reinhold, New York, Vol 3, (1962).

11. Bradley, D. and Entwistle, A. G. 'Temperature, Its Measurement and Control in Science and Industry,' 'Anomalous Resistance Effects in Small Diameter Platinum and Platinum-Rhodium Resistance Elements at Temperatures in Excess of 1000°C in a Gaseous Environment,' Reinhold, New York, Vol 3, (1962).

12. Barber, C. R. and Blanke, W.W., 'A platinum resistance thermometer for use at high temperatures,' J. Sci. Instr. Vol 38, pp. 17 (1961).

13. Corrucini, R. J., 'Annealing of platinum for thermometry,' J. Research Natl. Bur. Standards, Vol 47, pp. 94 (1951).

14. Ascoli, A., et al 'Activation energies for the production and migration of vacancies in platinum,' J. Phys. Chem. Solids, Vol 6, pp. 59 (1958).

15. Bacchella, G. L., et al. 'On the kinetics of quenched-in lattice vacancies in platinum,' J. Appl. Phys. Vol 30, pp. 748 (1959).

16. Piercy, G. R., 'Point defects in platinum,' Phil. Mag. Vol 5, pp. 201 (1960).

2C

Thermocouple and Radiation Thermometry above 900°K

BY HENRY J. KOSTKOWSKI AND GEORGE W. BURNS
National Bureau of Standards, Washington, D.C.

Summary

This chapter is largely an updating (1) or condensation (2) of sections of two previous publications and reviews the principles of thermocouple and radiation thermometry above 900°K, the present day precision and accuracy and the commercial
instruments currently available. The International Practical Temperature Scale
and the Thermodynamic Kelvin Temperature Scale are briefly described. With
regard to thermocouples, the presentation is confined to the more generally accepted
base, noble and refractory metal types. Characteristics such as temperature range,
stability and environmental limitations will be emphasized. The optical pyrometry
section includes a discussion of emittance corrections, recommendations for using
visual optical pyrometers and the status of photoelectric optical pyrometers.
Finally, two-colour, three-colour and total-radiation pyrometers are discussed,
primarily to show that, in spite of the recent interest in these instruments, they are
not generally as suitable for measuring temperature as optical (single-colour)
pyrometers.

Introduction

In determining the thermal radiation properties of solids, it is usually necessary
to measure the temperature of the solid or the temperature difference between the
solid and a blackbody. These measurements often have to be the order of ten
times more accurate than the accuracy required in the radiation properties. As a
consequence, it is desirable that those working on thermal radiation properties of
solids have a basic, up-to-date knowledge of the field of temperature measurements.

The instruments available for accurate thermometry above 900°K are primarily
thermocouples and optical pyrometers. The purpose of this paper is to review the
principles of thermocouple and radiation thermometry, the present day precision
and accuracy and the commercial instruments currently available. In order to
discuss accuracy meaningfully, it will also be necessary to consider the temperature scales in use today. With regard to thermocouples the review will be confined
to the more generally accepted base, noble and refractory metal types. Characteristics such as temperature range, stability and environmental limitations will be
emphasized. The optical pyrometry section will include a discussion of emmitance
corrections, recommendations for using visual optical pyrometers, and the status
of photoelectric optical pyrometers. Finally, two-color, three-color and total-
radiation pyrometers will be discussed, primarily to show that, in spite of the
recent interest in these instruments, they are not generally as suitable for measuring temperature as optical (single-color) pyrometers.

There are two major temperature scales in use today. These are the Thermodynamic Kelvin Temperature Scale (TKTS) (3) and the International Practical Temperature Scale (IPTS) (4).

Thermodynamic Kelvin Temperature Scale

As thermodynamic scale is derived from the second law of thermodynamics it is independent of the properties of any substance (5). However, in order to define such a scale uniquely it is necessary to select (or define) a number for the temperature of some one thermal state, or for a temperature interval between two states. The triple point of water was adopted (3) and (4) in 1954 by the General Conference on Weights and Measures as the fundamental fixed point on the thermodynamic scale and assigned the temperature 273.16°K. This thermodynamic scale is called the Thermodynamic Kelvin Temperature Scale and temperatures on this scale are designated degrees Kelvin or simply °K. It is considered to be the fundamental scale to which all temperature measurements should be referable.

Thermodynamic temperatures can be realized with a gas thermometer. At high temperatures, where a gas thermometer becomes impractical, radiation from a blackbody together with the Planck radiation equation can be used. In general, thermodynamic temperatures can be obtained from experimental measurements of the quantities in any equation arising from the second law of thermodynamics or the equilibrium theory of statistical mechanics.

International Practical Temperature Scale

Accurate measurements on the TKTS are very difficult, and therefore a practical scale called the International Temperature Scale was adopted by 31 nations in 1927 and revised in 1948. In 1960, its name was changed to the International Practical Temperature Scale (IPTS). This scale was designed to provide a means for specifying any temperature more conveniently and precisely than is possible on a thermodynamic scale. In addition, the scale was intended to be as close to the thermodynamic scale as existing knowledge and technique permitted.

The IPTS is based on six fixed points (oxygen, triple point of water, steam, sulfur, silver and gold) and methods for interpolating between these points. Temperatures on this scale are designated degrees Celsius or simply °C (Int. 1948). In this paper, unless stated otherwise, all temperatures will be given on the IPTS. Therefore, for simplicity, (Int. 1948) will be omitted. From 630.5°C to the gold point, defined as 1063°C temperatures are interpolated by means of a quadratic equation relating temperature to the electromotive force of standard thermocouple of platinum vs platinum-10% rhodium when one junction is at 0°C and the other is at the temperature being measured. Above the gold point, the IPTS is defined in terms of the Planck equation and the ratio of the spectral radiance of a blackbody at the temperature to be measured to the spectral radiance of a blackbody at the gold point. The instrument normally used to realize the scale in this range is the disappearing filament optical pyrometer.

For details on the definition of or recommendation for realizing the International Practical Temperature Scale, one should consult the official text (6) or its translation by Stimson (4).

Accuracy of Realizing the Temperature Scale

The concept of accuracy refers to how well a particular value agrees with the correct value. However, except in a situation where a material standard defines a unit of measurement, such as the metre bar previous to 1960, the correct value is not known and the accuracy of a particular result can never be exactly determined. An experimenter can make an estimate of the constant or systematic errors of a measurement, and this information is certainly useful. Since such estimates are a matter of judgement, they very greatly from one individual to another, and an objective interpretation on the meaning of the errors is even more difficult if not impossible to make.

There is a manner of obtaining an estimate of accuracy (2), at least for temperature measurements, which does not possess these limitations. Various national standards laboratories throughout the world independently attempt to realize the TKTS and the IPTS. Moreover, many of these laboratories are continually trying to improve their realization of the scales, and differences among the laboratories are probably the best indications available of how well the scales are being realized. Therefore, a very useful measure of the accuracy of how well the TKTS or the IPTS has been realized is the standard deviation of the population consisting of the means of the population of the temperature determinations performed in each of the national laboratories. In practice numerical results are usually not available from all the national laboratories, and therefore only a sample or estimated standard deviation can be determined. Of course, any constant systematic error that exists in all the national laboratories is not revealed in this manner. But neither would it be accounted for in any other manner. Thus it is believed that the above standard or sample standard deviation is the best available estimate of the accuracy of realizing the TKTS or IPTS, and this is how accuracy is defined in this paper. Similarly, precision is defined as the estimated standard deviation of the determination of any laboratory about the mean of the determinations in the same laboratory.

Table 2-C-1 gives the estimated accuracy of realizing the TKTS and the IPTS, the estimated precision of the thermometers used in realizing the IPTS, and reported differences between the two scales. Thermodynamic temperatures at and below the gold point have been obtained by gas thermometry and above the gold point by visual optical pyrometry. The table represents the best that can be done in temperature measurements as of 1962, and it should be emphasized that the accuracy of any temperature measurement can be no better that the accuracy of the scale to which it refers.

The precision and accuracy of realizing the TKTS and the IPTS above 900°K may improve significantly during the next few years as a result of the development of more accurate gas thermometers (7) (8), photoelectric pyrometers (9) (11), and high temperature platinum resistance thermometers (12). The latter two thermometers should also be useful for general laboratory use.

Thermocouples

The theory and use of thermocouples to determine temperature are well established. Three fundamental laws governing thermoelectric circuits have been formulated and are supported by a wealth of experimental evidence. They are often combined in the statement: "The algebraic sum of the thermoelectomotive forces generated in any given circuit containing any number of dissimilar homogeneous metals is a function only of the temperature of the junctions" (13). One of the major limitations in the use of thermocouples for high precision temperature measurements arises from the fact that unwanted emfs are generated in inhomogeneous thermoelements passing through temperature gradients. When selecting thermocouple materials, care should be taken to obtain as homogeneous a material as possible and to have the material in a well annealed state.

In any temperature measuring problem using a thermocouple, an important aspect is bringing the measuring junction of the thermocouple to the same temperature as the object or environment whose temperature is to be determined. Such a condition

Table 2-C-1: Estimated accuracy and precision in C of temperature scales as of 1962

Temperature C (Int. 1948)	Estimated accuracy of realizing I.P.T.S. of 1948	Estimated precision of thermometers used to realize I.P.T.S. of 1948	Estimated accuracy of realizing Thermodynamic Temperature scale of 1954 (7) (12)	Reported differences Therm. 1954 minus Int 1948 (7) (12)
630.5	0.02 .2	0.002 .1	0.3	+0.2
960.8 (silver point)	.2	.1	.4	+.5 +1.1
1063 (gold point)	.2 .4	.1 .3	.4	+.7 +1.5
2000	2	1	2	+3
4000	10	3	10	+10

can be approached if care is taken to minimize conduction and radiation losses (14) (15). Also, there must be sufficient electrical insulation between thermoelements of the thermocouples. This is so that emf determinations will be a true indication of the temperature of the measuring junction. Often in practice the experimenter may have geometrical or environmental limitations which make it impossible to exercise all the precautions necessary for good thermometry. However, usually the effects resulting from a lack of ideal conditions can be evaluated and accounted for to some extent. The proper use and testing of thermocouples are described in great detail in the literature (16 - 18).

In selecting a thermocouple for a particular application, one must consider a number of factors. Among these are the environment and temperature range in which the thermocouple is to be used, the stability which can be expected of the thermocouple in this range, the thermoelectric characteristics of the thermoucouple, and perhaps the cost of the thermocouple materials. For temperatures below 1200° C inexpensive base metal thermocouples find wide application. At higher temperatures, to 1800°C, it is necessary to use theromouples made of noble metals, metals which are more or less indifferent to their environment. At still higher temperatures, refractory metal thermocouples are required. These thermocouples are characterized by the high melting points of their constituents. All of these thermocouples may be used with some success at lower temperatures. They should be used at temperatures above their recommended range only in special situations, and then with the understanding that performance may be impaired.

Over the years a wide variety of thermocouples have been used for various temperature measuring situations. Some types have been found superior to others and have come into common use. In what follows the characteristics of the more common thermocouples will be described.

Base Metal Thermocouples (less than 1200°C)

For temperatures up to 1200°C base metal thermocouples having nickel as the major alloying components are used extensively in industry for measuring and controlling temperature. Examples are the Chromel P vs Alumel thermocouple, the Geminol-P vs Geminol-N thermocouple, and the Kanthal + vs Kanthal – thermocouple. They are inexpensive, have a high thermoelectromotive force, and are reasonably oxidation resistant. These thermocouples are considered to be reproducible to about 0.5°C when used for short periods of time and not used above 900°C. Dahl (19) showed that a Chromel P vs Alumel thermocouple could be used in air at 1000°C for 1000 hours with a maximum change in calibration of only 5°. At 1200°C however, a Chromel P vs Alumel thermocouple failed after 200 hours, its calibration change being 12° at the time of failure. Potts and McElroy (20), in more recent work have conducted extensive tests to 1000°C on nickel-base thermocouples. These tests include studies on homogeneity, cold working, annealing, oxidation, metallography and stability.

The maximum recommended operating temperature for nickel-base thermocouples is about 1250°C. Refractories such as porcelain, magnesia or alumina appear adequate for electrical insulation of nickel-base thermocouples throughout their useful temperature range.The use of a sheathed or swaged thermocouple assembly may appreciably extend the useful life and increase the reliability of these thermocouples in applications where corrosive atmospheres become a problem. Care should be taken to remove carbonaceous materials from insulating and protecting materials before thermocouple assembly, since nickel-base thermocouples may undergo large calibration changes at high temperatures in the presence of such materials. In addition, the use of nickel-chronium alloys under marginally oxidizing conditions should be avoided. Studies by Sibley (21) show the effect of heating a Chromel P vs Alumel Thermocouple under such conditions. Relatively large changes (88°F negative drift - see 'Notes') were observed in the thermocouple calibration after heating for 280 hours in a marginally oxidizing atmosphere at 2000°F (1093°C). The change was attributed to preferential oxidation of chromium in the Chromel P leg. Sibley also pointed out that marginally oxidizing conditions conducive to preferential oxidation can develop within protecting tubes through contamination or even through stagnation of air. Therefore, the use of large dia- meter protecting tubes is recommended to permit free circulation of air. However, recently a special grade of Chromel P alloy which is more resistant to preferential oxidation when subjected to marginally oxidizing conditions has been developed (21).

Noble Metal Thermocouples (less than 1800°C)

When cost is not a major problem, and it should not be except in situations where large numbers of thermocouples are used, the generally more stable noble metal thermocouples are preferred over the base metal types. A noble metal thermo- couple which has thermoelectrical characteristics similar to the nickel-base thermo- couples has been developed recently (22). This thermocouple is called Platinel. Tests by the manufacturer show that the temperature-emf curves of the Platinel and Chromel P vs Alumel thermocouples agree within 2% up to 1200°C. Under certain conditions, the Platinel thermocouple has proven to be more stable than nickel-base thermocouples. Stability tests in an oxidizing atmosphere of wet steam and carbon dioxide gas at 1200°C showed the Platinel thermocouple to be superior in performance to a Chromel P vs Alumel thermocouple of the same wire size. Data are also reported by the manufacturer for stability of the Platinel thermocouple in air. After about 1000 hours in air at 1300°C a Platinel thermocouple showed a maximum shift in calibration of only 3°. Platinel thermocouples are currently being studied at NBS by Freeze and Davis. In one test a Platinel thermocouple was elec- trically heated in air at about 1200°C and from time to time was checked against a reference thermocouple for changes in calibration. After a total of 1000 hours at 1200°C a shift in calibration equivalent to only 4°at 1200°C was observed. Details on this work by Freeze and Davis should be available in a future ASD technical report.

Another noble metal thermocouple has been developed recently for use in combus- tion-type atmospheres. The thermocouple has pure palladium for one leg and a platinum – 15% iridium alloy for the other. This thermocouple develops roughly three-fourths the electromotive force of a Chromel P vs Alumel thermocouple at 1100°C. Work by Ihnat (23) showed palladium vs platinum – 15% iridium thermo- couples were reliable to within ± 0.5% when used in an oxidizing atmosphere for periods as long as 400 hours in the 1000°to 1250°C temperature range. Ihnat recommended that the palladium vs platinum – 15% iridium thermocouple should not be used in a hydrogen atmosphere and that welded junctions be formed under pro- tection of an inert atmosphere. Also, the annealing procedure (24) (25) for the thermocouple appears to be important if good stability is to be obtained. Reference tables for the palladium vs platinum – 15% iridium thermocouple have been prepared at NBS by Freeze, Caldwell, and Davis (26).

The most accurate temperature measurements in the range from 630.5°C to about 1300°C are made with the platinum vs platinum – 10% rhodium thermocouple and the platinum vs platinum – 13% rhodium thermocouple. These thermocouples are used widely in laboratory applications for reference standards and for precise experi- mental work. In fact, since the platinum vs platinum – 10% rhodium thermocouple is used as the interpolating instrument on the International Practical Temperature Scale of 1948 in the range 630.5°to 1063°C (4), all other instruments used to measure temperature on the IPTS in this range must ultimately be compared with this thermocouple in some manner. The electromotive force of the platinum vs platinum − 13% rhodium thermocouple is slightly higher than the other, about 10% at 1300°C. Otherwise, for all practical purposes, the two can be considered similar in performance.

With carefully handled, well annealed (27), reference-grade platinum and platinum-rhodium wires, it is possible to obtain a precision with platinum vs platinum-rhodium thermocouples of 0.1° for short periods of time at least up to 1100°C. Thermoelements ranging from 30 to 60 inches in length can be cut randomly from 100 foot lengths of such platinum and platinum-10% rhodium wire, drawn from the same lot, and the calibration of thermocouples fabricated from these wires will seldom differ from the average of all the thermocouples by more than a few tenths of a degree at the gold point (1063°C). With wire of this quality, and in special situations where the temperature gradients along the wires can be expected to be the same from one determination to another, precision of better than 0.1° is possible. Platinum vs platinum − 10% rhodium thermocouples are tested at the freezing points of gold (1063°C) and silver (960.8°C) and at 630.5°C and 419.5°C during a primary calibration (16) at NBS. The uncertainties at each point do not exceed the equivalent of 0.2°C. Well annealed platinum vs platinum − 10% rhodium thermocouples fabricated from unused wire are expected to repeat from determination to determination at any of these points to within the equivalent of a few hundredths of a degree.

Platinum vs platinum − 10% or − 13% rhodium thermocouples are reliable to within ¼% up to 1300°C if used in a clean oxidizing atmosphere and not used for extended periods above 1300°C. High purity alumina is recommended for insulation and protection of these thermocouples when they are to be used for extended periods of time above 1000°C. Though recommended for use in oxidizing atmospheres, recent work (28) (29) indicates that they can be used with some reliability in vacuum, neutral, and even reducing atmospheres if precautions are taken to eliminate sources of possible contamination.

Experience indicates that the electromotive force of platinum vs platinum − 10% or − 13% rhodium thermocouples tends to decrease with time at a given temperature and depth of immersion. The changes are thought to be due to (a) rhodium migration, (b) preferential volatilization or oxidation in the alloy wire, and (c) chemical contamination. Rhodium migration (29-32) is the transfer of rhodium from the alloy wire to the pure platinum wire. It results in instability by decreasing the electromotive force of the thermocouple. Though not fully understood, the process is believed to progress more rapidly in situations where the measuring junction of the thermocouple is used in a region of sharp temperature gradient. Several investigators (29) (33-35) have reported that either platinum or rhodium may be preferentially removed from the alloy wire by volatilization or oxidation. The extent of this effect appears to depend strongly on the temperature and conditions under which the alloy wire is heated. In any event, the effect does not seem to cause any serious problems for temperatures up to 1300°C if the thermocouples are mounted in twin-bore insulating tubes and not used in a rapidly moving oxidizing atmosphere. In most practical applications, chemical contamination of the thermocouple from the surrounding environment is probably the principal factor that limits the useful life of platinum vs platinum-rhodium thermocouples used in the range 630.5°C. Common causes and effects of chemical contamination on platinum vs platinum-rhodium thermocouples can be found in the literature (36) (37).

For precise temperature measurements in the range 1300° to 1750°C thermocouples utilizing pure platinum as one thermoelement are declining in use in favor of thermocouples employing platinum-rhodium alloys in both legs. Using an alloy in both legs increases the mechanical strength of the thermocouples at high temperatures and appears to reduce the effects of chemical contamination and rhodium migration. Ehringer (38) studied the behaviour of platinum and platinum-rhodium alloy wires when heated for periods of time in air and hydrogen. He heated the wires in the presence of various refractory oxides such as alumina and silica. In this work alloys of platinum-rhodium were shown to be much less susceptible to changes in calibration than pure platinum. Metcalfe (32) showed that a platinum-1% rhodium vs platinum − 13%rhodium thermocouple was more stable in a vacuum at 1510°C than a platinum vs platinum − 13%rhodium thermocouple. This improved behaviour was attributed to a reduction in the effects of rhodium migration and chemical contamination. Recent studies have been made by Walker, Ewing and Miller at the Naval Research Laboratory on the instability of noble metal thermo-couples in the range 1000°to 1700°C. Effects of various grades of alumina sheath-ing on the thermoelectric characteristic of platinum and platinum-rhodium alloys in oxidizing and neutral atmosphere were investigated. They found that the platinum-rhodium alloys were more stable than pure platinum when used in similar environments at high temperatures. A paper covering this work should appear in the literature within a few months.

Three platinum-rhodium alloy combinations have gained general acceptance. These are the platinum − 5%rhodium vs platinum − 20%rhodium, platinum − 6%rhodium vs platinum − 30%rhodium, and platinum − 20%rhodium vs platinum − 40%rhodium thermocouples. The platinum − 5%rhodium vs platinum − 20%rhodium and platinum − 6%rhodium vs platinum − 30%rhodium thermocouples have nearly the same thermoelectric characteristics in the range 1300°to 1750°C. Their thermoelectric powers at 1600°C are 10 $\mu v/°C$ and 11 $\mu v/°C$, respectively. The platinum−20%rhod-ium vs platinum−40%rhodium thermocouple has a thermoelectric power of only 4.5 $\mu v/°C$ at 1600°C. However, Jewell, Knowles and Lord (39) have studied this thermocouple and recommend it for use in the 1700°to 1850°C temperature range. Wire manu-facturers in this country have standardized on the platinum − 6%rhodium vs platinum − 30%rhodium thermocouple. Reference tables are being prepared at NBS for this thermocouple, and reference tables for the platinum − 6%rhodium vs platinum − 30% rhodium thermocouple have appeared recently in a paper by Obrowski and Prinz (40). Though no long term stability experiments have been conducted at NBS, ex-cellent stability for short periods of time has been observed with this thermocouple at temperatures up to 1650°C. Recrystallized alumina has been used successfully for insulation and protection of platinum-rhodium alloys. However, at temperatures approaching 1800°C errors introduced by insufficient electrical insulation between thermo-elements should not be overlooked. Also, caution should be exercised in the use of alumina as an insulating material in the presence of carbonaceous mater-ials at temperatures above 1600°C (41). Though it is usually recommended that platinum-rhodium alloy combinations be used in oxidixing atmospheres, intermittent use in vacuum, neutral and hydrogen atmosphere appears possible. Except in cases where these thermocouples can be used in an exceptionally clean environment, protection by high purity alumina will most probably extend their useful life.

Refractory Metal Thermocouples

Increased demands from high temperature technology in the past ten years have led to accelerated programs in the search for thermocouples capable of reliable tempera-ture measurements above the range of platinum-rhodium types. Though the proper-ties of numerous combinations have been explored, only a few displayed promise and have been developed to any extent. Sanders (42) gives an extensive review of the many thermocouples that have been tried above 1800° C. The two high-temperature thermocouple systems receiving the most attention at present are the tungsten-rhenium and iridium-rhodium systems. Only refractory metal thermocouples of these two systems will be discussed in this paper.

The tungsten vs rhenium and tungsten vs tungsten − 26%rhenium thermocouples have been the most widely investigated in the tungsten-rhenium system. Of these two, the tungsten vs tungsten – 26% rhenium appears to offer the most promise in terms of high temperature capabilities and accuracy. A gradual decrease in the thermoelectric power of the tungsten vs rhenium thermocouple with increasing temperature limits its use for most practical applications to temperatures below 2200°C. The tungsten vs tungsten – 26% rhenium thermocouple has been reported as having a high thermoelectric power up to at least 2800°C and has shown excellent stability at temperatures as high as 2200°C. In recent work by Lachman (43) a tungsten vs tungsten – 26% rhenium thermocouple was heated for 100 hours at 4000°F (2204°C) in argon and showed a maximum change in calibration of 12°F. Lachman claimed that similar stability could be expected in a hydrogen atmosphere.

As a result of the increasing use of high temperature thermocouples and with improvements in the quality and availability of refractory metal wires, the NBS has initiated a project to investigate the thermoelectric properties of the more promising refractory metal materials. High temperature testing facilities (44) have been developed at NBS and Thomas is preparing reference tables for the tungsten vs rhenium thermocouple. Thermocouples, made from tungsten wire of different lots obtained from three different commercial sources, and rhenium wires from different lots from a single commercial source, have been tested in the range 1000° to 2000°C in a helium atmosphere. The maximum deviation for any thermocouple in the group from the average of all the thermocouples is about 20° at 2000°C. Though no long term stability tests on the tungsten vs rhenium thermocouple have been made at NBS, the thermocouple has, in general, proved to be stable for short periods of time at temperatures up to at least 2000°C in a purified helium atmosphere.

A major limitation in thermocouples employing pure tungsten as one thermoelement is the extreme brittleness of the tungsten in the recrystallized state. Handling of tungsten wire after it has been heated above about 1200°C requires utmost care. The fact that the tungsten - 26% rhenium alloy is still ductile at room temperature after being heated for extended periods above its recrystallization temperature suggests the possibility of obtaining a more useful high temperature thermocouple with improved mechanical properties by using tungsten-rhenium alloys in both legs. In a recent test at NBS a tungsten - 3% rhenium alloy wire was heated for 1 hour at 2000°C in a purified helium atmosphere. After this treatment it could be bent into a hairpin shape.

For reliable use at high temperatures, tungsten vs rhenium and tungsten vs tungsten – 26% rhenium thermocouples require a protective atmosphere free of oxidizing gases. Exposure to air above 1000°C will result in immediate failure of these thermocouples, and, all traces of water and carbonaceous materials should be removed from insulating and protecting parts before assembling these thermocouples. The behaviour of tungsten vs rhenium and tungsten vs tungsten – 26% rhenium thermocouples in vacuum (45) (46) hydrogen (47) (48) neutral (43) and carbon (41) (49) atmospheres has been studied, and the literature should be consulted for details.

Alumina appears satisfactory for electric insulation of these thermocouples up to about 1800°C. Above this range there are no completely satisfactory materials available today. In some cases, satisfactory results have been obtained with beryllia and thoria. Heath (41) and Sanders (42) have reviewed the merits and limitations of these and other high temperature refractory oxides. Thermocouples of the iridium-rhodium system are of particular interest because they show promise as being useful in oxidizing atmospheres above the range of platinum-rhodium types. One proven refractory thermocouple of this type is the iridium vs rhodium – 40% iridium thermocouple. It has been calibrated and used to 2100°C in a neutral atmosphere with a maximum uncertainty of 7°. Only minor changes in the calibration of this thermocouple have been reported after 50 hours at 2000°C in an

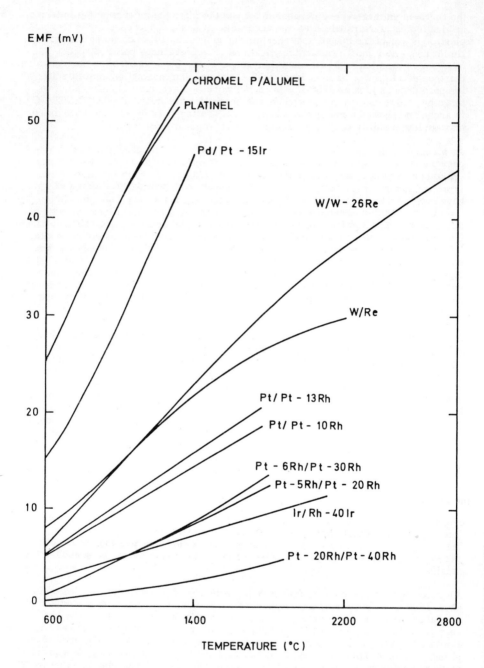

Fig. 2-C-1   EMF plotted against temperature for the more commonly used high temperature thermocouples, reference junction at 0° C

atmosphere containing 2% oxygen. The thermocouple failed after 12 hours in air at 2000°C, but was relatively stable during its lifetime. Moreover, the use of a protective sheath will prolong its life in air (42). Kuether and Lachman (45) have studied the behaviour of the iridium vs rhodium – 40% iridium thermocouple in vacuum at temperatures up to 2600°F (1427°C). They found a shift in calibration equivalent to 21°F at 2000°F (1093°C) after heating an iridium vs rhodium – 40% iridium thermocouple in a vacuum for a period of 20 hours at 2600°F (1427°C).

Caldwell and Blackburn at NBS have been working on a program to establish reference tables for several alloy combinations of iridium-rhodium against iridium. An iridium blackbody inductively heated in a high percentage helium atmosphere is being used in this work. Tables have been prepared for the iridium vs rhodium – 40% iridium thermocouple in the range 0° to 2100°C (50). Eight thermocouples fabricated from three different lots of wire from the same manufacturer were tested and the data used to construct the reference table. The maximum deviation of any of the eight thermocouples from the reference table was about 10° at 2000°C. They were able to use beryllia and thoria for electrical insulation but empirically determined corrections were necessary above 1800°C. Homogeneous iridium vs rhodium – 40% iridium thermocouples are available commercially and they are sufficiently ductile to permit bending on a quarter-inch radius. The major limitations in using this thermocouple are its high cost and relatively low thermoelectric power (5.5 $\mu v/°C$ at 1300°C and 6.5 $\mu v/°C$ at 2100°C).

The greatest problem in the reliable use of thermocouples above about 2100° or 2200°C is the lack of satisfactory materials for protection and electrical insulation. This seriousness of insufficient electrical insulation at high temperature is illustrated in a recent report by McGurty and Kuhlman (51). Due to lack of adequate insulating and protecting materials the use of bare thermocouples is mandatory at present if reliable temperature measurements are to be made at these high temperatures.

A summary of the temperature range, emf, thermoelectric power and stability of the thermocouples discussed in this paper is given in table 2-C-2. The numbers are estimates based on data found in the literature and on experience at NBS. Also, temperature-emf curves for the thermocouples are given in Figure 2-C-1. The curves cover the range of available calibration data, but it is not necessarily recommended that the thermocouple be used over the entire range.

Optical Pyrometers

When a thermocouple is undesirable because it disturbs the system significantly or unreliable because the temperature is too high, an optical pyrometer should be considered for determining the temperature. Moreover, because the IPTS above 1063°C is defined in terms of radiation, even thermocouples must be ultimately calibrated with a radiation thermometer above this temperature.

The radiation thermometry part of this paper will be organized differently and have significantly fewer references than the thermocouple part. This is due primarily to two reasons. First, there are a large number of thermocouples useful in different environments and temperature ranges while the optical pyrometer is the only radiation device recommended for temperature determinations. Second, one of the present authors was a co-author of a recent monograph on optical pyrometry (2) from which this review paper draws heavily. It was not thought worthwhile or necessary to repeat details of general pyrometry theory or methods, so only the results considered particularly appropriate are repeated or summarized.

The measurement of temperature by optical pyrometry is based on the fact that the

Table 2-C-2: Estimated stability for the more reliable high temperature thermocouples

Thermocouple	Atmosphere	Approx. e.m.f. at temp. indicated(mv)	Thermo-electric power at temp. indicated μv/ C	Temp. C (Int. 1948)	Estimated change in calibration after being at temp. for time indicated, deg.	
					10 hr	1000 hr
Chromel vs Alumel	Oxidizing	41	39	1000	0.5	5.0
		49	36	1200	2.0	F
Palladium vs platinum 15% iridium	Oxidizing	38	43	1200	0.5	5.0
Platinel + vs platinel	Oxidizing	48	32	1200	0.5	3.0
Platinum vs platinum 10%or13% rhodium	Oxidizing	11 ͼ 12	12 or 13	1100	0.1	2.0
		15 or 17	12 or 14	1500	1.0	---
Platinum-6% rhodium vs platinum-30% rhodium	Oxidizing	12	11	1700	4.0	----
Platinum-5% rhodium vs platinum-20% rhodium	Oxidizing	12	10	1700	4.0	---
Platinum-20% rhodium vs platinum-40% rhodium	Oxidizing	5	5	1800	6.0	---
Tungsten vs rhenium	Inert	28	7	2000	10.0	---
Tungsten vs tungsten 26% rhenium		37	14	2200	10.0	---
Iridium vs rhodium-40% iridium	Inert or slightly oxidising	11	7	2000	10.0	---

F means the thermocouple would fall before the time indicated

spectral radiance of a body depends on its temperature. For a blackbody, the spectral radiance is related to the temperature by the well-established Planck radiation equation (for units and notation, see (2),

$$N_b \lambda (T) = \frac{C_1 \lambda^{-5}/\pi}{e^{c_2/\lambda T} - 1} \qquad \text{(Eq. 2-C-1)}$$

where C_1 and C_2 are constants, λ is the wavelength, and T is the temperature expressed in degrees Kelvin. When the object is not a blackbody, the fractional reduction in spectral radiance for the same temperature is given by the spectral emittance ϵ_λ (T) and the spectral radiance becomes:

$$N_\lambda (T) = \epsilon_\lambda (T) N_{b\lambda} (T) \qquad \text{(Eq. 2-C-2)}$$

In this case, in order to determine the temperature of the object by optical pyrometry, it is necessary to determine not only the spectral radiance but also the spectral emittance. This need for spectral emmittance is probably the major problem in determining temperatures by optical pyrometry. This is particularly discouraging, because the temperature is needed to determine the spectral emittance and the spectral emittance to determine the temperature (with optical pyrometry). On the other hand, this clearly emphasizes the importance of spectral emittance data and the contributions that can be made in this field.

As a result of the above-mentioned paradox with temperature and spectral emittance, most spectral emittance studies utilizing optical pyrometry to obtain the temperature require a blackbody (spectral emittance equal to one). Nevertheless, it is possible to use a non-blackbody whose spectral emittance has been determined previously; and in addition, optical pyrometers are often checked or calibrated with non-blackbody sources. Therefore, problems inherent in determining the temperature of non-blackbody as well as blackbody sources will be discussed in this paper.

Temperature Determinations With Optical Pyrometers

Optical pyrometers are instruments which determine the spectral radiance of a radiating object at a particular wavelength. The determination is usually expressed as the temperature of a blackbody which has the same spectral radiance at this wavelength. Such a temperature is called the brightness and in general is a function of wavelength. Mathematically it is defined by the equation:

$$N_{\lambda'} (T) = \epsilon_{\lambda'} (T) N_{b\lambda'} (T) = N_{b\lambda'} (T'_B) \qquad \text{(Eq. 2-C-3)}$$

where T'_B is the brightness temperature at wavelength λ'. If the object being sighted on is a blackbody, the brightness temperature is the actual temperature and of course, is then independent of wavelength.

In order to obtain the temperature of a non-blackbody from an optical pyrometer determination, the spectral emittance at the wavelength associated with the pyrometer is required. The temperature can be obtained from equation (2-C-3) or more explicitly from:

$$\epsilon_{\lambda'} (t) = \frac{C_2}{e^{\lambda' (t + T_o)} - 1} \Big/ \frac{c_2}{e^{\lambda' (t_B + T_o)} - 1} \qquad \text{(Eq. 2-C-4)}$$

where $t + T_o = T$ and $t'_B + T_o = T'_B$, t is the temperature, and t'_B is the brightness temperature (at wavelength λ') in °C (Int. 1948), ϵ_λ (t) is the spectral emittance at λ' and t, $C_2 = 1.438$ cm deg, and $T_o = 273.15$ deg. Usually, the Wein radiation equation is an adequate approximation for the Planck equation as for a wavelength equal to 0.65μ and $t = 4000°C$ the error in using the Wein equation is about 5°. At 3000°C and 0.65μ the error is about 0.5°. Then equation 2-C-3 can be simplified to:

$$\frac{1}{T} = \frac{1}{T'_B} + \frac{\lambda'}{C_2} \ln \epsilon_{\lambda'} (T)$$

(Eq. 2-C-5)

The wavelength λ' is called the mean effective wavelength of the optical pyrometer. The accuracy required for λ' when determining non-blackbody temperatures depends on how rapidly $\epsilon_{\lambda'}$ varies with wavelength. However, the accuracy of the spectral emittance need be only $1/5$ to $1/15$ the accuracy required in the temperature. For example, in the vicinity of the gold point and at the wavelength of 0.65μ an error of 10% in the spectral emittance results in an error of only 0.65% in temperature. More generally, using Wein's approximation and assuming that the usually small variation of spectral emittance with temperature may be neglected one obtains:

$$\frac{dT}{T} = -\frac{\lambda' T}{C_2} \frac{d\epsilon_\lambda}{\epsilon_\lambda}$$

(Eq. 2-C-6)

If an accuracy of $\pm 0.01\mu$ for λ' is adequate, the value 0.65μ can usually be used for visual optical pyrometers manufactured in the United States (as of 1962).

The spectral emittance at 0.65μ has been determined for a number of substances (52 - 54). In addition Poland, Green and Margrave (55) have published a set of tables calculated from equation 2-C-4, giving the actual temperature as a function of the observed brightness temperature and spectral emittance at 0.65μ.

It is possible, with considerable effort, to determine the mean effective wavelength in visual optical pyrometers considerably better than $\pm 0.01\mu$ (probably about 0.001μ). However, in order to do this the spectral transmittance of the filters in the optical pyrometer, the relative visibility function of the observer and the colour temperature of the source are all required. Instead of determining the visibility function of the observer, a difficult feat, one can probably use a number of observers and assume their average is the CIE standard visibility function (2). This should be adequate because the standard deviation of the mean effective wavelength resulting from differences in the visibility function of observers has been reported (2) to be about 0.0008μ. If the colour temperature of the object is not available from the literature, it can be obtained experimentally by determining the spectral radiance of the object over the spectral bandpass of the pyrometer (approximately 0.62 to 0.75μ). The desired colour temperature is the temperature of the blackbody whose spectral radiance curve when multiplied by some constant best fits the observed spectral radiance curve of the source. The actual equations used for calculating the mean effective wavelength with the above data are rather lengthy and will not be given here. The equations as well as their derivations are available in the previously mentioned monograph (2).

Blackbodies

There are many substances for which the spectral emittance at 0.65μ is not known or not known sufficiently well to obtain an accurate temperature. In this situation, a blackbody must be built into the apparatus. A hollow opaque body containing a small hole can be made to approximate a blackbody extremely well, and sources used as blackbodies are usually of this type. In such bodies, the smaller the area of the hole relative to the area of the walls of the cavity, the higher the emittance or blacker the body. For a particular geometry the blackness of a hollow body also depends on the reflectivity of the inner surface of the cavity including how diffuse or specular it is. A factor often neglected is that the walls of the enclosure should have a uniform temperature. Lack of a uniform temperature can result in a large departure from blackbody conditions. Details for designing blackbodies and for calculating departures from an emittance of one may be found in the literature (56-58).

Intercomparison of Optical Pyrometers

When several optical pyrometers are used in a laboratory, they are often intercompared by using a tungsten strip lamp as a transfer source. These lamps are highly reproducible sources of radiant energy (2) (59) (60) and can be calibrated with respect to brightness temperature from 800°to 2300°C with an accuracy only slightly less than the accuracy of realizing the ITPS. In effect, the tungsten strip lamps when used under well defined conditions (orientation, direction of sighting, ambient temperature) serve as a continuous set of fixed points from 800°to 2300°C with a constancy of about 0.5°to 1.0°. One other point must be kept in mind when intercomparing optical pyrometers with tungsten strip lamps. The brightness temperature of a strip lamp is a function of wavelength, and the mean effective wavelengths of commercial optical pyrometers are sometimes different. Therefore, the brightness temperature of a strip lamp as determined with two different pyrometers, even though accurately calibrated, may be different. At 2200°C this difference has been observed to be as high as 5°in commercial optical pyrometers. At 1000°C it is usually less than 1°. For the most accurate optical pyrometer intercomparisons with strip lamps, the mean effective wavelengths of the pyrometers should be obtained and corrections made with the equation (2):

$$\frac{1}{T'} = \frac{(\lambda' - \lambda)}{\lambda}\left(\frac{1}{T} - \frac{1}{T^c}\right) + \frac{1}{T} \qquad \text{(Eq. 2-C-7)}$$

where, again, T and T' are brightness temperatures at wavelength λ and λ', respectively, and T^c is the colour temperature of the tungsten lamp.

Another very useful transfer or reference source that has become available commercially (Mole-Richardson Company), is the pyrometric carbon arc. The positive crater of an arc using pure graphite electrodes and operated just below the so-called arc overload current has a brightness temperature of about 3800°K (61) (62), reproducible to about 15°K. With appropriate absorbing glass filters such as those found in optical pyrometers, a carbon arc could also be used at brightness temperatures lower than 3800°K. At the apparent brightness temperature of 1000°K, the reproducibility of such an arc would be about 1°.

Recommendations for Using Optical Pyrometers

When high accuracy is the primary consideration in maintaining or making measurements on the IPTS, a few procedures should be emphasized. Both the small pyrometer lamps in optical pyrometers and tungsten strip lamps change with use. Therefore, in order to obtain high accuracy a laboratory should use one calibrated strip lamp or optical pyrometer infrequently and compare it to the strip lamps or pyrometers used regularly. For optimum results, the calibration of a visual optical pyrometer should be checked about every 200 hours of use. Great care should be taken concerning the orientation and alignment of the strip lamps; and vacuum strip lamps, which are generally more stable than gas-filled lamps below brightness temperatures (0.65μ) of about 1400°C (2), should be used whenever possible.

For optimum precision and accuracy in the use of optical pyrometers, laboratories should request NBS to calibrate their pyrometers as a function of pyrometer filament current. The laboratory should then use a standard resistor and sufficiently accurate potentiometer to determine this current. A multiturn smooth-turning rheostat is highly desirable for varying the filament current while making brightness matches. The precision of the matches can often be improved by having the pyrometer mounted rigidly in a comfortable position for a sitting observer. A black cloth thrown over the observer's head and part of the optical pyrometer to shield the observer from any distracting or annoying light is helpful. Observations should always be made from both a dark and bright filament to a match or disappearance and the two results averaged. If one or two individuals primarily use the pyrometer, make sure that their technique of matching or their visibility functions do not give results very different from the average of a larger number (at least 5 or 6) of observers. Blackbodies should be used whenever possible but if they cannot be used and high accuracy is required, the mean effective wavelengths of the pyrometers should be obtained.

Accuracy and Precision

The precision of visual optical pyrometers is limited by the sensitivity of the human eye. The precision possible by experienced observers using a good instrument under ideal conditions is shown in table 2-C-1.

The accuracy of brightness temperature determinations with visual optical pyrometers depends on the accuracy with which the IPTS can be realized in the national standards laboratories and how well a visual pyrometer can be calibrated and used relative to this scale. Brightness temperatures can be obtained with NBS calibrated commercial visual pyrometer to about 3° at the gold point, 6° at 2000°C and 40° at 4000°C. Using precisely determined current in the pyrometer lamp as a measure of the brightness temperature the above uncertainties can often be reduced. If one performs his own primary calibration with a carefully designed and constructed pyrometer and with all the precautions taken at a national standards laboratory, it is possible to approach the accuracy listed in column 2 of table 2-C-1.

Photoelectric Optical Pyrometers

Serious efforts have been underway at a number of national standards laboratories (9) (11) for the past five or six years to replace the visual optical pyrometer with a photoelectric optical pyrometer. Since a photomultiplier tube is more sensitive than the eye and can discriminate between smaller differences of radiance, errors in brightness matching and the mean effective wavelength can be reduced significantly. Photoelectric pyrometers developed in the standards laboratories have a precision about ten times greater than that listed for visual pyrometers in table 2-C-1. Little information is currently available on their accuracy, relative to the IPTS. However, based on the work at NBS, the accuracy realized in the near future is expected to be 2 or 3 times better than that of the visual pyrometer.

Photoelectric pyrometers are now available commercially from the Instrument Development Laboratories, Attleboro, Mass; the Leeds and Northrup Company, Philadelphia and the Pyrometer Instrument Company, Bergenfield. These instruments are reported to have sensitivities varying from 0.5° to that comparable to the photoelectric pyrometers in the national standards laboratories. Probably of greater significance in practice, is that these instruments make brightness matches automatically and therefore can be used remotely or to control a source of radiation as well as determine its temperature or brightness temperature.

Other Types of Radiation Thermometers

Two-Colour Pyrometers

Attempts have been made to circumvent the need for spectral emittance corrections when determining temperatures with an optical pyrometer by using a two-colour pyrometer (54). This instrument determines a two-colour temperature by measuring the ratio of the spectral radiances at two wavelengths. The two-colour temperature is equal to the temperature only if the spectral emittances at the two wavelengths are equal. Unfortunately, spectral emittance usually changes with wavelength. If the change is very small, the two-colour temperature will be close to the actual temperature. On the other hand, there are materials (Ag, Cu, Au) for which the spectral emittance changes with wavelengths so fast that the two-colour temperature differs a factor of two or more from the actual temperature. A detailed analysis of whether a two-colour pyrometer or an optical pyrometer determines a more accurate temperature is given by Pyatt (63). The idea to be emphasized is that a two-colour pyrometer is not generally more accurate than an optical pyrometer and some information concerning spectral emittances is needed before the instrument can be used with confidence. Furthermore, two-colour pyrometers are inherently less sensitive than optical (single colour) pyrometers. For example when determining the temperature of a blackbody at 2300°K with an optical pyrometer, a change in the spectral radiance at 0.66μ of 1.2% would modify the resulting temperature indication by 2°C. Using a two-colour pyrometer a change of 1.2% in spectral radiance at 0.66μ and 1.0% in the opposite direction at 0.56μ would modify the temperature indication by 30°C. Equation 2-C-8 is an expression for the sensitivity of a two-colour pyrometer when using the Wien approximation.

$$\frac{dT}{T} = \frac{\lambda_1\lambda_2 T}{C_2(\lambda_2-\lambda_1)} \frac{d(N_{\lambda_1}/N_{\lambda_2})}{N_{\lambda_1}/N_{\lambda_2}} \qquad\qquad (\text{Eq. } 2\text{-C-8})$$

In general, two-colour pyrometers are not recommended for determining temperatures accurately. However, there are applications where one is more interested in the control of temperature than in the measurement of temperature. In such cases, two colour pyrometers may be useful and a variety of such instruments are now available commercially.

Three-Colour Pyrometers

During the past few years three-colour pyrometers (64) (65) have received increasing attention and at first glance, are very promising as an instrument for obtaining the temperature of an object without having knowledge of its spectral emittance. This is true however, only if the spectral emittance of the object is exactly linear with respect to wavelength. Proponents of three-colour pyrometers claim that since many materials appear to have an approximately linear spectral emittance in the infrared, a three-colour infrared pyrometer will determine accurate temperatures for these materials. However, what they apparently do not realize is that a slight departure from linearity will result in a large temperature uncertainty. For example, if four different sources of radiation possessed the spectral emittances in Figure 2-C-2 and the temperatures indicated thereon, each would radiate the same between 1.2 and 2.0μ. Thus, one could not distinguish between any of these temperatures by spectral radiance measurements alone, and a three-colour pyrometer operating in this spectral region would indicate a temperature of 2000°K for all sources represented by the curves in Figure 2-C-2. Only in the case for which

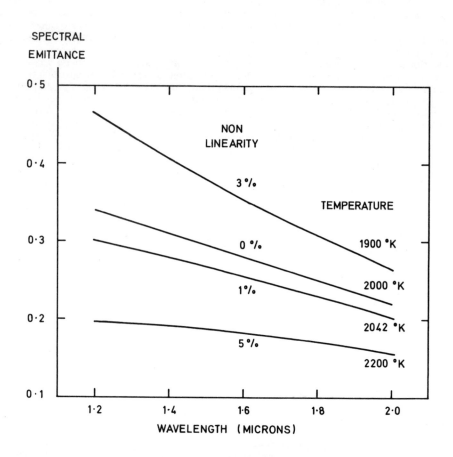

Fig. 2-C-2 Spectral emittance curves and temperatures for four radiation
sources.

the spectral emittance curve was linear, would this be the correct temperature. A nonlinearity in spectral emittance of 1% would result in a 42°error and a 5% nonlinearity in a 200°error. Where nonlinearity in Figure 2-C-2 is defined as the percent deviation of spectral emittance at 1.6μ from the spectral emittance calculated at 1.6μ for each curve by a linear interpolation between 1.2 and 2.0μ. The accuracy of the best available spectral emittance data probably falls in this range of 1 to 5%. Moreover, to the best of our knowledge, there is no theoretical basis for the spectral emittance to be exactly linear. On the other hand when using an optical pyrometer, an error in the spectral emittance at 0.65μ and 2000°K of 1 to 5% would result in a temperature error of only $1.8°$ to $9°$. As a result of the very demanding requirement on spectral emittance linearity, three-colour pyrometers are not recommended for (radiation) temperature measurements. To the best of our knowledge, as of 1962, there are no three-colour pyrometers available commercially.

Total-Radiation Pyrometers

Total radiation pyrometers are also not very suitable for accurate temperature measurements. Of course, knowledge of an effective emittance for a broad band of wavelengths is necessary, and this must be known more accurately than the spectral emittance for an optical pyrometer. As an example, the total radiance of a blackbody is proportional to the fourth power of temperature while the spectral radiance, say at 0.65μ and 2000°K is proportional to the eleventh power of temperature. In general, the broader the wavelength band of a radiation pyrometer, the greater the problems for determining accurate temperatures. In addition, many of the total-radiation pyrometers require larger targets than optical pyrometers. On the other hand, total-radiation pyrometers can be used to much lower temperatures (66) and are probably the least expensive radiation pyrometers which have an electrical output suitable for automatic control purposes. Thus they, as the two-colour pyrometers should be considered where control rather than a temperature determination is the primary objective. For those interested in total-radiation pyrometers, a recent book on this subject by Harrision (67) is recommended.

Conclusion

Temperature measurements are normally made on the International Practical Temperature Scale and reported in degrees Celsius, i.e. °C (Int. 1948) or in degrees Kelvin, i.e. °K (Int. 1948). The latter temperatures are obtained by adding 273.15°to the IPTS Celsius values. Differences between the IPTS when reported in degrees Kelvin and the Thermodynamic Kelvin Temperature Scale above 900°K are usually less than errors in determining the temperature in practice on the IPTS.

Thermocouples are very reliable for making accurate temperature determinations up to at least 1300°C. The use of platinum vs platinum-10% and -13% rhodium thermocouples is recommended in this range when the ultimate in precision and accuracy is desired. From 1300°C to about 1800°C, thermocouples are less reliable due to calibration uncertainties and to increased effects of chemical contamination. In this range thermocouples with a platinum-rhodium alloy in both legs are recommended. Above 1800°C all the previously mentioned difficulties increase and in addition there are no completely satisfactory materials for protection and electrical insulation. Thus in practice, accurate temperature determinations are very difficult. At present (1962) the more promising thermocouples for use above 1800°C are tungsten vs tungsten-26% rhenium and iridium vs rhodium-40% iridium.

For the determination of temperature of solids by radiation thermometry, an optical (single-colour) pyrometer is recommended. For the most accurate temperature determinations a blackbody and a number of observers (with a visual pyrometer) should be used. If a blackbody cannot be incorporated in the setup, the spectral emittance of the object at the mean effective wavelength of the pyrometer is required. Finally, the calibration of the optical pyrometer should be checked about every 200 hours of use. An infrequently used optical pyrometer or an infrequently used vacuum strip lamp is recommended for this check.

NOTES

There are no Fahrenheit units defined on either the International or Thermodynamic Scales. Nevertheless, they are still occasionally used in practice. When temperatures in the literature are given in Fahrenheit units, we have retained the usage in this section with the approximate Celsius units on the IPTS also given. For this purpose we have defined $°F = 9/5 \times °C$ (Int. 1948) + 32.

Temperature can be expressed on the TKTS or the IPTS. In the latter, usually preferred case, the temperature equals $t_{Int} + T_o$ where $T_o = 273.15°$.

In this section the symbol t designates temperature in $°C$ and T in $°K$. Though both temperatures are on the ITPS and should be designated t_{int} and T_{int}, for simplicity the subscripts have been omitted.

References

1. **Kostowski, H. J.**, 'Proc. of an Int. Svm. on High Temperature Technology,' The accuracy and Precision of Measuring Temperatures Above 1000°K.' McGraw-Hill, 1959, p. 33.

2. **Kostowski, H. J.**, and **Lee, R. D.**, 'Theory and Methods of Optical Pyrometry.' Monograph 41, Nat. Bur. Standards, 1962.

   Stimson, H. F., 'Heat Units and Temperature Scales for Calorimetry.' Am. Jour. Pys., vol. 23, 1955, p. 615.

4. **Stimson, H. F.**, 'International Practical Temperature Scale of 1948, Text revision of 1960.' Monograph 37, Nat. Bur. Standards, 1961; The International Temperature Scale of 1948, Jour. Res., Nat. Bur. Standards, vol. 42, 1949, p. 209.
5. **Zemansky, M. W.**, 'Heat and Thermodynamics.' McGraw-Hill., 1957.

6. Comptes Rendus de la Onizième Conférence Générale des Poides et Mesures, 1960, p. 1.

7. **Moser, H.**, 'Temperature, Its Measurement and Control in Science and Industry.' 'Review of Recent Determinations of Thermodynamic Temperatures of Fixed Points Above 419°C.' Reinhold, to be published.

8. **Guildner, L. A.**, 'Temperature, Its Measurement and Control in Science and Industry.' 'A National Bureau of Standards Gas Thermometer.' Reinhold, to be published.

9. **Lee, R. D.**, 'Temperature, Its Measurement and Control in Science and Industry.' 'The NBS Photoelectric Pyrometer of 1961.' Reinhold, to be published.'

10. **Middlehurst, J.**, and **Jones, T. P.**, 'A Precision Photoelectric Optical

Pyrometer'.' Temperature, Its Measurement and Control in Science and Industry.' Reinhold, to be published.

11. **Kandyba, V. A., and Kovalevskii, V. A.,** 'A Photoelectric Spectropyrometer of High Precision.' Doklady Akad. Nauk (U.S.S.R.), vol. 108, 1956, p. 633.

12. **Evans, J. P. and Burns, G. W.,** 'Temperature, Its Measurement and Control in Science and Industry.' A Study of Stability of 'High Temperature Platinum Resistance Thermometers.' Vol. 3, pt. 1. Reinhold, 1962, p. 313.

13. **Roeser, W. F.,** 'Temperature, Its Measurement and Control in Science and Industry.'' Thermoelectric Thermometry.' Reinhold, 1941.

14. **Thomas, A. R., Schurin, B., and Morris, J. C.,** ' Temperature Error Associated with Imbedded Thermocouples.' Rev. Sci. Instr., vol. 19, 1958, p. 1045.

15. **Pease, R. S.,** 'The Measurement of Specimen Temperature in a High Temperature X-ray Powder Camera.' Jour. Sci. Inst., vol. 32, 1955, p. 476.

16. **Roeser, W. F. and Lonberger, S. T.,** 'Methods of Testing Thermocouples and Thermocouple Materials.' Nat. Bur. Standards, Circular 590, 1958.

17. **Finch, D. I.,** 'General Principles of Thermoelectric Thermometry.' Leeds and Northrup Co., Tech. Pub. ENS2(1), 1962, p. 1161.

18. **Baker, H. D., Ryder, E. A., and Baker, N. H.,** 'Temperature Measurement in Engineering.' Vols. 1 and 2,' John Wiley., 1961.

19. **Dahl, A. I.,** Temperature, 'Its Measurement and Control in Science and Industry.' 'The Stability of Base Metal Thermocouples in Air From 800° to 2200°F.' Reinhold., 1941.

20. **Pitts, J. F., and McElroy, D. L.,** 'Thermocouple Research to 1000°C. — Final Report.' November 1, 1957, through June 30, 1959. ORNL–2773, Oak Ridge Nat. Lab.

21. **Sibley, F. S.,** 'High-Temperature Thermometry Seminar.' 'Effect of Environment on the Stability of Chromel-Alumel Thermocouples.' Oak Ridge Nat. Lab., Oct. 1-2, 1959, TID 7586 (pt. 1), p. 16.

22. **Accinno, D. J. and Schneider, J. F.,** 'Platinel – A Noble Metal Thermocouple To Replace Chromel-Alumel.' Engelhard, Tech. Bull., vol. 1, 1960, p. 53.

23. **Inhat, M. E.,** 'A Jet Engine Thermocouple System for Measuring Temperatures up to 2300°F.' WADC TR 57-744, Astia Doc. No. 203393.

24. **Clark R. B., and Hagel, W. C.,** 'High-Temperature Thermometry Seminar,' 'High-Output Noble-Metal Thermocouples and Matching Lead Wire.' Oak Ridge Nat. Lab., Oct. 1-2, 1959, TID 7586 (pt. 1), p. 37.

25. **Caldwell, F. R.,** 'Thermocouple Materials.' Nat. Bur. Standards, Monograph 40, 1962.

26. **Freeze, R. D., Caldwell, F. R., and Davis, E. R.,** 'Reference Tables for the Palladium vs Platinum-15% Iridium Thermocouple.' ASD–TDR–62–525.

27. **Corruccini, R. J.,** 'Annealing of Platinum for Thermometry.' Jour. Res., Nat. Bur. Standards, vol. 47, RP 2232, 1951, p. 94.

28. **Bennett, H. F.,** 'The Contamination of Platinum Metal Thermocouples.' Platinum Metals Rev., vol. 5, no. 4, 1961.

29. **McQuillan, M. K.,** 'Some Observations on the Behavior of Platinum/Platinum-Rhodium Thermocouples at High Temperatures.' Jour. Sci. Instr., vol. 26, 1949, p. 329.

30. **Mortlock, A. J.,** 'Error in Temperature Measurement Due to the Inter-diffusion at the Hot Junction of a Thermocouple.' Jour. Sci. Instr., vol. 35, 1958, p. 283.

31. **Darling, A. S.,** 'Rhodium-Platinum Alloys.' Platinum Metals Rev., vol. 5, no. 2, 1961.

32. **Metcalfe, A. G.,** 'The Use of Platinum Thermocouples in Vacuo at High Temperatures.' Brit. Jour. Appl. Phys., vol, 1, 1950, p. 256.

33. **Svec, H. J.,** 'Behavior of Platinum/Platinum-Rhodium Thermocouples at High Temperatures.' Jour. Sci. Inst., vol. 29, 1952, p. 100.

34. **Jewell, R. C., and Knowles, E. G.,** 'Behavior of Platinum/Platinum-Rhodium Thermocouples at High Temperatures.' Jour. Sci. Inst., vol. 28, 1951, p. 353.

35. **Powell, A. R.,** 'Behavior of the Platinum Metals at High Temperatures.' Platinum Metals Rev., vol. 2, no. 3, 1958.

36. 'A Symposium on the Contamination of Platinum Thermocouples.' Jour. of the Iron and Steel Inst., vol. 155, p. 213.

37. **Bennett, H. E.,** 'The Care of Platinum Thermocouples.' Platinum Metals Rev., vol. 2, No. 4, 1958.

38. **Ehringer, H.,** 'Uber die lebensdauer von pt-rh termoelementen.' Metall. 8, 1954, p. 596.

39. **Jewell, R. C., Knowles, E. G., and Land, T.,** 'High Temperature Thermocouple.' Metal Ind. (London), vol. 87, 1955, p. 217.

40. **Obrowski, W., and Prinz, W.,** 'Neu bestimmte grundwerte für die thermopaarkombination pt30%rh-pt6%rh.' Archiv für das Eisenhuttenwesen, vol. 33, 1962, p. 1.

41. **Heath, J. H.,** 'High Temperature Thermocouples-part 1,' Report to United Kingdom Atomic Energy Authority. AEEW-R 141, 1960.

42. **Sanders, V. D.,** 'Review of High Temperature Immersion Thermal Sensing Devices for In-Flight Engine Control.' Rev. Sci. Inst., vol. 29, 1958, p. 917.

43. **Lachman, J. C.,** 'New Developments in Tungsten/Tungsten-Rhenium Thermocouples.' Presented at the Instrument Scociety of America 16th National Conference, Los Angeles, Sept. 11, 1961.

44. **Thomas, D. B.,** 'A Furnace for Thermocouple Calibrations to 2200°C.' Jour. Res., Nat. Bur. Standards, 66C, 1962, p. 255.

45. **Kuether, F. W., and Lachman, J. C.,** 'How Reliable Are the Two New High-Temperature Thermocouples in Vacuum?' ISA Jour., vol. 7, 1960, p. 66.

46. **Sims, C. T., Gaines, G. B., and Jaffee, R. I.,** 'Refractory-Metal Thermocouples Containing Rhenium.' Rev. Sci. Inst., vol. 30, 1959, p. 112.

47. **Lachman, J. C., and Kuether, F. W.,** 'Stability of Rhenium/Tungsten Thermocouples in Hydrogen Atmospheres.' ISA Jour., vol. 7, 1960, p. 67.

48. **Lachman, J. C., and McGurty, J. A.,** 'Thermocouples for 5000°F Using Rhenium Alloys.' Presented at the Electrochemical Society on Rhenium, Chicago, May 4, 1960.

49. **Nadler, M. R.,** and Kempter, C. P., 'Thermocouples for Use in Carbon Atmospheres.' Rev. Sci. Instr., vol. 32, 1961, p. 43.

50. **Blackburn, G. F., and Caldwell, F. R.,** 'Reference Tables for 40 Percent Iridium-60 Percent Rhodium Versus Iridium Thermocouples.' Jour. Res., Nat. Bur. Standards, 66C, 1962, p. 1.

51. **McGurty, J. A., and Kuhlman, W. C.,** 'Tungsten/Rhenium Thermocouple Research and Development. Presented at SAE National Aeronautic Meeting and Production Engineering Forum, New York, Apr. 6, 1962.

52. **Worthing, A. G.,** 'Temperature, Its Measurement and Control in Science and Industry,' 'Temperature Radiation Emissivities and Emittances.' Reinhold, 1941, p. 1164.

53. **Gubareff, G. G., Janssen, J. E. and Torborg, R. H.,** 'Thermal Radiation Properties Survey.' Minneapolis-Honeywell Regulator Co., Minneapolis, 1960.

54. 'Temperature, Its Measurements and Control in Science and Industry.' Vol. 3, Reinhold., Parts 1 and 2, 1962. (Part 3 to be published).

55. **Poland, D. E., Green, J. W., and Margrave, J. L.,** 'Corrected Optical Pyrometer Readings.' Nat. Bur. Standards, Monograph 30, 1961.

56, **DeVos, J. C.,** 'Evaluation of the Quality of a Blackbody.' Physica, Vol. 20, 1954, p. 669.

57. **Vollmer, J.,** 'Study of the Effective Thermal Emittance of Cylindrical Cavities.' Jour. Opt. Soc. Am., vol. 47, 1957, p. 926.

58. **Gouffé, A.,** 'Corrections d'ouverture des corps-noirs artificiels compte tenu des diffusions multiples internes.' Revue d'optique, Vol. 24, 1945, p. 1.

59. **Barber, C. R.,** 'Factors Affecting the Reproducibility of Brightness of Tungsten Strip Lamps for Pyrometer Standardization.' Jour. Sci. Instr., vol. 23, 1946, p. 238.

60. **Lovejoy, D. R.,** 'Accuracy of Optical Pyrometry in the Range 800° C to 4000° C.' Canadian Jour. Phys., vol. 36, 1958, p. 1397.

61. **MacPherson, H. G.,** 'Temperature, Its Measurement and Control in Science and Industry,' 'The Carbon Arcs as a Radiation Standard.' Reinhold., 1941, p. 1141.

62. **Null, M. R., and Lozier, W. W.,** 'The Carbon Arc as a Radiation Standard.' 'Temperature, Its Measurement and Control in Science and Industry'(to be published by Reinhold Pub. Corp.).

63. **Pyatt, E. C.,** 'Some Consideration of the Errors of Brightness and Two Colour Types of Spectral Radiation Pyrometer.' Brit. Jour. Appl. Phys., vol. 5, 1954, p. 264.

64. **Brenden, B. B., and Newkirk, H. W.,** 'A Multicolour Pyrometer.' AEC Res. and Dev. Rep. HW-57162, Dept. of Commerce, Washington. 1958.

65. **Hornbeck, G. A.,** 'Temperature, Its Measurement and Control in Science and Industry,' 'A High-Speed Ratio Pyrometer.' Vol. 3, pt. 2, Reinhold, 1962.

66. **Magison, E. C., and Mellentin, K.,** 'Temperature, Its Measurement and Control in Science and Industry,''The Thermopile in Industrial Radiation Pyrometry.' Vol. 3, pt. 2, Reinhold, 1962.

67. **Harrison, T. R.,** 'Radiation Pyrometry and Its Underlying Principles of Radiant Heat Transfer.' John Wiley., 1960.

3

Temperature Measurement in Cryogenics

JOHN. A. CLARK,
University of Michigan, Ann Arbor, Michigan, U.S.A.

Summary

This section deals with the basic principles as well as the practical considerations of temperature measurement in the cryogenic range, i.e., below - 150°C. The following topics are included: The Concept of Temperature; The Absolute Thermodynamic Temperature Scale; The Gas Thermometer; The International Practical Temperature Scale; Temperature Scales Below 90°K; Thermo-electric Devices; Resistance Thermometers including Platinum Resistance Elements, Carbon Resistors, Thermistors and Germanium Thermometers; and Magnetic Thermometry or Adiabatic Demagnetization.

Introduction

The word cryogen is derived from the two Greek works kyros- and -gen, meaning literally "the production of icey-cold". More simply, a cryogen is a refrigerant. Cryogenic is the adjective form of the noun, and signifies physical phenomena below -150°C (123°K). This is the approximate temperature at which physical properties of many substances begin to show significant variation with temperature (1). Of natural importance to research, engineering design and operation at the low temperatures is the measurement of the temperature itself. The purpose of this paper is to discuss this question in a reasonably broad context within the framework of the 1968 state-of-the-art.

The selection of a suitable temperature sensing element depends on a number of important considerations. Perhaps most fundamental of all is the accuracy required in the measurement. Entirely different techniques will be employed, for example, if an accuracy of 0.001°K is necessary or if 1.0°K is sufficient. Other significant factors include the influence of transient effects, sensitivity, type of readout, nature of signal, availability or desirability of recording and control, durability, stability and ruggedness of the sensing element, and of course replacement, interchangeability and cost.

As of this writing (1968) no internationally accepted standard for temperature measurement exists below the defining fixed point temperature for oxygen (90.18°K, -182.97°C). In fact in 1960, the 11th General Conference on Weights and Measures dropped the notation Fundamental and Primary fixed points and adopted instead the terms defining fixed points and secondary reference points for the various two-phase reference states for temperature calibration (2)(3). This situation is expected soon to be resolved however, with the adoption of a uniform scale sometime during 1968 or 1969 which will extend the range of the present international scale to 13.8°K (4). Below this temperature no international scale will exist for some time although convenient and practical methods for measurement of temperatures to 0.2°K and lower have been developed during the past decade. These will be included in this discussion.

This section will cover the following topics: the concept of temperature, the absolute thermodynamic temperature scale, the gas thermometer, the International Practical Temperature Scale, temperature scales below 90°K, thermocouples, resistance thermometry, and magnetic thermometry or adiabatic demagnetization. The basic principles as well as practical considerations of measurement will be presented.

It will probably be of value at the outset if the principal sources of reference for cryogenic temperature measurement are listed. Most of these will be cited from time to time in the body of this paper and hence are also included among the references. However, in view of their value it is important to have them conveniently listed, as follows:

1.   Temperature, Its Measuement and Control in Science and Industry, Reinhold Co., American Institute of Physics.

Vol.   I, 1941, 1343 pages.
Vol.   II, Edited by Hugh C. Wolfe, 1955, 451 pages.
Vol   III, Charles M. Hertzfeld, Editor-in-Chief, 1962.
       (a) Part I, "Basic Concepts, Standards and Methods", F. G. Brickwedde, Editor, 1962, 838 pages.
       (b) Part II, "Applied Methods and Instruments", A. I. Dahl, Editor, 1962, 1087 pages.
       (c) Part III, "Biology and Medicine", J. D. Hardy, Editor.

2.   R. B. Scott, Cryogenic Engineering, Van Nostrand., 1959.

3.   R. W. Vance and W. M. Duke, Editors, Applied Cryogenic Engineering, John Wiley, 1962.

4.   R. W. Vance, Editor, Cryogenic Technology, John Wiley, 1963.

5.   Dirk De Klerk., 'Adiabatic Demagnetization', S. Flügge,Editor, Encyclopedia of Physics, Vol. XV, Low Temperature Physics 2.

6.   Journal of Research, NBS, Section A (Physics and Chemistry); Section C, (Engineering and Instrumentation).

7.   Advances in Cryogenic Engineering, K. D. Timmerhaus, Editor, Vol. 1-13, 1955-68 (to date).

8.   Cryogenics, Vol. 1-8, 1960-68 (to date).

9.   Metrologia, Vol. 1-4, 1964-68 (to date), Published under the auspices of the International Committee of Weights and Measures.

10.   The International Temperature Scale (ITS)

      (a) 1927 ITS
      G. F. Burgess, 'International Temperature Scale', J. Research NBS, Vol. 1, 1925. p. 635-37.
      See also, Temperature, Vol. 1, 1941, p. 21-23.

      (b) 1948 ITS
      J. A. Hall, Temperature, Vol. 1, 1955, p. 115-141.
      H. F. Stimson, 'The International Temperature Scale of 1948', J. Research NBS, Vol. 42, 1949, p. 209.

      (c) 1960 Text Revisions of the 1948 ITS
      H. F. Stimson, 'International Practical Temperature Scale of 1948. Text Revision of 1960', J. Research, NBS, Vol. 65A, No. 3, 1961. See also, H.F. Stimson, 'The Text Revision of the International Temperature Scale of 1948', Temperature, Vol. 3, Part I, 1962, p. 59-67.

The Concept of Temperature

The concept of temperature is old and doubtless stems from the desire to attach definite numerical quantities to a feeling of hotness or coldness. Galileo (1600) was one of the earliest to experiment with the design of an instrument to which a scale was attached for the purpose of indicating a numerical temperature. These early instruments were called 'Thermoscopes' and were said to have measured 'degrees of heat'. Today, 370 years later, we find the art of temperature measurement highly developed but under continued study. The basic standard instrument presently employed is the Gas Thermometer in some respects similar to the first of Galileo, but registering in degrees of absolute temperature, not in degrees of heat. This distinction was made only after the discovery of latent heats by Joseph Black and James Watt (1764) and the enunciation of the Second Law of Thermodynamics (about 1850).

A sensation of warmth or cold is of little value to the physical world when measurement and reproducibility of temperature is required. While it is of small value in measurement, the subjective sense might be used to indicate an equivalent 'hotness' or 'coldness' of two seperate bodies. It is common experience, for example, that two blocks of iron, one taken from an ice bath and the other from a furnace, will approach the same feeling of warmth if they are brought into thermal contact with one another. Of course, great doubt might reasonably be raised concerning the validity of the conclusion of equal 'hotness' if the indications were taken by touching the blocks with the skin of the hands. However, other schemes could be used which are less subjective and would produce the same result. One might not use the hands but use, for instance, a small rod of silver and place it in intimate thermal contact with each iron block. The increase or decrease in the length of the silver rod could then serve as an indicating device since by experience it is known that this dimension will change as the rod is heated or cooled; also, when the heating or cooling ceases the changes in length also cease. Hence, after some period of time following the bringing of the two blocks together very careful observations of the length (say with a powerful microscope) would show no subsequent change in length of the rod when it was placed successively in contact with each block. Furthermore, if the block and the silver rod were mutually in thermal contact with each other and with nothing else, the length of the rod would be the same when it was attached to each block.

This would define the measureable state known as the Equality of Temperature. The silver rod might also be called a temperature meter or, more simply, a thermometer. The process just described has led to a generalization, or law, called the Zeroth Law of Thermodynamics. This law, which is the logical basis of all temperature measurement, may be stated as follows:

Two bodies (the iron blocks) at the state of equality of temperature with a third body (the silver rod) are in a state of equality of temperature with each other.

Returning to the silver rod, which has been called a thermometer, one might be led to attempt to assign a sort of numerical scale ot its length so as to convert its elongation or contraction into some definite, reproducible scale of temperature. It is apparent that this could be done with no particular mechanical difficulty, although some amplification of the changes in the length might be necessary for convenience in use. The selection of the type and magnitude of the units on this scale is wholly arbitrary. It is known that when the rod is placed into a bath of ice and liquid water, or in a bath of saturated steam at constant pressure and allowed to reach a state of equality of temperature with the bath in each instance, it does not change in length, but has a greater length in the steam than in the ice. Because the length is greatest in the steam bath, it would seem reasonable to assign it the greatest level of temperature, although this is arbitrary and the reverse has been done, as in the Celsius Scale (1740). The temperature of the ice bath, for convenience, then could be established as zero while that of the steam bath could be taken as 100. And this would define a difference of 100 degrees of temperature between these two fixed points.

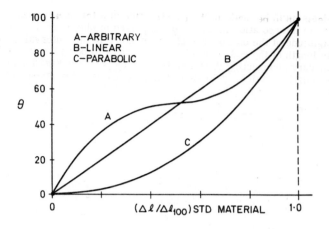

Fig. 3-1   Arbitrary scales of temperature

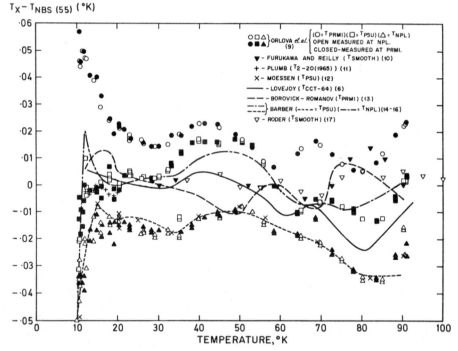

Fig. 3-2   Comparison of low temperature scales (10 to 90° K), including PSU, NPL, PRMI, CCT - 64, and NBS (2-20) 1965, with respect to NBS (55) scale. PSU = PSU = Pennsylvania State University; NPL = National Physical Laboratory (England); PRMI = USSR; CCT = Advisory Committee on Thermometry, International Committee on Weights and Measures; NBS = National Bureau of Standards (USA)

The final decision to be made in the construction of a temperature scale is the selection of an interpolation device to be employed to obtain the level of temperature and the magnitude of the unit degree of temperature in this interval from observations of the length of the rod. Freedom of choice is to be had in this selection also, that is, any curve connecting the 0 and 100 degree points in Fig. 3-1 may be chosen as the interpolation device. A scale of temperature is established both by the curves and the scale of the ordinate, as is evident, but freedom of choice is preserved if one fixes the scale of the ordinate and allows the curves to have an arbitrary shape. Some curves obviously are more convenient than others, for example, one would find a multivalued curve quite inconvenient to use.

Three curves or interpolating devices are shown in Fig. 3-1. The ordinate is divided arbitrarily into 100 equal divisions between 0 and 100. The abcissa is the ratio Δl, the difference between the length of the rod at intermediate levels of temperature and at the ice bath temperature to Δl_{100}, the difference between its length in the steam bath and the ice bath. Clearly, there are an infinite number of different scales one could select. One could take curve B which is a straight line joining the fixed points of temperature and have a linear scale which, if the silver rod were used as the thermometer, could be called the linear silver scale of temperature. By denoting this as the θ scale the relationship between length changes and θ is the simple one:

$$\frac{\Delta l}{\Delta l_{100}} = \frac{\theta}{100} \qquad\qquad \text{Eq. 3-1}$$

A question which might be raised now is this: Is this θ scale fundamental or if only the material in the rod is changed, will a different scale result? Indeed it turns out that this scale is not fundamental and different temperatures would be obtained with, say a linear copper scale. This important consequence of physics may be demonstrated as follows.

Consider that a linear silver scale has been adopted for reference with the silver rod being selected as the primary standard thermometer. All temperatures will be referred to this scale which we have called θ. We may take any property of matter which is measurable and which changes with heating and cooling as the indicating quantity. Changes in such properties may be called $\Delta p = p - p_0$ where p_0 is the magnitude of the property p at the level of temperature of the ice bath. In a rod of any other material the temperature coefficient of p based on the linear silver scale of temperature is defined as:

$$\alpha = \frac{\partial p}{\partial \theta} \qquad\qquad \text{Eq. 3-2}$$

Hence: $\Delta p = \displaystyle\int_0^\theta \alpha\, d\theta \qquad\qquad \text{Eq. 3-3}$

also: $\Delta p_{100} = \displaystyle\int_0^{100} \alpha\, d\theta \qquad\qquad \text{Eq. 3-4}$

so: $\dfrac{\Delta p}{\Delta p_{100}} = \dfrac{\displaystyle\int_0^\theta \alpha\, d\theta}{\displaystyle\int_0^{100} \alpha\, d\theta} \qquad\qquad \text{Eq. 3-5}$

Each of the integrals in equation 3-3 and 3-4 may be expressed as follows:

$$\int_0^\theta \alpha d\theta = \overline{\alpha_\theta} \cdot \theta \ ,$$

$$\int_0^{100} \alpha d\theta \ \overline{\alpha_{100}} \ 100 \ ,$$

where $\overline{\alpha}$ is the average value of α in a range of temperature.

Equation 3-5 is then written:

$$\frac{\Delta p}{\Delta p_{100}} = \frac{\overline{\alpha_\theta}}{\overline{\alpha_{100}}} \frac{\theta}{100} \qquad\qquad \text{Eq. 3-6}$$

It is a matter of experience that any property which changes with heating or cooling (such as length) does not do so at a constant rate of change in terms of the temperature of the scale of temperature employed to measure it. The exception, of course, is the property of the material used to define the linear scale of a selected standard temperature scale. But this is trivial.

A linear scale based on $\Delta p/\Delta p_{100}$ of any other material would be written:

$$\frac{\Delta p}{\Delta p_{100}} = \frac{t}{100} \qquad\qquad \text{Eq. 3-7}$$

where t is the temperature on the linear scale pertaining to this other material.

Combining equations 3-6 and 3-7 we have:

$$\frac{\overline{\alpha_\theta}}{\overline{\alpha_{100}}} \frac{\theta}{100} = \frac{t}{100}$$

or:

$$\frac{\theta}{t} = \frac{\overline{\alpha_{100}}}{\overline{\alpha_\theta}} \qquad\qquad \text{Eq. 3-8}$$

Equation 3-8 is the expression relating the linear scales of temperature (θ and t) of two different materials.

We find therefore, except in that rather improbable instance of $\overline{\alpha_{100}}/\overline{\alpha_\theta}$ being universally unity for all materials, a fundamental difference must be expected between scales of temperature defined in the manner outlined here. It is only for the case of a constant value of the temperature coefficient of change of a temperature dependent property that would produce a value of $\overline{\alpha_{100}}/\overline{\alpha_\theta}$ of unity and exact agreement between all linear scales of temperature. This circumstance cannot reasonably be expected in nature.

We conclude from these arguments that thermometers constructed after the fashion described, while useful as operational tools to measure and reproduce levels of 'temperature', would each produce different values of temperature when used to measure the state of a given system. This is roughly the present state of thermometry for temperatures below 90°K. In this range there presently exists no accepted standard thermometer nor scale although many working groups have defined their own 'wire' scales (5). However, these scales all differ from each other. This is demonstrated by Hust (6) in Fig. 3-2, where temperature scales from

several different laboratories in the U.S., Canada and Europe are compared with a
scale created by the National Bureau of Standards (NBS-55) in the range 10°K to
90°K. This scale is formed by lowering all temperatures on a previous scale
(NBS-39), (7) (8), by 0.01°K.

The Absolute (Thermodynamic) Temperature Scale

In 1848 Kelvin extended the reasoning of Carnot and demonstrated the existence of a
scale of temperature which, unlike those shown in Fig. 3-1, would be completely
independent of a thermometric substance. Such a scale is called an 'absolute' scale
and being deduced from the laws of thermodynamics only, it is known as the Absolute Thermodynamic Temperature Scale. Actually, there are an infinite number of
such scales of temperature possible, the final one selected being a matter of convenience. The scale we employ today is not the first scale Kelvin proposed but rather
his second. His first scale had $+\infty$ and $-\infty$ as the upper and lower bounds of
temperature, which is inconvenient, but his second scale remedied this having
bounds at 0 and $+\infty$.

From the Second Law of Thermodynamic, Kelvin was able to show that the rate of
the heat quantities from a cyclicly operating reversible heat engine could be written:

$$\frac{Q_1}{Q_0} = \frac{f(t_1)}{f(t_0)} \qquad\qquad \text{Eq. 3-9}$$

where $f(t)$ denotes an unknown but arbitrary function of temperature alone. The
form of this function is specified by the scale of temperature chosen and can therefore have an infinite number of possible forms. When a specific form is chosen a
scale of temperature is then defined which is independent in its definition of any
thermometric substance. The reversible engine becomes the thermometer but the
nature of such a device, as well as the ratio of its heat quantities, is quite independent of the fluid - the thermometric substance - employed to operate the engine.
Kelvin selected as his second scale the simple function $f(t) = T$ is called the Absolute Thermodynamic Temperature and is given in degrees Kelvin. Hence equation
3-9 becomes:

$$\frac{Q_1}{Q_0} = \frac{T_1}{T_0} \quad , \qquad\qquad \text{Eq. 3-10}$$

where T_1 and T_0 are the Kelvin temperatures of the heat source and the heat sink,
respectively.

The complete definition of the Kelvin scale including the establishment of the size
of the degree is dependent on a single arbitray constant. Originally this was
accomplished by defining the difference between the steam and ice points as 100
degrees Kelvin, exactly. The absolute temperature of the ice point was then determined experimentally using a gas thermometer. Since 1954 however, the arbitrary constant selected for defining the scale has been the temperature of the triple
point of water, taken to be 273.16°K exactly (2) (3). In 1854, one hundred years
earlier, Kelvin had stated that the triple point of water 'must be adopted ultimately'
as a defining fixed point (3). The triple point has been adopted to replace the ice
point owing to a greater reliability in establishing its temperature experimentally
and the fact that the triple point temperature is not pressure sensitive as are two-
phase states. The size of the degree in the interval between the ice and steam
points now must be determined experimentally. This interval will certainly not be
exactly 100°K but will probably be within 0.001°K or less of this value.

The dependence of the Kelvin scale on a single arbitrary constant may be shown by a simple argument. For fixed thermal states at say, T_1 (steam point) and T_0 (ice point) the ratio of the heat quantities in equation 3-10 is established by the constraints of nature. Thus:

$$\frac{Q_1}{Q_0} = \Gamma = \frac{T_1}{T_0} = \text{constant.} \qquad \text{Eq. 3-11}$$

If we define ΔT_{01} as $T_1 - T_0$, then the temperature of the ice point T_0 may be expressed in terms of ΔT_{01} as:

$$T_0 = \frac{\Delta T_{01}}{\Gamma - 1} \qquad \text{Eq. 3-12}$$

Hence, since Γ is fixed by the thermal states (T_0, T_1 whose numerical temperatures may be yet unknown), T_0 is determined by the value of ΔT_{01} or ΔT_{01} is determined by the value of T_0. One constant only, either T_0 or ΔT_{01}, is sufficient to define the scale. Prior to 1954 ΔT_{01} was chosen as $100°K$ and T_0 determined by the gas thermometer but since 1954 the reverse procedure has been adopted and T_0 is defined as the triple point of water at $273.16°K$. (It is defined by the International Practical Temperature Scale as $+0.01°C$ which gives the ice point as absolute temperature of $273.15°K$ (3). Now, the thermodynamic temperatures of all defining fixed points and secondary reference points must be determined by the gas thermometer.

The Absolute (Gas) Temperature Scale

The practical use of the Kelvin scale would require the operation of reversible engines. This of course is quite impossible and it is necessary to find an approximation to the Absolute Thermodynamic Scale. This is found from the properties of an ideal gas for if such a fluid is employed in a reversible engine it may be shown that:

$$\frac{Q_1}{Q_0} = \frac{\theta_1}{\theta_0}, \qquad \text{Eq. 3-13}$$

where an ideal gas is defined as a substance having an internal energy (U), a function only of temperature and an equation of state written as $pv = R\theta$, and θ is a 'temperature' on a new scale called the Absolute (Gas) Temperature Scale which would be determined from pressure and volume measurements on the gas, as:

$$\theta = \frac{pv}{R} \qquad \text{Eq. 3-14}$$

Further, if the difference $\theta_1 - \theta_0$ or θ_0 are defined to be identically the same as $T_1 - T_0$ or T_0, respectively, then it follows from equations 3-10 and 3-11 that:

$$\theta_1 = T_1,$$

$$\theta_0 = T_0$$

or, $\qquad \theta = T$ $\qquad \text{Eq. 3-15}$

In words, the Absolute (Gas) Temperature Scale is identical with the Absolute

(Thermodynamic) Temperature Scale if an ideal gas is employed in a reversible engine or any other device permitting the measurement of p and v. Such a device (which now replaces the reversible engine) is known as a gas thermometer and is the primary standard thermometer used to determine and establish the absolute thermodynamic temperature scale. Beattie (18) and Barber (19) describe the gas thermometer and the techniques of its use. Gas thermometers are either of constant pressure or constant volume and although both types give essentially identical results independent of the type of gas used, the constant volume type appears to be the more widely used. The M.I.T. thermometer used by Beattie (18) (20) (21) is of the constant volume type and uses nitrogen gas in a very pure state as the thermometric substance. Gas thermometry also has used H_2, He, Ne, A and Air as thermometric substances.

It was found by equation 3-15 that the requirement of a reversible engine as a thermometer was unnecessary to realize the Kelvin scale, if one could substitute a gas thermometer using an ideal gas. However, owing to the departure of the properties of a real gas from conditions of ideality, it becomes necessary to empirically correct the readings taken from a gas thermometer in order to determine the absolute temperature. Such temperatures are not actually Kelvin temperatures, but owing to the necessary corrections must be looked upon as approximations. They are called Absolute (Gas) Temperatures and represent the closest approximations to the absolute scale of Kelvin. The nature of these corrections is well established and is outlined by Keyes (22). However, it will be appropriate to indicate the nature of the result for a constant-volume gas thermometer. From thermodynamic theory and the properties of real gases it may be shown that for V^* = V:

$$\frac{p - p^*}{(T - T^*)p^*} = \frac{1}{T^*} + \frac{T}{(T - T^*)p^*} \int_{T^*}^{T} C_v \left(\frac{\partial T}{\partial v}\right)_u d\left(\frac{1}{T}\right) \qquad \text{Eq. 3-16}$$

The integral is the gas scale correction and is evaluated from measurements of the properties of real gases. For example, having once obtained the absolute temperature T^* of the triple point of water by definition at 273.16°K, then equation 3-16 can be used to obtain the absolute temperature T on the gas scale of any other thermodynamic state from gas thermometer measurements of p and p^* and the real properties of the gas. A simple constant-volume gas thermometer for cryogenic application is illustrated by Barber (19) and shown in Fig. 3-3. This gas thermometer is used for the calibration of platinum resistance thermometers in the liquid hydrogen temperature range. A typical gas bulb with platinum thermometer receptacles and auxiliary apparatus is shown in detail in Fig. 3-4 taken from Moessen, *et al* (12). Figure 3-5 shows temperature scale corrections for the non-ideality of the helium gas scale and the absolute temperature scale. This indicates that gas thermometer temperatures from various laboratories may differ from each other in the cryogenic temperature range by as much as 0.03°K. These differences are attributed to the various methods used to account for gas imperfectability and do not include the influence of dead space volume, gravity and other deviations from ideal measuring conditions.

A negative absolute temperature may seem to be a suitable subject for a discussion of cryogenic temperatures. The concept of a negative absolute temperature is presented by Ramsey (24) and Hertzfeld (25). Such a condition may be described whenever the population of an energy state of higher energy is greater than the population of a lower energy state (25) under conditions which permit a statistical mechanical interpretation of thermodynamics. Hertzfeld (25) lists these conditions as: '(1) The system must be fairly well isolated from its surroundings, but must come to internal equilibrium rapidly; (2) the states of the system must be quantized; and (3) the system must have a highest state in the same sense that a system has a lowest

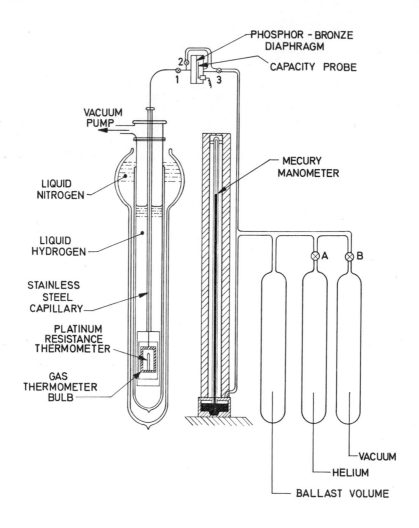

Fig. 3-3   Constant volume thermometer used for calibration of a platinum resistance thermometer (19)

state.' Examples of such systems are the nuclear magnetic moments of the constituents of certain crystals. No violation of the principles of thermodynamics is envisioned in this phenomenon. Interestingly, states at negative absolute temperatures are 'hotter' than those at infinite temperature. This results from the fact that at T equal to ∞ all states are equally populated. However, if higher energy states have larger populations than lower energy states the system must be 'hotter' than those states having a temperature of infinity. This naturally removes the discussion from the cryogenic range!

The International Temperature Scale (ITS)

Owing to its size and complexity the gas thermometer is impractical to use for laboratory or industrial measurement of temperature, as most gas thermometers occupy a room-sized space and require elaborate and time consuming preparations for their use. For these reasons a simple, reproducible and convenient secondary temperature standard is required even for precise laboratory measurements. The gas thermometer remains of course, the primary standard and is employed to determine the gas scale absolute temperature of the various defining fixed points and to calibrate precision laboratory secondary standard thermometers.

The definition of the secondary standard thermometers is established by international agreement by the General Conference on Weight and Measures, a body consisting of scientific representatives from 36 nations which meets every six years. This parent body is assisted by a smaller executive group known as the International Committee on Weights and Measures which consists of 18 elected members from the various nations and normally meets every two years. It is this group that supervises the International Bureau of Weights and Measures at Sévres, near Paris, France. This committee also oversees the publication of Metrologia, a journal devoted to original papers on research 'directed towards the significant improvement of fundamental measurements in any field of physics'. An Advisory Committee on Thermometry (Comité Consultatif de Thermométrie), the CCT, actively assists the International Committee on Weights and Measures in all matters relating to temperature measurement.

International Temperature Scales (ITS) have been adopted in 1927 (26) and in 1948 (27) (28). In 1960 a textual revision of the 1948 scale was made (2) (3) but this revision did not significantly affect the numerical values on the scale. The principle changes were:

(a)   Replace the ice-point with the triple point of water (0.01°C, exactly)

(b)   Use zinc point (pressure insensitive) instead of the sulphur point (pressure sensitive)

(c)   Change the name to the International Practical Temperature Scale (IPTS).

The ITS (1927 and 1948) is a Celsius (°C, 1948) scale and no mention was made in the text of an international Practical Kelvin Temperature Scale (IPTS). However, in practice this conversion was made on the basis of the accepted value of T_0, the Kelvin scale temperature of the ice-point. The 1960 revision of the ITS (1948) specifically mentions the IPKTS and relates it to the IPTS by:

$$T°K(IPKTS) - t°c(IPTS) + T_0,$$ Eq. 3-17

where T_0 is now defined to be 273.15°K. This was done so that the IPKTS will have the same value (273.16°K) for the triple point of water as the Kelvin Absolute Temperature Scale. The IPTS and the Celsius scale both are defined to have a value of

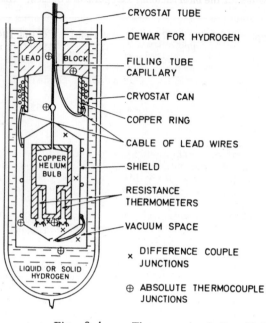

CRYOSTAT TUBE

DEWAR FOR HYDROGEN

FILLING TUBE
CAPILLARY

CRYOSTAT CAN

COPPER RING

CABLE OF LEAD WIRES

SHIELD

RESISTANCE
THERMOMETERS

VACUUM SPACE

× DIFFERENCE COUPLE
JUNCTIONS

⊕ ABSOLUTE THERMOCOUPLE
JUNCTIONS

LEAD   BLOCK

COPPER
HELIUM
BULB

LIQUID OR SOLID
HYDROGEN

Fig. 3-4   Thermometer bulb, shields, and cryostat

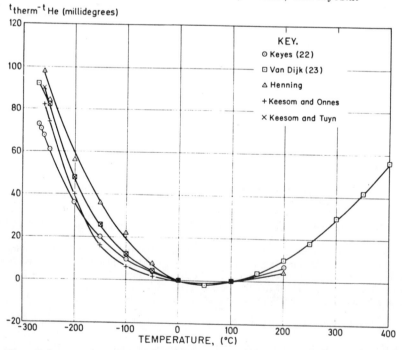

KEY.
⊙ Keyes (22)
⊡ Van Dijk (23)
△ Henning
+ Keesom and Onnes
× Keesom and Tuyn

Fig. 3-5   Gas imperfection corrections for constant volume helium gas thermometer

TABLE 3-1 Defining Fixed Points for the International Temperature Scales. Hust (6)

Description (all at 1 atm) except triple point of water	°C (Int 1927) ITS	°C (Int 1948) ITS	°C (Int 1948) 1960 text rev. IPTS
Oxygen point: Equilibrium between liquid and gaseous oxygen	-182.97	-182.97	-182.97
Ice Point: Equilibrium between ice and air saturated liquid water	0.000	0.000	
Triple point of water: Equilibrium between ice liquid water and gaseous water			0.010
Steam point: Equilibrium between liquid and gaseous water	100.00	100.000	100.000
Sulfur point: Equilibrium between liquid and gaseous sulfur	444.60	444.60	(444.60).
Zinc point: Equilibrium between solid and liquid zinc (Recommended to replace the sulfur point)			419.505
Silver point: Equilibrium between solid and liquid silver	960.5	960.8	960.8
Gold Point: Equilibrium between solid and liquid gold	1063.0	1063.0	1063.0

TABLE 3-2: Official Interpolation Procedures for the 1927 and 1948 International Temperature Scales. Hust (6)

(t in °C; T in °K; T_0 is temperature of ice point, $T_0 = 273.15°K$)

1927 Scale	1948 Scale
-190 to 0°C	-182.97 to 0°C
platinum resistance thermometer	platinum resistance thermometer
$R_t = R_0 [1 + At + Bt^2 + C(t - 100) t^3]$	$R_t = R_0 [1 + At + Bt^2 + C(t - 100) t^3]$
calibrate at 0_2, ice, steam, S-points	calibrate at 0_2, ice, steam, S-points
0 to 660°C	0 to 630.5°C
$R_t = R_0 (1 + At + Bt^2)$	$R_t = R_0 (1 + At + Bt^2)$
$R_{100}/R_0 \geqslant 1.390$; $R_{444.6}/R_0 \geqslant 2.645$	$R_{100}/R_0 > 1.3920$
calibrate at ice, steam, S-points	calibrate at ice, steam, S-points
660 to 1063°C	630.5 to 1063°C
Pt-Pt 10%Rh thermocouple	Pt-Pt 10%Rh thermocouple
$e = a + bt + ct^2$	$e = a + bt + ct^2$
calibrate at Sb, Ag, Au-points	calibrate at Sb, Ag, Au-points
above 1063°C	above 1063°C
monochromatic optical pyrometer	monochromatic optical pyrometer

$$\log \frac{J_t}{J_{Au}} = \frac{c_2}{\lambda} \left[\frac{1}{1336} - \frac{1}{t + T_0} \right] \qquad \log \frac{J_t}{J_{Au}} = \frac{\exp \frac{c_2}{(tAu + T_0)} - 1}{\frac{c_2}{(t + T_0)} - 1}$$

with $c_2 = 1.432$ cm deg $c_2 = 1.438$ cm deg

TABLE 3-3: Difference Between ITS (1927) and IPTS (1948).   Hust (6)

Platinum Thermometer Range

t °C (Int) 1948   Δt°C (Int) 1948 - °C (Int) 1927

t °C (Int) 1948	Δt°C (Int) 1948 - °C (Int) 1927
630.5	0.00*
650	.08*
700	.24
750	.35
800	.42
850	.43
900	.40
950	.32
1000	.20
1050	.05
1063	.00

* These values are uncertain since platinum thermometers are defined only up to 630.5°C on 1948 scale (see Corruccini (29)).

Radiation Law Range

It is difficult to determine exact differences of the ITS and IPTS in this range because of the variability of λ ; the wavelength of the radiation on the 1927 scale is restricted only to the visible spectrum and is not restricted at all on the 1948 scale. The following table contains the differences calculated at $\lambda_1 = 0.4738 \times 10^{-4}$ cm and $\lambda_2 = 0.65 \times 10^{-4}$ cm according to

Corruccini (29).

t °C (Int) 1948	Δt°C (Int) 1948 λ_1	°C (Int) 1927 λ_2
1063	0	0
1500	-2	-2
2000	-6	-6
2500	-12	-12
3000	-19	-20
3500	-28	-30
4000	-38	-43

TABLE 3-4: Relation Between the International Practical Scale and the Thermodynamic Scale (1960)

International Practical Scales

Celsius	Absolute
Names	
International Practical Temperature	International Practical Kelvin Temperature
Symbols	
t_{int}	$T_{int} = t_{int} + T_0$
Designations	
°C (Int. 1948) degrees Celsius international practical 1948	°K (Int. 1948) degrees Kelvin international practical 1948

Thermodynamic Scales

Celsius	Absolute
Names	
Thermodynamic Celsius temperature	Thermodynamic Kelvin temperature
Symbols	
$t = T - T_0$	T
Designations	
°C (therm.) degrees Celsius thermodynamic	°K degrees Kelvin

Notes: For the international practical temperature, the subscript "int" after t
may be omitted if there is no possibility of confusion.

$T_0 = 172.15°$

0.01°C as the triple point of water. Stimson (2) observes that for precision no greater than 0.001°C, the zero on the 1948 Celsius scale (ITS 1948) may be realized with an ice bath as described in the 1948 ITS.

The International Practical Temperature Scale (IPTS) specified four things: (a) the gas scale temperatures of reproducible defining fixed points and the secondary reference points at which instruments are calibrated, (b) the types of instruments to be used in realizing the scale, (c) the equations to be used for interpolating or extrapolating from the fixed points, and (d) the experimental procedures recommended for both measurement and calibration. A summary of the IPTS and a comparison of the 1927, 1948 and the 1960 revision of the 1948 scale are given in Tables 3-1, 3-2 and 3-3, taken from Hust (6). The complete range of temperatures from -182.97°C to 1063°C is included for completeness. Twenty-two secondary reference points from -78.5°C to 3380°C including their vapor temperature-pressure relations are given by Stimson (3). The relationship between the International Practical Temperature Scale (1948) and the thermodynamic scale is shown in Table 3-4 (2).

Because of the polynomial form of the interpolating equations used to describe the International Practical Temperature Scale (IPTS) between the defining fixed points, an inherent difference exists between the IPTS and the thermodynamic temperature scale (TTS). This difference is determined by comparing gas thermometer readings with those from standard thermometers as prescribed by the IPTS. Hust (6) reports the data of several investigators who examined the differences between the TTS and the IPTS in the range - 190°C to 0°C. These results are shown in Fig. 3-6. As may be noted, fairly large discrepancies exist between these various results probably because of differences in the gas thermometers measurements as suggested by the data in Fig. 3-5. In order to examine and define these differences systematically, Preston-Thomas and Kirby (35) redetermined part of the TTS, in terms of platinum resistance thermometer readings, by means of a constant volume helium gas thermometer of reasonably high accuracy. These authors expect to extend similar measurement to -219°C, the triple point of oxygen. Their measurements in the range -183°C to 100°C are given in Fig. 3-7. As may be seen by the data in Fig. 3-6 and 3-7, the IPTS and the TTS differ by a maximum of about 0.04°C in the cryogenic range.

Temperature Scales Below 90°K

Below the oxygen point (-182.97°C, 90.18°K) no International Temperature Scale presently exists. During the past few years however, a great deal of study has been devoted to this problem by the CCT and a number of proposals for extending the IPTS to 13.8°K, the triple point of equilibrium hydrogen, have been made. It now seems probable that the IPTS in force since 1948 will be abandoned and replaced with a new scale (4) (5). This new scale, which may take effect as early as late 1968 or perhaps during 1969, will conform to the best experimental values of the thermodynamic temperatures now available. If these events transpire as expected, it will mark a period of 20 years between the new scale and the 1948 scale which itself replaced the 1927 scale after about a similar 20 year tenure. This will, of course, leave the important range below 13.8°K undefined by an international standard and since this includes the entire region of the He[4] and He[3] it can only be hoped that similar efforts by the CCT will bring about a standard scale at these very low temperatures.

Because of the absence of an international standard below 90°K several 'national' or 'laboratory' scales have been developed, each of which is different from the others and from the thermodynamic scale. They are based on the resistance characteristics of platinum calibrated against a gas thermometer and several of these scales were compared in Fig. 3-2. Scott (36) compares several other scales as

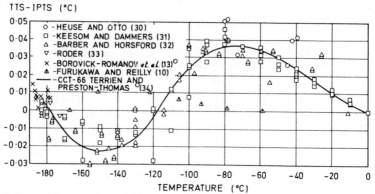

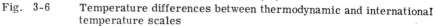

Fig. 3-6 Temperature differences between thermodynamic and international temperature scales

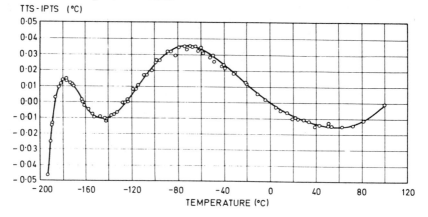

Fig. 3-7 Comparison of measurements of TTS-IPTS (35)

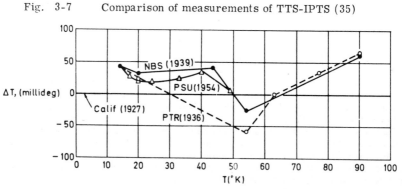

Fig. 3-8 Comparison of temperature scales (36) Calif = University of California (37); NBS = National Bureau of Standards (F 18); PSU = Pennsylvania State University (12); PTR = Physikalishe Technistlae Reichsanstalt (36)

indicated in Fig. 3-8. The NBS (1939) scale has been superseded by the NBS (1955) scale formed by lowering all temperatures on the NBS (1939) scale by 0.01°C and these scales have been the basis for all NBS calibrations in the interval 12°to 90°K since 1939. The agreement of the NBS (1939) scale with the thermodynamic scale was ± 0.02°C in the range 12°to 90°K. It is interesting to note that the scale identified as 'Calif (1927)' in Fig. 3-8 is formulated on the basis of a copper-constantan thermocouple which was stable over a period of 3 years having an estimated accuracy of 0.05°K in the range 12°to 90°K (37).

In 1964 the CCT established a provisional temperature scale to be considered as a replacement for the IPTS below 273.15°K. This scale is referred to as CCT-64 and is in the form of a resistance-temperature table for platinum thermometers, extending from 10°K to 273.15°K. The derivation for the range 90°K to 273.15°K is given by Barber and Hayes (38). Currently, certain modifications are being considered in it prior to its recommendation as an international scale (5) but, any modification in CCT-64 will doubtless be small, and the low temperature part is assumed (6) to be the best approximation to the thermodynamic scale in this region. Calibration of thermometers below 90°K may be accomplished using a number of multi-phase equilibrium states, called fixed points and Timmerhaus (39) lists several of these states which are given here in Table 3-5.

TABLE 3-5: Fixed Points Below 90°K (39)

Point	Temp., °K
Lambda point of helium	2.173
Boiling point of helium (1 atm)	4.215
Triple point of equilibrium hydrogen	13.81
Triple point of normal hydrogen	13.95
Boiling point of equilibrium hydrogen (1 atm)	20.27
Boiling point of normal hydrogen (1 atm)	20.39
Triple point of neon	24.57
Boiling point of neon (1 atm)	27.17
Triple point of oxygen	54.36
Triple point of nitrogen	63.14
Boiling point of nitrogen (1 atm)	77.35

These are not presently 'secondary reference points' as prescribed by an International Temperature Scale, but represent the best literature values. An equilibrium cell or vapor pressure thermometer is employed to determine these states and would be similar to the oxygen vapor-pressure thermometer described by Timmerhaus (40) and shown in Fig. 3-9.

For precise calibration of thermometers in the range 0.20°K to 5.2°K the vapor pressure scales of He^4 and its light isotope He^3 are available. For temperatures between 1°K and 5.2°K the International Committee on Weights and Measures in October 1958 recommended for international use a scale based on equilibrium between He^4 liquid and its vapor now known as the '1958 He^4 scale of temperatures'. This scale is described by Brickwedde, et al. (41) where the vapor pressure of He^4 is tabulated for intervals of 0.001°K from 0.50°K to 5.22°K. Clement (42) concludes that the He^4 1958 scale is accurate within 0.001 to 0.002°K with a roughness less than 0.0001°K. Values of the vapor pressure of He^4 in microns (10^{-3} mm Hg) for intervals of 0.01°K are given in Table 3-15, taken from ref. 41.

A comparison of the 1958 He^4 scale with previous scales is shown in Fig. 3-11, taken from Hust (6). The identification of the various scales is given by Brickwedde, et al (41). The acoustical thermometer of Plumb and Cataland (11) provides an

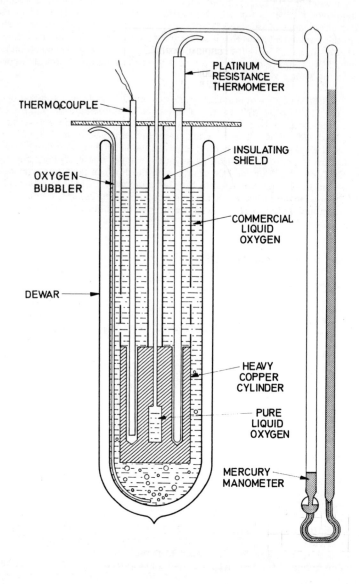

Fig. 3-9   Oxygen vapor-pressure thermometer for calibrating working
thermometers (40)

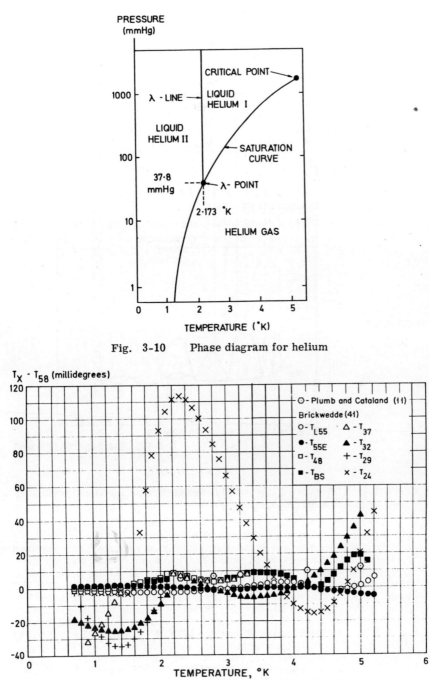

Fig. 3-10   Phase diagram for helium

Fig. 3-11   Deviations of earlier helium vapor-pressure scales from 1958 He^4 scale (6)

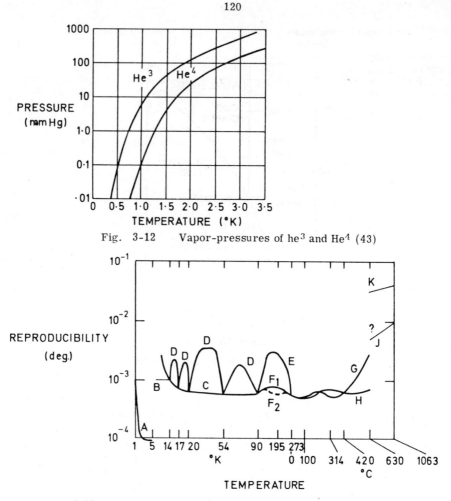

Fig. 3-12   Vapor-pressures of he³ and He⁴ (43)

Fig. 3-13   Estimated reproducibilities of various actual and postulated
temperature scales (5)

(A). Vapour pressure measurement. 1958 He- scale;   (B). Estimated
reproducibility of a Ge resistance thermometer 'wire scale';   (C). Estimated
reproducibility of any of the Pt resistance thermometer 'national' scales;
(D). Reproducibility of the Barber van Dijk scale (46) on the (optimistic)
assumption of the fixed points being realisable to 0.2 millikelvin;   (E). IPTS
in the 90 (K) to 273 (K) range assuming the indeterminacy shown by Barber
(32);   (F). IPTS in the 90 (K) to 273 (K) range assuming the indeterminacy
shown by Lovejoy (47) (F_1) or alternatively the use of an additional fixed
point (CO_2 point) in a modification of the IPTS (F_2);   (G). IPTS in the range
0°C to 630°C;   (H). Reproducibility of a modification of the IPTS in the
manner suggested by McLaren (48);   (J). Estimated reproducibility of a Pt
resistance thermometer scale in the 630°C to 1063°C range;   (K). Reproducibility of the IPTS (using Pt 10 Rh/Pt thermocouples) in the 630°C to
1063°C range.

interesting comparison with the results of the vapor pressure scale.

The phase diagram for He^4 is shown in Fig. 3-10. Below the λ-point at $2.173\,^{\circ}K$ liquid helium experiences a transition to its superfluid state. The tendency of superfluid helium to flow makes vapor pressure measurements difficult below the λ- point and furthermore, below $1\,^{\circ}K$ the vapor pressure of He^4 is less than 120 microns adding additional problems in measurement. To overcome both of these drawbacks the vapor pressure of the light isotope He^3 was determined and developed into the He^3 scale. A comparison of the vapor pressures of He^3 and He^4 is given in Fig. 3-12, taken from Arp and Kropschot (43). For comparison it will be noted that the vapor pressure of He^3 at $1\,^{\circ}K$ is 8,842 microns and that of He^4 at the same temperature is only 120 microns. The International Committee on Weights and Measures in 1962 recommended the use of the He^3 vapor pressure temperature data for international use. This scale, which is known as the '1962 He^3 scale of temperatures', is tabulated in intervals of $0.001\,^{\circ}K$ from $0.20\,^{\circ}K$ to $3.324\,^{\circ}K$ by Sherman, *et al* (44). Vapor pressure data in intervals of $0.01\,^{\circ}K$ for He^3 are given in Table 3-16, taken from the summary table of Sydoriak, *et al* (45).

Preston-Thomas and Bedford (5) have examined the reproducibilities of various actual and postulated temperature scales in the range $1\,^{\circ}K$ to $1063\,^{\circ}K$. Their results are given in Fig. 3-13 indicating a general reproducibility of 10^{-2} to 10^{-3} over the full range.

Thermometers for Cryogenic Temperatures

The remaining sections of this paper will consider the principle devices which are employed to measure cryogenic temperatures, including thermoelectric, electrical resistance and magnetic thermometers. A survey of available low temperature thermometers is illustrated in Fig. 3-14 for the temperature range $0.05\,^{\circ}K$ to $300\,^{\circ}K$. This is an extension of a similar chart presented by Timmerhaus (40). A comparison of the performance of several of these devices has been prepared by Corruccini (63) in a survey of temperature measurements at cryogenic temperatures. His results are given in Table 3-6.

TABLE 3-6: Comparison of Cryogenic Temperature Measuring Devices

	Type	Range, $^{\circ}K$	Best Reproducibility, $^{\circ}K$	Best Accuracy, $^{\circ}K$
1	Platinum Resistance	10-900	10^{-3} to 10^{-4}	10^{-2} to 10^{-4}
2	Carbon	1-30	10^{-2} to 10^{-3}	10^{-2} to 10^{-3}
3	Germanium	1-100	10^{-3} to 10^{-4}	10^{-2} to 10^{-3}
4	Gold-Cobalt vs Copper Thermocouple	4-300	10^{-1} to 10^{-2}	0.10

Thermocouples

The familiar thermo-electric circuit - the thermocouple - in which an EMF is produced by subjecting the junctions of dissimiliar metallic combinations to different temperatures is commonly used in the cryogenic temperature range. In circum-

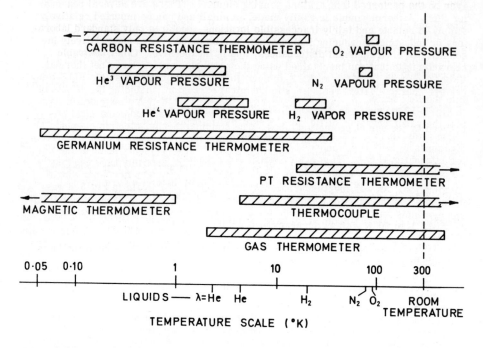

Fig. 3-14   Temperature ranges normally associated with various low temperature thermometers

stances where measurement accuracy is from 0.25 to 0.50°K a thermocouple may even be the preferred temperature sensing element. There are several reasons for this. A thermocouple is easily made, is small and can be mounted relatively simply in remote and fairly inaccessible locations, requires only standard laboratory or industrial measuring instruments, can be made rugged and relatively insensitive to environmental disturbances, and is inexpensive. Other desirable characteristic that can be obtained using themocouples are: a large net thermal EMF, a monotonic or linear EMF-temperature characteristic, a stable EMF-temperature characteristic, resistance to chemical corrosion, including the effects of both oxidizing and reducing atmospheres, uniformity of the wire material in large batches and high thermal response. The influence of the environment must often be reduced by the use of protection tubes. The common thermo-electric elements in use today at temperatures from 4°K to 300°K are the gold-cobalt vs copper and the constantan vs copper junctions, described below. Measurements made at the liquid nitrogen, liquid oxygen and liquid hydrogen temperature probably have used the constantan vs copper thermocouple with greater frequency than any other single combination. As was mentioned earlier, the 'Calif (1927)' scale in Fig. 3-8 was formulated on the basis of a copper-constantan thermocouple (37) and this particular thermocouple was found to be stable for a period of 3 years in the temperature range 12°K to 90°K with an accuracy of 0.05°K.

Although thermocouples are commonly used at temperature below 300°K the International Practical Temperature Scale is not specified in terms of thermo-electric systems in the cryogenic range of temperatures. The principal reasons for this are accuracy and reproducibility as compared with the platinum resistance thermometers.

The general principles of thermo-electric thermometry and the various thermo-electric circuits and instrumentation are of course, important to design for the installation of thermocouples. In view of space limitations here and the generally wide availability of this kind of information, it will not be included in this discussion. Finch (49) has given a thorough presentation of the principles of thermoelectricity. Some improved reference tables for iron-constantan, chromel-alumel, copper-constantan and chromel-constantan thermocouples are presented by Benedict and Ashby (50). Caldwell (51) discusses the properties of various materials that could be used as thermocouple elements at temperatures above 0°C and the use of thermocouples in engineering measurements and their circuits are given by Weber (52), Baker, *et al* (53) and Dike (54), among others.

The behavior of a thermocouple element is usually characterized by its thermo-electric potential of EMF, E, and its thermoelectric power, dE/dT. Its EMF, E, is always related to an arbitrarily selected reference temperature. At cryogenic temperatures the common thermoelectric combinations are gold-cobalt (Au + 2.11 atomic percent Co) vs copper, copper vs constantan (60 percent Cu and 40 percent Ni), gold-cobalt vs normal silver (Ag + 0.37 atomic percent Au), Iron vs constantan and chromel-P (90 percent Ni and 10 percent Cr) vs Alumel (95 percent Ni and 5 percent (Al, Si, Mn). The more frequently used thermocouples, however, are the gold-cobalt vs copper and the copper vs constantan combinations. These thermocouples have been used to temperatures as low as 0.2°K. Their best accuracy in the temperature range 4 to 300°K is 0.10°K for gold-cobalt vs copper and 0.50°K for copper vs constantan.

The thermoelectric potential differences for these 5 thermocouples is given in Table 3-7, taken from Powell, *et al* (55).

The principal advantage of the use of the gold-cobalt vs. copper combination is evident from these data as it has a significantly higher thermal EMF. However, owing to inhomogeneities in its chemical constituency this combination produces irregular EMF's that are uncompensated for in its calibration and therefore give rise to measurement errors. In fact, this lack of homogeneity in composition is

TABLE 3-7: Thermoelectric Potential Differences in Microvolts for Several Thermocouple Combinations (55)

Temp. °K	Constantan vs. Copper	Gold- Cobalt vs. Copper	Normal Silver vs Copper	Iron vs. Constantan	Chromel P vs. Alumel
4-20	57.8	171.4	0.2	59	41
20-76	646.9	1562.5	37.9	805	616
76-273	5545.6	8123.2	133.7	8252	6182

TABLE 3-8: Inhomogeneity of Thermoelectric Voltages Obtained from Dip Tests (50)

Samples		Bath temperatures			
		4-300°K		76-300°K	
		Voltage (uV)		Voltage (uV)	
		Maximum	Average	Maximum	Average
(a)	Cu	4.5	2.5	2.0	0.8
(b)	Cu	1.8	0.7	1.0	0.3
(c)	Constantan	0.5	0.2	0.5	0.2
(d)	Au-Co	5.0	3.0	4.0	2.5
(e)	Au-Co	5.5	3.5	4.0	2.5
(f)	Ag-Au	2.2	1.2	1.2	0.8

Samples were: (a) Instrument grade copper, 32 A.W.G.; (b) Thermocouple grade copper, 36 A.W.G.; (c) Thermocouple grade constantan, 36 A.w.g.; (d) Gold-cobalt, Bar 9, 36 A.w.g. (1960); (e) Gold-cobalt, Bar 5, 36 A.w.g. (1958); (f) 'Normal' silver, 36 A.w.g.

the greatest single defect in the Au-Co vs. Cu thermocouple. When the chemical metallurgy of the Au-Co wires can produce a product having a constant, controllable and stable composition this thermocouple will come into much wider use at very low temperatures. The effects of inhomogeneity are usually greatest when the measuring and reference junctions are at widely different temperatures. In such cases the thermocouple lead wires are subjected to steep temperature gradients and at the points of greatest temperature change in the wire chemical inhomogeneity will produce an EMF. Thus, the Au-Co vs. Cu combination is best used where temperature differences to be measured are small. A convenient and practical application is the use of the Au-Co vs. Cu combination as a differential thermocouple in an installation where the temperature differences are small or zero, as in constant temperature baths, cryostats and equilibrium cells for temperature calibration.

The Fe vs. Con and Ch vs. Al thermocouples are infrequently used at low temperatures principally because of voltage uncertainties resulting from inhomogeneities in the wires.

TABLE 3-9: Thermoelectric Potential Differences in Microvolts for Gold-Cobalt and Constantan vs. Copper Thermocouples (56)

Temp., °K	Au-Co	Con-stantan	Temp., °K	Au-Co	Con-stantan
0	0.00	0.00	90	2246.8	946.7
2	2.09	0.66	95	2433.3	1038.5
4	8.22	2.62	100	2622.6	1133.7
6	18.20	5.83	110	3008.5	1333.7
8	31.83	10.26	120	3402.8	1546.4
10	48.93	15.88	130	3804.1	1771.7
12	69.30	22.64	140	4211.2	2009.5
14	92.75	30.50	150	4623.2	2260.0
16	119.1	39.43	160	5039.1	2522.7
18	148.1	49.40	170	5458.4	2797.1
20	179.6	60.40	180	5880.4	3083.1
25	269.1	92.31	190	6304.6	3380.3
30	372.5	130.3	200	6730.6	3688.6
35	483.0	173.9	210	7158.0	4007.7
40	614.2	222.9	220	7586.4	4337.4
45	749.9	276.8	230	8015.7	4677.5
50	893.9	335.6	240	8445.5	5027.8
55	1045.2	398.8	250	8875.6	5388.0
60	1202.9	466.2	260	9305.9	5757.9
65	1366.2	537.5	270	9736.2	6137.3
70	1534.5	612.7	280	10166.3	6526.0
75	1707.1	691.2	290	10596.1	6923.7
80	1883.5	773.0	300	11025.5	7330.2
85	2063.4	858.1			

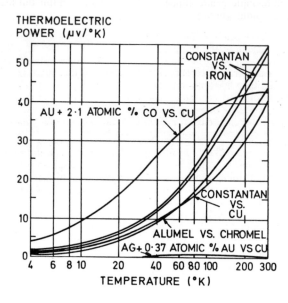

Fig. 3-15   Thermoelectric power as a function of temperature for various thermocouple combinations (63)

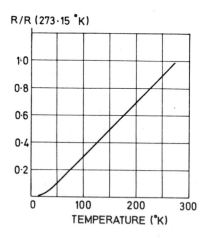

Fig. 3-16   Resistance ratio of platinum as a function of temperature

An estimate of the inhomogeneity of thermoelectrical voltages obtained by placing one section of a wire sample in a cryogen while the two ends of the wire are attached to a potentiometer is reported by Powell, *et al* (56) and shown in Table 3-8. As is evident from this sampling, the gold-cobalt wire is subject to the greatest voltage uncertainty. Thermocouple grade copper and constantan exhibit the least voltage uncertainty owing to inhomogeneity.

Powell, *et al* (55)(56) have studied the thermoelectric characteristics of several thermocouple combinations in the temperature range 4°K to 300°K. A summary of their results for the Au-Co vs. Cu and Cu vs. Con thermocouples is given in Table 3-9 for a 0°K reference temperature. An extensive tabulation of the thermo-electric potentials and thermoelectric power in 1°K intervals for these combinations from 0°K to 300°K is found in ref (56). These results represent the best average or smoothed data for a family of thermocouple combinations and thus, they may be used as the standard reference data for each thermocouple. Such data are of great value in thermocouple calibration, as is discussed later.

The thermoelectric power, dE/dT, in microvolts per degree Kelvin for the five thermocouple combinations in Table 3-17 is given in Fig. 3-15 as a function of temperature. At temperatures from 4°K to about 200°K, the Au-Co vs. Cu thermo-couple is clearly the superior combination from the standpoint of thermoelectric power. Below about 40°K the Fe vs. Con, Ch vs. Al and Cu vs. Con thermocouples have about the same thermoelectric power. Normal silver vs. copper produces an almost insignificant thermoelectric power at low temperatures. The thermoelectric power, dE/dT, in Fig. 3-15 may be used to give an indication of the sensitivity of temperature measurement when it is related to the measurement sensitivity of the potentiometer ΔE^* in microvolts, used to measure the thermal EMF of the thermo-couple. That is, the uncertainty in temperature indication, ΔT^*, may be written:

$$\Delta T^* = \frac{\Delta E^*}{(dE/dT)} \qquad \text{Eq. 3-18}$$

Thus, thermocouples having large thermoelectric power will enable a smaller measurement uncertainty for a given measuring instrument.

The calibration of a thermocouple is conveniently done by establishing its deviation characteristic as compared with Standard thermocouple EMF. Standard thermo-couple potentials at cryogenic temperatures are given in Table 3-9 in summary form for Au-Co vs. Cu and Cu vs. Con and may be found in much greater detail in ref. 56. The thermocouple 'Deviation' is defined as:

$$\Delta E_{DEV} = E_{STD} - E_{OBS} , \qquad \text{Eq. 3-19}$$

where E_{STD} is the standard EMF corresponding to the temperature of the thermo-couple for which E_{OBS} is its observed EMF. A deviation plot is usually constructed by obtaining several corresponding values of ΔE_{DEV} and E_{OBS} over a range of temp-erature and generally, when these data are plotted as ΔE_{DEV} vs. E_{OBS} a smooth, frequently almost linear, curve may be used to join the data points. This is a re-sult of the fact that while each individual thermocouple wire combination will differ slightly from others of similar composition, the EMF-temperature characteristics of a 'family' of similar wires are essentially parallel. Thus, their deviations will be almost linear and exactly zero at a common reference temperature.

The use of a deviation plot provides a very convenient method for making accurate temperature measurements with thermocouples. Owing to the essential linearity of a deviation curve, interpolation between a minimum number of calibration points may be done with confidence. The determination of an unknown temperature in measurement is made by computing E_{STD} from equation 3-19 using ΔE_{DEV} taken from the deviation plot corresponding to the E_{OBS} for the thermocouple. The unknown temperature is found from the 'standard' table of E_{STD} vs. temperature.

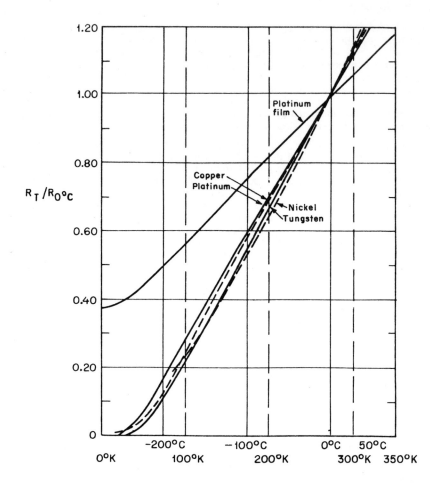

Fig. 3-17   Resistance-temperature relationships for various resistance-type
            temperature sensors - high range sources of data: platinum, mean of
            NBS calibration; tungsten; copper and nickel. (Courtesy of
            Rosemount Engineering Company).

The 'standard' table is usually formulated in great detail and represents the best, smoothed data for a family of thermocouple combinations.

A potentiometer is probably the most satisfactory instrument for precision temperature measurement using thermocouples. These instruments are described in detail elsewhere (52) (53) (57). Instruments presently available by the Leeds and Northrup Co., the K-5 (facility) and K-3 have sensitivities 0.02-0.1 μV and 0.5 μV, respectively. The Wenner potentiometer has a sensitivity of 0.1 μV and a potentiometer manufactured by the Minneapolis Honeywell Co. also has a sensitivity of 0.1 μV. Similar potentiometers are produced by other companies. Comparing these sensitivities with the thermoelectric power of the Au-Co vs. Cu thermocouple, temperature sensitivities will range from 0.002°K to 0.01°K at a level of temperature of 10°K.

Resistance Thermometry

The variation of electrical resistance with temperature provides a very convenient, accurate and practical method for temperature measurement. This method is enhanced when the material from which the thermometer is made has a stable and easily reproducible composition. Otherwise, the method becomes impractical owing to inherent instabilities in the resistance-temperature characteristic and consequent uncertainties in the temperature. The basic measurement required is that of electrical resistance and this can be done with great precision using available resistance bridges or potentiometers. Hence, with a stable material and present instrumentation a resistance thermometer can be used to measure temperature to a high degree of accuracy (52) (53) (58 - 60). For precision measurements the platinum resistance thermometer is the most widely used temperature measuring device in the range 1°K to 300°K. As mentioned earlier, the International Practical Temperature Scale (1948) is defined in terms of the resistance characteristics of platinum from -183°C to 630.5°C. Undoubtedly, when the new International temperature scale is introduced (4) (5) (6) some time in the period 1968-69, as expected, it also will employ the resistance characteristic of platinum as the standard below 300°K, as well as above that temperature. The reason for this of course, is the unusually high degree of purity that can be achieved in the production of platinum, the reproducibility of the purity from batch to batch, its monotonic resistance-temperature curve in the strain-free, annealed state, and its inertness to chemical contamination. Its cost is high which may be a factor in its use. Other materials which are also used include copper, nickel, carbon, germanium and certain semi-conductors known as thermistors. These will be discussed later.

The resistance-temperature characteristic of platinum is shown in Fig. 3-16. Above 50°K this relationship is essentially linear. The 1948 IPTS requires that the resistance ratio in Fig. 3-16 be equal to or greater than 1.3920 at 373.15°K (100°C) to insure purity in the platinum wire. The resistance-temperature characteristics of platinum film on a non-conducting substrate, nickel, tungsten and copper are shown in Fig. 3-17.

Precision platinum-resistance thermometers are made of a fine coil of highly purified, strain-free platinum wire wound around a non-conducting frame. A typical method of construction is shown in Fig. 3-18. The ice-point resistance of these thermometers is commonly set at approximately 25.5 absolute ohms. The platinum thermometer is usually manufactured as a capsule (Fig. 3-18) or as a cane. In each case four lead wires are provided for resistance measurement. Precision resistance is best measured using a Mueller Bridge with a four lead wire thermometer as shown in 3-19. The accuracy of this bridge circuit is 10^{-5} ohms (39) which would correspond to approximately 0.003°K at 12°K and 0.00009°K at 100°K. Except at very low temperatures accuracies from 0.001°K to 0.0001°K can be obtained using a platinum thermometer and Mueller Bridge. As indicated in Fig. 3-19, the four lead

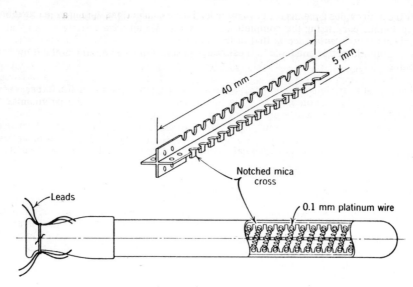

Fig. 3-18   Capsule-type, strain-free resistance thermometer (40)

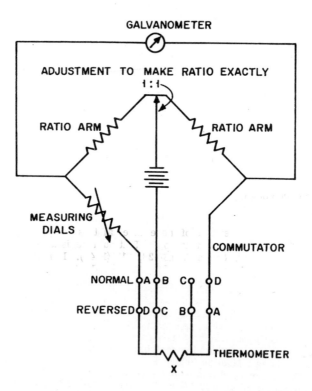

Fig. 3-19   Mueller bridge with a four-lead platinum resistance thermometer

wire circuit provides a means for reversing lead wire connections during a measurement, this technique permitting the complete cancellation of lead wire resistance so that the net measured resistance is that of the platinum resistance thermometer wire itself. Potentiometric methods for resistance measurement are summarized by Dauphinee (61).

Calibration of a platinum thermometer can be made using a gas thermometer, another standard thermometer or using the defining fixed-points and a polynomial equation between resistance and temperature, such as the Callendar or Callendar-VanDusen equations (28) which are equivalent to those given in Table 3-2. In the United States calibration is frequently done by the National Bureau of Standards, Institute for Basic Standards. Typical calibration data for a platinum thermometer is given in Table 3-10. The constants α, δ and β were found from the Callendar-VanDusen formula:

$$t = \frac{R_t - R_o}{\alpha R_o} + \delta \left[\frac{t}{100} - 1 \right]\left[\frac{t}{100} \right] + \beta \left[\frac{t}{100} - 1 \right]\left[\frac{t}{100} \right]^3 \qquad \text{Eq. 3-20}$$

TABLE 3-10: Report of Calibration of Platinum Resistance Thermometer, L & N No. 1653433. Submitted by The University of Michigan (62)

Constant	Value
α	0.003925780
δ	1.49168
β	0.11116 (t below 0°C)
β	0 (t above 0°C)
R_o	25.5510 abs. ohms

Additional qualifying information was provided by the NBS for this calibration as follows: "The value of δ was estimated using the assumption, based on experience with similar thermometers, that the product $\alpha \cdot \delta$ is a constant. The uncertainty in the estimated value of δ is equivalent to an uncertainty at the sulphur point of less than ± 0.01 deg C. The other values given are determined from measurements at the triple point of water, the steam point, and the oxygen point. The uncertainty of the measurements at these points, expressed in temperature, is less than ± 0.0003, ± 0.0015 and ± 0.005 deg C respectively. About one-half of each of these uncertainties is an allowance for systematic errors, including the differences among national laboratories, the remaining part representing the effect of random errors in the measurement process. The effects of these uncertainties on other measured temperatures are discussed in Intercomparison of Platinum Resistance Thermometers between -190 and 445°C, J. Research NBS 28, 217 (1942). During calibration the value of R_o changed by the equivalent of 5×10^{-4} deg C. These results indicate that this thermometer is satisfactory for use as a defining standard in accordance with the text of the International Practical Temperature Scale."

Resistance-temperature data on the thermometer described in Table 3-11 are listed in Table 3-17 for a small range of temperatures above 90°K. These data are computed from the following equation and represent a few of the numerical results abstracted from the original calibration:

$$\frac{R_t}{R_o} = 1 + \alpha t \left[1 + \delta \left[1 - \frac{t}{100} \right]^{10^{-6}} + \beta t^2 \left[1 - \frac{t}{100} \right]^{10^{-6}} \right] \text{Eq. 3-21}$$

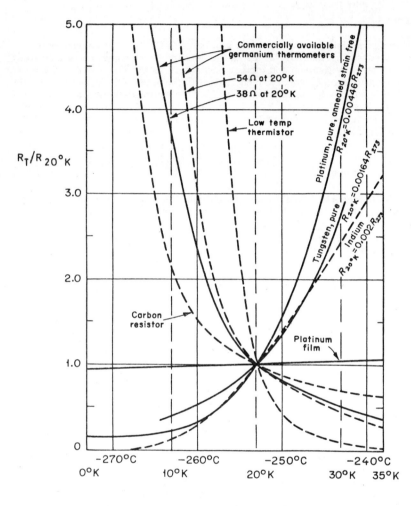

Fig. 3-20   Resistance-temperature relationship for various resistance-type
temperature sensors-low range sources of data: platinum, mean of
NBS calibrations; carbon resistor; germanium thermometer;
thermistor; tungsten; and indium (Courtesy of Rosemount
Engineering Company)

The first column is the temperature in °K (IPTS 1948), the second column is the thermometer resistance in absolute ohms and the third column gives the inverse (reciprocal) of the difference between each two successive values in the second column. These reciprocal first differences are included to facilitate interpolation. The error introduced by using linear interpolation will be less than 0.0001°C. The third column may also be expressed as dT/dR, °K/ohm, as the tabular difference in the first column is 1.0°K. The thermometer described in Table 3-11 was also calibrated and the results tabulated in 0.1°K intervals from 11°K to 92°K by the NBS using the NBS-1955 temperature scale. This temperature scale was referred to earlier and Fig. 3-2 and defines the temperature in terms of the electrical resistance of platinum in the range 10°K to 90°K.

An important class of low temperature thermometers are those whose electrical resistance increases with decrease in temperature, rather than the opposite, as is the case with platinum. Below 20°K these thermometers become most practical. This class of thermometers includes carbon, germanium, and the semi-conductors (thermistors) and are the most sensitive resistance elements to temperature changes at low temperatures available. The electrical resistance characteristics of these materials is shown in Fig. 3-20 in comparison with platinum, tungsten and indium.

The most common resistance element, which also is readily available and inexpensive, is the conventional carbon radio resistor. In addition to its high thermal sentivity at low temperatures, the carbon resistor can be made small, is rather insensitive to magnetic fields and has a small heat capacity for rapid thermal response. It is slightly pressure sensitive, having temperature changes of 0.31°K at 20°K and 0.02°K at 4°K for an increase in pressure of 1000 psi (64), and is subject to thermal instabilities or ageing. This lack of reproducibility is particularly significant after the resistor has been exposed to thermal cycling. Carbon in the form of thin graphite coatings has been used as a thermometer (65), this type of thermometer being especially useful where high response is required, as in low temperature (0.1°K) adiabatic demagnetization experiments.

Lindenfeld (66) reports on the use of carbon and germanium thermometers between 0.30°K and 20°K. One problem in the use of carbon radio resistors below 1°K is the difficulty in measuring their high resistance. Maximum power dissipated in these resistors is about 10^{-8} watts for temperatures 1°K and higher and using a Wheatstone Bridge temperature changes of 10^{-5} to 10^{-6}°K can be detected. The use of the carbon resistor in measurement is greatly aided if a reasonably simple and accurate formula can be written relating resistance to temperature. Clement and Quinnell (67) found that Allen-Bradley Company cylindrical carbon radio resistors has a resistance temperature relationship below 20°K which could be expressed to within ± 1/2 percent by a semi-empirical expression of the form:

$$\log_{10}R + \frac{K}{\log_{10}R} = A + \frac{B}{T} \qquad \text{Eq. 3-22}$$

The constants K, A and B are determined by a calibration of the resistor at a minimum of three known temperatures. Typical resistance-temperature curves for two Allen-Bradley carbon resistors are shown in Fig. 3-21. Schulte (68) calibrated an Allen-Bradley 0.1 W, 270 ohm carbon resistor between 4°K and 296°K and found his results to correlate within 7 percent of equation 3-22. For a range of temperatures from 2°K to 20°K Mikhailov and Kaganovskii (69) also found that equation 3-22 gave satisfactory results for carbon thermometers. In this case the constants in the equation were determined from calibrations at 2°K, 4.2°K and 20.4°K. This permitted temperatures to be calculated with an accuracy of a few hundredths of a degree in the range 2°K to 4.2°K. After 100 heating and cooling cycles between 300°K and 77°K, uncertainty in the temperature measurements in the same 2.2°K interval did not exceed 0.01°K.

i*

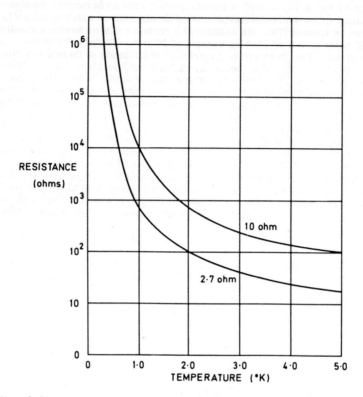

Fig. 3-21   Resistance-temperature curve for two Allen-bradley carbon resistors
(39)

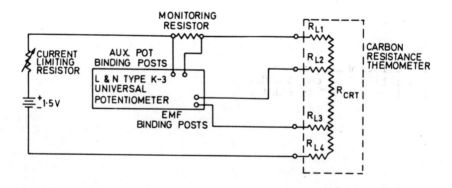

Fig. 3-22   Schematic diagram of the L & N type K-3 universal potentiometer
circuit (70)

Measurement of the resistance of a carbon thermometer may be made with a resistance bridge, as in Fig. 3-19, or with a potentiometer using an accurately calibrated monitoring resistor of known resistance, a schematic diagram of which is shown in 3-22 as used by Greene (70). He calibrated a carbon resistor having a nominal resistance of 82 ohms with a measuring current of 10 μ A. The results of this calibration are given in Fig. 3-23 which illustrates the influence of thermal cycling, the reproducibility of the calibration before and after a calibration run and heat conduction along the thermometer lead wires. The ordinate in Fig. 3-23 is the voltage drop across the resistor for a 10 μ A current. During any one calibration the accuracy amounts to ± 0.022°K and is within the precision of the measurements. Although thermal cycling did produce a shift in the calibration curve, its slope remains constant and thermal conduction along the lead wires raised the calibration curve by approximately 0.10°K in this instance.

The use of carbon resistors for field measurement where laboratory precision is not demanded has been studied by Herr, et al (71). Allen-Bradley Co. 0.1 watt, 100 ohm (± 5 percent at 300°K) resistors were found to be reproducible within ± 1 percent of the absolute temperature in the range 19.5°K to 55.5°K (35°R to 100°R). The measurement of resistance ratio rather than absolute resistance was found to be a more satisfactory method owing to drift in the resistance values of the carbon resistor.

The word 'thermistor' is a trade name for a class of semi-conducting solids having a large negative temperature coefficient of electrical resistance. It is a name derived from the word combination thermal-sensitive-resistor. In a physical description these substances are classed as electronic semi-conductors whose characteristics have been given much theoretical and experimental examination since World War II.

Semi-conductors may be classed with those substances having electronic conductivities in the range 10^{-5} to 10^3 (ohm-cm)$^{-1}$, or resistivities falling between 10^{-3} and 10^5 ohm-cm (72). This can be compared with the pure metals and metallic alloys whose resistivities (73) are generally less than 10^{-4} ohm-cm or with the electrical insulators, as mica and quartz, having resistivities above 10^6 ohm-cm at ordinary temperatures. Figure 3-24 shows these relationships. The important difference between semi-conductors and metals for thermal sensitive uses is not, however, their orders of magnitude of resitivity but the great differences in the change of resistivity with temperature as compared with the metals. This may be illustrated by a typical thermistor which will increase in resistance from 780 to 17,800 ohms for a temperature change from +30 to -30°C. This is a total change of approximately 17,000 ohms or a percentage change of about 2000 percent. Compared with standard platinum and copper resistance thermometers the corresponding change is about 6 and 100 ohms, respectively, over the same range of temperature, both changing about 20 percent. The thermistor, then, undergoes a percentage change in resistivity of about 100 times that of the metals in this range of temperature. Should a greater interval of temperature be examined, as in Fig. 3-24, the percentage change for the thermistor might be as large as 2×10^6.

Possibly of greater significance in the field of thermal measurements is (dR/dT), the rate of change of resistance with temperature, of this thermistor as a function of temperature. At 25°C, for example, dR/dT is 44 ohms/°C and at -30°C it is 1120 ohms/°C, while for a standard 25-ohm platinum resistance thermometer, dR/dT is about 0.10 ohms/°C in this same range of temperature. This means that if one is able to measure changes in resistance, say, to 0.01 ohm, the temperature change capable of detection with this thermistor is 0.0002°C at 25°C and 0.000009°C at -30°C but some commercially available thermistors have sensitivities 100 to 1000 times greater than this. The ordinary resistance thermometer would detect a temperature change of 0.1°C under these same circumstances. It is quite generally

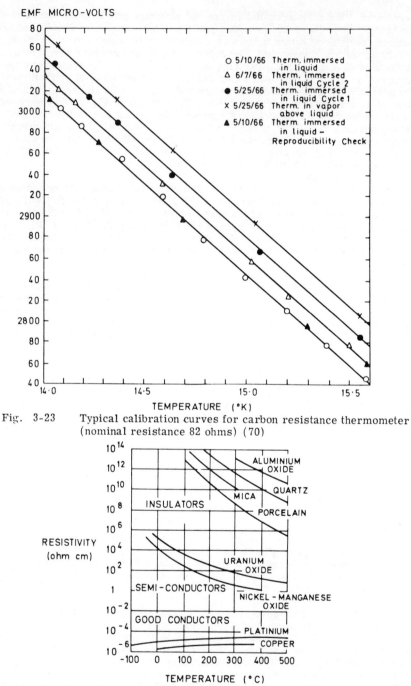

Fig. 3-23   Typical calibration curves for carbon resistance thermometer
(nominal resistance 82 ohms) (70)

Fig. 3-24   Temperature-resistivity relationship of insulators, semi-conductors,
and good conductors (84)

true that thermistors have greatest sensitivity at lower temperatures. For absolute temperature measurement other considerations, naturally, are necessary, not least among which is the thermal stability of the thermistor element, a property possessed in the highest degree by an annealed, strain free platinum resistance thermometer.

Thermistors are available from the manufacturers in a variety of shapes and sizes: discs, beads, rods, washers, and wafers. The shape selected depends on the use to be made of the element and sizes range from 0.0152mm to 2.54mm diameter for beads, 5.08mm to 19.05mm diameter and 1.02mm to 12.7mm thick for discs, wafers and washers, and from 0.0254mm to 12.7mm diameter, 6.35mm to 50.8mm long for rods. Lead wires of various lengths and diameters consist of platinum, platinum-iridium alloys, or copper which can be butt-soldered, wrapped and soldered or fired in place on the thermistor element. Silver paste contacts are available to which the user can soft-solder lead wires, if desired. Washer type elements have terminals which may be mechanically clamped into place against the faces of the element. Protective coatings are frequently placed over the thermistor to prevent or retard atmospheric attack. These consist of a thin or thick layer of glass or enamel coating. For certain applications the element can be placed in an evacuated or gas-filled bulb.

The recommended maximum temperature for continuous service varies but it can be as high as 300°C, however some manufacturers recommend a temperature no greater than 150°C. To a large extent this will depend upon such things as the accuracy required, the atmosphere surrounding the element and the melting point of the solder, if any, used to fasten the lead wires to the element. In any event, the thermistor is used to its greatest advantage, from a thermal-sensitive considera- tion, at lower temperatures.

Most thermal-sensitive semi-conductors (thermistors) are manufactured by sintering various mixtures and combinations of metallic-oxides, the common materials being the oxides of manganese, nickel, cobalt, copper, uranium, iron, zinc, titanium, and magnesium. For the commercial thermistors the oxides of manganese, nickel and cobalt, however, are the most commonly used substances for the mixtures. The result of this type of manufacturing process is a hard, dense ceramic type of material. Other materials (72) (74) which may be classed with the semi-conductors and which possess a large negative temperature coefficient of electrical resistance include chlorides such as NaCl, some sulphides like Ag_2S, CuS, PbS, CaS and some iodides, bromides, and nitrides. Lead sulphide has been used as a detector of infra-red radiation in a radiation pyrometer and is marketed commercially. Its response is high (10,000 cps) and it can detect temperatures as low as 89°K. The uses of thermistors in a radiation-type pick-up is reported (77) for measurement of sub-zero temperatures.

Some pure materials such as silicon, tellurium, germanium and selenium (74) which are monatomic become semi-conductors in the presence of certain impurities. This effect is shown qualitatively in Fig.3-25 and 3-26 for silicon containing an un- known impurity and for cuprous oxide with varying amounts of oxygen in excess of the stoichiometric. Figure 3-25 taken from Becker, *et al* (75), shows a 10^7 in- crease in the conductivity of pure silicon by the addition of a foreign impurity. A similar large increase in conductivity is seen in the case of cuprous oxide, Fig. 3-26, also taken from (75) where the increase is due to an excess of oxygen up to 1 percent. These effects vary greatly with the type of impurity, its amount, its dispersion within the solid, and the heat treatment of the solid.

Generally speaking, a thermistor can be considered for use in any application re- quiring a thermal sensitive electrical resistance element, the obvious and perhaps most widley employed application being that of temperature measurement. As was

138

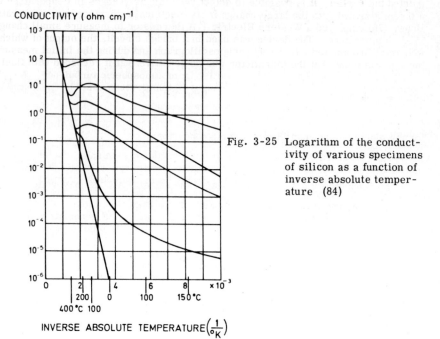

CONDUCTIVITY (ohm cm)$^{-1}$

INVERSE ABSOLUTE TEMPERATURE$\left(\frac{1}{°K}\right)$

Fig. 3-25 Logarithm of the conductivity of various specimens of silicon as a function of inverse absolute temperature (84)

CONDUCTIVITY (ohm cm)$^{-1}$

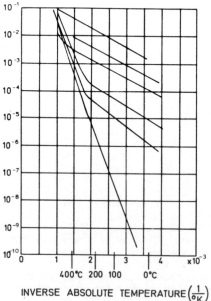

Fig. 3-26 Logarithm of the conductivity of various specimens of cuprous oxide as a function of inverse absolute temperature.

INVERSE ABSOLUTE TEMPERATURE$\left(\frac{1}{°K}\right)$

pointed out earlier, it is possible to detect very minute changes in temperature with a thermistor owing to the large change in its electrical resistance with temperature. Brown (76) employed a Western Electric 17A thermistor to measure small changes in air temperature. The device was used in a bridge circuit, the output of which was amplified and fed into a recording oscillograph and during the initial measurement it was found that the thermistor was so sensitive that it recorded with fidelity the fluctuation in air temperature resulting from atmospheric turbulence. A typical oscillograph is shown in Fig. 3-27. Changes in temperature could be measured to an estimated $0.0007°C$.

Theoretical work of Wilson (78) (80) and others has lead to the following expression for the electronic conductivity of a semi-conductor:

$$\rho = Ae^{-B/T} \qquad \text{Eq. 3-23}$$

Since the conductivity δ is the reciprocal of the resistivity ζ we may write:

$$\rho = Ce^{B/T}$$

or:

$$\rho = \rho_o\, e^{B\left(\frac{1}{T} - \frac{1}{T}\right)} \qquad \text{Eq. 3-24}$$

Also, since the electrical resistance is a geometric extension of the resistivity equation 3-24 may be written:

$$R = R_o e^{B\left(\frac{1}{T} - \frac{1}{T_o}\right)} \qquad \text{Eq. 3-25}$$

Because of the form of equations 3-24 and 3-25, the logarithm of the resistivity or resistance is frequently plotted against the reciprocal of the absolute temperature, as shown in Fig. 3-28, in order to demonstrate the electrical characteristics of a thermistor and to compare it with others. These data are experimental and are taken from Becker, *et al* (75).

The experimental curves in Fig. 3-28 are almost straight, as required by Equation 3-24. However, close inspection will disclose a slight curvature which may be shown to increase linearly with increase in level of temperature (75). Hence, the equation is sometimes modified as:

$$\rho = ET^{-c}e^{D/T} \qquad \text{Eq. 3-26}$$

where C is a small number compared with D or B and may be positive, negative or zero depending on the material (75). For our present purpose we shall employ equation 3-25, since if the interval $T - T_o$ is not too great this equation will adequately represent the data and it is somewhat easier to handle mathematically.

As was mentioned above the relationship of resistance to absolute temperature, given by equation 3-25, has the same shape as the curve shown in Fig. 3-28, from which several important characteristics may be obtained relative to the suitability of a thermistor as a temperature sensing element. A curve of R vs. $1/T$ is also a convenient chart for comparing several different thermistors for use in temperature measurement. By taking logarithms and differentiating equation 3-25 the following equations are obtained:

$$\frac{dR}{R} = -\frac{B}{T^2}\, dT \qquad \text{Eq. 3-27}$$

or:

$$\frac{1}{R}\frac{dR}{dT} = -\frac{B}{T^2} \qquad \text{Eq. 3-28}$$

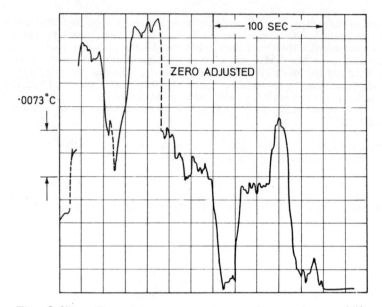

Fig. 3-27   Thermistor response to room temperature variations (84)

SPECIFIC RESISTANCE (ohm cm)

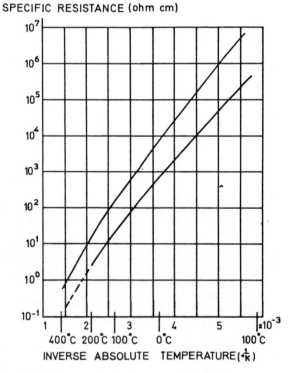

Fig. 3-28   Logarithm of the specific resistance of two thermistor materials as a function of inverse absolute temperature (84)

and:
$$\frac{dR}{dT} = - B \frac{R}{T^2} \qquad\qquad \text{Eq. 3-29}$$

Equation 3-29 may be interpreted in relation to a curve similar to Fig. 3-28 or Log R vs. 1/T. It will be noted that the slope of a curve on such a chart is written:

$$\frac{d (\text{Log } R)}{d(1/T)} = \frac{dR/R}{-dR/T^2} = (\text{slope of Log R - 1/T curve}) \qquad\qquad \text{Eq. 3-30}$$

Comparison of equations 3-29 and 3-30 disclosed that the right hand side of equation 3-30, the slope of a curve plotted as Log R vs 1/T, is equal to the parameter B in equation 3-25. Hence:

$$B = (\text{slope of Log R vs. 1/T curve}). \qquad\qquad \text{Eq. 3-31}$$

Equation 3-29 is then rearranged to:

$$\frac{dR}{dT} = - (\text{slope}) \frac{R}{T^2} \qquad\qquad \text{Eq. 3-32}$$

Interpretation of equation 3-32 is as follows. For use as a temperature sensing element it is desirable that a thermistor have as large a value of dR/dT as possible in order that it be sensitive and capable of detecting small changes in temperature for any given resistance measuring system. From equation 3-32 it follows that at any given temperature, that thermistor which has the greatest slope on a Log R vs. 1/T plot and the greatest resistance will also be the most sensitive as a temperature sensing element. In this way, therefore, a series of thermistors can be very rapidly evaluated as to their thermal sensitivity.

Another method for evaluation of thermistors consists of plotting Log R_o vs. B, where B is determined from experimental thermistor data in the region of T_o, which may be taken to be 0°C; R_o is then the resistance of the thermistor at 0°C. Because most thermistors have similar characteristics it will be generally true that a thermistor with superior thermal sensitivity at 0°C will also have superior sensitivity at other temperatures. In any event the resistance-temperature characteristics of the thermistor can be obtained approximately from equation 3-25 or from the manufacturer's published data. Equation 3-25 is approximate owing to the non-linear nature of Log R vs. 1/T, as mentioned above in connection with equation 3-26 and Fig. 3-28.

The technical literature does not contain a large body of data on the stability or ageing effects of thermistors so what is reported here are heterogeneous results of a number of observers on a few isolated tests. It may be generally concluded, however, that an ageing effect may be expected which usually is of the nature of an increase with time of the electrical resistance which is not linear but logarithmic, resulting in smaller percentage changes in resistance with increased time. Pre-ageing may be accomplished by heating or by the passage of higher than service current through the thermistor (79). These have the effect also of accelerating the ageing if the temperature is high enough.

The change of electrical resistance is sometimes attributed to a rearrangement in the distribution of the components of the mixture of oxides making up a semiconductor. Heat treatment is believed to play a major role in the dispersion of the components so that ageing and pre-ageing usually involve some kind of heat treatment. Muller and Stolen (81) tested two Western Electric 14A thermistors at 25°C over a period of six months and they report a decrease in resistance of about 50 ohms out of a total of approximately 100,000 ohms. This corresponds to an ageing effect of about 0.012°C.

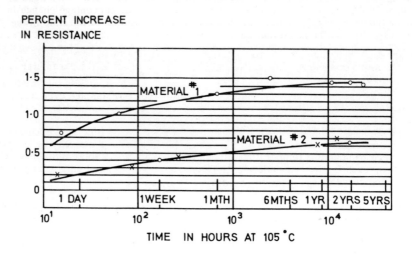

PERCENT INCREASE
IN RESISTANCE

Fig. 3-29   Effect of ageing in 105° C oven on thermistor characteristics;
materials 1 and 2 (84)

TABLE 3-11: Short Range Stability of a Western Electric 14A Thermistor .

Time Mins	Thermistor A	Thermistor B
0	96, 234. 0	96, 234. 7
5	96, 234. 6	96, 234. 6
10	96, 234. 2	96, 234. 9
15	96, 235. 0	96, 234. 4
20	96, 234. 8	96, 234. 4
25	96, 234. 8	96, 234. 8
30	96, 234. 7	96, 234. 2
35	96, 234. 8	96, 234. 7
40	96, 234. 6	96, 234. 0
45	96, 235. 0	96, 234. 6

Figure 3-29 shows ageing data (75) taken on three quarter-inch diameter discs of material No. 1 and No. 2 (No. 1 is composed of manganese, nickel oxides; No. 2 is composed of oxides of manganese, nickel and cobalt) with silver contacts and soldered leads. These discs were measured soon after production, were aged in an oven at 105°C and were periodically tested at 24°C. The percentage change in resistance over its initial value is plotted versus the logarithm of the time in the ageing oven. It is to be noted that most of the ageing takes place in the first day or week so that if these discs were pre-aged for a week or a month and the subsequent change in resistance referred to the resistance after pre-ageing, they would age only about 0.2 percent in one year. In a thermistor thermometer, this change in resistance would correspond to a temperature change of 0.05°C while thermistors mounted in an evacuated tube, or coated with a thin layer of glass age even less than those shown in the figure. For some applications such high stability is not essential and it is not necessary to give the thermometers special treatment. Thermistors have been used at high temperatures with satisfactory ageing characteristics. Extruded rods of material No. 1 have been tested for stability by treating them for two months at a temperature of 300°C and -75°C for a total of 700 temperature cycles, each lasting one-half hour. The resistance of typical units changed by less than one percent.

In order to determine the life of a 1A thermistor, Pearson (82) placed it in a circuit where an off-and-on current of 10 mA. a.c. was repeated 30 seconds over an extended period of time. Resistance measurements were made on the units periodically in order to determine their stability with time and the general trend was a rise in resistance during the first part of its life, after which the resistance became quite constant. Over a period of 15 months, during which time the thermometer was put through 650,000 heating cycles, the cold resistance did not increase by more than 7 percent. The resistance of the thermistor when hot was found to be equally stable.

The characteristics of both thermistors and thermocouples shift when exposed to high temperatures for lengthy periods of time (83). For thermistors the resistance change varies logarithmically with time with higher temperatures accelerating the change. This suggests that if thermistors are subjected for several days or weeks to temperatures somewhat higher than those to encountered in actual use, the major portion of the change would have occurred. For thermocouples, the change in voltage output becomes greater as the exposure time to high temperature is increased. Over a three month period in which thermistors and thermocouples were exposed to 365°K for about 15 hours, the thermistor shifted a maximum of 0.11°K, while the thermocouple shifted 0.17°K. However, when new elements were tested and aged for 100 hours at 530°K, the thermistors still shifted only 0.11°K while the thermocouples shifted twice as much or 0.33°K.

It was found by Muller and Stolen (81) that if the exciting potential is left impressed across the thermistor, a steady state is reached. This implied a resistance change of less than 1 ohm on daily measurement, the cold resistance of this thermistor at 0°C being 350,000 ohms. Short range stability of a Western Electric 14A thermistor measured at five minute intervals at 25°C (in ohms) is shown in the table opposite. The authors (81) used the thermistor to measure small temperature difference in a laboratory experiment. The conclusion is that no significant change in resistance was detected which could not be attributed to measurement uncertainty.

To obtain a stable thermistor the following steps are generally thought to be necessary (75). By these precautions remarkably good stabilities can be attained.

(a)   Select only semi-conductors which are pure electronic conductors.

(b)   Select those which do not change chemically when exposed to the atmosphere at elevated temperatures.

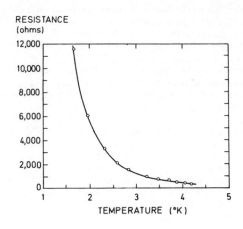

RESISTANCE
(ohms)

TEMPERATURE (°K)

Fig. 3-30   Calibration curve for a germanium thermometer (79)

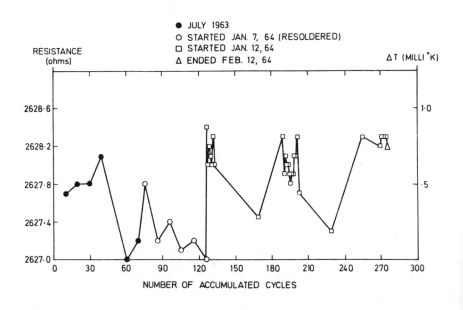

● JULY 1963
○ STARTED JAN. 7, 64 (RESOLDERED)
□ STARTED JAN. 12, 64
△ ENDED FEB. 12, 64

RESISTANCE
(ohms)

ΔT (MILLI °K)

NUMBER OF ACCUMULATED CYCLES

Fig. 3-31   Equilibrium resistance as a function of the number of accumulated
cycles T = 4.2°K (87)

(c)   Select one which is not sensitive to impurities likely to be encountered in
        manufacture or in use.

(d)   Treat it so that the degree of dispersion of the critical impurities is in
        equilibrium or else that the approach to equilibrium is very slow at opera-
        ting temperatures.

(e)   Make a contact which is intimate, sticks tenaciously, has an expansion coef-
        ficient compatible with the semi-conductor, and is durable in the atmosphere
        to which it will be exposed.

(f)   In some cases, enclose the thermistor in a thin coating of glass or a material
        impervious to gases and liquids, the coating having a suitable expansion
        coefficient.

(g)   Pre-age the unit for several days or weeks at a temperature somewhat higher
        than that to which it will be subjected.

Clark and Kobayashi (84) (85) have studied the general characteristics of thermistors to be used for temperature measurement. This includes the theory of their
conductance properties, the dynamic response and steady-state error of the thermistor temperature-sensing element, their stability and the resistance-temperature
characteristics of approximately 300 commercially available thermistors from 8
different manufacturers. Friedberg (79) describes a semi-conducting film of ZnO
used as a thermometer at $2°K$ which had an electrical resistance of $5(10^5)$ ohms at
liquid helium temperatures, and a sensitivity of approximately $5(10^4)$ ohms per
degree K at $2°K$.

Germanium, with impurities consisting variously of arsenic, gallium or indium,
has become one of the most satisfactory materials for thermal resistance elements
in the range $0.2°K$ to $20°K$. This material possesses a negative temperature coefficient of resistance, a moderate level of resistance, high sensitivity of resistance
change to temperature change, high reproducibility and stability to thermal cycling
and is readily manufactured and fabricated. The impurities are included in the
germanium in controlled quantities to influence both the resistance-temperature
characteristics and the sensitivity and a typical resistance-temperature curve for
germanium 'doped' with 0.001 At per cent indium is shown in Fig. 3-30 for the temperature range $1°K$ to $5°K$. This particular element was found to be highly reproducible over a period of several months and the thermometer was subjected to a
number of warming and cooling cycles following which its resistance-temperature
characteristic could be reproduced to within ± $0.001°K$. The measuring current
used was 0.01 ma although the author reports an increase of current to 0.1 ma did
not appreciably influence the R-T characteristic (79).

Edlow and Plumb (86) (87) studied the reproducibility and temperature-resistance
characteristics of a number of commercially available germanium thermometers,
the germanium having either arsenic or gallium as the impurity. Their purpose was
to find out if a germanium thermometer was sufficiently stable to be used as a basic
secondary standard thermometer. As a consequence of their study the NBS adopted
the germanium resistance thermometer as the basis for the NBS scale from $2°K$ to
$20°K$ and used it for basic temperature calibration in this range. The determination
of reproducibility was made by cycling the resistance element from $4.2°K$ to $300°K$
and measuring the resistance change at $4.2°K$ which was then related to the corresponding temperature change. Two typical heating-cooling cycle tests are shown in
Fig. 3-31 and 3-32. In each case the reproducibility is within ± $0.001°K$. In the
case of resistor D, Fig. 3-32, the reproducibility is within $0.0005°K$ after 86 cycles.
Because of this high degree of stability the resistor of Fig. 3-32 became one of the
NBS standard thermometers. This result is quite typical of that found by others.

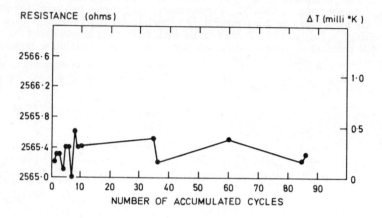

Fig. 3-32   Equilibrium resistance as a function of the number of accumulated
cycles for a resistor D. T = 4.2°K (87)

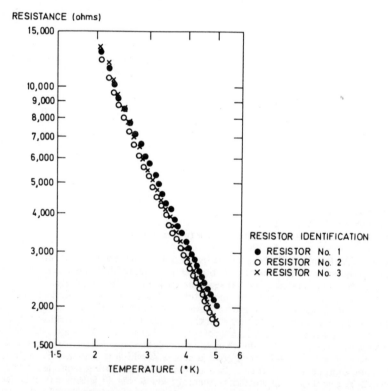

Fig. 3-33   A plot of the resistance-temperature calibration data for resistors
1, 2, and 3. (86)

Temperatures were derived from liquid helium-4 vapour pressures

Kunzler, *et al* (88) for example, cycled arsenic 'doped' germanium encapsulated in helium-filled thermometers as many as 50 times and found no evidence of calibration change of as much as 0.0001°K. Furthermore, they report two such thermometers in use for 3 years on low temperature experimental apparatus with no observable change in calibration. From results such as these it seems safe to conclude that germanium 'doped' with a selected impurity is a suitable material for low temperature thermometers below 20°K.

The resistance-temperature calibration data for a number of encapsulated, hermetically sealed, arsenic 'doped' germanium thermometers was determined by Endlow and Plumb (86) in the range 2.1°K to 5.0°K. The resistance was measured at temperature intervals of 0.1°K in a pressure-controlled helium liquid-vapor equilibrium cell and other measurements were made in a calibration comparator apparatus. The results agreed to within 0.001°K, the basic standard temperature reference was the NBS 1958 He^4 scale, Table 3-15 and some typical data are given in Fig. 3-33. A polynomial function was derived for each thermometer to represent its resistance-temperature calibration in the range 2.1°K to 5.0°K. The sensitivity of a germanium thermometer, dR/dT, manufactured by Cryo Cal, Inc. (89), is shown in Fig. 3-34 for the temperature range 2°K to 28°K. At 20°K the sensitivity of this thermometer is 3 ohms per °K which be compared with a sensitivity of 0.0185 ohms per °K for a platinum thermometer at the same temperature. The very large increase in sensitivity for germanium at temperatures below 20°K is characteristic of this type of resistance thermometer.

The use of arsenic-doped germanium prepared from a single germanium crystal is reported by Kunzler, *et al* (88), the germanium element being cut into the form of a bridge of dimensions 0.06 × 0.05 × 0.52 cm with side arms near each end for electrical connections. An encapsulated thermometer design is illustrated in Fig. 3-35. When covered with a platinum case it is filled with helium gas which limits its lowest useful temperature to about 0.25°K. Bare bridges have also been used in applications such as adiabatic demagnetization experiments where a thermometer with minimum heat capacity is required to give high response and in this case a lag time between the thermometer and sample was 0.1 second. Higher currents are permitted with the bare bridge than with encapsulated models owing to the improved cooling permitted by the exposed germanium element. The resistance-temperature characteristics of the encapsulated model were found to be unaffected (within ± 0.0001°K) by thermal cycling or aging over a period of several years. Cycling of the bare bridge between 4.2°K and 293°K several times produced only a few thousandths of a degree change in its calibration. The resistance-temperature characteristics of four typical encapsulated thermometers are shown in Table 3-12 and Fig. 3-36.

The R-T characteristics of a carbon thermometer is shown for comparison. At low temperatures the germanium thermometers have widely different electrical properties because the arsenic impurity concentration is not the same in each sample even though they were cut from the same germanium crystal. This is a good example of the extreme sensitivity of the electrical properties of these resistors to impurity concentration. However, the resistivity – temperature characteristics of an element are defined approximately by its resistivity at 4.2°K (88) and in the range 2°K to 35°K, the ratio (dR/R)(dT/T) is of the order of unity for all samples, a result found with germanium bridges cut from other crystals as well. This characteristic is responsible for the tremendous temperature sensitivity of the resistance thermometers. The sensitivity dR/dT at 4.2°K of several thermometers, including those in Table 3-12, is shown in Fig. 3-37. An increased sensitivity may be achieved roughly according to R$^{3/2}$, by selecting a thermometer of higher resistance providing the instrumentation is compatible with the selected resistor.

The resistance of germanium is influenced by a magnetic field. The variation of the magnetoresistance with temperature was studied by Kunzler, *et al* (88) using a

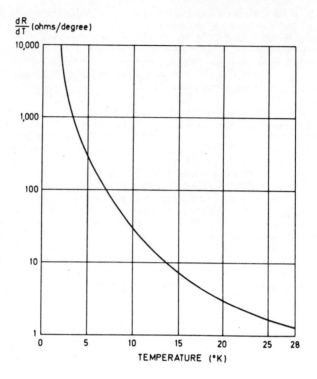

Fig. 3-34   Sensitivity dR/dT typical standard cryoresitor (Courtesy Gryo. Cal, Inc.) (89)

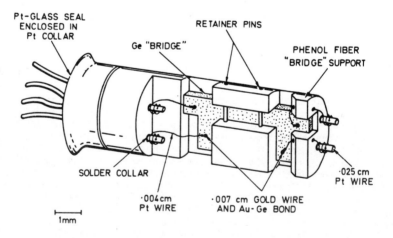

Fig. 3-35   Encapsulated germanium thermometer–model II, with cover removed (88)

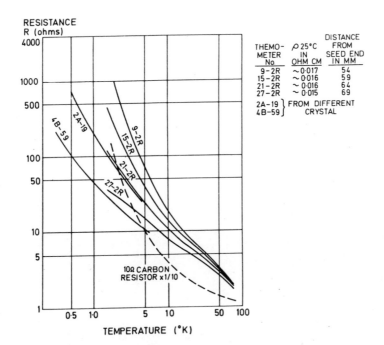

Fig. 3-36   Resistance-temperature characteristics of germanium thermal sensing elements.

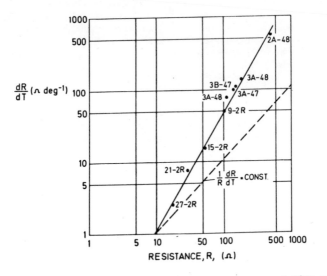

Fig. 3-37   Variation of dR/dT with resistance at 4.2° K (88)

TABLE 3-12: Resistance-Temperature Characteristics of Germanium Thermometers Fabricated from Arsenic-Doped Crystal 8-899-N (88)

T°K	Sample No			
	9-2R		15-2R	
	R Ω	dR/dT	R Ω	dR/dT
273	~ 1		~ 1	
77	2.0		1.9	
35	4.6	0.16	4.3	0.13
20	8.0	0.5	7.0	0.3
15	10.5	0.8	9.0	0.6
10	18.3	2.8	14.1	1.8
4.2	101	50	53	15.5
2	789	1000	216	200
1.5	2300		450	

T°K	21-2R		27-2R	
	R Ω	dR/dT	R Ω	dR/dT
273	~ 1		~ 1	
77	1.8		1.7	
35	3.9	0.11	3.4	0.07
20	5.9	0.22	4.9	0.15
15	7.3	0.4	5.9	0.25
10	10.7	1.1	8.0	0.67
4.2	29	7.7	16.7	2.6
2	77	46	29.5	11.2
1.5	120		36.5	

germanium bridge having a zero field resistance ($R_{H=0}$) of 200 ohms at 4.2°K. The magnetoresistance ($\Delta R/R_{H=0}$) at 18 kilogauss was found to be 0.16 at 4.2°K and gradually increased with decreasing temperature, reaching a maximum value of 0.28 at 1.9°K. Below 1.9°K the magnetoresistance decreased to a value of $\Delta R/R_{H=0}$ equals 0.21 at 1.2°K. At 4.2°K the corresponding change in temperature calibration as a result of the magnetic field would be approximately 0.20°K. The magnetoresistance of germanium is also slightly anisotropic, being somewhat less than 10 percent of the total magnetoresistance over 180 angular degrees at 4.2°K and in an 18 kilogauss field.

Other papers treating the germanium resistance thermometers have been published by Low (90) and Orlova, et al (91). Antcliffe, et al. (92) report the use of germanium thermometers below 1°K. Their lowest temperature was 0.40°K obtained by a He³ bath and the range of temperatures investigated was 4.20°K to 0.40°K. Between 4.20°K and 1.20°K the data were fitted to:

$$R = CT^{-A} e^{-B/T} ,$$

Eq. 3-33

with representative values of the constants as A = 0.507 - 1.004, -B = 1.245 - 1.399 and C = 71.89 - 112.8 for three resistors calibrated.

Magnetic Thermometry

The practical minimum temperature which may be produced by pumping helium is about 1°K for He⁴ and 0.5°K for He³ as below these temperatures the vapor pressure is too low to be maintained for most useful experimental purposes. To produce as well as measure temperatures below 0.5°K the properties of paramagnetic substances, usually paramagnetic alums, are used. The low temperatures are achieved

TABLE 3-13: Temperatures Attained by Adiabatic Demagnetization of Various Paramagnetic Salts (96)

Experimenters	Date	Paramagnetic salt	Initial field, oersteds	Initial temp. °K	Final magnetic temp. T^* °K
Giauque and MacDougall	1933	Gadolinium sulfate	8,000	1.5	0.25
De Haas, Wiersma, and Kramers	1933	Cerium fluoride	27,600	1.35	0.13
		Dysprosium ethyl sulfate	19,500	1.35	0.12
		Cerium ethyl sulfate	27,600	1.35	0.085
De Haas and Wiersma	1934	Chromium potassium alum	24,600	1.16	0.031
	1935	Iron ammonium alum	24,075	1.20	0.018
		Alum mixture	24,075	1.29	0.0044
		Cesium titanium alum	24,075	1.31	0.0055
Kurti and Simon	1935	Gadolinium sulfate	5,400	1.15	0.35
		Maganese ammonium sulfate	8,000	1.23	0.09
		Iron ammonium alum	14,100	1.23	0.038
		Iron ammonium alum	8,300	1.23	0.072
		Iron ammonium alum	4,950	1.23	0.114
MacDougall and Giauque	1936	Gadolinium nitrobenzene sulfonate	8,090	0.94	0.098
Kurti, Laine, Rollin, and Simon	1936	Iron ammonium alum	32,000	1.08	0.010
Kurti, Laine, and Simon	1939	Iron ammonium alum	28,800	9.5	0.36
Ashmead	1939	Copper potassium sulfate	35,900	1.17	0.005
DeKlerk (95)	1956	Chromium potassium alum	--	--	0.0029

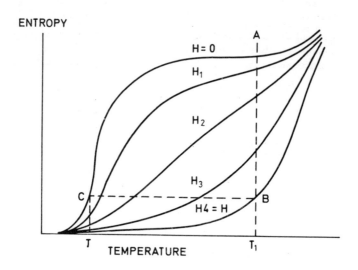

Fig. 3-38   Temperature-entropy diagram for a paramagnetic salt under the influence of different magnetic fields (40)

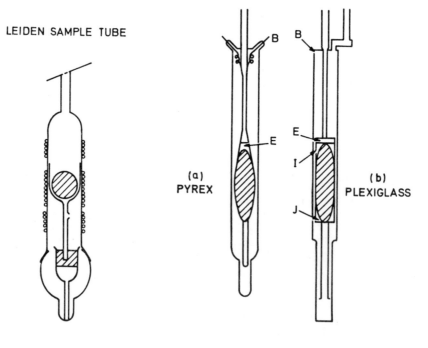

Fig. 3-39   Typical paramagnetic salt samples (94)

by demagnetizing these salts adiabatically from an initial state of a high magnetic field and a temperature of approximately 1°K as the process of adiabatic demagnetization produces a rapid drop in the temperature of the salt owing to a decrease in its energy by the work of demagnetization. This is analogous to the drop in temperature of a compressed gas as it expands isentropically or adiabatically while doing work on its environment. Garrett (93) reports the limit of cooling by this process (electronic) is about 10^{-4}°K but if the energy of nuclear spin is involved a temperature of 10^{-6}°K is thought possible. A two stage demagnetization of a diluted chromium alum has produced a final temperature of 10^{-3}°K with a field of 9000 gauss but to reach this temperature in a single demagnetization from 1°K a field of 25,000 gauss would be required. Temperatures of a few hundredths of a degree absolute can be achieved without exceptional difficulties and those of the order of one-thousandths of a degree can be obtained with somewhat greater effort (94)(95). Table 3-13, prepared by Zemansky (96), summarizes some results of adiabatic demagnetization experiments and identified the paramagnetic salts used. Certain properties of commonly used paramagnetic salts are given in Table 3-14 (96).

At liquid helium temperatures the orientation of the magnetic ions in the paramagnetic salts are influenced by a magnetic field in a significant way and contribute to both the energy and the entropy of the salt. Lattice vibrations also have energy and entropy contributions but at the low temperatures (< 1°K) associated with adiabatic demagnetization experiments these effects are small. The partial spacial ordering of the paramagnetic ions in the presence of a magnetic field at constant temperature results in a decrease of the system entropy, as would be expected in an isothermal transition from a less-ordered to a greater ordered state. Thus, the effect of an increase in the magnetic field on a paramagnetic salt is exactly analogous to the isothermal compression of a fluid or the isothermal extension of an elastic substance. This is illustarted in Fig. 3-38 which shows the temperature-entropy diagram of a paramagnetic salt for magnetic fields of strength H. States of lower entropy at a given temperature correspond to the magnetic fields of greater strength, i.e., $H_4 > H_3$, etc.

The process of magnetic cooling consists first of cooling a sample of paramagnetic salt to as low a temperature as possible in the absence of any significant magnetic field ($H \approx 0$) shown as state A, Fig. 3-38. This is usually accomplished in a helium cryostat pumped to a temperature T_1 of approximately 1°K. While maintained at this temperature by the helium bath a magnetic field is introduced into the system which causes the entropy to decrease to state B, Fig. 3-38. In state B the paramagnetic salt is removed from the immediate influence of its cooling bath, usually accomplished by pumping away the helium surrounding the salt, and the magnetic field switched off. With the removal of the field the paramagnetic ions are reoriented to a state of greater disorder in a reversible-adiabatic process with a corresponding flow of work to the environment by virtue of the magnetic rearrangement. The consequence of this is an isentropic drop in energy of the salt to a state of zero magnetic field and lower temperature T, shown as state C, Fig. 3-38. A cryostat for doing this is described by DeKlerk and Steenland (97) and shown in Fig. 3-40. The time required to reduce the magnetic field is about 1 second which may be compared with the spin-spin relaxation time of 10^{-9} seconds and the spin-lattice relaxation time of 10^{-3} seconds (93) (98).

The temperature T to which the paramagnetic salt was cooled is computed from 'Curie's Law':

$$M = \frac{C}{T} H \qquad\qquad \text{Eq. 3-34}$$

or:

$$M = \chi H \qquad\qquad \text{Eq. 3-35}$$

154

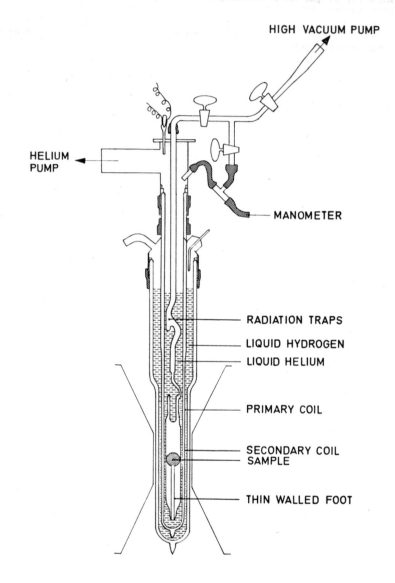

HIGH VACUUM PUMP

HELIUM
PUMP

MANOMETER

RADIATION TRAPS

LIQUID HYDROGEN

LIQUID HELIUM

PRIMARY COIL

SECONDARY COIL
SAMPLE

THIN WALLED FOOT

Fig. 3-40   Typical leiden demagnetization cryostat, one-fifth of real size (97)

TABLE 3-14: Properties of Paramagnetic Salts (96)

Paramagnetic salt	Gram-ionic weight M (gm)	Density, $\frac{gm}{cm^3}$	Curie const., $C \frac{cm^3 \ deg}{gm \ ion}$
Cerium magnesium nitrate $2Ce(NO_3)_3 3Mg(NO_3)_2 24H_2O$	765	--	0.318
Chromium potassium alum $Cr_2(SO_4)_3 K_2SO_4 24H_2O$	499	1.83	1.86
Chromium methylammonium alum $Cr_2(SO_4)_3 CH_3NH_3SO_4 24H_2O$	492	1.645	1.87
Copper potassium sulfate $CuSO_4 K_2SO_4 6H_2O$	442	2.22	0.445
Iron ammonium alum $Fe_2(SO_4)_3(NH_4)_2SO_4 24H_2O$	482	1.71	4.35
Gadolinium sulfate $Gd_2(SO_4)_3 8H_2O$	373	3.010	7.85
Manganese ammonium sulfate $MnSO_4(NH_4)_2SO_4 6H_2O$	391	1.83	4.36
Titanium cesium alum $Ti_2(SO_4)_3 Cs_2SO_4 24H_2O$	589	~2	0.118

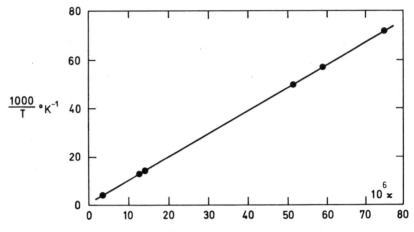

Fig. 3-41 Plot of susceptibility per gm vs reciprocal temperature for powdered $CuSO_4 \cdot K_2SO_4 \cdot 6H_2O$, showing the curie law temperature dependence (100)

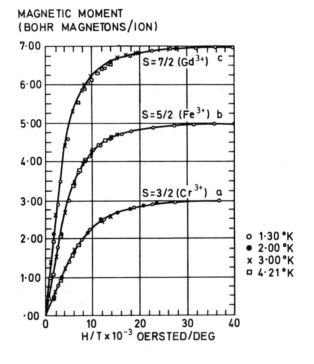

Fig. 3-42 Plot of magnetic moment H/T for spherical samples of (a) potassium chromium alum - (b) ferric ammonium alum and (c) gadolinium sulfate octahydrate (100)

with:
$$\chi = \frac{C}{T} ,$$
Eq. 3-36

where M is the magnetization or magnetic moment, C is Curie's constant, H is the magnetic field strength and χ is the magnetic susceptibility. The magnetic suscept-ibility is related to the permeability, μ, and the magnetic flux intensity, B,

by: $B = \mu H$
Eq. 3-37

and: $4 \pi \chi = \mu - 1.$
Eq. 3-38

Substances are classified according to the value of χ: diamagnetic for $\chi < 0$, para-magnetic for $\chi > 0$, and ferromagnetic $\chi >> 0$.

Departures from Curie's Law result from the effects of the shape of the paramag-netic salt and are expressed by the Curie-Weiss Law:

$$\chi = \frac{C}{T - \Delta}$$
Eq. 3-39

where Δ is the Curie-Weiss constant and is equal to zero for a spherical sample. For this reason spherical samples are used, as in Fig. 3-40, if possible or, if not, the results are corrected to that of a spherical sample. Typical spherical and spheroidal sample tubes are illustrated by DeKlerk (94) in Fig. 3-39. The magnetic temperature computed from equation 3-36 or 3-39 is not a true thermodynamic temperature owing to the empirical constants C and Δ which do not follow from considerations of the second law of thermodynamics. These temperatures will be denoted as T^* and will be related to the thermodynamic temperature T later.

For either spherical or spheroidal samples the defined magnetic temperature is written (94) as:

$$T^*_{sphere} = \frac{C}{\chi_{sphere}}$$
Eq. 3-40

where:
$$\chi_{sphere} = \chi_{spheroid} / [1 + (4\pi/3 - \alpha) \chi_{spheroid}] ,$$
Eq. 3-41

$$\alpha = 4\pi \left(\frac{1-e^2}{e^2} \right) \left[\frac{1}{2e} \log_e \left(\frac{1+e}{1-e} \right) - 1 \right] ,$$
Eq. 3-42

and:
$$e = (1 - \epsilon^2)^{1/2} ,$$
Eq. 3-43

ϵ is defined as the eccentricity of the spheroid as outlined by Maxwell (99).

The magnetic behavior of four paramagnetic salts showing their conformance with Curie's Law at liquid helium temperatures and higher is given in Figs. 3-41 and 3-42, taken from Kittel (100). At low temperatures saturation effects cause de-parture from Curie's Law at a certain magnetic field strength, as illustrated in Fig. 3-42.

The determination of T^*_{sphere}, or $T - \Delta$, is made by measuring the magnetic inductance produced by the paramagnetic salt in an electrical measuring circuit, as shown in Fig. 3-43 and the magnetic inductance is proportional to the magnetic susceptibility, χ. The magnetic susceptibility of the salt is determined at 1°K and 4°K using the 1958 He[4] scale and then extrapolated to lower temperatures for use during demagnetization experiments. T^*_{sphere} is a good approximation to T for a few tenths of a degree below 1°K but at lowest temperatures it fails to represent T

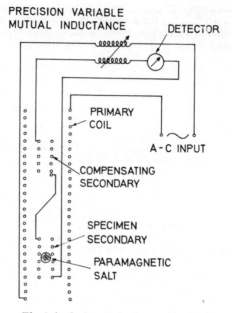

PRECISION VARIABLE
MUTUAL INDUCTANCE

DETECTOR

PRIMARY
COIL

A - C INPUT

COMPENSATING
SECONDARY

SPECIMEN
SECONDARY

PARAMAGNETIC
SALT

Fig. 3-43   Electrical circuit for magnetic thermometer (40)

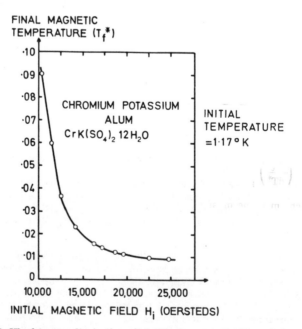

FINAL MAGNETIC
TEMPERATURE (T_f^*)

CHROMIUM POTASSIUM
ALUM
$CrK(SO_4)_2 \cdot 12H_2O$

INITIAL
TEMPERATURE
$= 1 \cdot 17\,°K$

INITIAL MAGNETIC FIELD H_i (OERSTEDS)

Fig. 3-44   DeKlerk's results in the adiabatic demagnetization of chromium
potassium alum (96)

since for all known salts a maximum in χ has been found which produces a minimum in T^*_{sphere}. Demagnetization from still higher fields results in progressively lower values of x and higher T^*_{sphere} and T may differ by an order of magnitude. The final temperature T^*_{sphere} for a chromium potassium alum as a function of magnetic field strength is shown Fig. 3-44. In this case a minimum T^*_{sphere} is approached asympotically for progressively higher fields.

The thermodynamics of a paramagnetic salt indicate (93) (94) that the entropy S is a function of T and H. Thus:

$$S = f\ (T,\ H). \qquad\qquad \text{Eq. 3-44}$$

This may also be written (93) (94), as

$$Tds = C_H\,dT + T\left(\frac{\partial M}{\partial T}\right)_H dH \qquad\qquad \text{Eq. 3-45}$$

where:
$$C_H = \left(\frac{\partial E}{\partial T}\right)_H = T\left(\frac{\partial S}{\partial T}\right)_H \qquad\qquad \text{Eq. 3-46}$$

For the isentropic demagnetization, state B to C, Fig. 3-38, then equation 3-45 indicates that:

$$T - T_1 = \int_0^H \frac{T}{C_H}\left(\frac{\partial M}{\partial T_H}\right) dH \qquad\qquad \text{Eq. 3-47}$$

Since, $(\partial M/\partial T)_H < 0$ by equation 3-34, the temperature T will always be less than T_1 for adiabatic demagnetization processes.

The relation between T^*_{sphere} (to be identified as T^* hereafter) and the thermodynamic temperature T is determined from the thermodynamic definition:

$$T = \left(\frac{dQ}{dS}\right)_{Rev} \qquad\qquad \text{Eq. 3-48}$$

This may also be written:
$$T = \frac{(dQ/dT^*)_{H=0}}{(dS/dT^*)_{H=0}} \qquad\qquad \text{Eq. 3-49}$$

Now (dQ/dT^*) may be found from heating experiments in which:

$$\left(\frac{dQ}{dT^*}\right)_{H=0} = m\left(\frac{dh}{dT^*}\right)_{H=0} \qquad\qquad \text{Eq. 3-50}$$

in which, m is the mass of a sample of paramagnetic salt and h is its enthalpy per unit mass.

The quantity $(dS/dT^*)_{H=0}$ is determined from a series of demagnetization experiments from T_1, Fig. 3-38, and a number of different magnetic fields such as H_1, H_2, H_3 and H_4. The entropies corresponding to the isotherm T_1 and the various fields is determined from equation 3-45 as:

$$S(H, T_1) - S(O, T_1) = \int_0^H \left(\frac{\partial M}{\partial T}\right)_H dH \qquad\qquad \text{Eq. 3-51}$$

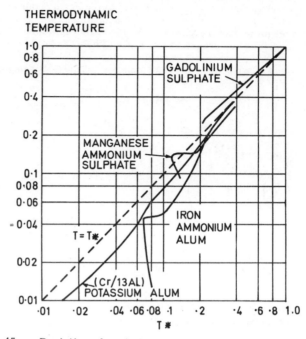

Fig. 3-45   Deviation of curie temperature, T∗, from thermodynamic
temperature for several paramagnetic salts (40)

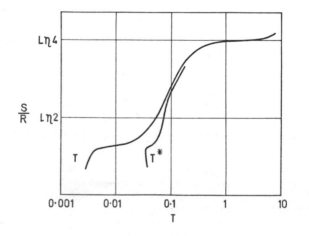

Fig. 3-46   Entropy of potassium chrome alum as a function of absolute temperature and of T∗. (100)

The corresponding temperatures are then computed from equation 3-47, giving a curve of S vs. T^* for a zero field (H = 0). From this the slope (dS/dT^*) may be derived and T computed from equation 3-49.

The relationship between T and T^* for several paramagnetic salts is shown in Figs. 3-45 and 3-46.

References

1.　　Clark, J. A.　'Advances in Heat Transfer', Cryogenic Heat Transfer, Vol. 5, edited by Irvine, Jr. T. F., and Hartnett, J. P., Academic Press, N.Y., 1968.

2.　　Stimson, H. F.　'Temperature','The Text Revision of the International Temperature Scale of 1948,'Vol. 3, 1, pp. 59-66.

3.　　Stimson, H. F.　'International Practical Temperature Scale of 1948: Text Revision 1960', NBS Monograph 37, Sept. 8, 1961. See also paper of same title and author in J. Research, NBS (A, Physics and Chemistry) Vol. 65A, No. 3, 1961.

4.　　Terrien, J.　'News from the International Bureau of Weights and Measures', Metrologia, Vol. 4, No. 1, 1968, p. 41.

5.　　Preston-Thomas, H. and Bedford, R. E.　'Practical Temperature Scales Between 11°K and 273°K', Metrologia, Vol. 4, No. 1, 1968, pp. 14-30.

6.　　Hust, J. G.　Personal communication, Cryogenics Division, National Bureau of Standards, Boulder, Colorado. April 4, 1968.

7.　　Hoge, H. J. and Brickwedde, F. G.　'Establishment of a Temperature Scale for the Calibration of Thermometers Between 14 and 83°K', Vol. 22, 1939, pp. 351-73.

8.　　Hoge, H. J.　'Temperature', 'A Practical Temperature Scale Below the Oxygen Point and a Survey of Fixed Points in this Range', Vol. 1, Reinhold, N.Y., 1941, pp. 141-56.

9.　　Orlova, M. P. Sharevskaya, D. I. Astrov, D. N. and Krutikova. 'The Derivation of the Provisional Reference Table CCT-64, T = f(W) for Platinum Resistance Thermometers for the Range from 12 to 273.15°K, Part I. The Derivation of the Table for the Range from 12 to 95°K', Metrologia, Vol. 2, No. 1, 1966, pp. 6-10.

10.　　Furukawa, G. T. and Reilly, M. L.　'Application of Precise Heat Capacity Data to the Analysis of the Temperature Intervals of the NBS (1955) and the International Practical Temperature Scales in the Region of 90°K', J. Research NBS (A. Physics and Chemistry) Vol. 69A, No. 1, 1965, pp. 5-12.

11.　　Plumb, H. H. and Cataland, G.　'Acoustical Thermometer and the National Bureau of Standards Provisional Temperature Scale 2-20, (1965)', Metrologia, Vol. 2, No. 4, 1966, pp. 127-39.

12.　　Moessen, G. W., Astonand, J. G. Ascah, R. G.　'Temperature' 'The Pennsylvania State University Thermodynamic Temperature Scale Below 90°K and the Normal Boiling Points of Oxygen and Normal Hydrogen on the Thermodynamic Scale, Vol. 3, Reinhold, N.Y., 1962, pp. 90-102.

162

13. Borovick-Romanov, A.S., Strediclov, P.R., Orlova, M.P., and Astrov, D.N., 'Temperature', 'The I.M.P.R. Temperature Scale for 10 to 90°K Region', Vol.3, Reinhold, N.Y., 1962, pp.113-28.

14. Barber, C. R. 'Progress in Refrigeration Science and Technology', 'New Gas-Thermometer Measurements Over the Range from 10° to 90°K and the Extension of the International Temperature Scale Below 90°K', Vol. 1, Pergamon, 1960, pp. 174-78.

15. Barber, C. R. 'The Construction of a Practical Scale of Temperature at Sub-Zero Temperatures', Proceedings, Inst. of Refrigeration, Vol. 58, 1961, pp. 153-68.

16. Barber, C. R. 'The Establishment of a Practical Scale of Temperature for the Range 10 - 90°K', J. Applied Physics, (British) Vol. 13, 1962, pp. 235-41.

17. Roder, H. M.,'Irregularities in the NBS (1955) Provisional Temperature Scale', J. Research NBS, (A. Physics and Chemistry), Vol. 69A, 1965. pp. 527-30.

18. Beattie, J. A. 'Temperature', 'Gas Thermometry', Vol. 2, Reinhold, N.Y., 1955, pp. 63-97.

19. Barber, C. R. 'Temperature', 'Helium Gas Thermometry at Low Temperatures', Vol. 3, Reinhold, N.Y., 1962, pp. 103-12.

20. Beattie, J. A. 'Temperature', 'The Thermodynamic Temperature of the Ice-Point,' Vol. 1, Reinhold, N.Y., 1941, pp. 74-88.

21. Beattie, J. A. Benedict, M. and Kaye, J. 'An Experimental Study of the Absolute Temperature Scale', Proceedings American Academy of Arts and Sciences, Vol. 74, No. 11, Dec. 1941, pp. 327-98.

22. Keyes, F. G. 'Temperature', 'Gas Thermometer Scale Corrections Based on an Objective Correlation of Available Data for Hydrogen, Helium and Nitrogen', Vol. 1, Reinhold, N.Y., 1941, pp. 45-59.

23. Van Dijk, H. 'Concerning Temperature Units and Temperature Scales', Z. Angew. Phys., Vol. 15, 1963, pp. 561-66.

24. Ramsey, N. F. 'Temperature', 'Thermodynamics and Statistical Mechanics of Negative Absolute Temperatures', Vol. 3, part 1, Reinhold, N.Y., 1962.

25. Hertzfeld, C. M. 'Temperature', 'The Thermodynamic Temperature Scale, Its Definition and Realization', Vol. 3, part 1, Reinhold, N.Y., 1962, p. 49.

26. Burgess, G. F. 'International Temperature Scale', J. Research NBS, Vol. 1, 1928, pp. 635-37.

27. Stimson, H. F. 'The International Temperature Scale of 1948', J. Research NBS, Vol. 42, 1949, p. 209.

28. Hall, J. A. 'Temperature, Vol. 2, ''The International Temperature Scale,' Reinhold, N.Y., 1955, pp. 115-139.

29. Corruccini, R. J. Differences Between the International Temperature Scales of 1948 and 1927, J. Research NBS, Vol. 43, 1949, pp. 133-36.

30. Heuse, W. and Otto, J. 'A New Gas Thermometer Determination of Some fixed Points Below 0° in Connection with Pressure and Resistance Thermometers', Ann. Physics, Vol. 9, No. 5, 1931, pp. 486-504.

31. Keesom, W. H. and Dammers, B. G. 'Comparison of Some Platinum Thermometers with the Helium Thermometer Between 0 and -183°C, Physica. Vol. 2, 1935, pp. 1080-90.

32. Barber, C. R. and Horsford, A. 'Differences Between the Thermodynamic Scale and the International Practical Temperature Scale from 0°C to -183°C,' Metrologia, Vol. 1, No. 3, 1956, pp. 75-80.

33. Roder, H. M. 'Irregularities in the NBS (1955) Provisional Temperature Scale', J. Research NBS, (A. Physics and Chemistry), Vol. 69A, 1965, pp. 527-30.

34. Terrien, J. and Preston-Thomas, H. 'Progress in the Definition and in the Measurement of Temperature', Metrologia, Vol. 3, No. 1, 1967, pp. 29-31.

35. Preston-Thomas, H. and Kirby, C. G. M. 'Gas Thermometer Determinations of the Thermodynamic Temperature Scale in the Range -183°C to 100°C', Metrologia, Vol. 4, No. 1, 1968, pp. 30-40.

36. Scott, R. B. 'Temperature, Vol. 2,' Low Temperature Scales from 90° to 5°K, Reinhold, N.Y., 1955, pp. 179-84.

37. Giauque, W. F., Buffington, R. M. and Schulze, W. A. 'Copper-Constantan Thermocouples and the Hydrogen Thermometer Compared from 15° to 283° Absolute,' J. Am. Chem. Soc., Vol. 49, 1927, p. 2343.

38. Barber, C. R. and Hayes, J. G. 'The Derivation of the Original Reference Table CCT-64, T = f(W) for Platinum Resistance Thermometers for the Range from 12 to 273.15°K. Part II. The Derivation of the Table for the Range from 90 to 273.15°K', Metrologia, Vol. 2, No. 1, 1966, pp. 11-13.

39. Timmerhaus, K. D. 'Low Temperature Thermometry', Applied Cryogenic Engineering, Editors, Vance, R. W., and Duke, W. M., John Wiley, N.Y., 1962.

40. Timmerhaus, K. D. 'Measurement of Low Temperatures', Cryogenic Technology, Editor, Vance, R. W., John Wiley, N.Y., 1963.

41. Brickwedde, F. G. 'The 1958 He[4] Scale of Temperatures' part 1, Introduction; Van Dijk, H., Durieux, M., Clement, J. R., Logan, J.K. part 2, 'Table for the 1958 Temperature Scale', NBS Monograph 10, June 17, 1960. See also J. Research NBS, (A Physics and Chemistry), Vol. 64A, No. 1, 1960.

42. Clement, J. R. 'Temperature, Vol. 3, 'The 1958 He[4] Temperature Scale,' part 1, Reinhold, N.Y., 1962, pp. 67-74.

43. Arp, V. and Kropschot, R. H. 'Helium', Applied Cryogenic Engineering, Editors, Vance, R. W., and Duke, W. M., John Wiley N.Y., 1962.

44. Sherman, R. H., Sydoriak, S. G. Roberts, T. R. 'The 1962 He[3] Scale of Temperatures, 4. Tables', J. Research NBS, Vol. 68A, No. 6, 1964, pp. 579-88.

45. Sydoriak, S. G.,Sherman, R. H. and Roberts, T. R. 'The 1962 He[3] scale of Temperatures,(Parts 1-3),' J. Research NBS, Vol. 68A, No. 6, 1964, pp. 547-78.

46. Barber, C. R. and Van Dijk, H. 'The Provisional International Practical Temperature Scale of Temperatures of 1967', Document No. 3, Presented to the CCT 1967.

47. Lovejoy, D. R. 'Quelque points d'ebullition et point triples au-dessons de 0°C', CCT 6th Session, 23, 1962.

48. McLaren, E. H. and Murdock, E. G. 'The Freezing Points of High Purity Metals as Precision Temperature Standards VIII b. Sb: Liquidus Points and Alloy Melting Ranges of Seven Samples of High Purity Antimony; Temperature Scale Realization and Reliability in the Range 0 - 631°C', Canadian J. Physics (in press).

49. Finch, D. I. 'Temperature, Vol. 3, ' 'General Principles of Thermoelectric Thermometry', Reinhold, N.Y., 1962, pp. 3-32.

50. Benedict, R. P. and Ashby, H. F. 'Temperature, Vol. 3, part 2, ' 'Improved Reference Tables for Thermocouples', Reinhold, N.Y., 1962, pp. 51-64.

51. Caldwell, F. R. 'Temperature', 'Thermocouple Materials', Vol. 3, Reinhold., 1962, pp. 81-134.

52. Weber, R. L. 'Heat and Temperature Measurement', Prentice-Hall, 1950.

53. Baker, H. D., Ryder, E. A. and Baker, N. H. 'Temperature Measurement in Engineering, ' Vol. 1, John Wiley, 1955.

54. Dike, P. H. 'Thermoelectric Thermometry, ' Leeds and Northrup Co., 1954.

55. Powell, R. L. Bunch, M. D. and Caywood, L. P. 'Advances in Cryogenic Engineering', 'Low Temperature Thermocouple Thermometry', Vol. 6, 1961, pp. 537-42. See also, Temperature, Vol. 3, 1962, pp. 65-67.

56. Powell, R. L. Bunch, M. D. and Corruccini, R. J. 'Low Temperature Thermocouples - 1. Gold Cobalt or Constantan vs. Copper or 'Normal Silver', Cryogenics, March 1961, pp. 139-50.

57. White, W. P. 'Temperature', 'Potentiometers for Thermoelectric Measurements, Vol. 1,' Reinhold, 1941, pp. 265-79.

58. Mueller, E. F. 'Temperature','Precision Resistance Thermometry,'Vol. 1, Reinhold, 1941, pp. 162-179.

59. Stimson, H. F. 'Temperature', 'Precision Resistance Thermometry and Fixed Points,'Vol. 2, Reinhold, 1955, pp. 141-68.

60. Werner, F. D. 'Temperature'' Some Recent Developments in Applied Platinum Resistance Thermometry,' Vol. 3, part 2, Reinhold, 1962, pp. 297-304.

61. Dauphinee, T. M. 'Temperature','Potentiometric Methods of Resistance Measurement,'Vol. 3, part 1, Reinhold, 1962, pp. 269-83.

62.   Report of Calibration, National Bureau of Standards, Test No. G35936A, completed Sept. 24, 1965. Communication to J. A. Clark by Professor R. E. Sonntag, University of Michigan.

63.   Corruccini, R. J. 'Advances in Cryogenic Engineering, "Temperature Measurements in Cryogenic Engineering,' Vol. 8, 1963, Plenum, pp. 315-34.

64.   Dean, J. W. and Richards, R. J. 'Advances in Cryogenic Engineering, ' 'Hydrostatic Pressure Effects in Carbon and Germanium Thermometers,' Vol. 14, Plenum, 1969.

65.   Dupre, A., Itterbeek, A., Michiels, L. and Van Neste, L. 'The Use of Graphite Thermometers in Heat Conductivity Experiments below $1°K$', Cryogenics, Vol. 4, No. 6, Dec. 1964, pp. 354-57.

66.   Lindenfeld, P. 'Temperature', 'Carbon and Semiconductor Thermometers for Low Temperatures, ' Vol. 3, part 1, Reinhold, 1962, pp. 339-405.

67.   Clement, J. R. and Quinell, E. H. 'Low Temperature Characteristics of Carbon-Composition Thermometers, ' Review of Scientific Instruments, Vol. 23, No. 5, May 1952, pp. 213-17.

68.   Schulte, E. H. 'Carbon Resistors for Cryogenic Temperature Measurement, ' Cryogenics, Vol. 6, No. 6, December 1966, pp. 321-23.

69.   Mikhailov, M. N. and Kaganouskii, A. Ya. 'Carbon Resistance Thermometers for Low Temperatures', Cryogenics, Vol. 2, No. 6, December 1961, pp. 98-100.

70.   Greene, N. E. 'Three-Phase, Solid-Liquid-Vapor, Equilibrium in the System Hydrogen-Helium', Ph.D. Thesis, University of Michigan, Department of Mechanical Engineering, December, 1966.

71.   Herr, A. C. Terbeek, H. G. and Tieferman, M. W. 'Temperature', 'Suitability of Carbon Resistors for Field Measurement of Temperatures in the Range 30 to $100°R$, ' Vol. 3, part 2, Reinhold, 1962, pp. 355-59.

72.   Maurer, R. J. 'The Electrical Properties of Semi-Conductors, J. Applied Physics, Vol. 16, Oct. 1945, pp. 563.

73.   'Handbook of Physics and Chemistry, ' The Chemical Rubber Publishing Co., 34th Edition 1952-53, pp. 2185-2193.

74.   Seitz, F. 'The Basic Principles of Semi-Conductors', J. Applied Physcis, Vol. 16, October 1945, pp. 553.

75.   Becker, J. A., Green, C. B. and Pearson, G. L. 'Properties and Uses of Thermistors-Thermally Sensitive Resistors', Electrical Engineering, Vol. 65, 1946, p. 711.

76.   Brown, L. G. 'Air Rate Measurement in Vertical Down Flow of Fluidized Solids,' S. B. Thesis, Department of Mechanical Engineering, M.I.T., June 1955.

77.   Stoll, A. M. 'Wide Range Thermistor Radiometer for Measurement of Skin Temperatures and Environmental Radiant Temperature', Review of Scientific Instruments, Vol. 25, No. 2, 1954, p. 184.

78.   Wilson, A. H.   'Theory of Electronic Semi-Conductors', Proceedings of the
       Royal Society of London, Vol. CXXXIII, 1931, p. 458.

79.   Friedberg, S. A.   'Temperature', 'Semi-Conductors as Thermometers',
       Vol. 2, Reinhold, N. Y., 1955, pp. 359-82.

80.   Wilson, A. H.   Semi-Conductors and Metals, Cambridge University Press,
       New York, 1939.

81.   Muller, R. H. and Stolen, H. J.   'Use of Thermistors in Precise Measure-
       ment of Small Temperature Differences', Analytical Chemistry, Vol. 25,
       July 1953, pp. 1103-06.

82.   Pearson, G. L.   'Life Characteristics of a 1A Thermistor', Bell Telephone
       Laboratory Record, Vol. 19, Dec. 1940, p. 107.

83.   Benedict, R. P.   'Thermistors vs. Thermocouples', Electrical Manufac-
       turing, August 1954, p. 120.

84.   Clark, J. A. and Kobayashi, Y.   'Property of Thermistors', Technical
       Report 188, Contract DA-19-016-ENG-3204, U. S. Army Material Command,
       New Hampshire, May 1967, 23 pages.

85.   Clark, J. A. and Kobayashi, Y.   'Resistance-Temperature Characteristics
       of Some Commercially Available Thermistors', Supplement to Technical
       Report 188 (above), May 1967.

86.   Edlow, M. H. and Plumb, H. H.   'Germanium Resistance Thermometry in
       the Range 2.1 to 5.0°K,' J. Research NBS, Vol. 71C, No. 1, Jan-Mar 1967,
       pp. 29-41.

87.   Edlow, M. H. and Plumb, H. H.   'Reproducibility of Germanium Resistance
       Thermometers at 4.2°K', J. Research NBS, Vol. 70C, No. 4, Oct-Nov 1966,
       pp. 245-55.

88.   Kunzler, J. E., Geballe, T. H. and Hall, Jr., G. W.   'Temperature',
       'Germanium Resistance Thermometers', Vol. 3, part 1, Reinhold, 1962,
       pp. 391-97.

89.   Herder, T.   'Properties of Germanium Thermometers', private communi-
       cation, Fla. to J. A. Clark, Cryo Cal, Inc., Riviera Beach, Oct. 1968.

90.   Low, F. J.   'Gallium-Doped Germanium Resistance Thermometers',
       'Advances in Cryogenic Engineering', Plenum, Vol. 7, 1962, pp. 514-16.

91.   Orlova, M. P., Astrov, D. N. and Medvedeva, L. A.   'A Germanium
       Thermometer for Low Temperatures', Cryogenics, June 1965, pp. 165-67.

92.   Antcliffe, G. A. Einspruch, N. G. Pinatti, D. G. and Rorschauch, Jr., H.E.
       'Germanium Resistance Thermometry at Temperatures Below 1°K', Review
       of Scientific Instruments, Vol. 39, Feb. 1968, pp. 254-55.

93.   Garrett, C. G. B.   'Magnetic Cooling, ' Harvard University Press, 1954.

94.   De Klerk, D.   'Adiabatic Demagnetization', Low Temperature Physics II,
       Vol. XV Encyclopedia of Physics, S. Flugge, Editor, Springer-Verlag,
       1956, pp. 38-209.

95.　De Klerk, D.　'Temperature', 'Thermometry Below 1°K, 'Vol. 2, Reinhold, 1955, pp. 251-64.

96.　Zemansky, M. W. 'Heat and Thermodynamics,' 4th Ed, McGraw-Hill, 1957.

97.　De Klerk, D. and Steenland, M. J.　'Progress in Low Temperature Physics', 'Adiabatic Demagnetization', Chap. XIV, Vol. 1, Editor, C. J. Corter, Inter-Science, N. Y. 1955.

98.　Jackson, L. C.　'Low Temperature Physics', Fourth Ed. John Wiley, N. Y., 1955.

99.　Maxwell, J. C. 'A Treatise on Electricity and Magnetism,' 3rd Ed.　Oxford University Press, Vol. 2, 1904, p. 69.

100.　Kittel, C.　'Introduction to Solid State Physics', Second Ed.　John Wiley, 1956.

3-APPENDIX

The International Practical Temperature Scale of 1968.

Shortly after the present manuscript was submitted to the publishers in September 1968, the Comité International des Poids et Mesures met in October 1968 and agreed to adopt the International Practical Temperature Scale of 1968 (IPTS-68).　Because of the sequencing of these two events it is necessary to up-date this chapter with a brief appendix dealing with the latest International Practical Temperature Scale.

A description of the new IPTS-68 is found in a series of three papers in METROLOGIA, Vol. 5, No. 2, April, 1969, p. 35-49.　C.R. Barber states in the forward in the lead paper the following:

"There were two important reasons for revising the IPTS-48.　The first of these was the need to extend the Scale to lower temperatures to achieve a unification of the existing National Scales in the region 10K-90K.　Secondly the Scale had not been revised significantly over the range from -183°C to 1063°C since its inception in 1927 and modern gas thermometer measurements showed that the Scale gave values considerably different from the thermodynamic temperatures.

"The CCT agreed on the basic data and the methods of interpolation for a new definition of the IPTS at its 8th meeting held in Washington and Ottawa on September 1967.　Provision was made to extend the Scale down to 13.81K, the triple-point of equilibrium hydrogen and for the use of the best known values of the thermodynamic temperatures...."　For detailed information concerning the International Practical Temperature Scale of 1968, it will be necessary to refer to the above listed papers in METROLOGIA.　However, it might be of value here to indicate the nature of the new Scale in the range of temperatures considered in this chapter, that is, the cryogenic range.

The standard instrument used from 13.81K to 630.74C is the strain-free platinum resistance thermometer made from annealed pure platinum.　Interpolation between the fixed point temperatures is provided by formula used to describe the relation between indications of the standard instruments and values of the International Practical Temperature.　From 13.81K to 273.15K the temperature T_{68} (International Practical Temperature of 1968) is defined by the relation

$$W(T_{68}) = W_{CCT-68}(T_{68}) + \Delta W(T_{68})$$

where $W(T_{68})$ is the resistance ratio of the platinum resistance thermometer and

$W_{CCT-68}(T_{68})$ is a resistance ratio as given by a set of tabular values provided in the above reference. The last term in the above relationship is a deviation in the resistance ratio and is determined at the temperatures of the defining fixed points from measured values of $W(T_{68})$ and from tabular values which are provided. At intermediate temperatures interpolation formula are provided to determine values of the deviations. These deviations are determined by separate polynomial functions in the following ranges of temperature, 13.81K to 20.28K, 20.28K to 54.361K, 54.361K to 90.188K and 90.188K to 273.15K.

A detailed study of the relationships between the IPTS-68 and the NBS-55, NPL-61, PRMI-54 and PSU-54 temperature scales in the range 13.81K to 90.188K is provided. All scale differences are less than 40×10^{-3}°K in this range of temperature.

TABLE 3-15: Vapor pressure of He[4] (1958 scale) in microns (10^{-3} mm) mercury at 0°C and standard gravity (980.665 cm/sec^2)   Brickwedde, *et al* (41)

T°K	Microns	T°K	Microns	T°K	Microns
0.50	0.016342	0.90	41.581	1.30	1208.51
.51	.022745	.91	46.656	1.31	1284.81
.52	.031287	.92	52.234	1.32	1364.83
.53	.042561	.93	58.355	1.33	1448.73
.54	.057292	.94	65.059	1.34	1536.61
.55	.076356	.95	72.386	1.35	1628.62
.56	.10081	.96	80.382	1.36	1724.91
.57	.13190	.97	89.093	1.37	1825.58
.58	.17112	.98	98.567	1.38	1930.79
.59	.22021	.99	108.853	1.39	2040.67
0.60	0.28121	1.00	120.000	1.40	2155.35
.61	.35649	1.01	132.070	1.41	2274.99
.62	.44877	1.02	145.116	1.42	2399.73
.63	.56118	1.03	159.198	1.43	2529.72
.64	.69729	1.04	174.375	1.44	2665.09
.65	.86116	1.05	190.711	1.45	2805.99
.66	1.0574	1.06	208.274	1.46	2952.60
.67	1.2911	1.07	227.132	1.47	3105.04
.68	1.5682	1.08	247.350	1.48	3263.48
.69	1.8949	1.09	269.006	1.49	3428.07
0.70	2.2787	1.10	292.169	1.50	3598.97
.71	2.7272	1.11	316.923	1.51	3776.32
.72	3.2494	1.12	343.341	1.52	3960.32
.73	3.8549	1.13	371.512	1.53	4151.07
.74	4.5543	1.14	401.514	1.54	4348.79
.75	5.3591	1.15	433.437	1.55	4553.58
.76	6.2820	1.16	467.365	1.56	4765.68
.77	7.3365	1.17	503.396	1.57	4958.18
.78	8.5376	1.18	541.617	1.58	5212.26
.79	9.9013	1.19	582.129	1.59	5447.11
0.80	11.445	1.20	625.025	1.60	5689.88
.81	13.187	1.21	670.411	1.61	5940.76
.82	15.147	1.22	718.386	1.62	6199.90
.83	17.348	1.23	769.057	1.63	6467.42
.84	19.811	1.24	822.527	1.64	6743.57
.85	22.561	1.25	878.916	1.65	7028.47
.86	25.624	1.26	938.330	1.66	7322.31
.87	29.027	1.27	1000.87	1.67	7625.21
.88	32.800	1.28	1066.67	1.68	7937.40
.89	36.974	1.29	1135.85	1.69	8259.02

T°K	Microns	T°K	Microns	T°K	Microns
1.70	8590.22	2.11	32271.1	2.52	80572.2
		2.12	33128.0	2.53	82142.9
1.71	8931.18	2.13	33998.6	2.54	83734.6
1.72	9282.06	2.14	34882.8	2.55	85347.2
1.73	9643.02	2.15	35780.3		
1.74	10014.3			2.56	86981.2
1.75	10395.9	2.16	36690.9	2.57	88636.7
		2.17	37614.3	2.58	90313.8
1.76	10788.2	2.18	38550.2	2.59	92012.6
1.77	11191.2	2.19	39500.3		
1.78	11605.1			2.60	93733.4
1.79	12030.1	2.20	40465.6		
				2.61	95476.0
1.80	12466.1	2.21	41446.6	2.62	97240.8
		2.22	42443.5	2.63	99028.2
1.81	12913.7	2.23	43456.5	2.64	100838
1.82	13372.8	2.24	44485.7	2.65	102669
1.83	13843.6	2.25	45531.3		
1.84	14326.1			2.66	104525
1.85	14820.7	2.26	46593.5	2.67	106403
		2.27	47672.5	2.68	108304
1.86	15327.3	2.28	48768.6	2.69	110228
1.87	15846.3	2.29	49881.8		
1.88	16377.7			2.70	112175
1.89	16921.7	2.30	51012.3		
				2.71	114145
1.90	17478.2	2.31	52160.2	2.72	116139
		2.32	53325.8	2.73	118156
1.91	18047.7	2.33	54509.2	2.74	120198
1.92	18630.1	2.34	55710.5	2.75	122263
1.93	19225.5	2.35	56930.0		
1.94	19834.1			2.76	124353
1.95	20455.9	2.36	58167.8	2.77	126465
		2.37	59423.8	2.78	128603
1.96	21091.1	2.38	60698.8	2.79	130765
1.97	21739.7	2.39	61992.0		
1.98	22402.0			2.80	132952
1.99	23077.9	2.40	63304.3		
				2.81	135164
2.00	23767.4	2.41	64635.2	2.82	137401
		2.42	65985.4	2.83	139663
2.01	24470.9	2.43	67354.8	2.84	141949
2.02	25188.1	2.44	68743.5	2.85	144260
2.03	25919.2	2.45	70152.0		
2.04	26664.2			2.86	146597
2.05	27423.3	2.46	71580.2	2.87	148961
		2.47	73028.1	2.88	151349
2.06	28196.3	2.48	74496.0	2.89	153763
2.07	28983.2	2.49	75984.2		
2.08	29784.2			2.90	156204
2.09	30599.1	2.50	77493.1		
				2.91	158671
2.10	31428.1	2.51	79022.2	2.92	161164

T°K	Microns	T°K	Microns	T°K	Microns
2.93	163684	3.36	299178	3.79	495317
2.94	166230	3.37	303008		
2.95	168802	3.38	306871	3.80	500688
		3.39	310768		
2.96	171402			3.81	506098
2.97	174028	3.40	314697	3.82	511547
2.98	176682			3.83	517036
2.99	179364	3.41	318659	3.84	522564
		3.42	322654	3.85	528132
3.00	182073	3.43	326684		
		3.44	330747	3.86	533739
3.01	184810	3.45	334845	3.87	539387
3.02	187574			3.88	545075
3.03	190366	3.46	338976	3.89	550805
3.04	193187	3.47	343141		
3.05	196037	3.48	347341	3.90	556574
		3.49	351575		
3.06	198914			3.91	562383
3.07	201820	3.50	355844	3.92	568234
3.08	204755			3.93	574126
3.09	297719	3.51	360147	3.94	580059
		3.52	364485	3.95	586034
3.10	210711	3.53	368860		
		3.54	373269	3.96	592051
3.11	213732	3.55	377714	3.97	598110
3.12	216783			3.98	604210
3.13	219864	3.56	382194	3.99	610352
3.14	222975	3.57	386710		
3.15	226115	3.58	391262	4.00	616537
		3.59	395849		
3.16	229285			4.01	622764
3.17	232484	3.60	400471	4.02	629033
3.18	235714			4.03	635345
3.19	238974	3.61	405130	4.04	641700
		3.62	409825	4.05	648099
3.20	242266	3.63	414556		
		3.64	419324	4.06	654541
3.21	245587	3.65	424128	4.07	661026
3.22	248939			4.08	667554
3.23	252322	3.66	428968	4.09	674125
3.24	255736	3.67	438846		
3.25	259182	3.68	438760	4.10	680740
		3.69	443713		
3.26	262658			4.11	687399
3.27	266166	3.70	448702	4.12	694103
3.28	269706			4.13	700851
3.29	273278	3.71	453729	4.14	707643
		3.72	458794	4.15	714479
3.30	276880	3.73	463897		
		3.74	469038	4.16	721360
3.31	280516	3.75	474218	4.17	728185
3.32	284183			4.18	735255
3.33	287883	3.76	479435	4.19	742269
3.34	291615	3.77	484691		
3.35	295380	3.78	489985	4.20	749328

T°K	Microns	T°K	Microns	T°K	Microns
4.21	756431	4.64	1107699	5.06	1547912
4.22	763579	4.65	1117002	5.07	1559698
4.23	770772			5.08	1571546
4.24	778010	4.66	1126359	5.09	1583458
4.25	785294	4.67	1135772		
		4.68	1145239	5.10	1595437
4.26	792623	4.69	1154761	5.11	1607481
4.27	799999			5.12	1619589
4.28	807422	4.70	1164339	5.13	1631761
4.29	814893			5.14	1644000
		4.71	1173972	5.15	1656305
4.30	822411	4.72	1183662		
		4.73	1193407	5.16	1668673
4.31	829978	4.74	1203209	5.17	1681108
4.32	837592	4.75	1213066	5.18	1693612
4.33	845255			5.19	1706180
4.34	852966	4.76	1222981		
4.35	860725	4.77	1232955	5.20	1718817
		4.78	1242983	5.21	1731521
4.36	868533	4.79	1253069	5.22	1744290
4.37	876390				
4.38	884296	4.80	1263212		
4.39	892252				
		4.81	1273414		
4.40	900258	4.82	1283673		
		4.83	1293991		
4.41	908313	4.84	1304367		
4.42	916418	4.85	1314802		
4.43	924573				
4.44	932778	4.86	1325297		
4.45	941033	4.87	1335850		
		4.88	1346462		
4.46	949338	4.89	1357136		
4.47	957693				
4.48	966099	4.90	1367870		
4.49	974556				
		4.91	1378662		
4.50	983066	4.92	1389516		
		4.93	1400429		
4.51	991628	4.94	1411404		
4.52	1000239	4.95	1422438		
4.53	1008905				
4.54	1017621	4.96	1433533		
4.55	1026390	4.97	1444690		
		4.98	1455911		
4.56	1035213	4.99	1467191		
4.57	1044087				
4.58	1053014	5.00	1478535		
4.59	1061995				
		5.01	1489940		
4.60	1071029	5.02	1501409		
		5.03	1512940		
4.61	1080114	5.04	1524535		
4.62	1089254	5.05	1536192		
4.63	1098449				

TABLE 3-16: He³ vapor pressure on the 1962 He³ scale at 0°C and standard gravity, 980.665 cm/sec². Sydoriak *et al* (45).

The units of pressure are microns (10^{-3} mm) of mercury below 1°K and millimeters of mercury at higher temperatures

T	0.00	0.01	0.02	0.03	0.04
0.20	0.012	0.024	0.046	0.084	0.144
0.30	1.877	2.636	3.633	4.921	6.561
0.40	28.11	34.54	42.08	50.86	61.01
0.50	159.2	183.3	210.1	239.8	272.5
0.60	544.4	604.3	668.9	738.4	813.0
0.70	1381	1498	1622	1753	1892
0.80	2892	3089	3295	3511	3736
0.90	5304	5603	5914	6237	6572
1.00	8.842	9.267	9.704	10.156	10.622
1.10	13.725	14.295	14.881	15.484	16.102
1.20	20.163	20.900	21.655	22.428	23.220
1.30	28.360	29.285	30.229	31.193	32.177
1.40	38.516	39.646	40.799	41.973	43.169
1.50	50.822	52.178	53.558	54.961	56.389
1.60	65.467	67.068	68.694	70.345	72.022
1.70	82.638	84.501	86.391	88.309	90.254
1.80	102.516	104.660	106.833	109.035	111.266
1.90	125.282	127.724	180.197	132.701	135.236
2.00	151.112	153.870	156.661	159.485	162.342
2.10	180.184	183.276	186.403	189.564	192.760
2.20	212.673	216.117	219.597	223.113	226.665
2.30	248.757	252.570	256.420	260.309	264.236
2.40	288.613	292.813	297.053	301.333	305.653
2.50	332.425	337.031	341.679	346.368	351.100
2.60	380.383	385.414	390.489	395.608	400.771
2.70	432.686	438.164	443.687	449.256	454.872
2.80	489.549	495.495	501.488	507.531	513.622
2.90	551.203	557.642	564.131	570.672	577.264
3.00	617.907	624.866	631.879	638.945	646.066
3.10	689.949	697.459	705.026	712.650	720.332
3.20	767.656	775.753	783.910	792.128	800.408
3.30	851.406	860.130	868.918	877.773	

T	0.05	0.06	0.07	0.08	0.09
0.20	0.239	0.382	0.592	0.891	1.308
0.30	8.619	11.173	14.304	18.105	22.673
0.40	72.68	86.02	101.17	118.31	137.61
0.50	308.5	347.9	391.1	438.0	489.1
0.60	893.0	978.7	1070.1	1167.6	1271.4
0.70	2038	2192	2355	2525	2704
0.80	3971	4216	4472	4739	5016
0.90	6918	7277	7649	8034	8431
1.00	11.102	11.597	12.106	12.631	13.170
1.10	16.737	17.388	18.056	18.741	19.443
1.20	24.029	24.857	25.704	26.571	27.456
1.30	33.181	34.206	35.252	36.319	37.407
1.40	44.388	45.629	46.893	48.179	49.489
1.50	57.840	59.316	60.817	62.342	63.892
1.60	73.726	75.455	77.211	78.993	80.802
1.70	92.228	94.229	96.258	98.315	100.402
1.80	113.527	115.818	118.138	120.489	122.870
1.90	137.803	140.401	143.031	145.692	148.386
2.00	165.232	168.155	171.112	174.102	177.126
2.10	195.990	199.256	202.557	205.894	209.266
2.20	230.255	233.881	237.544	241.244	244.982
2.30	268.202	272.206	276.249	280.331	284.452
2.40	310.013	314.414	318.855	323.337	327.861
2.50	355.874	360.690	365.549	370.450	375.395
2.60	405.978	411.230	416.526	421.868	427.254
2.70	460.534	466.242	471.998	477.801	483.651
2.80	519.762	525.951	532.189	538.477	544.815
2.90	583.907	590.602	597.349	604.149	611.002
3.00	653.241	660.472	667.757	675.098	682.496
3.10	728.072	735.871	743.728	751.644	759.620
3.20	808.750	817.155	825.622	834.153	842.747

TABLE 3-17: August 1965 Table for Platinum Resistance Thermometer 1653433

TEMP ° K	RESISTANCE ABS OHMS	INVERSE DIFF.	TEMP ° K	RESISTANCE ABS OHMS	INVERSE DIFF.
90	6.20974		140	11.66916	9.305
91	6.32084	9.001	141	11.77656	9.311
92	6.43186	9.008	142	11.88390	9.316
93	6.54279	9.015	143	11.99118	9.322
94	6.65364	9.022	144	12.09840	9.327
95	6.76440	9.029	145	12.20556	9.332
96	6.87507	9.035	146	12.31265	9.337
97	6.98567	9.042	147	12.41969	9.343
98	7.09617	9.049	148	12.52667	9.348
99	7.20660	9.056	149	12.63358	9.353
100	7.31695	9.063	150	12.74044	9.358
101	7.42721	9.069	151	12.84724	9.363
102	7.53739	9.076	152	12.95399	9.368
103	7.64749	9.083	153	13.06067	9.373
104	7.75751	9.089	154	13.16730	9.379
105	7.86745	9.096	155	13.27387	9.384
106	7.97732	9.102	156	13.38038	9.389
107	8.08710	9.109	157	13.48684	9.393
108	8.19681	9.115	158	13.59324	9.398
109	8.30644	9.122	159	13.69959	9.403
110	8.41599	9.128	160	13.80588	9.408
111	8.52546	9.135	161	13.91212	9.413
112	8.63486	9.141	162	14.01830	9.418
113	8.74419	9.147	163	14.12443	9.423
114	8.85343	9.153	164	14.23050	9.427
115	8.96261	9.160	165	14.33653	9.432
116	9.07171	9.166	166	14.44249	9.437
117	9.18074	9.172	167	14.54841	9.441
118	9.28969	9.178	168	14.65428	9.446
119	9.39857	9.184	169	14.76009	9.451
120	9.50738	9.190	170	14.86585	9.455
121	9.61612	9.196	171	14.97156	9.460
122	9.72479	9.202	172	15.07722	9.464
123	9.83338	9.208	173	15.18283	9.469
124	9.94191	9.214	174	15.28839	9.473
125	10.05036	9.220	175	15.39390	9.478
126	10.15875	9.226	176	15.49936	9.482
127	10.26707	9.232	177	15.60477	9.487
128	10.37532	9.238	178	15.71013	9.491
129	10.48350	9.244	179	15.81545	9.495
130	10.59162	9.249	180	15.92071	9.500
131	10.69967	9.255	181	16.02593	9.504
132	10.80765	9.261	182	16.13110	9.508
133	10.91556	9.267	183	16.23623	9.513
134	11.02341	9.272	184	16.34130	9.517
135	11.13120	9.278	185	16.44633	9.521
136	11.23892	9.283	186	16.55132	9.525
137	11.34657	9.289	187	16.65625	9.529
138	11.45417	9.294			
139	11.56169	9.300			

List of **Mathematical Symbols**

A	Constant
B	Constant
C	Constant, Curie constant (eq. 3-33)
D	Constant
dE/dF	Thermoelectric power
E	Thermocouple EMF, constant (eq. 3-25), internal energy
$F(t)$	Arbitrary function of temperature
H	Magnetic field strength
h	Enthalpy
K	Constant
l	Length
M	Magnetic moment
m	Mass
P	Arbitrary temperature dependent property, pressure
Q_o	Quantity of heat rejected by a Carnot engine to a heat reservoir at temperature t_o.
Q_1	Quantity of heat absorbed by a Carnot engine from a heat reservoir at temperature t_1
R	Resistance
R_o	Resistance at the ice point
R_t	Resistance at temperature t
r	Ratio of two thermodynamic temperatures
T	Absolute thermodynamic temperature (Kelvin scale)
T^*	Thermodynamic temperature of the triple point of water, magnetic temperature
t	Temperature according to an arbitrary temperature scale, platinum resistance temperature
V	Volume

Greek Symbols

α	Temperature coefficient of any arbitrary property, P; constant
β	Constant
Δ	Curie-Weiss constant
ΔE^*	Potentiometer sensitivity
ΔT^*	Uncertainty in temperature indication
δ	Constant
θ	Temperature according to an arbitrary temperature scale
ρ	Electrical resistivity
σ	Electrical conductivity
χ	Magnetic susceptibility

4

Optical Measurement of Temperature

R. J. GOLDSTEIN
University of Minnesota, Minneapolis.

Summary

Shadowgraph, Schlieren and interferometric systems are described. The physical principles of the three methods are reviewed and the equations necessary to evaluate density and temperature fields are derived. Design problems and the ranges of application are indicated with examples. Errors which affect the evaluating equations are considered including quantitative corrections which can be used. The application of lasers to some optical measuring systems is discussed.

Introduction

There are many optical techniques that have been used in the measurement of temperature. Among these are (a) spectroscopic methods in which the emitted or absorbed electromagnetic radiation of a gas (possibly with a tracer added) is measured, (b) total or spectral radiation methods in which the temperature of an opaque surface is measured by comparison with the Stefan-Boltzmann or Planck radiation laws, (c) a scattered radiation technique in which the Doppler broadening of a light beam is measured to get the temperature level (usually of scattering electrons) and (d) what might be called index of refraction methods in which the index of refraction or spatial derivatives of the index of refraction of a medium is measured and from this temperature field is inferred.

Only the methods falling under the last category are examined in this paper. This includes Schlieren, shadowgraph, and interferometer techniques (Refs. 1-7 have considerable information and extensive bibliographies on these methods) which are used to study the temperature fields in transparent media - (usually gases or liquids). Although all three methods depend on variation of the index of refraction in a transparent medium and the resulting effects on a light beam passing through the test region, quite different quantities are measured in each one. Shadowgraph systems are used to indicate the variation of the second derivative (normal to the light beam) of the index of refraction. With a Schlieren system the first derivative of the index of refraction (in a direction normal to the light beam) is determined. Interferometers permit direct measurement of differences in optical path length essentially giving the index of refraction field directly.

Optical measurement of a temperature field has many advantages over other techniques but perhaps the major one is the absence of an instrument probe which could influence the temperature field. The light beam can also be considered as essentially inertialess so that very rapid transients can be studied. The sensitivities of the three methods are quite different so that they can be used to study a variety of systems. Thus interferometers are often used to study free convection boundary layers where temperature gradients are very small while Schlieren and shadowgraph systems are often employed in studying shock and flame phenomena where very large temperature and density gradients are present.

Shadowgraph, Schlieren and interferometric measurements are essentially integral ones in that they integrate the quantity measured over the length of the light beam. For this reason they are best suited to measurements in two (or one) dimensional fields where there is no index of refraction or density variation in the field along the light beam, except at the beam's entrance to and exist from the test (disturbed) region. These latter variations can be considered as sharp discontinuities or appropriate end corrections can be made. Axisymmetric fields can also be studied, as is demonstrated in the Appendix specifically for inteferometric measurements. If the field is three dimensional, an average of the measured quantity (along the light beam) can still be determined. Since both Schlieren and shadowgraph systems are primarily used for qualitative studies this is often acceptable and even in interferometric studies the averaging done by the light beam can sometimes be quite valuable (8).

Since the three methods to be studied really measure the index of refraction (or one of its spatial derivatives) the relationship between this property and the temperature must be known. Actually, the index of refraction of a homogeneous medium is a function of the thermodynamic state and not necessarily of the temperature alone. According to the Lorenz-Lorentz relation the index of refraction of a homogeneous transparent medium is primarily a function of density:

$$\frac{1}{\rho} \frac{n^2 - 1}{n^2 + 2} = \text{a constant} \qquad \qquad \text{Eq. 4-1}$$

In particular, when $n \sim 1$, this reduces to the Gladstone-Dale equation:

$$\frac{n - 1}{\rho} = C,$$

or

$$\rho = \frac{n - 1}{C} \qquad \qquad \text{Eq. 4-2a}$$

which holds quite well for gases. The constant C, called the Gladstone-Dale constant is a function of the particular gas and varies slightly with wave length. Usually instead of using C directly, the index of refraction at standard temperature and pressure, n_o, is given:

$$n - 1 = \frac{\rho}{\rho_o} (n_o - 1) \qquad \qquad \text{Eq. 4-2b}$$

When the first or second derivative (say with respect to y) is determined as in a Schlieren or shadowgraph apparatus then, for gases, from equation 4-2a:

$$\frac{\partial \rho}{\partial y} = \frac{1}{C} \frac{\partial n}{\partial y} \qquad \qquad \text{Eq. 4-3}$$

$$\frac{\partial^2 \rho}{\partial y^2} = \frac{1}{C} \frac{\partial^2 n}{\partial y^2} \qquad \qquad \text{Eq. 4-4}$$

If the pressure can be assumed constant and the ideal gas equation of state $(\rho = p/RT)$ holds:

$$\frac{\partial n}{\partial y} = -\frac{Cp}{RT^2} \frac{\partial T}{\partial y} = -\frac{n_o - 1}{T} \frac{\rho}{\rho_o} \frac{\partial T}{\partial y} \qquad \qquad \text{Eq. 4-5a}$$

or:

$$\frac{\partial T}{\partial y} = -\frac{T}{n_o - 1} \frac{\rho_o}{\rho} \frac{\partial n}{\partial y} \qquad \qquad \text{Eq. 4-5b}$$

and:

$$\frac{\partial^2 n}{\partial y^2} = C \left[-\frac{\rho}{T} \frac{\partial^2 T}{\partial y^2} + \frac{2\rho}{T^2} \left(\frac{\partial T}{\partial y} \right)^2 \right] \qquad \text{Eq. 4-6}$$

Note that equation 4-5b which would apply in a Schlieren study shows a relatively simple relationship between the gradient of the temperature and the gradient of the index of refraction which is measured. For a shadowgraph the equivalent relation (Eq. 4-6) is more complicated, although under many conditions the second term may be small.

The index of refraction of a gas as measured in an interferometer can indicate the temperature directly. From equations 4-2a and 4-2b assuming constant pressure and the perfect gas equation of state:

$$T = \frac{C}{n-1} \frac{p}{R} = \left(\frac{n_o - 1}{n - 1} \right) \frac{p}{p_o} \times T_o \qquad \text{Eq. 4-7}$$

The index of refraction of a liquid is primarily a function of temperature and for accurate results should be obtained from direct measurements. For comparison table 4-1, derived from Ref. (9) and (10), cites values at 20°C and one atmosphere for air and water. The two wave lengths chosen are a commonly used mercury line (546.1 mμ) and the visible line from a CW He-Ne laser (632.8mμ).

Of the three systems to be discussed, two of them -Schlieren and shadowgraph - can be described by geometrical or ray optics although under certain conditions diffraction effects can be significant. Interferometers, as the name implies, depend on the interference of coherent light beams and some discussion of physical (wave) optics will be required.

Schlieren

To study both Schlieren and shadowgraph systems the path of a light beam in a medium whose index of refraction is a function of position must be analysed Consider Fig. 4-1 where a light beam, traveling initially in the z direction, passes through a medium whose index of refraction varies (for simplicity) only in the y direction. At time, τ, the beam is at position z and the wave front (surface normal to the path of the light) is as shown. After a time interval $\Delta\tau$ the light has moved a distance of $\Delta\tau$ times the velocity of light which in general is a function of y so the wave front or light beam may have turned an angle $d\alpha'$. The local value of the speed of light is c_o/n. With reference to Fig. 4-1, and assuming that only small deviations occur, the distance that the light beam (Δz) travels during time interval $\Delta\tau$ is:

$$\Delta z = (c_o/n) \ \Delta\tau$$

Now:

$$\Delta^2 z = \Delta z_y - \Delta zy + \Delta y$$

or:

$$\Delta^2 z = -c_o \ \frac{\Delta(\frac{1}{n})}{\Delta\tau} \ \Delta\tau \Delta y$$

and the angular deflection of the ray is:

$$\Delta\alpha' \approx \frac{\Delta^2 z}{\Delta y} = -n \ \frac{\Delta(\frac{1}{n})}{\Delta y} \ \Delta z$$

In the limit if Δy and Δz are considered to be very small:

$$d\alpha' = \frac{1}{n} \ \frac{\partial n}{\partial y} \ dz = \frac{\partial(\ln n)}{\partial y} \ dz \qquad \text{Eq. 4-8}$$

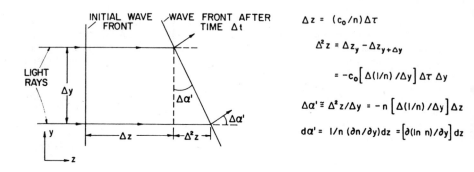

$$\Delta z = (c_o/n)\Delta\tau$$

$$\Delta^2 z = \Delta z_y - \Delta z_{y+\Delta y}$$

$$= -c_o\left[\Delta(1/n)/\Delta y\right]\Delta\tau\,\Delta y$$

$$\Delta\alpha' \cong \Delta^2 z/\Delta y = -n\left[\Delta(1/n)/\Delta y\right]\Delta z$$

$$d\alpha' = 1/n\,(\partial n/\partial y)dz = \left[\partial(\ln n)/\partial y\right]dz$$

Fig. 4-1   Bending of a light ray in an inhomogeneous medium

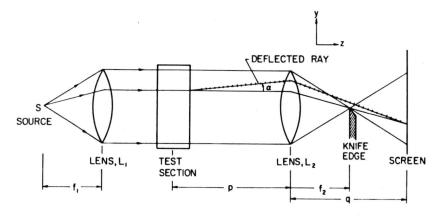

Fig. 4-2   Typical schlieren system using lenses

Table 4-1

λ	$n_{air} - 1$	n_{H_2O}	$\dfrac{dn}{dT}_{air}$ ($^\circ$C)$^{-1}$	$\dfrac{dn}{dT}_{H_2O}$ ($^\circ$C)$^{-1}$
546.1 mμ	2.732×10^{-4}	1.3345	-0.932×10^{-6}	-0.895×10^{-4}
632.8 mμ	2.718×10^{-4}	1.3317	-0.928×10^{-6}	-0.880×10^{-4}

Since α' is also the slope $(\frac{dy}{dz})$ of the light beam for small deviations:

$$\frac{\partial^2 y}{\partial z^2} = \frac{1}{n} \frac{\partial n}{\partial y} \qquad\qquad \text{Eq. 4-9}$$

If the angle α' remains small this expression will hold over the light path through the disturbed region and the angle at the exit of the test region is then:

$$\alpha' = \int \frac{1}{n} \frac{\partial n}{\partial y} \, dz = \int \frac{\partial (\ln n)}{\partial y} \, dz \qquad\qquad \text{Eq. 4-10}$$

where the integration is performed over the entire length of the light beam in the test region.

If the test region is enclosed by glass walls and the index of refraction within the test section is considerably different from the ambient air then, from Snell's Law, an additional angular deflection is present. If α is the angle of the light beam after it has passed through the test section and emerged into the surrounding air:

$$n_a \sin \alpha = \sin \alpha'$$

Assuming the test section windows are plane and of uniform thickness, for small values of α and α':

$$\alpha = \frac{n}{n_a} \alpha'$$

Using equation 4-10

$$\alpha = \frac{n}{n_a} \int \frac{1}{n} \frac{\partial n}{\partial y} \, dz$$

Assuming $\frac{1}{n}$ within the integrand does not change greatly through the test section

$$\alpha = \frac{1}{n_a} \int \frac{\partial n}{\partial y} \, dz \qquad\qquad \text{Eq. 4-11}$$

$$\cong \int \frac{\partial n}{\partial y} \, dz$$

since $n_a \approx 1$.

Note that if a gas (not at extremely high density) is the test fluid, $\alpha' \cong \alpha$. The angle α in equation 4-11 is in the y - z plane. If there is also a variation of index of refraction in the x direction then, again assuming small angular deviation, a similar expression would give the angle in the x - z plane proportional to $\frac{\partial n}{\partial x}$.

If variations in the x and z direction, as well as the effect of significant angular deviation are included, the resulting equation for the path of the light beam, would be equivalent to equation 4-9 (2),

$$y'' = \frac{1}{n} \, [1 + x'^2 + y'^2] \, [\frac{\partial n}{\partial y} - y' \frac{\partial n}{\partial z}] \qquad\qquad \text{Eq. 4-12}$$

where primes refer to differentiation with respect to z. A similar equation could be written for x''. Note that the light beam is turned in the direction of increasing

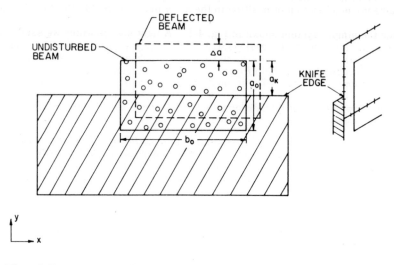

Fig. 4-3   View of deflected and undisturbed beam at knife edge of schlieren system.

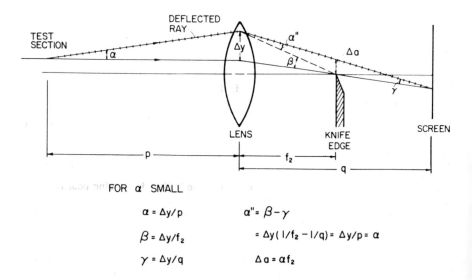

FOR α SMALL

$$\alpha = \Delta y/p \qquad\qquad \alpha'' = \beta - \gamma$$

$$\beta = \Delta y/f_2 \qquad\qquad = \Delta y(1/f_2 - 1/q) = \Delta y/p = \alpha$$

$$\gamma = \Delta y/q \qquad\qquad \Delta a = \alpha f_2$$

Fig. 4-4   Ray displacement at knife edge for a given angular deflection

index of refraction. In most media this means that the light is bent towards the region of higher density or lower temperature. Basically a Schlieren system is a device to measure or indicate this small angle (typically of the order of 10^{-6} to 10^{-3} radians) as a function of position in the x - y plane normal to the light beam.

Consider the simple system shown in Fig. 4-2. A light source which we shall assume to be rectangular (dimensions a_s by b_s), is at the focus of lens L_1. The resulting parallel light beam enters the field of disturbance in the test section. The deflected rays when the disturbance is present are indicated by cross-hatched lines. The light is collected by a second lens L_2 at whose focus a knife edge is placed and passes onto a screen located at the conjugate focus of the test section. As will be shown below, if the screen is not at the focus of the disturbance, shadowgraph effects will be superimposed on the Schlieren pattern.

If no disturbance is present then ideally the light beam at the focus of L_2 would be as shown in Fig. 4-3, having dimensions a_o - b_o which are related to the initial dimensions by:

$$\frac{a_o}{a_s} = \frac{b_o}{b_s} = \frac{f_2}{f_1}$$

Eq. 4-13

where f_1 and f_2 are the focal lengths of L_1 and L_2 respectively. As shown in the figure, the shorter dimension a_o is usually at right angles to the knife edge to maximize sensitivity (see below). The knife edge (typically a razor blade) is adjusted, when no disturbance is present, to cut off all but an amount "a_K" (typically $a_K = a_o/2$) of the height a_o. When the knife edge is moved across the beam exactly at the focus, the illumination at the screen will decrease uniformly but if the knife edge is not right in the focal plane the image at the screen will not darken uniformly. The illumination at the screen when no knife edge is present is I_o, and with the knife edge inserted in the focal plane the illumination is:

$$I_K = \frac{a_K}{a_o} I_o$$

Eq. 4-14

The light passing through any part of the test region comes from all parts of the source. Thus at the focus not only is the image of the source composed of light coming from the whole field of view but light passing through every point in the field of view gives an image of the source at the knife edge. If the light beam at a position (x, y) in the test region is deflected by an angle α then from Fig. 4-4 the image of the source coming from that position will be shifted at the knife edge by an amount:

$$\Delta a = \pm f_2 \cdot \alpha$$

Eq. 4-15

where the sign is determined by the position of the knife edge, being positive when (as in Fig. 4-4), $\alpha > 0$ gives $\Delta a > 0$ and negative if the knife edge were reversed so that $\alpha > 0$ led to $\Delta a < 0$. The illumination at the image of x, y on the screen will be (c.f. Fig. 4-3):

$$I_d = I_K \left(\frac{a_K + \Delta a}{a_K} \right)$$

$$= I_K \left(1 + \frac{\Delta a}{a_K} \right)$$

Eq. 4-16

where Δa is positive if the light is deflected away from the knife edge and negative if the light is deflected towards the knife edge. The relative intensity or contrast is:

$$\text{Contrast} = \frac{\Delta I}{I_K} = \frac{I_d - I_K}{I_K} = \frac{\Delta a}{a_K} = \pm \frac{\alpha f_2}{a_K} \qquad \text{Eq. 4-17}$$

using equation 4-15. Note that the sensitivity of the Schlieren system for measuring the deflection is:

$$\frac{d\,\text{Contrast}}{d\alpha} = \frac{f_2}{a_K} \qquad \text{Eq. 4-18}$$

or proportional to f_2 and inversely proportional to a_K. For a given optical system minimizing a_K by movement of the razor blade would maximize the contrast. However, this would limit the range for deflection of the beam towards the knife edge to:

$$\alpha_{max} = \frac{a_K}{f_2} \qquad \text{Eq. 4-19}$$

as all deflections this large or larger would give (neglecting diffraction) no illumination. The maximum angle of deflection away from the knife edge that could be measured is:

$$\alpha_{max'} = \frac{a_o - a_K}{f_2} \qquad \text{Eq. 4-20}$$

as a deflection of this magnitude would permit all the source illumination to pass to the screen. For equal range in both directions, $a_K = a_o/2$ and:

$$\alpha_{max} = \alpha_{max'} = \frac{a_o}{2f_2} = \frac{a_s}{2f_1} \qquad \text{Eq. 4-21}$$

Note from Fig. 4-3 that deflections in the x direction are parallel to the knife edge and will not affect the illumination at the screen so if density gradients in the x direction within the test region are to be studied, the knife edge must be turned at right angles. For maximum sensitivity (since a_s is less than b_s) the source should also be rotated ninety degrees.

Combining equation 4-11 and equation 4-17

$$\text{Contrast} = \frac{\Delta I}{I_K} = \pm \frac{f_2}{a_K n_a} \int \frac{\partial n}{\partial y} \, dz \qquad \text{Eq. 4-22}$$

Assuming a two dimensional field with $\frac{\partial n}{\partial y}$ constant at a given x, y position over the length L in the z direction,

$$\text{Contrast} = \pm \frac{f_2}{a_K} \frac{1}{n_a} \frac{\partial n}{\partial y} L \qquad \text{Eq. 4-23a}$$

$$\approx \pm \frac{f_2}{a_K} \frac{\partial n}{\partial y} L \qquad \text{Eq. 4-23b}$$

This equation holds for every (x, y) position in the test section and gives the contrast at the equivalent position in the image on the screen.

If the deflection is towards the knife edge the field will darken and the contrast will be negative. Using the coordinate system of Fig. 4-3, if the knife edge covers up the region y < 0 at the focus:

$$\frac{\Delta I}{I_K} = +\frac{f_2}{a_K} \frac{1}{n_a} \frac{\partial n}{\partial y} L \qquad\qquad \text{Eq. 4-24a}$$

While if the knife edge is reversed and covers the region y > 0:

$$\frac{\Delta I}{I_K} = -\frac{f_2}{a_K} \frac{1}{n_a} \frac{\partial n}{\partial y} L \qquad\qquad \text{Eq. 4-24b}$$

Changing the knife edge reverses the dark and light images on the screen. The brighter areas of the image represent regions in the test section where the index of refraction (and thus usually density) increases in the direction away from the knife edge (Fig. 4-5). Dark areas represent regions where the index of refraction increases in the direction of the opaque side of the knife edge (Fig. 4-5).

Equation 4-22 can be rewritten in the case of a gas at constant pressure using equation 4-5a:

$$\frac{\Delta I}{I_K} = \pm \frac{f_2}{a_K n_a} \int \frac{(n_o - 1)}{T} \frac{\rho}{\rho_o} \frac{\partial T}{\partial y} \, dz \qquad\qquad \text{Eq. 4-25}$$

and equivalent to equation 4-23:

$$\frac{\Delta I}{I_K} \approx \pm \frac{f_2}{a_K} \left(\frac{n_o - 1}{\rho_o} \right) \frac{p}{RT^2} \frac{\partial T}{\partial y} L \qquad\qquad \text{Eq. 4-26}$$

since $n_a \approx 1$.

For a liquid:

$$\frac{\Delta I}{I_K} = \pm \frac{f_2}{a_K n_a} \int \frac{\partial T}{\partial y} \frac{dn}{dT} \, dz \qquad\qquad \text{Eq. 4-27}$$

If the field is ever two-dimensional and n does not change greatly:

$$\frac{\Delta I}{I_K} = \pm \frac{f_2}{a_K n_a} \frac{\partial T}{\partial y} \frac{dn}{dT} \cdot L \qquad\qquad \text{Eq. 4-28a}$$

$$\approx \pm \frac{f_2}{a_K} \frac{\partial T}{\partial y} \frac{dn}{dT} \cdot L \qquad\qquad \text{Eq. 4-28b}$$

In a quantitative study, measurements of the illumination or contrast, usually of the image on a photographic negative, must be made. These are quite time consuming and the resulting accuracy has not usually warranted the effort. Thus standard Schlieren systems are usually employed for qualitative studies of a temperature or density field. The minimum value of the contrast that can easily be observed is of the order of .05 which can be used in determining the overall sensitivity of the system. Since $\frac{dn}{dT}$ varies slightly with wave length it is preferable that the light source be relatively monochromatic, although for both Schlieren and shadowgraph systems this is usually not a major criterion.

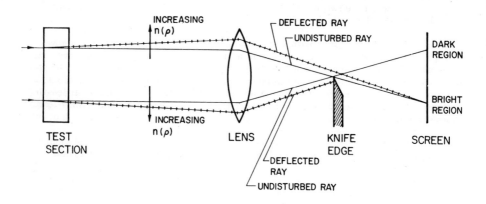

INCREASING n(ρ)

DEFLECTED RAY

UNDISTURBED RAY

DARK REGION

BRIGHT REGION

INCREASING n(ρ)

TEST SECTION

LENS

KNIFE EDGE

SCREEN

DEFLECTED RAY

UNDISTURBED RAY

Fig. 4-5   Effect of index of refraction gradient on illumination at screen

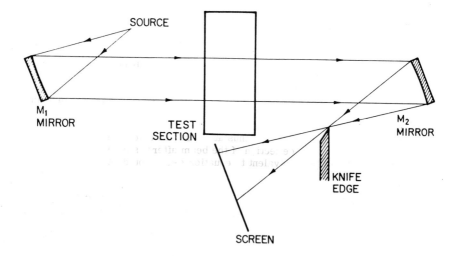

SOURCE

M_1 MIRROR

TEST SECTION

M_2 MIRROR

KNIFE EDGE

SCREEN

Fig. 4-6   Typical shclieren system using converging mirrors

The high cost of large aberration-free lenses usually precludes construction of the system shown in Fig. 4-2. but the optically similar system using concave mirrors shown in Fig. 4-6 is widely used.   The source and knife edge should be in the same plane and on opposite sides of the axes of the two mirrors in the "Z" arrangement shown. This eliminates the aberration coma although in the off-axis system astigmatism is still present. The legs of the "Z" should each be at the same angles to the line between the two mirrors and this angle should be as small as possible to reduce astigmatism (11).

Schlieren photographs taken with a system similar to that of Fig. 4-6 are shown in Figs. 4-7 and 4-8. The light source is a zirconium arc lamp with a source size of about 0.76 mm. Each mirror has an aperture of about 20 cm and a focal length of about 170 cm. The disturbed region is about three and one half meters from the second mirror. In place of a screen a 35 mm camera with a 135 mm focal length lens is used to record the image. To focus on the test section a -1 auxiliary lens is also used.

Figure 4-7 is a Schlieren image of a burning gas flame and jet leaving a standard propane torch. Figure 4-8 shows different images of the free convection field around a heated cylinder (3.2 cm diameter by 20 cm long) in air. Although the temperature of the cylinder and thus the Rayleigh number only varies slightly for the different photographs, the difference in knife edge orientation shown for each view dramatically changes the image. As mentioned above the Schlieren image lightens when the index of refraction increases in the direction away from the knife edge. Thus the lighter regions on the photo show that the local temperature gradient is positive in the direction towards the knife edge while the reverse is true for the darker regions.

A number of variations on the Schlieren systems shown in Figs. 4-2 and 4-6 have been used, and two of these are shown in Fig. 4-9.   In Fig. 4-9a one plane and one converging mirror are used. Since plane mirrors are easier to make than converging ones this apparatus would be somewhat less expensive than the one in figure 4-6. The main reason for its use however is the amplification of the angle representative of the disturbance, as the beam passes through the test section twice, the deflection angle will be doubled and, all other parameters being the same, so will the sensitivity. However, this double passage will in general cause a slight blurring of the image as the beam does not go through the exact same part of the test section on each passage. In addition, since the screen cannot be at the focus of both views of the test section some shadowgraph effects will be present. A single mirror system shown in Fig. 4-9b is still simpler although the blurring of the image would be still more serious than in Fig. 4-9a because the light is not parallel. The source and knife edge are at conjugate foci and for convenience they are often kept close together and thus at a distance twice the focal length, f, from the mirror. If α is the deflection of the beam after a single transit of the test section the sensitivity, equivalent to equation 4-18, would be $\frac{4f}{a_K}$. Since the

source and knife edge with the two systems in Fig. 4-9 are in such close proximity a splitter plate is sometimes used to give them a larger physical separation. Optical geometries similar to those shown in Figs. 4-9a and 4-9b but with a converging lens replacing the converging mirror can also be used. It should be apparent that in all of these systems a camera placed in the beam after the knife edge and focused on the test section can be used in place of the screen.

Other Schlieren systems have used one of the optical arrangements shown above, usually that of Fig. 4-6, but without the knife edge. In a color Schlieren the knife edge is replaced by colored filters held at the focus and the deflection of the light beam (necessarily non-monochromatic) then gives rise to different colors depending on its magnitude. In some systems an aperture is placed at the focus and gives a

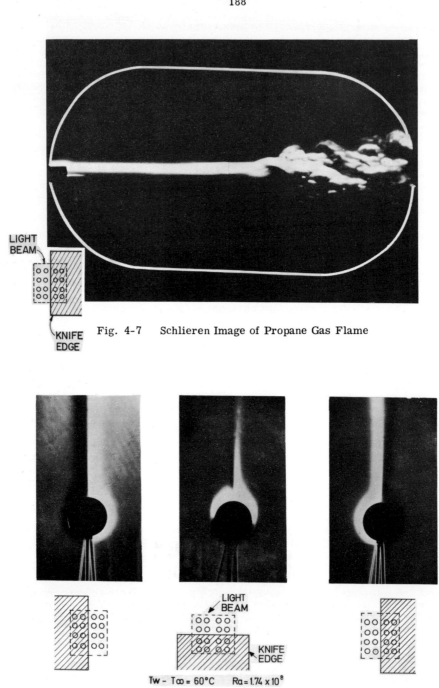

Fig. 4-7   Schlieren Image of Propane Gas Flame

Tw − T∞ = 60°C   Ra = 1.74 x 10⁸

Fig. 4-8   Free Convection Field Around a Heated Cylinder

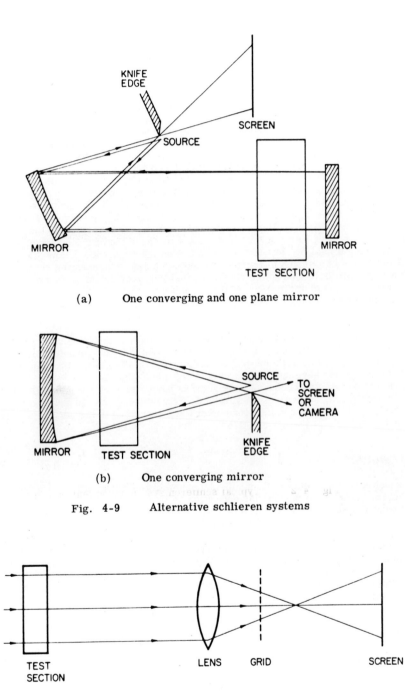

(a)   One converging and one plane mirror

(b)   One converging mirror

Fig. 4-9   Alternative schlieren systems

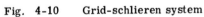

Fig. 4-10   Grid-schlieren system

darker image for any deflection or temperature gradient irrespective of the direction of the gradient. An opaque disc at the focus gives a brightening of the image for a light deflection in any direction. A system of this latter type is related to the Schlieren interferometer which is described in a later section of this paper.

Of particular interest for quantitative studies is the Ronchi or grid Schlieren, (12), (13), (14). A grid is shown as part of a focusing lens Schlieren in Fig. 4-10 which could be used in any of the optical arrangements previously described, although quantitative studies are best performed using parallel light which passes through the test section only once. The grid has equally spaced opaque lines (whose width is usually set equal to the spacing) on a transparent sheet. It is placed before the focus as shown in Fig. 4-10. The resulting Schlieren image is a series of lines, parallel if no disturbance is present. When a disturbance is present the displacement of these fringes will be directly proportional to the local angular deflection, α. The grid could also be placed right at the focus where the knife edge is located in a standard Schlieren system and in this system the beam should just pass through one of the gaps between two opaque lines when no disturbance is present. Thus the spacing between the lines would equal a_o, (cf Fig. 4-3) and the screen would be uniformly illuminated. When a disturbance is present the deflection of the light beam at the focus, Δa, will cause the beam to traverse the grid producing a light or dark image depending on the magnitude of Δa. The resulting image is a series of fringes, called isophotes, representing regions of constant angular deflection (often constant density or temperature gradient). Placement of the grid at the focus of the second lens however is often impractical. The required line spacing on the grid may be so small as to cause significant diffraction effects.

Other systems which may be of interest in heat transfer studies include: a self-illuminated Schlieren system for study of plasma jets (15), a sharp-focusing Schlieren system (16) and stereoscopic Schlieren (17). The latter two though cumbersome to use have application to study of three-dimensional fields. Schlieren systems using lasers as light sources have also been studied (18). The Schmidt-Schlieren, because of its similarity to a shadowgraph, is outlined in the next section while Schlieren interferometers are described in the section on interferometry.

SHADOWGRAPH

In a shadowgraph system the linear displacement of the perturbed light beam is measured, rather than the angular deflection as in a Schlieren system. The shadowgraph image can be understood with reference to Fig. 4-11 in which a parallel light beam enters a non-uniform test section. To simplify the derivation, variations are assumed to exist only in the y direction. At the exit to the test section the beam is not usually parallel having been deflected by an angle α which is a function of y. Consider the illumination at the exit of the test section. The linear displacement of the light beam is probably not too great there, because of the relatively short distance the light has travelled and if the illumination is uniform entering the test section it should still be closely uniform there. The light, however, is bent through an angle α. The illumination within the region defined by Δy at this position will be within the region defined by Δy_{sc} at the screen. If the initial intensity is I_T, then at the screen:

$$I_o = \frac{\Delta y}{\Delta y_{sc}} I_T$$

Eq. 4-29

If z_{sc} is the distance to the screen:

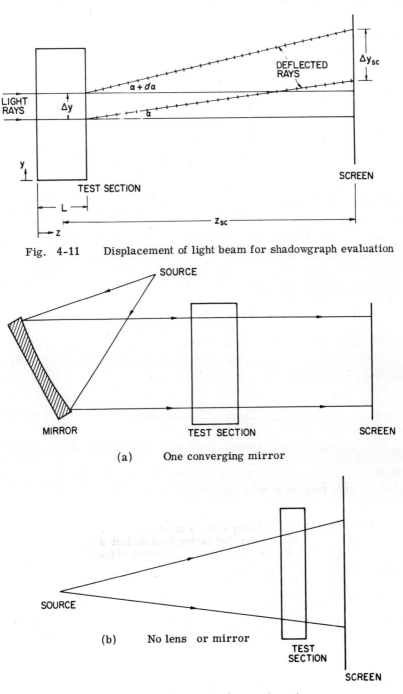

Fig. 4-11   Displacement of light beam for shadowgraph evaluation

(a)   One converging mirror

(b)   No lens or mirror

Fig. 4-12   Alternative shadowgraph systems

$$\Delta y_{sc} = \Delta y + z_{sc}\, d\alpha \qquad\qquad \text{Eq. 4-30}$$

The contrast is:

$$\frac{\Delta I}{I_T} = \frac{I_o - I_T}{I_T} = \left(\frac{\Delta y}{\Delta y_{sc}} - 1\right)$$

$$\approx -z_{sc}\frac{\partial \alpha}{\partial y} \qquad\qquad \text{Eq. 4-31}$$

Combining this with equation 4-11:

$$\frac{\Delta I}{I_T} = -\frac{z_{sc}}{n_a}\int \frac{\partial^2 n}{\partial y^2}\, dz \qquad\qquad \text{Eq. 4-32}$$

If the index of refraction is only a function of temperature, as with most liquids:

$$\frac{\Delta I}{I_T} = -\frac{z_{sc}}{n_a}\int \frac{\partial^2 T}{\partial y^2}\ \frac{dn}{dT}\, dz$$

$$\approx -z_{sc}\int \frac{\partial^2 T}{\partial y^2}\ \frac{dn}{dT}\, dz \qquad\qquad \text{Eq. 4-33}$$

assuming $\frac{dn}{dT}$ is constant. For a gas, equation 4-6 could be substituted into equation 4-32.

If there are additional variations of the index of refraction in the x direction, then equivalent to equation 4-33b:

$$\frac{\Delta I}{I_T} = -\frac{z_{sc}}{n_a}\int \left(\frac{\partial^2 n}{\partial x^2} + \frac{\partial^2 n}{\partial_y{}^2}\right)\, dz \qquad\qquad \text{Eq. 4-34}$$

The shadowgraph, like the Schlieren and interferometer methods, is best utilized in a two-dimensional system where there is no variation in the z direction aside from the sharp change at entrance and exit of the test region. Note that variation of index of refraction in both x and y directions are obtained from a single image, while Schlieren systems usually only indicate variations normal to the knife edge.

Different optical geometries are possible for shadowgraph systems as shown in Fig. 4-12. Parallel light optics as in Fig. 4-12a are easiest to understand although the lensless and mirrorless system of Fig. 4-12b is also usable if the distance from the (small) source to the test region is large. Other combinations of mirrors and lenses analogous to the Schlieren systems of Figs. 4-2, 4-6 , and 4-9 have been used. It should be noted that if a mirror or lens is used after the test region in a shadowgraph system it should not be placed such that the conjugate focus of the test section is in the plane of the screen. At the conjugate focus the parts of the beam deflected at different angles in the test region are all brought back together so there is no linear displacement there and thus no shadowgraph effect.

The standard shadowgraph is rarely used for quantitative studies as the difficulty in evaluating equation 4-33 essentially rules out direct measurement of the temperature field. The contrast would have to be measured accurately and the equation integrated twice to get the density or temperature distribution. Even the temperature gradient which is of interest in heat transfer studies would require one integration. If, however, very large gradients of density or temperature are present as in a shock wave or a flame, shadowgraph pictures can be very useful. As with a Schlieren system quantitative measurements such as shock angles can be made. In addition, a shadowgraph is quite useful in indicating a boundary layer transition (3, p. 28).

Figure 4-13 shows a shadowgraph of the flame whose Schlieren photo is in Fig. 4-7. The same optical system was used as described above in reference to Fig. 4-7 and Fig. 4-8 (i.e. a system similar to Fig. 4-6) with the knife edge removed and the camera set out of focus to get the shadowgraph image.

One particular modification of the shadowgraph has been used in heat transfer studies to obtain surface heat fluxes. It is sometimes called the Schmidt Schlieren system and is relatively simple to use and evaluate. (19) (20). Although a shadow picture is taken, a deflection is measured that is proportional to the index of refraction gradient at a solid-fluid interface. From this deflection the wall temperature gradient, and thus the surface heat flux, can be obtained.

Consider the light path in Fig. 4-14a, where the light enters the disturbed or test region parallel to the test surface. There is no variation of properties in the z direction within or outside the test section and at first only deflections in the y - z plane are considered. From equation 4-9 the path of the light beam for small angular deflections, is described by:

$$\frac{\partial^2 y}{\partial z^2} = \frac{1}{n} \frac{\partial n}{\partial y}$$

Integrating once gives the value of the slope of a light ray at the exit of the test section:

$$\left(\frac{\partial y}{\partial z}\right)_T = \frac{1}{n} \frac{\partial n}{\partial y} L \qquad \text{Eq. 4-35}$$

Integrating again to get the value of y at this position for a ray that entered at y_i:

$$y_T - y_i = \frac{1}{n} \frac{\partial n}{\partial y} \frac{L^2}{2} \qquad \text{Eq. 4-36}$$

In these integrations we have assumed that $\frac{1}{n} \frac{\partial n}{\partial y}$ is constant along the beam even though the y position changes slightly. This is valid if $\frac{\partial^2 n}{\partial y^2}$ is small (20). If no other variation in index of refraction is present, after leaving the test section the ray travels in a straight line to the screen. The ray height at the screen is given by:

$$y_{sc} = y_T + \left(\frac{\partial y}{\partial z}\right)_T (z_{sc} - L/2)$$

or:

$$(y_{sc} - y_i) = \frac{1}{n} \frac{\partial n}{\partial y} z_{sc} L \qquad \text{Eq. 4-37a}$$

$$\approx \frac{\partial n}{\partial y} z_{sc} L \qquad \text{Eq. 4-37b}$$

when $n \approx 1.0$.

If the test fluid has an index of refraction differing greatly from the surrounding air then upon emerging from the test section windows the slope of the light beam

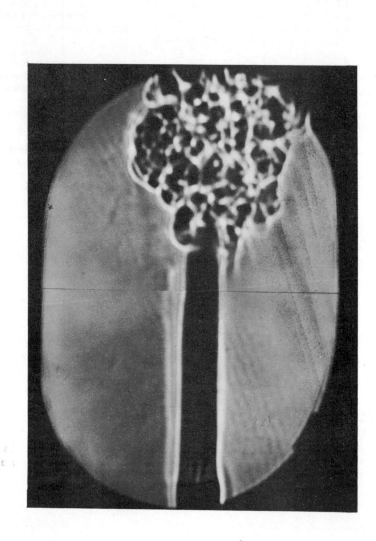

Fig. 4-13   Shadowgraph of Flame used in Fig. 4-7

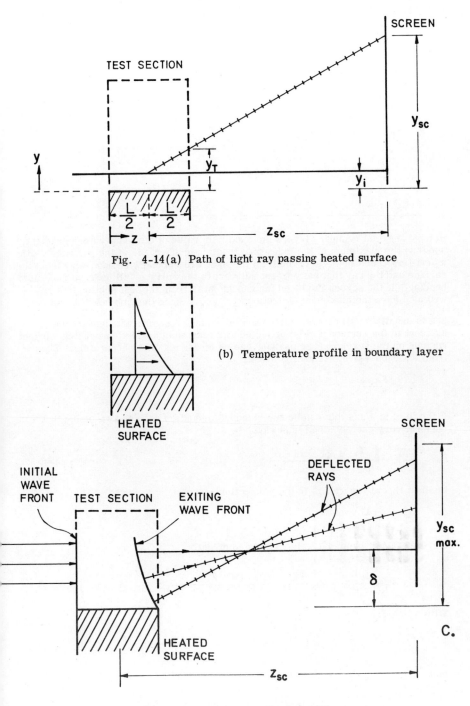

Fig. 4-14(a) Path of light ray passing heated surface

(b) Temperature profile in boundary layer

(c) Light beam passing heated surface

would be:

$$\frac{1}{n_a} \frac{\partial n}{\partial y} L$$

or neglecting displacement of the beam during passage through the windows:

$$y_{sc} - y_i = \frac{1}{n} \frac{\partial n}{\partial y} \frac{L^2}{2} + \frac{1}{n_a} \frac{\partial n}{\partial y} L \left(z_{sc} - L/2\right) \qquad \text{Eq. 4-38}$$

and if:

$$L << z_{sc}$$

$$(y_{sc} - y_i) = \frac{1}{n_a} \frac{\partial n}{\partial y} L z_{sc} \qquad \text{Eq. 4-39a}$$

$$\approx \frac{\partial n}{\partial y} L z_{sc} \qquad \text{Eq. 4-39b}$$

In most thermal boundary layers the maximum value of the temperature gradient, and thus the maximum of the index of refraction gradient, is at the surface. With a heat flow from the solid to the fluid the light will normally be bent away from the surface and the ray that passed just adjacent to the surface will undergo maximum bending. If the screen is placed far enough away from the test section this ray will also have the maximum deflection, $y_{sc\,max}$. Since the value of $\frac{\partial^2 T}{\partial y^2}$ and thus $\frac{\partial^2 n}{\partial y^2}$ is usually small or even zero near the surface a significant light bundle adjacent to the surface will be deflected this maximum amount, producing a bright contour on the screen whose position can be measured fairly accurately. Then from equation 4-37b or equation 4-39b:

$$\frac{\partial n}{\partial y} = \frac{y_{sc\,max}}{z_{sc} \ L} .$$

If the fluid is a gas this can be combined with equation 4-5b and assuming that T does not vary greatly along light ray:

$$\left. \frac{\partial T}{\partial y} \right) = \frac{T_w}{-n_o - 1} \frac{\rho_o}{\rho} \frac{y_{sc\,max}}{z_{sc} \ L} . \qquad \text{Eq. 4-40}$$

the heat flux at the wall is in the y direction:

$$qw = -k \left. \frac{\partial T}{\partial y} \right)_w$$

and the Nusselt number can be calculated directly,

$$Nu = \frac{q_w \ D}{k(T_w - T_\infty)} = \frac{T_w}{(n_o - 1)} \frac{\rho_o}{\rho} \frac{D}{z_{sc} \ L} \frac{y_{sc\,max}}{(T_w - T_\infty)} . \qquad \text{Eq. 4-41}$$

With a liquid:

$$\left. \frac{\partial T}{\partial y} \right)_w = \frac{y_{sc\,max}}{\left(\frac{dn}{dT} \right)_w z_{sc} \ L} \qquad \text{Eq. 4-42}$$

and:

$$Nu = \frac{-y_{sc\,max}}{(T_w - T_\infty)} \frac{D}{z_{sc} \ L \left(\frac{dn}{dT} \right)_w} \qquad \text{Eq. 4-43}$$

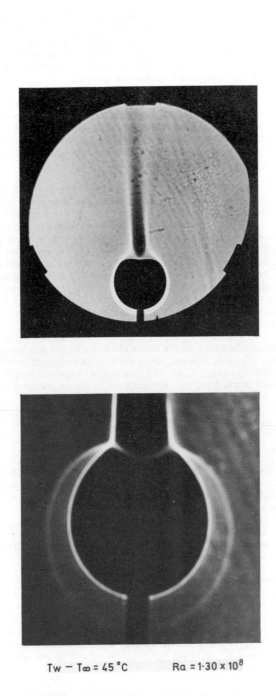

Tw − T∞ = 45 °C   Ra = 1·30 × 10⁸

Fig. 4-15   Shadowgraphs of Cylinder used in Fig. 4-8

It should be noted that to measure the displacement on the screen the zero position for y must be known. This must usually be determined when no disturbance is in the test region so the rays passing the wall are not deflected. If a slit is placed in the light beam before the test section such that primarily the solid-fluid interface is illuminated a somewhat sharper image of the maximum deflection can be obtained although care must be taken to avoid diffraction effects.

If a thermal boundary layer as in Fig. 4-14b and 4-14c is present all light within the boundary layer will be deflected at least to some extent. If the distance to the screen is large a shadow will appear which is representative of the thickness of the boundary layer. Since the boundary layer does not have a truly finite thickness however this shadow height at the screen is somewhat a function of the screen position even for large values of z_{sc}.

Shadowgraphs of a heated horizontal circular cylinder (the same as in Fig. 4-8 in air are shown in Fig. 4-15. The same optical system as described in relation to Fig. 4-7 and 4-8 and modified for Fig. 4-13 was used. The first photo shows the cylinder and plume while the second photo is an enlargement of the region near the cylinder. The heart-shaped halo around the cylinder is indicative of the local heat transfer coefficient variation around the periphery. For quantitative measurements the position of the solid surface intself could be put on the figure and measurements of $y_{sc\,max}$ (in this case in the radial direction) could be taken using that surface as the datum. From the figure one can observe the relatively large heat flux and thus large heat transfer coefficient (since the cylinder wall temperature was uniform) at the bottom of the cylinder. The heat transfer coefficient gradually decreases as one goes up around the cylinder reaching a minimum at the top.

A number of other modifications of the basic shadow system can be used for quantitative studies. Several designs use a narrow inclined slit in the light beam before the test section ((1) chap. VI). The distortion of the slit image on the screen is particularly useful in studying one dimensional temperature or density fields.

Interferometer

Basic Principles

The third optical device for measurement of temperature (or density) is the inter-ferometer which is often used for quantitative studies. Interferometry, unlike Schlieren and shadowgraph systems, does not depend upon the deflection of a light beam to determine density. In fact refraction effects are usually of second order and undesirable in interferometers as they introduce deviations or errors in the evaluating equations. To understand interferometric measurements one must consider the wave nature of light and this is perhaps best done by first examining a particular system that is widely used.

The Mach-Zehnder interferometer is often employed in heat transfer and aerodyna-mic studies. One of the main advantages of the Mach-Zehnder system over other interferometers is the large displacement of the reference beam from the test beam. In this way the reference beam can pass through a uniform field. In addition, since the test beam passes through the disturbed region only once the image is sharp and optical paths can be clearly defined. References (7), (21), (22), (23), (24), (25), (26) and (27) discuss some of the details of the optics of the Mach-Zehnder interferometers.

Figure 4-16 is a schematic diagram of a Mach-Zehnder interferometer. A mono-chromatic light source is used in conjunction with a lens to obtain a parallel beam of light. The requirement of a very narrow spectral width for the light source is

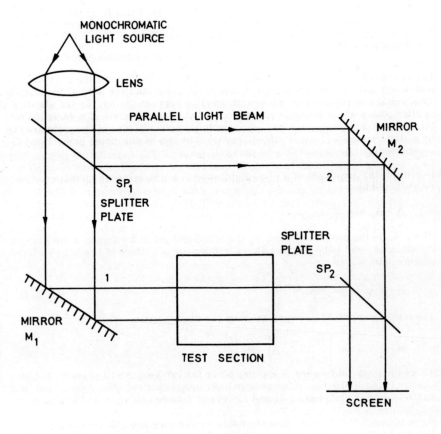

Fig. 4-16   Diagram of Mach-Zehnder interferometer

more critical in an interferometer than with Schlieren or shadowgraph systems. The parallel light beam strikes the first splitter plate, Sp_1 which is a partially silvered mirror permitting approximately half the impinging light to pass directly through it. This transmitted light follows path 1 to mirror M, where it is reflected towards the second splitter plate, Sp_2 The light reflected by Sp_1 follows path 2 going to mirror M where it is also reflected towards Sp_2. The second splitter plate also transmits about half the impinging light and reflects most of the rest and the recombined beams pass on to the screen. Note that there would also be another recombined beam leaving Sp_2, but in general only one beam from the final splitter is used. The mirrors and splitter plates are usually set at corners of a rectangle (25). They should then be all closely parallel and at an angle of $\pi/4$ to the initial parallel beam.

Let us consider that in Fig. 4-12 the mirrors are perfectly parallel and that in both path 1 and path 2 there are no variations in optical properties normal to either beam. This would require not only uniform properties between the mirror but also that the splitter plates are uniform in properties. (Note that the effect of a variation in thickness of a splitter plate can be corrected if both surfaces of the plate are flat by a slight rotation of one of the mirrors.) The two beams (from paths 1 and 2) emerging from Sp_2 would then be parallel.

In general the amplitude of a plane light wave in a homogeneous medium can be represented by:

$$A = A_0 \sin \frac{2\pi}{\lambda} (c_0 T - z) \qquad\qquad \text{Eq. 4-44}$$

where A_0 is the peak amplitude, c_0 the speed of light in a vacuum, t the time, z the distance, and λ the wavelength. Consider the amplitude of beam 1 at a fixed position past S_2 to be:

$$A_1 = A_{01} \sin \frac{2\pi c_0 T}{\lambda} \qquad\qquad \text{Eq. 4-45}$$

The other beam could be represented at the same position by:

$$A_2 = A_{02} \sin \left[\frac{2\pi c_0 T}{\lambda} - \Delta \right] \qquad\qquad \text{Eq. 4-46}$$

where the phase difference Δ appears since the two beams will probably not be exactly in phase due to a difference in their optical path length. Before the first splitter plate the two beams (1 and 2) were of course one beam and in phase.

Since beams 1 and 2 come from the same source they are coherent and can interfere with each other. This is really implicit in equations 4-45 and 4-46 if Δ is not a function of time, but only of the path difference. Summing equations 4-45 and 4-46 and assuming that:

$$A_{01} = A_{02} = A_0$$
$$A_T = A_1 + A_2 = A_0 \quad \sin \left[\left[\frac{2\pi c_0 T}{\lambda} - \Delta \right] + \sin \left[\frac{2\pi c_0 T}{\lambda} \right] \right] \qquad\qquad \text{Eq. 4-47}$$

which can be rewritten:

$$A_T = 2 A_0 \cos \left(\frac{\Delta}{2}\right) \quad \sin \left[\frac{2\pi c_0 T}{\lambda} - \theta \right] \qquad\qquad \text{Eq. 4-48}$$

where θ is a new phase difference. Thus the sum of the two waves is a new wave of the same frequency and wave length.

Of particular importance is the intensity of the combined beam which is the quantity observed visually or measured by a photographic plate. The intensity, I, is proportional to the square of the peak amplitude or:

$$I \sim 4 A_o^2 \cos^2 \left(\frac{\Delta}{2}\right)$$

Eq. 4-49

Note that when $\frac{\Delta}{2\pi}$ is an integer (say j), the peak intensity is four times that of either of the two beams but when $\frac{\Delta}{2\pi}$ is a half integer $(j + \frac{1}{2})$ the intensity is zero. The interesting yet not too difficult paradox in this latter case is where did the energy go?

The optical path along a light beam is defined by:

$$PL = \int ndz$$

Eq. 4-50

$$= \int \frac{c_o}{c} \, dz = \lambda_o \int \frac{dz}{\lambda}$$

Eq. 4-51

Thus the optical path length is the vacuum wave length times the real light path in wave lengths (which can vary along the path). In Fig. 4-16 the difference between paths 1 and 2 would be:

$$\overline{\Delta PL} = PL_1 - PL_2 = \lambda_o \left[\int_1 \frac{dz}{\lambda} - \int_2 \frac{dz}{\lambda} \right]$$

Eq. 4-52

or:

$$\overline{\Delta PL} = \int_1 ndz - \int_2 ndz$$

Eq. 4-53

The phase change when a light wave progresses a distance dz (cf equation 4-44) is:

$$\frac{2\pi \ dz}{\lambda}$$

Thus the difference in phase of the two beams upon recombination is, from equations 4-45, 4-46, and 4-52:

$$\Delta = 2\pi \left[\int_1 \frac{dz}{\lambda} - \int_2 \frac{dz}{\lambda} \right]$$

or:

$$\frac{\Delta}{2\pi} = \frac{\overline{\Delta PL}}{\lambda_o}$$

Eq. 4-54

If $\frac{\overline{\Delta PL}}{\lambda_o}$ is zero or an integer then, from equations 4-49 and 4-54 there will be constructive interference and the field on the screen in Fig. 4-16 would be uniformly bright.

Fringe Pattern with Mach-Zehnder Interferometer

Consider a Mach-Zehnder interferometer with beams 1 and 2 passing through homogeneous media such that initially the recombined beam is uniformly bright ($\overline{\Delta PL}$ assumed to be zero). If a disturbance (inhomogeneity) were put in part of the field of light beam 1 then the path difference $\overline{\Delta PL}$ would no longer be zero nor would the field be uniform. At any position in the cross section of the beam (neglecting refraction) equation 4-53 can be written to give ϵ , the path length difference in terms of vacuum wave lengths:

$$\epsilon = \frac{\overline{\Delta PL}}{\lambda_o} = \frac{1}{\lambda_o} \int (n - n_{ref}) \, dz \qquad \text{Eq. 4-55}$$

where n_{ref} is the reference value of the index of refraction that was initially present throughout beam 1 and is in the reference beam, 2. If $\frac{\overline{\Delta PL}}{\lambda_o}$ is an integer the field will be bright while if $\Delta PL/\lambda_o$ is a half integer the field will be dark. Thus the initially uniformly bright field will have a series of bright and dark regions (fringes) each one representative of a specific value of $\overline{\Delta PL}$ and differing in mag-nitude from the adjacent fringe of the same shade by a value $\epsilon = \frac{\overline{\Delta PL}}{\lambda_o} = 1.$ If a gas in light beam 1 is causing the variation in optical path the Gladstone-Dale relation, equation 4-2, can be used in equation 4-55:

$$\epsilon = \frac{C}{\lambda_o} \int (\rho - \rho_{ref}) \, dz \qquad \text{Eq. 4-56}$$

If the field is two dimensional in that the only variation in the index of refraction along the light beam (i.e. in the z direction) are the sharp discontinuities at the entrance and exit of the test section, (see Appendix for a treatment of axisymmetric density fields) and ρ only varies over a length L, the fringe shift ϵ is given by:

$$\epsilon = \frac{(n - n_{ref})}{\lambda_o} L \qquad \text{Eq. 4-57}$$

For a gas:

$$\epsilon = \frac{C}{\lambda_o} (\rho - \rho_{ref}) L \qquad \text{Eq. 4-58}$$

or:

$$\rho = \frac{\lambda_o \epsilon}{CL} + \rho_{ref} \qquad \text{Eq. 4-59}$$

If the pressure is constant and the ideal gas law is used:

$$\frac{1}{T} = \frac{\lambda_o R}{pCL} \epsilon + \frac{1}{T_{ref}} , \qquad \text{Eq. 4-60}$$

$$T = \frac{p}{p} \frac{CL}{CL} \frac{T_{ref}}{+ \lambda_o R \epsilon T_{ref}} , \qquad \text{Eq. 4-61}$$

or:

$$T - T_{ref} = \left(\frac{-\epsilon}{\dfrac{p CL}{\lambda_o R T_{ref}} + \epsilon} \right) T_{ref} \qquad \text{Eq. 4-62}$$

For a two dimensional field in a liquid, equation 4-57 would be written:

$$n = \frac{\lambda_o \epsilon}{L} + n_{ref} \qquad \text{Eq. 4-63}$$

where n and n_{ref} would have to be known as functions of temperature. For small temperature differences:

$$\epsilon = \frac{L}{\lambda_o} \frac{dn}{dT} (T - T_{ref})$$

Eq. 4-64

and:

$$T - T_{ref} = \frac{\epsilon \, \lambda_o}{L} \frac{1}{dn/dT}$$

Eq. 4-65

If $\lambda_o = 546.1$ mμ and L is 30 cm then each fringe (i.e. $\epsilon = 1$) would represent a temperature difference of about 2°C in air at 20°C and one atmosphere. In water under the same conditions each fringe represents a temperature difference of about 0.02°C.

Even if the initial optical path lengths of 1 and 2 were not exactly equal the above equations are still valid in determining temperature and density differences between different parts of the cross section in the disturbed beam 1. This is the usual manner in which interferometers are employed which only requires a known reference point in the cross section of the test beam 1 where the properties are known and of course, uniform optical path length across the cross section of the reference beam. Then n_{ref}, ρ_{ref} and T_{ref} would refer to this specific, hopefully uniform, portion of the test region, and all properties at other locations in the test section are measured in terms of the properties there.

With the two beams parallel to each other when recombined (which is often called infinite fringe setting as discussed below), each fringe is the locus of points in a two-dimensional field where the density or temperature is constant. When the fringes represent isotherms in heat transfer studies they delineate thermal boundary layers and are very useful for qualitative temperature field visualization as well as for quantitative studies.

In practice a Mach-Zehnder interferometer is not always used with the beams perfectly parallel upon recombination as in the discussion above. Consider two beams each of which is uniform (in phase) normal to the direction of its propogation, although diverging slightly, at a small angle θ, from each other as represented by the two wave trains shown in Fig. 4-17. Lines are shown drawn through the crests (maxima of amplitude) for each wave train to represent the planes (wave fronts) normal to the direction of propogation. Constructive interference occurs where the maxima of the two beams coincide and dashed line representing the locus of these positions are also shown. If a screen is placed approximately normal to the two beams the intensity distribution on the screen would follow a cosine-squared law (Eq. 4-49) as shown on the figure. Thus parallel equally spaced alternately dark and light fringes (called wedge fringes) appear on the screen when there are no disturbances in either field. The difference in optical path length between the two beams varies linearly across the field of view with wedge fringes so that only one fringe in the field (the "zero-order fringe") represents exactly equal path lengths. From Fig. 4-17 the spacing between the fringes is:

$$d = \frac{\lambda/2}{\sin \theta/2} \text{ or } \sim \frac{\lambda}{\theta}$$

Eq. 4-66

To observe fringes, θ must be very small. For example if d is about 5 mm then θ (using the green mercury line) is about 10^{-4} radians. As θ is decreased to zero the fringes get further and further apart approaching the "infinite fringe" pattern found when the two beams are parallel.

When a Mach-Zehnder interferometer is adjusted to give wedge fringes the fringes are localized as shown in Fig. 4-18. Only a pair of rays is shown and these are diverging and brought to a focus on the screen (or film in a camera) by a focusing lens. The angular separation of the beams is greatly exaggerated on the figure. The dashed lines represent the paths from the virtual object of the beams in 1 and

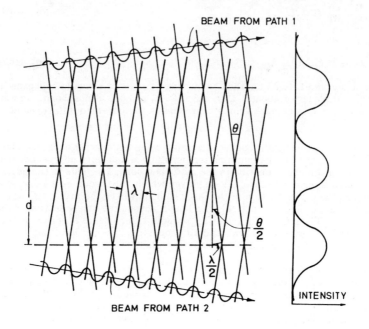

Fig. 4-17   Intensity pattern from two intersecting plane light beams

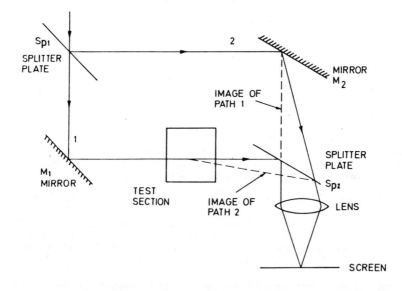

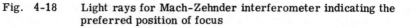

Fig. 4-18   Light rays for Mach–Zehnder interferometer indicating the preferred position of focus

2 as they would appear along the other path. The fringes are localized where, tracing backwards along the real and image paths, the rays intersect. The plane of localization can be adjusted, once the beams are close enough to parallel to see fringes (i.e. "d" not too small) by rotation primarily of SP_2 (and also of M_2 to keep the fringes in view) about two orthogonal axes in the plane of SP_2. If the fringes are localized at M_2 then the rotation of M_2 will not affect the plane of localization and will only change the fringe spacing and orientation. To have both the fringes (localized at M_2) and the test section (actually the center of the test section - as discussed below) in focus on the screen or in the camera, the interferometer mirrors can be placed on the corners of a 2 to 1 rectangle, the distance from SP_2 to M_2 then being the same as the distance from SP_2 to the middle of the test section.

When a disturbance is present within the test section (which is in beam 1 in Fig.4-18) the optical path is no longer uniform in this beam 1. The fringes then are no longer straight, but curved as in Fig. 4-19 and in this figure the original (undisturbed) position of the fringes is shown by dashed lines. In general the undisturbed fringes should be aligned in a direction in which the expected temperature (index of refraction) gradient will be large. The difference in optical path length from the original value or from the reference position in the field of view where the fringes have not changed is shown on the figure in terms of the fringe shift, ϵ. If the total fringe shift is large, only integral values of ϵ are usually measured but for small differences in optical path length, fractional values of ϵ can be measured as shown. One of the major advantages of wedge fringes is the possibility of measuring fractional values of ϵ. In addition it is difficult to be certain with infinite fringe spacing that the undisturbed (or reference) field is at the maximum brightness so that there is an uncertainty in the reference position. This problem does not occur with wedge fringes as long as there is a region of known uniform properties in the field of view. Contours of constant optical path length can also be obtained with wedge fringes by superposing the disturbed interference pattern over the undisturbed pattern. The resulting Moiré fringe pattern gives grey lines usually representing isotherms in a two-dimensional test region. If there are irregularities in the undisturbed image due to faulty optical parts this superposition method can still be used to obtain quantitative results.

The versatility of interferometry in heat transfer studies can be observed in Figs. 4-20 to 4-24. Figures 4-20 to 4-22 are obtained from an initially infinite fringe spacing. Figures 4-20 and 4-21 indicate the free convection isotherms in air about a heated horizontal flat plate and a heated horizontal cylinder respectively. The cylinder is the one for which Schlieren and shadowgraph (Schmidt Schlieren) patterns are presented in Figs. 4-8 and 4-13. Figure 4-22 shows how transient boundary layer development, in this case with free convection on a vertical foil in air, can be followed with an interferometer. Figure 4-23 shows the Moiré fringe pattern obtained when a double exposure is made, indicating the free convection boundary layers on both sides of a thin foil in water. Figure 4-24 shows the temperature field in a forced flow using wedge fringes. The flow is of air over a rearward facing step with approximately uniform heating all along the surface.

Design and Adjustment

A diagram of an operating Mach-Zehnder interferometer is shown in Fig. 4-25. Instead of lenses, mirrors are used to obtain the initial parallel light beam and to focus the final combined beam. Light from a low pressure mercury vapor lamp is focused, through a filter to have a more monochromatic beam, on a small (0.25 mm diam.) illuminating mirror, D, which acts as a near-point light source for paraboidal mirror F. The parallel light from this mirror goes to the first splitter plate, SP_1. The light that passes directly through the splitter plate goes to mirror M_1 where it is turned at right angles and directed through the test section and then to the second splitter plate SP_2. The reference beam, after being reflected at SP_1

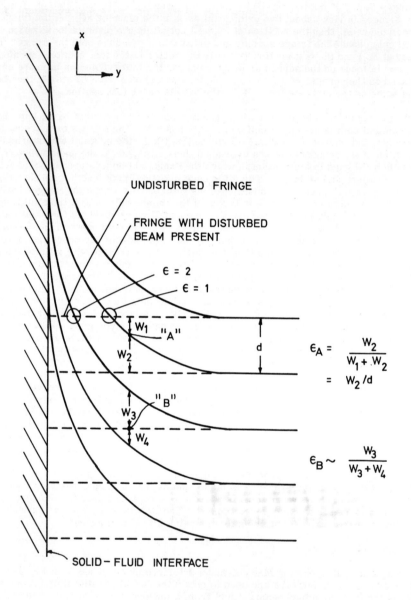

Fig. 4-19   Fringe shift pattern with wedge fringes

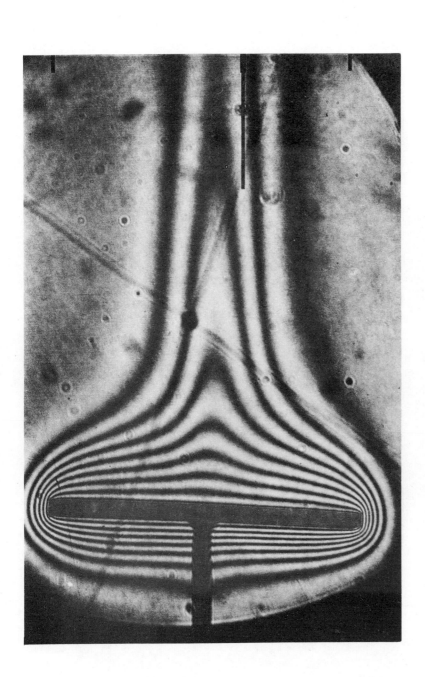

Fig. 4-20   Free Convection Isotherms about a Heated Plate (2'' x 1/8'') where
$T_W - T_\infty = 27\,^\circ F$

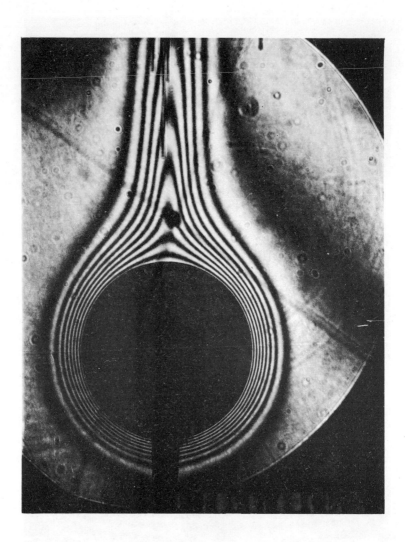

Fig. 4-21   Similar Isotherms about a Heated Horizontal Cylinder

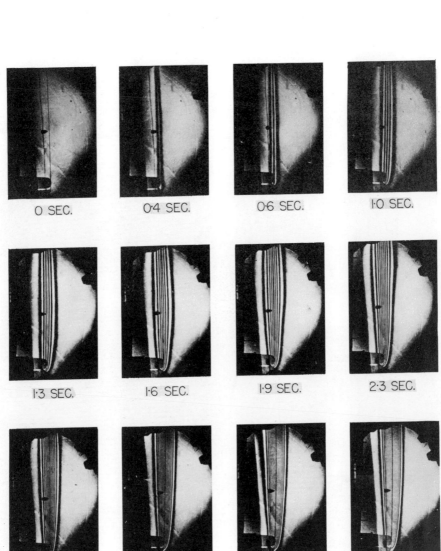

O SEC. 0·4 SEC. 0·6 SEC. 1·0 SEC.

1·3 SEC. 1·6 SEC. 1·9 SEC. 2·3 SEC.

3·1 SEC. 5·5 SEC. 10·3 SEC. 17·5 SEC.

Fig. 4-22 Transient boundary layer development

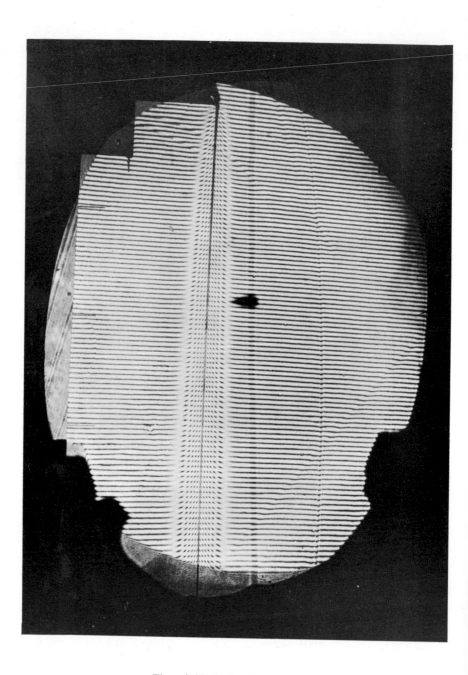

Fig. 4-23 Moire fringe pattern

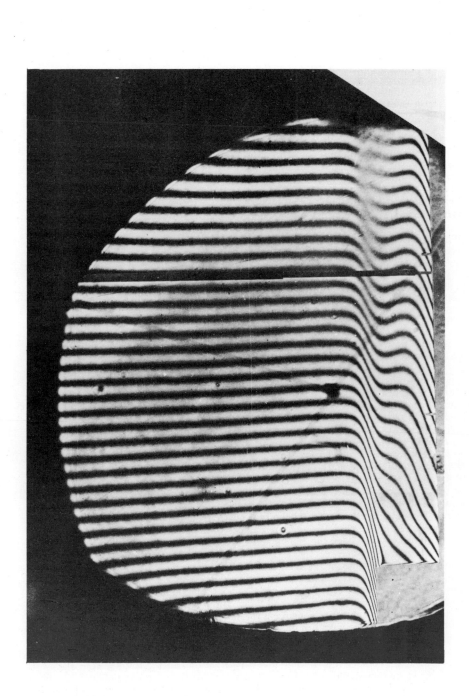

Fig. 4-24 Temperature field in a forced flow of air using wedge fringes

goes to the mirror M_2 and is there reflected to SP_2. The two beams, after recombining at SP_2, are reflected by plane mirror M_3 to the spherical mirror M_4, then onto a small plane mirror H and finally into a camera or onto a viewing plate. If thick windows must be used on the test section or if the fluid in the test section has a refractive index very different from that of air, it may be necessary to have a compensating tank Q to ensure that the path lengths of the beams are not too different.

Note that the test section should be placed in beam 1 rather than beam 2. In this way the beam representing the shadow image of the test section does not pass through the last splitter plate which could cause considerable astigmatism (28).

The alignment of an interferometer such as shown in Figs. 4-16 and 4-25 though somewhat complicated and time consuming is not so horrendous a task as is often stated. A number of methods have been described (21), (25), (29), (30) which greatly simplify the task. The chief concern is to align the reference and test beams so that they are closely parallel. If they are not, from equation 4-66, the fringe spacing is so small that the fringes cannot be detected.

When first aligning the interferometer the two path lengths are set approximately equal. The difference in length must be less than the coherence length of the source-filter combination which increases as the light becomes more monochromatic. If the light intensity variation with wave length is Gaussian with a bandwidth of $\Delta\lambda$, the coherence length or optical path difference over which fringes can still be observed is approximately $\frac{\lambda^2}{\Delta\lambda}$ (31). The parallelism of the beam leaving the paraboidal mirror, F, can be determined by measuring its dimensions at various positions along its path or, more accurately, by having it reflected back to F by a plane mirror and observing the proximity of the focus of this returned beam to the small illuminating mirror, D.

To obtain fringes, beams 1 and 2 (Fig. 4-18) must be nearly parallel to each other. This can be accomplished by aligning the images of two objects observed by looking back through SP_2 preferably with a small telescope. The two objects examined should be far apart and must both be located before the first splitter plate, SP_1, so that images are obtained for both paths (1 and 2). In practice the illuminating mirror (D in Fig. 4-25) or point source (Figs. 4-16 and 4-18) which can be considered at infinity is used as well as some observable object (perhaps the illuminated cross-hairs holding the mirror) placed in the field of view before SP_1. Rotation of M_2 and SP_2 about two orthogonal axes moves each pair of virtual images of the two objects. When both images of each object are superimposed the two beams leaving SP_2 are closely parallel and fringes should appear in the field of view. Focusing on the center of the test section and M_2 with the telescope, camera or screen, fringes are made as sharp as possible by further rotation of SP_2 meanwhile rotating M_2 to keep the fringe spacing from getting too small.

When the plane of focus of the fringes is in M_2 (and the center of the test section) the final adjustment of optical path length can be made. It is advantageous to keep the interferometer set close to the zero order fringe as that is the position for sharpest fringes even for the filtered light. In addition, white light and the zero order fringe are useful for measuring the index of refraction for fluids whose optical properties are unknown or in tracing fringes through regions of large density gradients. In the apparatus shown in Fig. 4-25 the path length of the test beam can be altered by translation of the mirror M_1. If white light (an incandescent bulb suffices) replaces the filtered mercury light on half the field of view the mirror can be translated until the zero order white light fringe is observed. In practice it is often helpful, in particular if the initial setting is far from the zero order fringe, to use light of varying coherence lengths from the most monochromatic to white light to make each set of fringes as sharp as possible while translating the mirror.

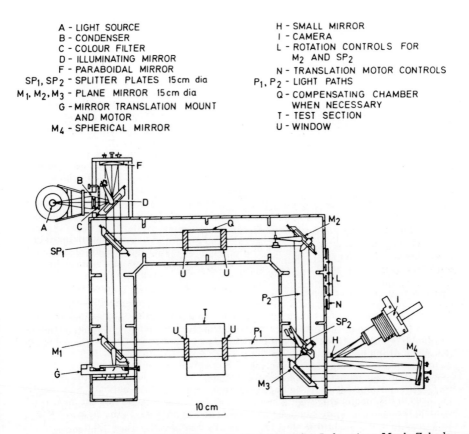

A - LIGHT SOURCE
B - CONDENSER
C - COLOUR FILTER
D - ILLUMINATING MIRROR
F - PARABOIDAL MIRROR
SP$_1$, SP$_2$ - SPLITTER PLATES 15cm dia
M$_1$, M$_2$, M$_3$ - PLANE MIRROR 15cm dia
G - MIRROR TRANSLATION MOUNT
AND MOTOR
M$_4$ - SPHERICAL MIRROR

H - SMALL MIRROR
I - CAMERA
L - ROTATION CONTROLS FOR
M$_2$ AND SP$_2$
N - TRANSLATION MOTOR CONTROLS
P$_1$, P$_2$ - LIGHT PATHS
Q - COMPENSATING CHAMBER
WHEN NECESSARY
T - TEST SECTION
U - WINDOW

10 cm

25.   Fig. 4-25 University of Minnesota Heat Transfer Laboratory Mach-Zehnder
Interferometer

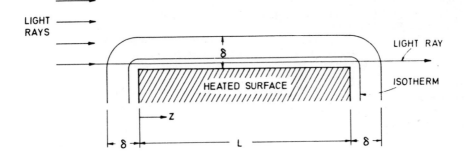

Fig.   4-26 Assumed temperature distribution to determine end effect
correction

Once adjusted the interferometer if properly constructed mechanically usually needs only minor re-adjustment. Placing the unit in a vibration-free constant-temperature area helps to maintain alignment.

Interferometer Error Analysis in a Two Dimensional Field

Since the Mach-Zehnder interferometer is of great value for quantitative studies in two dimensional fields considerable attention (32), (33), (34), (35), (36), (37), (38), (40) has been directed towards the corrections that must be applied when the idealizations assumed in the derivation of equations 4-62 and 4-65 are not strictly met. The two most significant errors usually encountered are due to refraction and end effects. Refraction occurs when there is a density (really index of refraction) gradient normal to the light beam causing the beam to 'bend'. The resulting error increases with increasing density gradient and with increasing path length in the disturbed region L. It is refraction that usually prevents accurate interferometric measurements in thin forced convection boundary layers. End effects are caused by deviation from two dimensionality of the actual density field in particular where the light beam enters and leaves the disturbed region. The end effects are usually large when the disturbed region is large normal to the light beam direction and relatively short along the light beam. End effects are often significant with thick thermal boundary layers. Thus if an experimental apparatus is designed to minimize refraction error the end effect error may be large and vice-versa.

The end effects will be considered in detail first. At the two ends of the test section, where the light enters and leaves, the density field may no longer be truly two-dimensional and some correction to the calculation of the two-dimensional field in the center of the test piece must be made. The exact correction depends on the design of the test apparatus including the presence or absence of windows at the edges of the test section. For the purposes of demonstration, consider fig. 4-26 where a horizontal cross-section of a constant temperature heated vertical plate losing heat by natural convection is shown. In the region near the center of the plate the temperature field is two-dimensional (one-dimensional in the section shown). As an approximation to the effect of the ends assume that the isotherms or constant density lines are arcs of circles at the corners in the figure. The fringe shift of the ray at the wall is, from equation 4-55:

$$\epsilon_w = \frac{1}{\lambda_0} \int (n - n_{ref}) \, dz$$

$$= \frac{2}{\lambda_0} \left\{ \int_{(L/2)}^{L} (n_w - n_{ref}) \, dz + \int_{L}^{L+\delta} (n - n_{ref}) \, dz \right\}$$

integrated along y = 0. To a first approximation from equation 4-64:

$$\epsilon_w = \frac{2}{\lambda_0} \frac{dn}{dT} \left[\int_{L/2}^{L} (T_w - T_{ref}) \, dz + \int_{L}^{L+\delta} (T - T_{ref}) \, dz \right] \qquad \text{Eq. 4-67}$$

where n_{ref} and T_{ref} are respectively the index of refraction and temperature outside the boundary layer. A reasonable polynomial approximation to the temperature distribution in the boundary layer is:

$$T - T_{ref} = (T_w - T_{ref}) \left(1 - \frac{y}{\delta}\right)^2 \qquad \text{Eq. 4-68}$$

Then at y = 0, for L < z < L + δ:

$$T - T_{ref} = (T_w - T_{ref}) \left[1 - \frac{z - L}{\delta}\right]^2 \qquad \text{Eq. 4-69}$$

and from equation 4-67:

$$\epsilon_w = \frac{2dn}{dT} \frac{1}{\lambda_o} (T_w - T_{ref}) \left[\frac{L}{2} + \frac{\delta}{3}\right] \qquad \text{Eq. 4-70}$$

The fractional change error in the fringe shift due to the end effect is the difference between the values calculated using equations 4-70 and 4-65 (i.e. the effect of finite δ):

$$\frac{\Delta\epsilon}{\epsilon} \approx +\frac{2}{3} \frac{\delta}{L} \qquad \text{Eq. 4-71}$$

The error as calculated above is positive in that a temperature larger than the true wall temperature would be indicated if no correction is used. More complicated temperature distributions near the edge of a test section have also been studied (32) (33) (41). In some cases the end effect error in the outer region of a boundary layer may be negative.

Refraction of the light beam leads to two different deviations from the evaluating equations. When the light ray is bent in the assumed two-dimensional field [say $n = n(x, y)$] no longer does it go through a fixed value of x - y along its path. Equation 4-55 should be used along the true optical path rather than assuming that the index of refraction is constant along the path and can be taken outside the integral sign. Another refraction effect is the apparent displacement of the beam which leads to an error in the x - y position assigned to a particular fringe displacement. If the interferometer is focused at the center of the test section the displacement error is essentially zero whether the index of refraction is close to unity (37) or not (42) and this should be done in most precision measurements.

To determine the remaining part of the refraction error consider, for simplicity, a one-dimensional problem where the index of refraction varies only in the y direction as in Fig. 4-14. This is often a reasonable assumption as the gradient of the index of refraction in one direction is usually quite small. Additionally, let us assume that $\frac{\partial n}{\partial y}$ is constant over the path of a given light ray. Although other variations can be chosen this is a good approximation in a thermal boundary layer close to the solid-fluid interface. Then equation 4-9, which applied to Fig. 4-14 as long as the angles are small, can be integrated twice (cf equation 4-36) yielding:

$$(y - y_i) = \frac{1}{2} \frac{1}{n} \frac{\partial n}{\partial y} z^2 \qquad \text{Eq. 4-71}$$

Since $\frac{\partial n}{\partial y}$ is constant:

$$n = n_i + \frac{\partial n}{\partial y} (y - y_i) \qquad \text{Eq. 4-72}$$

where n_i is the value of the index of refraction at y_i. Then, from

$$\epsilon = \frac{1}{\lambda_o} \int_o^L \left[(n_i - n_{ref}) + \left(\frac{\partial n}{\partial y}\right) \frac{1}{2n} \frac{\partial n}{\partial y} z^2\right] dz \qquad \text{Eq. 4-73}$$

or:

$$\epsilon = \frac{(n_i - n_{ref}) L}{\lambda_o} + \frac{1}{\lambda_o} \left(\frac{\partial n}{\partial y}\right)^2 \frac{1}{6n} L^3 \qquad \text{Eq. 4-74}$$

for a two-dimensional field with only small changes in n. Subtracting the value of ϵ obtained by neglecting refraction (i.e. $\frac{n_i - n_{ref}}{\lambda_o} L$) the error in fringe shift is:

$$\Delta\epsilon = \frac{1}{\lambda_o} \left(\frac{\partial n}{\partial y}\right)^2 \frac{L^3}{6n} \qquad \text{Eq. 4-75}$$

The error in temperature, using (64), is:

$$\Delta T = \frac{\lambda_o \Delta \epsilon}{L \; dn/dT}$$

Eq. 4-76

and taking:

$$\frac{\partial n}{\partial y} = \frac{dn}{dT} \frac{\partial T}{\partial y}$$

$$\Delta T = \left(\frac{dn}{dT}\right) \left(\frac{\partial T}{\partial y}\right)^2 \frac{L^2}{6n}$$

Eq. 4-77

This is the normal refraction correction that should be considered in an experiment. According to more exact analyses the refraction error is a function of the location of the focal plane. When the interferometer is focused at the center of the test section the refraction error is half of the value given by equation 4-77 (33), (40), (42). Additional refraction effects appear when the test beam passes through a test section window, but this correction is usually quite small (38).

An additional error may appear when measuring the fringe positions. Fringe shifts are usually determined visually with a traveling microscope which permits quite accurate measurement (43). Other refinements (44), (45) have led to more exotic measuring systems.

Other Interferometers

A number of interferometric systems other than the Mach-Zehnder have been used in heat transfer and aerodynamic studies. These in general are used to produce interferograms which can be evaluated in a similar manner to the Mach-Zehnder patterns. In some systems gratings have been used to divide the initial beam into two coherent beams one of which traverses the test region. The beams are recombined on another grating yielding an interference pattern. One systen (46) (47) uses two gratings but the reference and test beams then pass very close to each other. In a four grating apparatus (48) the beams are further apart but residual fringes are often superimposed on the pattern. A laser light source has also been used with a grating interferometer (49).

Several laser light source interferometers have been used or suggested for temperature measurement (50), (51), (52). Direct use of a laser as the light source in a Mach-Zehnder interferometer increases the coherence length to the point where a compensating tank may not be required even for a relatively large difference in path length of the two beams in the interferometer. A specific laser-interferometer system (50) is shown in Fig. 4-27. This interferometer is similar in some respects to the Mach-Zehnder interferometer. Light from a laser (for convenience a CW gas laser) is directed onto the first splitter plate. The reflected illumination passes through the diverging lens to the paraboidal mirror. The focal point of this mirror is off-axis and a parallel beam results. This beam traverses the test section and is reflected by the second off-axis paraboidal mirror through the second diverging lens. The resulting narrow parallel beam is recombined at the second splitter plate with the reference beam that had passed through the first splitter plate. Although the coherence length of the laser is large, it is best that the difference in the undisturbed path length of the two beams be zero or an integral multiple of twice the laser cavity length.

The interferometer shown has several advantages over a conventional Mach-Zehnder system. Far fewer large precision optical components are used. Additionally since the beams are combined when they are small the severe requirements of parallelism of the two beams is greatly reduced simplifying the instrument alignment. The small beam diameter also reduces the error introduced by a given

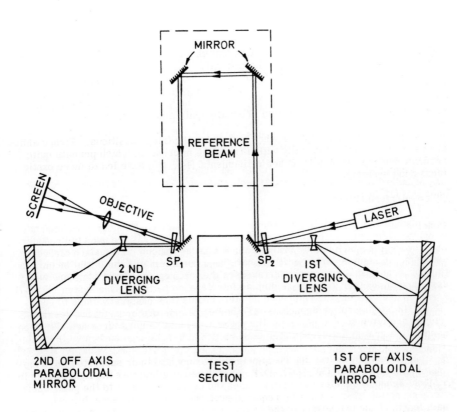

Fig. 4-27 Interferometer using laser light source

disturbance (per unit length) in the region of the reference beam as the total effect is then proportional to the beam diameter. With a small enough beam diameter the reference beam could pass through the test section without seriously affecting the fringe pattern.

Other systems that are used with laser sources include Schlieren interferometers. In one such system (53), (54), (55) a very small wire or stop is placed at the focus of a standard Schlieren system to block the central maximum of the Fraunhofer diffraction pattern. Then the phase distribution produced when the beam passed through a disturbance in the test region can be observed in reference to an undisturbed part of the test beam. The result is a fringe pattern similar to that observed with a Mach-Zehnder interferometer set for infinite fringe spacing. Interferometers in which the reference beams are sheared slightly (52) (56) in a lateral direction have been used with conventional and laser light sources. A polarization interferometer (7) (57) is a wave shearing interferometer in which two coherent beams polarized at right angles to one another are produced from a single incoming beam. The two beams often diverge at a finite angle and when recombined after passage through the test section, a fringe pattern results. If the shear is very small the fringe pattern represents the first derivative of the index of refraction field rather than the index of refraction directly. A gas laser has been used as a light source for a Twyman-Green interferometer in heat transfer studies (58). In addition the use of lasers in holography can be specifically applied to interferometric systems (59) (60) (61) (62).

Conclusion

The physical properties of shadowgraph, Schlieren and interferometric systems have been described. The basic operating equations for all three systems have been derived with emphasis on their use in determining density and temperature distributions in two dimensional fields.

Shadowgraph and Schlieren systems are principally used for qualitative description of a density or temperature field. However, they can be used for quantitative studies in particular if a grid-Schlieren or Schmidt-Schlieren apparatus is used. Because Schlieren and shadowgraph photographs yield information on the first and second derivatives of density (or temperature) they find their widest application in systems where there are steep gradients of density and temperature as with flame fronts and shock waves.

Interferometers, usually in the form of a Mach-Zehnder system, are often used in quantitative determination of two-dimensional (including axisymmetric) density and temperature fields. For this reason details of the evaluating equations and the possible error corrections have been presented. Interferometers are often employed with systems in which density or temperature gradients are relatively small, such as free convection boundary layers.

The advent of lasers permits novel and useful interferometric designs. Lasers can be used in Schlieren interferometers and holography for temperature and density measurements.

Acknowledgment

The author wishes to express his thanks to W. Aung and T.Y. Chu for their aid during the preparation of the photographic plates and the review of the manuscript.

References

1. Weinberg, F.J., 'Optics of Flames', Butterworths, London, 1963.

2. Ladenburg, R.W., Lewis, B., Pease, R.N., and Taylor, H.S., 'Physical Measurements in Gas Dynamics and Combustion,' Vol. 9 of High-Speed Aerodynamics and Jet Propulsion, Princeton University Press, Chapters A1, A2, A3, 1954.

3. Holder, D.W., North, R.J., and Wood, G.P., 'Optical Methods for Examining the Flow in High-Speed Wind Tunnels,' Parts I, II AGARD, 1965. Holder, D.W., and North, R.J., 'Schlieren Methods,' Notes on Applied Science No. 31, National Physical Laboratory, London, 1963.

4. Barnes, N.F., 'Optical Techniques for Fluid Flows,' J. Soc. of Motion Picture Television Engineer, 61, 1953, p. 487.

5. Dean, R.C., Jr., 'Aerodynamic Measurements', Gas Turbine Lab., Massachusetts Inst. of Tech., 1953,

6. Shardin, H., 'Toepler's Schlieren Method; Basic Principles for its Use and Quantitative Evaluation,' Navy Translation 156, 1947.

7. Françon, M., 'Optical Interferometry,' Academic Press, New York, 1966.

8. Goldstein, R.J., and Chu, T.Y., 'Thermal Convection in a Horizontal Layer of Air', HTL-TR No. 81, Univ. of Minnesota 1968.

9. Landolt - Börnstein, 'Physikalisch-Chemische Tabellen,' Sup. #3, 1935, p. 1677.

10. Tilton, L., and Taylor, J., 'Refractive Index and Dispersion of Distilled Water for Visible Radiation at Temperatures 0 to 60°C,' NBS J. of Res., 20, 1938, p. 419.

11. Speak, G.S., and Walters, D.J., 'Optical Considerations and Limitations of the Schlieren Method', ARC Tech. Rept., R and M No. 2859 London, 1954.

12. Ronchi, V., 'Due Nuovi Metodi per lo Studio delle Superficie e dei Sistemi Ottici', Annali della R. Scuola Normale Sup. di Pisa, 15 1923 (bound 1927)

13. Darby, P.F., 'The Ronchi Method of Evaluating Schlieren Photograph,' Tech. Conf. on Optical Pheno. in Supersonic Flow, NAVORD Report 74-46, 1946.

14. Didion, D.A., and Oh, Y.H., 'A Quantitative Schlieren-Grid Method for Temperature Measurement in a Free Convection Field', Tech. Rept. 1, Mech. Eng. Dept., Catholic University of America 1966.

15. Watermeier, L.A., 'Self-Illuminated Schlieren System', Rev. of Sci. Instru., 37, 1966, p. 1139.

16. Kantrowitz, A., and Trimpi, R.L., 'A Sharp Focusing Schlieren System', J. Aero. Sci., 17, 1950, p. 311.

17. Hett, J.H., 'A High Speed Stereoscopic Schlieren System', J. Soc. Motion Picture and Television Engineers, 56, 1951, p. 214.

18. Ackerman, J.A., and Brill, G.A., Jr., 'Final Report on Research on the Adaptability of Lasers to Schlieren Systems', ARL 65-139, 1965.

19. Schmidt, E., 'Schlierenaufnahmen des Temperaturfelds in der Nähe Wärmeabgebender Körper,' Forschung Ing., Wesen, 3, 1932, p. 181.

20. Boelter, L.M.K., and Cherry, V.H., 'Measurement of Heat Transfer by Free Convection from Cylindrical Bodies by the Schlieren Methods', ASHVE Transaction, 44, 1938, p. 499.

21. Eckert, E.R.G., Drake, R.M., Jr., and Soehngen, E., 'Manufacture of a Zehnder-Mach Interferometer,' Wright-Patterson Air Force Base, Tech. Rept. 5721, ATI-34235, 1948.

22. Bennett, F.D., and Kahl, G.D., 'A Generalized Vector Theory of the Mach-Zehnder Interferometer', J. Opt. Soc. of America, 43, 1953, p. 71.

23. Zobel, T., 'The Development and Construction of an Interferometer for Optical Measurement of Density Fields', NACA/TN/1184 1947.

24. Shardin, H., 'Theorie und Anwendung des Mach-Zehnderschen Interferenz-Refraktometers', Zeits. f. Instrumentenk, 53, 1933, p. 396 and p. 424. DRL Translation No. 3, Univ. of Texas.

25. Tanner, L.H., 'The Optics of the Mach-Zehnder Interferometer', ARC Technical Report, R and M No. 3069, 1959.

26. Tanner, L.H., 'The Design and Use of Interferometers in Aerodynamics', R and M 3131, 1957.

27. Wilkie, D., and Fisher, S.A., 'Measurement of Temperature by Mach-Zehnder Interferometry', Proc. Instn. Mech. Engrs., 178, 1963-1964, p. 461.

28. Prowse, D.B., 'Astigmatism in the Mach-Zehnder Interferometer', Appl. Opt., 6, 1967, p. 773.

29. Price, E.W., 'Initial Adjustment of the Mach-Zehnder Interferometer', Rev. Sci. Instrum., 23, 1952, p. 162.

30. Prowse, D.B., 'A Rapid Method of Aligning the Mach-Zehnder Interferometer', Australian Defence Scientific Service, Tech. Note 100, 1967.

31. Born, M., and Wolfe, E., 'Principles of Optics', 3rd Ed. Pergamon Press, Oxford, 1965, p. 322.

32. Eckert, E.R.G., and Soehngen, E.E., 'Studies on Heat Transfer in Laminar Free Convection with the Zehnder-Mach Interferometer', Air Force Tech. Rept. 5747, ATI-44580, 1948.

33. Wachtell, G.P., 'Refraction Effect in Interferometry of Boundary Layer of Supersonic Flow Along Flat Plate,' Phys. Rev., 78, 1950, p. 333.

34. Blue, R.E., 'Interferometer Corrections and Measurements of Laminar Boundary Layers in Supersonic Stream', NACA/TN/2110, 1950.

35. Eckert, E.R.G., and Soehngen, E.E., 'Distribution of Heat-Transfer Coefficients Around Circular Cylinders in Crossflow at Reynolds Numbers from 20 to 500', Trans. of the ASME, 74, 1952, p. 343.

36. **Kinsler, M.R.,** 'Influence of Refraction on the Applicability of the Zehnder-Mach Interferometer to Studies of Cooled Boundary Layers,' NACA/TN/2462, 1951.

37. **Howes, W.L., and Buchele, D.R.,** 'A Theory and Method for Applying Interferometry to the Measurement of Certain Two-Dimensional Gaseous Density Fields', NACA/TN/2693, 1952.

38. **Howes, W.L., and Buchele, D.R.,** 'Generalization of Gas-Flow Interferometry Theory and Interferogram Evaluation Equations for One-Dimensional Density Fields', NACA/TN/3340, 1955.

39. **Howes, W.L., and Buchele, D.R.,** 'Practical Considerations in Specific Applications of Gas-Flow Interferometry', NACA/TN/3507, 1955.

40. **Howes, W.L., and Buchele, D.R.,** 'Optical Interferometry of Inhomogeneous Gases', J. Opt. Soc. of America, 56, 1966, p. 1517.

41. **Goldstein, R.J.,** 'Interferometric Study of the Steady State and Transient Free Convection Thermal Boundary Layers in Air and in Water about a Uniformly Heated Vertical Flat Plate,' Ph.D. Thesis, Univ. of Minnesota, 1959.

42. **Chu, T.Y.,** personal communication, 1968.

43. **Howes, W.L., and Buchele, D.R.,** 'Random Error of Interference Fringe Measurements Using a Mach-Zehnder Interferometer', Appl. Opt. 5, 1966, p. 870.

44. **Werner, F.D., and Leadon, B.M.,** 'Very Accurate Measurement of Fringe Shifts in an Optical Interferometer Study of Gas Flow,' Rev. Sci. Instr. 24, 1953, p. 121.

45. **Dew, G.D.,** 'A Method for the Precise Evaluation of Interferograms', J. Sci. Instr., 41, 1964, p. 160.

46. **Kraushaar, R.,** 'A Diffraction Grating Interferometer', J. Opt. Soc. America, 40, 1950, p. 480.

47. **Sterrett, J.R., and Erwin, J.R.,** 'Investigation of a Diffraction Grating Interferometer for use in Aerodynamic Research', NACA/TN/2827, 1952.

48. **Weinberg, F.J., and Wood, N.B.,** 'Interferometer Based on Four Diffraction Gratings', J. Sci. Instr., 36, 1959, p. 227.

49. **Sterrett, J.R., Emery, J.C., and Barber, J.B.,** 'A Laser Grating Interferometer', AIAA J., 3, 1965, p. 963.

50. **Goldstein, R.J.,** 'Interferometer for Aerodynamic and Heat Transfer Measurements', Rev. Sci. Instr., 36, 1965, p. 1408.

51. **Oppenheim, A.K., Urtiew, P.A., and Weinberg, F.J.,** 'On the Use of Laser Light Sources in Schlieren-Interferometer Systems', Proc. Roy. Soc. A., 291, 1966, p. 279.

52. **Tanner, L.H.,** 'The Design of Laser Interferometers for Use in Fluid Mechanics', J. Sci. Instr., 43, 1966, p. 878.

53.   **Gayhart, E.L., and Prescott, R.,** 'Interference Phenomenon in the Schlieren System', J. Opt. Soc. Amer., 39, 1949, p. 546.

54.   **Temple, E.B.,** 'Quantitative Measurement of Gas Density by Means of Light Interference in a Schlieren System', J. Opt. Soc. Amer., 47, 1957, p. 91.

55.   **Brackenridge, J.B., and Gilbert, W.P.,** 'Schlieren Interferometry. An Optical Method for Determining Temperature and Velocity Distributions in Liquids', Appl. Opt., 4, 1965, p. 819.

56.   **Bryngdahl, O.,** 'Applications of Shearing Interferometry', Progress in Optics, Vol. 4, **E. Wolf ed.,** John Wiley, New York, 1965.

57.   **Chevalerias, R., Latron, Y., and Veret, C.,** 'Methods of Interferometry Applied to the Visualization of Flows in Wind Tunnels', J. Opt. Soc. Amer., 47, 1957, p. 703.

58.   **Grigull, U., and Rottenkolber, H.,** 'Two-Beam Interferometer Using a Laser', J. Opt. Soc. Amer., 57, 1967, p. 149.

59.   **Horman, M.H.,** 'An Application of Wavefront Reconstruction to Interferometry', Appl. Opt., 4, 1965, p. 333.

60.   **Heflinger, L.O., Wuerker, R.F., and Brooks, R.E.,** 'Holographic Interferometry', J. Appl. Phys., 37, 1966, p. 642.

61.   **Tanner, L.H.,** 'Some Applications of Holography in Fluid Mechanics', J. Sci. Inst., 43, 1966, p. 81.

62.   **Bryngdahl, O.,** 'Shearing Interferometry by Wavefront Reconstruction', J. Opt. Soc. of Amer., 58, 1968, p. 865.

63.   **Hildebrand, F.B.,** 'Methods of Applied Mathematics', 2nd Ed., Prentice Hall, Englewood, N.J., 1965, p. 276.

64.   **Kahl, G.D., and Mylin, D.C.,** 'Refractive Deviation Errors of Interferograms' J. Opt. Soc. Amer., 55, 1965, p. 364.

Nomenclature

A amplitude of light beam

A_1 amplitude of light beam from path 1

A_2 amplitude of light beam from path 2

A_o maximum of amplitude

$A_o 1$ maximum of amplitude of beam from path 1

$A_o 2$ maximum of amplitude of beam from path 2

A_T amplitude of recombined light beams from path 1 and 2

Δa deflection of light beam away from Schlieren knife edge

a_s, a_o, a_K dimension of Schlieren beam normal to knife edge at source, at knife edge, and above knife edge when no disturbance is present respectively.

b_o, b_s dimension of Schlieren beam parallel to knife edge at source and knife edge respectively.

C   Gladstone-Dale constant

c   speed of light

c_o speed of light in vacuum

D   diameter of cylinder and dimension in Nusselt number

d   fringe spacing

f   focal length of lens or mirror

h   heat transfer coefficient

I   light intensity

I_d illumination at screen of disturbed field when knife edge is present

I_K illumination at screen of undisturbed field when knife edge is present

I_o illumination at screen with no knife edge

I_T illumination at exit of test section (and at screen if no deflection) in shadow-graph system

K   knife edge

k   thermal conductivity

L   length of test section in light beam (z) direction

n   index of refraction

n_a index of refraction of air outside test section

n_o index of refraction at standard conditions

n_{ref} index of refraction in reference region

Δn $(n - n_{ref})$

Nu   Nusselt number

p   pressure and object distance from lens or mirror

PL   optical path length

$\overline{\Delta PL}$ difference in optical path length

q   image distance from lens or mirror

q_w wall heat flux

R   gas constant in terms of mass

r   radial position in axisymmetric field

r_o value of r such that at $r > r_o$ the index of refraction is that of the reference region

Ra   Rayleigh number, based on diameter for circular cylinder

S   source

Sc   screen

Sp   splitter plate

t   dummy variable used in equation 4-A-7.

T   temperature

T_{ref} temperature in reference region

T_∞ free stream temperature

x   direction normal to y and z

y   direction perpendicular to z and it is usually the direction in which the gradient of density and temperature lies

y_i height of light ray at entrance to test section

y_{sc} height of light ray at screen

$y_{sc\,max}$ maximum value of y_{sc}

y_T height of light ray at exit from test section

$\frac{\partial y}{\partial z})_T$ slope of light ray at exit of test section

z   direction along light beam

z_{sc} distance from test section to screen

Greek symbols

α angular deflection of light ray as measured in air outside test section and is same as α' if $n \approx n_a$

α_{max} maximum deflection angles that can be measured with Schlieren system
α_{max}'

α' angular deflections of light ray within test fluid; $\alpha' \cong \alpha$ if $n \approx n_a$ (i.e., if test fluid is gas)

α'' angle defined and used in Fig. 4-4

β angle defined and used in Fig. 4-4

γ angle defined and used in Fig. 4-4

δ boundary layer thickness

Δ phase difference

ϵ interferometer fringe shift, optical path length difference in vacuum wave lengths

θ angle between interferometer beams when recombined

λ wave length of light

λ_o vacuum wave length

λ_{sc} wave length at screen or when beams are recombined

$\Delta\lambda$ spectral width of light source

ρ density

ρ_o density at standard condition

ρ_{ref} density in reference region

σ dummy variable introduced into equation (4-A-5)

τ dummy variable used in equation 4-A-7

Subscript

w   refers to condition at the wall

Appendix

Interferogram Analysis of Axisymmetric Fields

Although the optical techniques described in this paper have found their widest use in two dimensional-rectangular coordinate systems they are also applicable to other geometries. In particular, interferograms of axisymmetric density or temperature distributions can be quantitatively evaluated using the Abel transformation (63).

Consider Fig. 4-28a which is a cross section of a field in which the index of refraction is a function only of r, and possibly position normal to the section (x), but not of the angular position. We shall only consider the field in this particular section (i.e. constant x). A light beam from an interferometer passes through the test region in the direction z. At radial positions greater than r_o the field is assumed to be uniform with an index of refraction of n_{ref}. This is no real limitation as we can make r_o as large as we want. Neglecting refraction [cf (64)] the fringe shift from the light ray at a particular position y is, from equation 4-55:

$$\epsilon \, (y) = \frac{1}{\lambda_o} \int_{-z_o}^{z_o} [n(r) - n_{ref}] \; dz \qquad \text{Eq. 4-A-1}$$

where the integration is carried out at constant y. The integration limits are functions of y but could with full generality be extended to $\pm \infty$. Since:

$$z = \sqrt{r^2 - y^2} \qquad \text{Eq. 4-A-2}$$

and at constant y:

$$dz = \frac{r \; dr}{\sqrt{r^2 - y^2}} \qquad \text{Eq. 4-A-3}$$

equation 4-A-1 can be written as:

$$\epsilon \, (y) = \frac{2}{\lambda_o} \int_{y}^{r_o} \frac{\Delta n(r) \, r \, dr}{\sqrt{r^2 - y^2}} \qquad \text{Eq. 4-A-4}$$

Multiplying both sides of equation 4-A-4 by:

$$\frac{y \; dy}{\sqrt{y^2 - \sigma^2}}$$

and integrating between σ and r_o:

$$\int_{\sigma}^{r_o} \frac{\epsilon \, (y) \, y \, dy}{\sqrt{y^2 - \sigma^2}} = \frac{2}{\lambda_o} \int_{\sigma}^{r_o} \left[\int_{y}^{r_o} \frac{\Delta n(r) \, r \, y \, dr}{\sqrt{y^2 - \sigma^2} \sqrt{r^2 - y^2}} \right] dy \qquad \text{Eq. 4-A-5}$$

Note that the integration on the right-hand side is first over r between y and γ_o and then over y between σ and r_o. This is shown in Fig. 4-28b where the integration is carried out over the whole shaded area by first integrating to obtain the horizontal element shown and then in the second integration (over y) to sweep out the finite area. Integration of the integrand over this same region can be performed as shown in Fig. 4-28c by first getting the vertical element (i.e. integrating over y between σ and r) and then over the whole area (a second integration over r between σ and r_o). Thus:

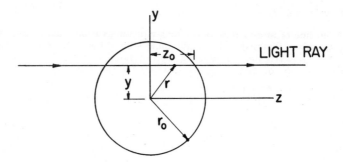

Fig. 4-28a Light beam passing through axisymmetric field

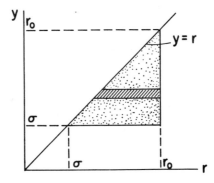

b Region of integration for equation 4-A-5

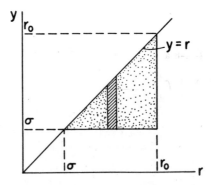

c Region of integration for equation 4-A-6

$$\int_{\sigma}^{r} \frac{\epsilon(y)\ y\ dy}{\sqrt{y^2 - \sigma^2}} = \frac{2}{\lambda_o} \int_{\sigma}^{r} \Delta n(r) \cdot r \left[\int_{\sigma}^{r} \frac{y\ dy}{\sqrt{y^2 - \sigma^2}\ \sqrt{r^2 - y^2}} \right] dr \qquad \text{Eq. 4-A-6}$$

The significance of this change in the order of integration can be observed by considering the inner integral on the right-hand side of equation 4-A-6. Let:

$$\tau = \frac{y^2 - \sigma^2}{r^2 - \sigma^2}$$

and since r and σ are constant over the inner integration:

$$d\tau = \frac{2y\ dy}{r^2 - \sigma^2}$$

Thus:

$$\int_{\sigma}^{r} \frac{y\ dy}{\sqrt{y^2 - \sigma^2}\ \sqrt{r^2 - y^2}} = \frac{1}{2} \int_{0}^{1} \frac{d\tau\ (r^2 - \sigma^2)}{\sqrt{y^2 - \sigma^2}\ \sqrt{r^2 - y^2}}$$

$$= \frac{1}{2} \int_{0}^{1} \frac{d\tau}{\sqrt{\tau\ (1 - t)}} \qquad \text{Eq. 4-A-7}$$

The right-hand side of equation 4-A-7 is in the form of a Beta function and is equal to $\frac{\pi}{2}$.

Equation 4-A-6 thus becomes:

$$\int_{\sigma}^{r_o} \frac{\epsilon(y)\ y\ dy}{\sqrt{y^2 - \sigma^2}} = \frac{\pi}{\lambda_o} \int_{\sigma}^{r_o} \Delta n(r)\ r\ dr \qquad \text{Eq. 4-A-8}$$

If the left hand side is integrated by parts:

$$\int_{\sigma}^{r_o} \frac{\epsilon(y)\ y\ dy}{\sqrt{y^2 - \sigma^2}} = \epsilon(y)\ \sqrt{y^2 - \sigma^2} \Bigg] \int_{\sigma}^{r_o} \sqrt{y^2 - \sigma^2}\ \frac{d\epsilon(y)}{dy}\ dy \qquad \text{Eq. 4-A-9}$$

$$= -\int_{\sigma}^{r_o} \sqrt{y^2 - \sigma^2}\ \frac{d\epsilon(y)}{dy}\ dy \qquad \text{Eq. 4-A-10}$$

since the first term on the right-hand of equation 4-A-9 is zero at both limits. Combining equations 4-A-8 and 4-A-10:

$$\int_{\sigma}^{r_o} \Delta n(r)\ r\ dr = -\frac{\lambda_o}{\pi} \int_{\sigma}^{r_o} \sqrt{y^2 - \sigma^2}\ \frac{d\epsilon(y)}{dy} \qquad \text{Eq. 4-A-11}$$

Differentiating both sides of Equation 4-A-11 with respect to σ^2,

$$-\frac{\Delta n(\sigma)}{2} = +\frac{\lambda_o}{2\pi} \int_{\sigma}^{r_o} \frac{\dfrac{d\epsilon(y)}{dy}}{\sqrt{y^2 - \sigma^2}}\ dy \qquad \text{Eq. 4-A-12}$$

or if σ is set equal to r,

$$\Delta n(r) = -\frac{\lambda_o}{\pi} \int_r^B \frac{\dfrac{d\epsilon(y)}{dy}}{\sqrt{y^2 - r^2}} \, dy \qquad\qquad \text{Eq. 4-A-13}$$

This equation can be used to evaluate interferograms of axisymmetric fields. It relates the measured fringe shift, really its derivative, which is a function of y to the desired index of refraction which is a function of the radial position r. In practice the measured $\epsilon(y)$ can be represented by best-fit least-square polynomials. This representation and the required differentiation and integration can be easily done on a high speed computer to yield $n(r)$ and from this the density or temperature distribution. Since the original presentation of this material a convenient method for interferometric analysis of axisymmetric fields has appeared (65).

5

Spectroscopic Temperature Determination in High Temperature Gases

E. PFENDER
University of Minnesota, Minneapolis, U. S. A.

Summary

In the first part of this survey the various physical laws and definitions of gaseous radiation are reviewed including the different types of radiation which are emitted by a high temperature gas. The second part contains a discussion of the most important direct and indirect spectrometric methods which have been developed for temperature measurements of emitting-absorbing high temperature gases.

Introduction

For a description of the heat transfer situation in a medium or between adjoining media, the temperature or enthalpy field must be known. Temperature and heat flux measurements at moderate temperature levels are thoroughly covered in the other review papers. In this review, techniques will be discussed which are suitable for temperature measurements at very high temperature levels at which matter is in a gaseous, more or less ionized state. The term plasma has been adopted to describe such gases, and this paper will survey the most important spectrometric methods which have been suggested for the determination of temperatures in plasmas.

The upper limit of temperatures considered in this survey will be approximately $30 \times 10^3 °K$ which corresponds to the maximum temperatures experienced in present engineering applications, as for example, in plasma propulsion devices, in arc or high frequency gas heaters and in plasma torches for welding, cutting and spraying. The lower temperature limit is in the order of $10^4 °K$. Such temperatures are of importance for molecular radiation and spectrometric methods have been developed to determine temperatures in this range and at least one of them will be included in this report.

Another limitation in this survey is imposed by the pressure of the high temperature plasma. In general, such plasmas represent multi-component mixtures (molecules, atoms, ions, electrons) in which numerous chemical reactions may occur. A single temperature concept of this mixture is meaningful only when thermodynamic (TE) or local thermodynamic equilibrium (LTE) prevails. Otherwise the various components may have different temperatures and the possible chemical reactions can no longer be described by an equilibrium temperature. One of the decisive parameters which determines whether or not LTE may be expected is the pressure, as low pressure plasmas of laboratory dimensions frequently show strong deviations from LTE, whereas high temperature plasmas at atmospheric or higher pressures approach a state of LTE. Since the majority of the spectrometric temperature measurement techniques are based on the existence of LTE, the discussion will be essentially restricted to these situations.

Spectrometric methods offer two important advantages compared with methods which use probes or thermocouples for sensing the temperature. Since radiation emitted by the plasma is used for the temperature evaluation, the diagnostic tool may be in a remote location relative to the plasma and does not have any influence on the plasma, in that it does not alter the quantity to be measured and the method provides an excellent spatial resolution of the measured temperature field. In general, gaseous radiation sources do not have a uniform temperature distribution but in many cases of practical interest, however, such sources display rotational symmetry. In such cases, conversion of the observed side-on radiation intensities into local intensities is a straight-forward procedure.

The first part of this review will be devoted to a discussion of the important laws and concepts in gaseous radiation. Since most of the spectrometric methods to be discussed in this review are based on the existence of TE or LTE in the plasma, the second part will review the conditions which are favorable for this situation. In the next part the various types of radiation which are emitted by a plasma, and which are crucial for the development of spectroscopic methods are considered. Finally, in the last section the most important spectroscopic methods will be discussed, those which have been adopted for diagnostic purposes in high temperature gases. References to specific research papers will not be included in this review because they may be found in texts, proceedings of symposiums and/or special review articles (1 - 15). This survey covers only the methods which are well known today in high temperature spectroscopy; it does not include spectrometers and the associated hardware.

Basic Concepts of Gaseous Radiation

In this section the most important general definitions and laws which govern radiation in a gaseous medium will be reviewed. When electromagnetic radiation passes through a medium with varying index of refraction, the wavelength λ as well as the propagation velocity c of the wave vary with the index of refraction. As the frequency $\nu = c/\lambda$ does not depend on the particular properties of the medium, it will be used as a wave parameter in this review, although the index of refraction in gases is usually close to unity.

Intensity and density of gaseous radiation

The monochromatic radiation intensity I_ν is defined as the amount of radiant energy $\Delta\chi$ which passes per unit time Δt through an area element Δa which is perpendicular to the direction of a radiation pencil of solid angle $\Delta\omega$. This definition includes only radiation which is emitted in a frequency interval from ν to $\nu + \Delta\nu$. Writing this definition as a formula yields:

$$I_\nu = \frac{\Delta\chi}{\Delta t \Delta a \Delta\omega \Delta\nu} \quad \left(\frac{\text{Joule}}{\text{sterad cm}^2} \right) \qquad \text{(Eq. 5-1)}$$

The unit solid angle is measured in steradians (sterad). The total radiation intensity, I, is obtained by integrating over the entire spectrum:

$$I = \int_0^\infty I_\nu d\nu \left(\frac{\text{Watt}}{\text{sterad cm}^2} \right) \qquad \text{(Eq. 5-2)}$$

The dimension of monochromatic and total radiation intensity is, of course, not the same.

The nomochromatic radiation density, u_ν, is defined as the amount of monochromatic radiant energy, $\Delta\chi$, contained in a volume element ΔV:

$$u_\nu = \frac{\Delta\chi}{\Delta V \Delta\nu} \quad \left(\frac{\text{Joule sec}}{\text{cm}^3}\right) \qquad \text{(Eq. 5-3)}$$

This radiation density is connected with the radiation intensity through the relation:

$$u_\nu = \frac{1}{c} \int_\omega I_\nu d\omega \qquad \text{(Eq. 5-4)}$$

or for isotropic radiation:

$$u_\nu = \frac{4\pi}{c} I_\nu$$

The total radiation density is then:

$$u = \int_o^\infty u_\nu d\nu \quad \left(\frac{\text{Joule}}{\text{cm}^3}\right) \qquad \text{(Eq. 5-5)}$$

Emission and absorption in gases

The monochromatic radiant energy, $\Delta\chi$, which is emitted by a volume element ΔV into a solid angle $\Delta\omega$ per unit time Δt is termed the emission coefficient, ϵ_ν:

$$\epsilon_\nu = \frac{\Delta\chi}{\Delta\nu\Delta V\Delta\omega\Delta t} \quad \left(\frac{\text{Joule}}{\text{sterad cm}^3}\right) \qquad \text{(Eq. 5-6)}$$

ϵ_ν, as it stands here, shall describe spontaneous emission only. The total radiation flux stemming from the volume element ΔV may be expressed as:

$$\phi = \Delta V \int_o^\infty \int_\omega \epsilon_\nu d\nu d\omega \quad \text{(Watt)} \qquad \text{(Eq. 5-7)}$$

For isotropic radiation:

$$\phi = 4\pi \Delta V \int_o^\infty \epsilon_\nu d\nu$$

Intensity loss by absorption - if monochromatic radiation of intensity I_ν passes in the normal direction through an absorbing gaseous slab of thickness $d\ell$, an attenuation of the initial radiation intensity occurs, according to:

$$dI_\nu = -\kappa_\nu' I_\nu d\ell \qquad \text{(Eq. 5-8)}$$

where κ_ν' (cm^{-1}) represents the monochromatic absorption coefficient. This absorption coefficient is in general a function of the state and the properties of the gas, of the radiation frequency, and of the direction in which the radiation propagates. Besides the usual volume absorption coefficient, the mass absorption coefficient $\kappa_{\nu_m}' = 1/\rho \; \kappa_\nu'$ is sometimes used where ρ represents the mass density of the gas.

If I_{ν_t} is the radiation intensity entering a gaseous layer of finite thickness L, integration of equation 5-8 yields:

$$I_\nu = I_{\nu, o} \exp \left(-\int_o^L \kappa'_\nu d\ell \right) \qquad \text{(Eq. 5-9)}$$

$$= I_{\nu, o} \exp \left(- \tau_\nu \right)$$

where $\tau_\nu = \int_o^L \kappa'_\nu d\ell$ represents the optical depth of the layer. For the special case of a homogeneous gas with uniform temperature distribution, the optical depth becomes $\tau_\nu = \kappa'_\nu L$.

An analogous derivation for the attenuation of radiation by scattering yields:

$$I_\nu = I_{\nu, o} \exp \left(- \int_o^L \gamma_\nu d\ell \right) \qquad \text{(Eq. 5-10)}$$

with γ_ν as the monochromatic scattering coefficient which like the absorption coefficient is a function of the state and the properties of the gas, of the radiation frequency, and sometimes also of the direction in which the radiation travels.

The similarity of equations 5-9 and 5-10 permits a description of radiation attenuation due both to absorption and scattering with $\beta_\nu = \kappa'_\nu + \gamma_\nu$ as the monochromatic extinction coefficient.

Radiation in perfect thermodynamic equilibrium

The conditions under which an emitting-absorbing gas is in a state of thermodynamic equilibrium (TE) or local thermodynamic equilibrium (LTE) will be discussed in the next paragraph. In this section a radiation field in a gaseous medium will be considered which is in equilibrium with its boundaries (cavity radiation). Such a radiation field is isotropic with a blackbody radiation intensity, B_ν, corresponding to an equilibrium temperature T. In such a system Kirchhoff's law, connecting the emission and absorption coefficient with the intensity of the radiation field, may be applied, viz:

$$\frac{\epsilon'_\nu}{\kappa'_\nu} = B_\nu \qquad \text{(Eq. 5-11)}$$

ϵ'_ν is a modified emission coefficient which includes the contribution of induced or forced emission. This emission coefficient is always larger than that for spontaneous emission, as can be readily seen from the Einstein relation:

$$\epsilon'_\nu = \frac{\epsilon_\nu}{1-e^{-h\nu/kT}} \qquad \text{(Eq. 5-12)}$$

In this equation h is Planck's and k is Boltzmann's constant. T is the equilibrium temperature. The blackbody radiation intensity B_ν may be expressed by the Planck function:

$$B_\nu = \frac{2h\nu^3}{c^2} \frac{1}{e^{h\nu/kT}-1} \qquad \text{(Eq. 5-13)}$$

and the radiation density of blackbody radiation assumes the value:

$$u_\nu = \frac{8\pi h\nu^3}{c^3} \frac{1}{e^{h\nu/kT}-1} \qquad \text{(Eq. 5-14)}$$

By adding the emission term, ϵ'_ν, to equation 5-8 and retaining the assumptions under which it has been derived, the radiation transport equation for an emitting-absorbing medium becomes:

$$\frac{dI_\nu}{d\ell} = \epsilon'_\nu - \kappa'_\nu I_\nu = \kappa'_\nu(B_\nu - I_\nu) \tag{Eq. 5-15}$$

Integration of equation 5-15 for a layer of finite thickness L with the boundary condition $I_\nu = 0$ for $L = 0$ yields:

$$I_\nu = B_\nu(1 - e^{-\kappa'_\nu L}) \tag{Eq. 5-16}$$

From this relation it follows for an optically thin medium $(K'_\nu L \ll I)$

$$I_\nu = \kappa'_\nu L B_\nu \tag{Eq. 5-17}$$

By applying Kirchhoff's law (Eq. 5-11) Equation 5-17 becomes:

$$I_\nu = \epsilon'_\nu L \tag{Eq. 5-18}$$

which states that the radiation intensity of an optically thin layer increases proportionally with the layer thickness. Without the contribution of induced emission equation 5-18 reads:

$$I_\nu = \epsilon_\nu L \tag{Eq. 5-19}$$

For large optical depths $(\kappa'_\nu L \gg 1)$ follows from equation 5-16 :

$$I_\nu = B_\nu$$

i.e., the highest possible radiation intensity which a high temperature gas is able to emit is the blackbody radiation of its own equilibrium temperature.

Temperature definitions

High temperature, high density gases are able to emit spectra in which continuous radiation predominates. The various radiation mechanisms which contribute to these spectra will be discussed in the next section under, 'Radiation Emitted by a High Temperature Plasma'. The nature of a predominantly continuous spectrum suggests a comparison with the spectrum of a blackbody radiator. Depending on the basis of such a comparison, different temperature definitions of gaseous radiation sources have been suggested.

Color temperature - the observed intensity distribution of a gaseous radiator is matched on a relative scale with that of a blackbody radiator over a frequency interval from ν_1 to ν_2. The temperature of the blackbody radiator is then identified with the color temperature of the gaseous radiator in the specified frequency interval. By shrinking the frequency interval to a single value $\bar{\nu}$ the slopes $(dI_\nu/d\nu)_{\bar{\nu}}$ of the two distributions have to be matched resulting in a definition of the color temperature for a single frequency $\bar{\nu}$.

Radiation temperature ('black temperature') - the same comparison as above, based on absolute intensities, results in the definition of the radiation temperature or 'black temperature' of the radiation source in the specified frequency interval. Again, shrinking of the frequency interval to a single frequency $\bar{\nu}$ and matching of the two absolute intensity distributions at this frequency determines the radiation temperature of the gaseous radiation at $\bar{\nu}$.

Effective temperature - a comparison of the gaseous radiator with a blackbody radiator based on the total emissive power leads to the definition of an effective temperature.

These temperature definitions, which are in use in the literature, are based on descriptions of the measurements. No specific physical meaning can be attached to them. The color temperature, for example, may be higher or lower than the corresponding LTE gas temperature whereas the effective and radiation temperature are always lower than the LTE temperature of the gaseous radiator.

Einstein's transition probabilities

The knowledge of the energies which are involved in an emission or absorption process is not sufficient to predict the intensity of the emitted or absorbed radiation. In addition, we need to know the number of radiation processes per time and volume unit. The latter is given by the number density of particles participating in the radiation process, whereas the rate of the radiation process is governed by the transition probabilities. In this paragraph transition probabilities for spontaneous and induced emission as well as those for absorption will be discussed along with the relationships among them.

Spontaneous emission - an excited atom in a higher quantum states may return to a lower energy state t by giving off a photon of energy $h\nu$ according to Bohr's frequency relation:

$$X_s - X_t = h\nu \qquad \text{(Eq. 5-20)}$$

This equation refers to an energy jump within a neutral atom. A similar jump may occur in an r-times ionized atom as long as $r \leq Z-1$, where Z is the number of protons in the nucleus. Equation 5-20 may be rewritten for this more general case as:

$$X_{r,s} - X_{r,t} = h\nu \qquad \text{(Eq. 5-20a)}$$

With $n_{r,s}$ r-times ionized atoms per cm^3 in an excited state s, the number of quantum transitions per sec and cm^3 becomes:

$$A_{r,t}^{r,s} \, n_{r,s} \qquad \text{(Eq. 5-21)}$$

$A_{r,t}^{r,s}$ is the transition probability for spontaneous transition in an r-times ionized atom from a higher energy state s to a lower state t.

Induced or forced emission - an ionized gas imbedded in a radiation field of density u_ν may also radiate by induced emission. In the elementary process of induced emission a photon of frequency ν interacting with an excited ion in a higher quantum state will force this ion to emit a photon of the same frequency and in the same direction as the oncoming photon. The number of such transitions per sec and cm^3 is given by:

$$B_{r,t}^{r,s} \, n_{r,s} \, u_\nu \qquad \text{(Eq. 5-22)}$$

Note that the dimension of the transition probability for induced emission, $B_{r,t}^{r,s}$, is $cm^3/Joule\ sec^2$ whereas the dimension for the transition probability of spontaneous emission, $A_{r,t}^{r,s}$, is sec^{-1}.

Absorption - in the case of absorption, transitions occur within an r-times ionized atom from a lower quantum state t to a higher quantum state s. If $n_{r,t}$ is the number density of r-times ionized atoms in the quantum state t, the number of absorption processes for photons of frequency ν per sec and cm^3 is given by:

$$B_{r,s}^{r,t} \; n_{r,t} \; u_\nu \qquad\qquad (\text{Eq. 5-23})$$

with $B_{r,s}^{r,t}$ as the transition probability for an r-times ionized atom from a lower quantum state t to a higher quantum state s.

If an ionized gas is in a state of perfect thermodynamic equilibrium, a balance of the radiation process must exist, in other words, the number of processes s→t per sec and cm^3 must be equal to the number of opposite processes t→s. From equations 5-21 5-22 and 5-23 it follows for this balance:

$$A_{r,t}^{r,s} \; n_{r,s} \; + \; B_{r,t}^{r,s} \; n_{r,s} \; u_\nu \; = \; B_{r,s}^{r,t} \; n_{r,t} \; u_\nu \qquad\qquad (\text{Eq. 5-24})$$

In addition, TE requires that the excited states follow a Boltzmann distribution:

$$\frac{n_{r,s}}{n_{r,t}} = \frac{g_{r,s}}{g_{r,t}} \exp \frac{-(\chi_{r,s} - \chi_{r,t})}{kT} = \frac{g_{r,s}}{g_{r,t}} \exp \left[\frac{-h\nu}{kT} \right] \quad (\text{Eq. 5-25})$$

The symbols $g_{r,s}$ and $g_{r,t}$ represent the statistical weights of the energy states s and t, respectively.

Replacing $n_{r,s}/n_{r,t}$ in equation 5-24 with equation 5-25 and solving for u_ν yields:

$$u_\nu = \frac{A_{r,t}^{r,s}}{\frac{g_{r,s}}{g_{r,t}} B_{r,s}^{r,t} e^{h\nu/kT} - B_{r,t}^{r,s}} \qquad\qquad (\text{Eq. 5-26})$$

Since TE requires also that the radiation density is that of blackbody radiation, a comparison of equations 5-14 and 5-26 establishes the following relationships between the transition probabilities:

$$B_{r,t}^{r,s} \; g_{r,t} = B_{r,s}^{r,t} \; g_{r,s} \qquad\qquad (\text{Eq. 5-27})$$

$$A_{r,t}^{r,s} = B_{r,t}^{r,s} \; \frac{8\pi h\nu^3}{c^3}$$

If, for example, $A_{r,t}^{r,s}$ is known, the other two transition probabilities can be calculated from equation 5-27.

Radiation from a non-homogeneous layer (Abel inversion)

The radiation transport equation (see Eq. 5-15) may be integrated in closed form for a homogeneous emitting-absorbing layer of uniform temperature. Equation 5-15 may still be applied for radiation emitted from a non-homogeneous source of varying temperature, but the integration of this equation is now much more complex because κ'_ν as well as B_ν are functions of the temperature and therefore, of the position in the source.

An optically thin, rotationally symmetric plasma source is of interest, since it is obtained in the laboratory as well as in numerous applications. From such a source, the side-on radiation intensity of a spectral line, $I_L(x)$, includes contributions from layers having different emission coefficients, $\epsilon_L(r)$ (see Fig. 5-1).

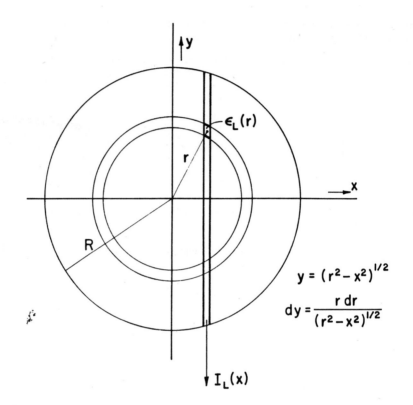

$$I_L(x) = 2\int_0^{(R^2-x^2)^{1/2}} \epsilon_L(r)\,dy = 2\int_{r=x}^{R} \epsilon_L(r)\frac{r\,dr}{(r^2-x^2)^{1/2}}$$

OBSERVED SIDE-ON INTENSITY:

ABEL INVERSION:

$$\epsilon_L(r) = -\frac{1}{\pi}\int_r^R \frac{I_L'(x)}{(x^2-r^2)^{1/2}}\,dx$$

Fig. 5-1   Abel inversion for a rotationally symmetric, optically thin source

$$I_L(x) = 2\int_0^y \epsilon_L(r)\, dy$$

$$= 2\int_{r=x}^R \epsilon_L(r)\frac{r\,dr}{(r^2-x^2)^{\frac{1}{2}}} \qquad (\text{Eq. } 5\text{-}28)$$

The solution of the Abel integral equation (Eq. 5-28) is given by:

$$\epsilon_L(r) = -\frac{1}{\pi}\int_r^R \frac{dI_L/dx}{(x^2-r^2)^{\frac{1}{2}}} \qquad (\text{Eq. } 5\text{-}29)$$

The experimentally determined distribution $I_L(x)$ may be approximated by poly-nomials in order to solve for $\epsilon_L(r)$. Frequently, equation 5-28 is solved numer-ically by using a finite difference approach adaptable to a digital computer.

Thermodynamic State of a High Temperature Plasma

Since most of the spectrometric methods to be discussed in the last section of this review are based on the assumption of TE or LTE, the main requirements imposed by these concepts will be included in this survey. A more comprehensive treat-ment of this subject may be found in the literature (1), (3), (4) and (5). As already mentioned in the introduction, emphasis will be on high temperature plasmas which do not contain molecular species, i.e., the temperature level is either so high that molecules are completely dissociated, or the plasma is generated from an atomic gas.

High temperature plasmas in perfect thermodynamic equilibrium (TE)

Thermodynamic equilibrium prevails in a uniform, homogeneous plasma volume if kinetic and chemical equilibria as well as every conceivable plasma property are unambiguous functions of the temperature. In turn, the temperature is the same for all plasma constituents and their possible reactions. More specifically, the following conditions must be met:

a)   The velocity distribution functions for particles of every species r which exist in the plasma, including the electrons, follow a Maxwell-Boltzmann distribution:

$$f(v_r) = \frac{4v_r^2}{\sqrt{\pi}\ (\frac{2kT}{m_r})^{3/2}}\ \exp\left(-\frac{m_r v_r^2}{2kT}\right) \qquad (\text{Eq. } 5\text{-}30)$$

v_r is the velocity of particles of species r, m_r is their mass, and T is their temp-erature, which is the same for every species r, and which is, in particular, iden-tical to the plasma temperature.

b)   The population density of the excited states of every species r follows a Boltzmann distribution:

$$n_{r,s} = n_r\ \frac{g_{r,s}}{Z_r}\ \exp\left(-\chi_{r,s}/kT\right) \qquad (\text{Eq. } 5\text{-}31)$$

n_r is the total number density of ions of species r, Z_r is their partition function, and $\chi_{r,s}$ is the energy of the sth quantum state. the excitation temperature T which appears explicitly in the exponential term and implicitly in the partition function Z_r is identical to the plasma temperature.

c)   The particle densities (neutrals, electrons, ions) are described by the Saha-Eggert equation which may be considered as a mass action law:

$$\frac{n_{r+1} n_e}{n_r} = \frac{2 Z_{r+1}}{Z_r} \frac{(2\pi m_e kT)^{3/2}}{h^3} \exp\left(-\chi_{r+1}/kT\right) \qquad \text{(Eq. 5-32)}$$

χ_{r+1} represents the energy which is required to produce an $(r+1)$ times ionized atom from an r-times ionized atom.   The ionization temperature T in this equation is identical to the plasma temperature.

d)   The electromagnetic radiation field is that of blackbody radiation of the intensity B_ν as described by the Planck function (see Eq. 5-13):

$$B_\nu = \frac{2h\nu^3}{c^2} \frac{1}{e^{h\nu/kT} - 1} \qquad \text{(Eq. 5-33)}$$

The temperature of this blackbody radiation is again identical to the plasma temperature.

In order to generate a plasma which follows this ideal model as described by equations 5-30 to 5-33, the plasma would have to dwell in a hypothetical cavity whose walls are kept at the plasma temperature, or the plasma volume would have to be so large that the central part of this volume, in which TE prevails, would not sense the plasma boundaries.   In this way the plasma would be penetrated by a blackbody radiation of its own temperature.   An actual plasma will, of course, deviate from these ideal conditions.   The observed plasma radiation, for example, will be much less than the blackbody radiation because most plasmas are optically thin over a wide wavelength range.   Therefore, the radiation temperature as de-fined earlier of a gaseous radiator deviates appreciably from the kinetic tempera-ture of the plasma constituents, or the already mentioned excitation and ionization temperatures.   In addition to radiation losses, plasmas suffer irreversible energy losses by conduction, convection and diffusion which also disturb the thermodynamic equilibrium.   Thus, laboratory plasmas as well as some of the natural plasmas cannot be in a perfect TE state.   In the following parts, deviations from TE and their significance will be discussed.

The Concept of Local Thermal Equilibrium (LTE)

Since an actual plasma does not exhibit a uniform distribution of its properties (for example, in temperature and density), equilibrium considerations can only be applied locally.   For this reason the concept of local thermodynamic (or thermal) equilibrium was introduced.   This is, in addition, less restrictive than the perfect thermodynamic equilibrium concept as LTE does not require a radiation field which corresponds to the blackbody radiation intensity of the respective LTE tempera-ture.   It does require, however, that collision processes and not radiative pro-cesses govern transitions and reactions in the plasma and that there is a micro-reversibility among the collision processes.   In other words, a detailed equili-brium of each collision process with its reverse process is necessary.   Steady state solutions of the respective collision rate equations will then yield the same energy distribution pertaining to a system in complete thermal equilibrium with the exception of the rarefied radiation field.   LTE further requires that local gradients of the plasma properties (temperature, density, heat conductivity, etc.) are suffi-ciently small .   This is so that a given particle which diffuses from one location to another in the plasma finds sufficient time to equilibrate, i.e., the diffusion time should be of the same order of magnitude or larger than the equilibration time. From the equilibration time and the particle velocities an equilibration length may be derived which is smaller in regions of small plasma property gradients (for example in the center of an electric arc). Therefore, with regard to spatial variations LTE is more probable in such regions. Heavy particle diffusion and resonance radiation from the center of a non-uniform plasma source help to reduce the effective equilibrium distance in the outskirts of the source.

In the following, a systematic discussion of the important assumptions for LTE will be undertaken, based on laboratory-generated plasmas. In practice, the electric arc appears as a simple and convenient method to generate a high temperature, high density plasma.

Kinetic Equilibrium - it may be safely assumed that each species (electron gas, ion gas, neutral gas) in a dense, high temperature plasma will assume a Maxwellian distribution. However, the temperatures defined by these Maxwellian distributions may be different from species to species. Such a situation, which leads to a two temperature description, will be discussed for an arc plasma.

The electric energy fed into an arc is dissipated in the following way. The electrons, according to their high mobility, pick up energy from the electric field which they partially transfer by collisions to the heavy plasma constituents. Because of this continuous energy flux from the electrons to the heavy particles, there must be a temperature gradient between these two species, so that $T_e > T_a$. T_e is the electron temperature and T_a the temperature of the heavy species, assuming that ion and neutral gas temperatures are the same.

In the two-fluid model of a plasma defined in this manner, two distinct temperatures T_e and T_a deviate from each other will depend on the thermal coupling between the two species. The difference between these two temperatures can be expressed by the following relation (1):

$$\frac{T_e - T_a}{T_e} = \frac{m_a}{8m_e} \frac{(\lambda_e eE)^2}{(3/2kT_e)^2} \qquad \text{(Eq. 5-34)}$$

m_a is the mass of the heavy plasma constituents, λ_e the mean free path length of the electrons, and E the electric field intensity. Since the mass ratio $m_a/8m_e$ is already about 230 for hydrogen, the amount of (directed) energy $(\lambda_e eE)$ which the electrons pick up along one mean free path length has to be very small compared with the average thermal (random) energy $3/2kT_e$ of the electrons. Low field intensities, high pressures $(\lambda_e \sim 1/p)$ and high temperature levels are favorable for a kinetic equilibrium among the plasma constituents. For example, at low pressures, appreciable deviations from kinetic equilibrium may occur. Figure 5-2 shows in a semi-schematic diagram how electron and gas temperatures separate in an electric arc with decreasing pressure. For atmospheric argon high intensity arc with E = 13V/cm, $\lambda_e = 3\times10^{-4}$cm, $m_A/m_e = 7\times10^4$ and $T_e = 30\times10^3$K, the deviation between T_e and T_a is only 2%(1).

Excitation Equilibrium - in order to determine the excitation equilibrium, every conceivable process which may lead to excitation or de-excitation has to be considered. This discussion is restricted to the most prominent mechanisms which are collisional and radiative excitation and de-excitation.

Excitation
(a)   electron collision
(b)   photo absorption

De-excitation
(a)   collision of the 2nd kind
(b)   photo emission

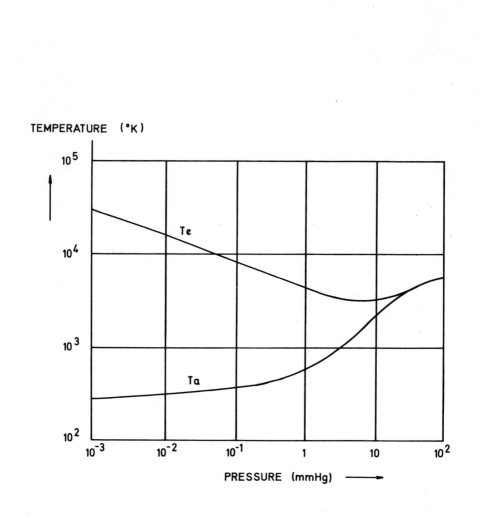

Fig. 5-2   Electron and gas kinetic temperatures in an arc-generated plasma

For the case of TE, micro-reversibilities have to exist for all processes, i.e., in the above scheme, excitation by electron collisions will be balanced by collisions of the 2nd kind, the reverse process. Also, excitation by the photo absorption process will be balanced by photo emission processes which include spontaneous and induced emission. Furthermore, the population of excited states is given by a Boltzmann distribution (see Eq. 5-31). The micro-reversibility for the radiative processes holds only if the radiation field in the plasma reaches the intensity B_ν of blackbody radiation. However, actual plasmas are frequently optically thin over most of the spectral range, so that the situation for excitation equilibrium seems to be hopeless. Fortunately, if collisional processes dominate, photo absorption and emission processes do not have to balance. Only the sum on the left-hand side and the right-hand side of the scheme above have to be equal. Since the contribution of the photo processes to the number of excited atoms is almost negligible when collisional processes dominate, the excitation process is still close to LTE.

Ionization Equilibrium - for the ionization equilibrium again only the most prominent mechanisms which lead to ionization and recombination will be considered:

Ionization   Recombination

(a) electron collision   (a) three body recombination
(b) photo absorption   (b) photo recombination

In a perfect thermodynamic equilibrium state with cavity radiation, a micro-reversibility among the collisional and radiative processes would exist and the particle densities would be described by the Saha-Eggert equation. Without cavity radiation, the number of photo ionizations is almost negligible requiring instead of the micro-reversibility, a total balance of all processes involved. Photo recombinations are not negligible, especially at lower electron densities. The frequency of the three remaining elementary processes is a function only of the electron density leading, for $n_e = 7 \times 10^{15} \text{cm}^{-3}$, to the same order of magnitude frequency of these elementary processes. The result is an appreciable deviation between actual and predicted values (Eq. 5-32) of the electron densities. Only for values $n_e > 7 \times 10^{15} \text{cm}^{-3}$ does the Saha-Eggert equation predict correct values. For smaller electron densities the Corona formula has to be used, which considers ionization by electron impact and photo recombination only:

$$\frac{n_e}{n_o} = \frac{\sqrt{27}}{16\alpha^3} \frac{\zeta_n}{n} \frac{\chi_{i,H}^2}{\chi_i^3} \frac{kT}{g} \exp(-\chi_i/kT) \qquad \text{(Eq. 5-35)}$$

In this equation α is Sommerfeld's fine structure constant, ζ_n the number of valence electrons, n the principal quantum number of the valence shell, $\chi_{i,H}$ the ionization energy of hydrogen and g a constant with a value between 1.4 and 4. The particle concentrations in low density arcs at atmospheric pressure, for example, have to be calculated with this formula. Significant deviation of the electron density predicted by the Saha equation from the true electron density may also occur in the fringes of high intensity arcs and plasma jets.

In summary, it has been found that LTE exists in a steady state optically thin plasma when the following conditions are simultaneously fulfilled:

(a) The different species which form the plasma have a Maxwellian distribution.

(b) Electric field effects are small enough, and the pressure and the temperature are high enough to make $T_e = T_a$.

(c) Collisions are the dominating mechanism for excitation (Boltzmann distribution) and ionization (Saha-Eggert equation).

**RATIO OF IONIZATION AND
RECOMBINATION COEFFICIENT (S/a)**

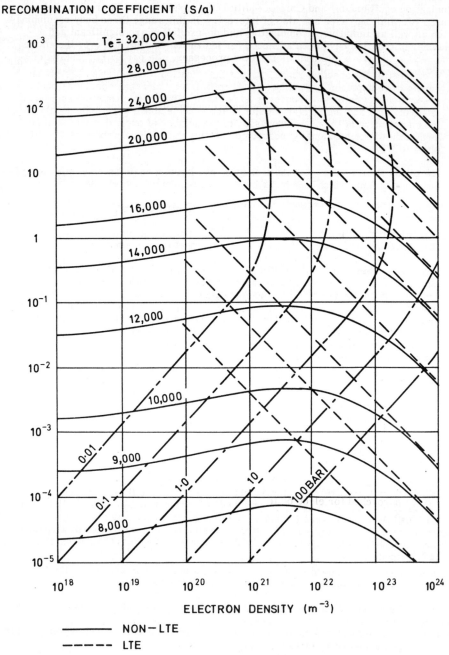

Fig. 5-3   State diagram for hydrogen in LTE and non-LTE

(d)   Spatial variations of the plasma properties are sufficiently small.

Besides the conditions for the two extreme cases, namely LTE (based on Saha ionization equilibrium) and Corona equilibrium, conditions in the regions between these two limiting cases are also of interest.   In this range three body recombination as well as radiative recombination and de-excitation are significant and a number of theories have been advanced for ionization equilibrium over the entire range of radiative-collisional elementary processes.   In particular, detailed calculations of optically thin and optically thick hydrogen plasmas have been reported. Some results of these calculations follow for the optically thin case.

If α is the combined collisional-radiative recombination coefficient and S the corresponding ionization coefficient, rate equations may be established which describe the effective rate of population and depopulation.   The rate of population of the ground state is described by:

$$\left(\frac{d\, n_{o,\,o}}{dt} \right)_{pop.} = \alpha\, n_e n_1 \tag{Eq. 5-36}$$

In this relation, $n_{o,\,o}$ represents the number of neutral hydrogen atoms in the ground state and n_e and n_1 are the electron and ion densities, respectively.   The rate of depopulation of the ground state is given by:

$$\left(\frac{d\, n_{o,o}}{dt} \right)_{depop.} = -S\, n_e n_{o,o} \tag{Eq. 5-37}$$

Under steady state conditions:

$$\left(\frac{d\, n_{o,o}}{dt} \right)_{pop} + \left(\frac{d\, n_{o,o}}{dt} \right)_{depop.} = 0 \tag{Eq. 5-38}$$

$$\text{or } \frac{S}{\alpha} = \frac{n_1}{n_{o,o}} = \frac{n_e}{n_{o,o}} \tag{Eq. 5-39}$$

Figure 5-3 shows a state diagram for values of S/α as a function of the electron density with pressure and electron temperatures as parameters.   At high electron densities ($\geqslant 10^{24} m^{-3}$) pairs of LTE and non-LTE curves plotted for the same electron temperature merge.   At low electron densities ($\leqslant 10^{21} m^{-3}$) the non-LTE curves merge into curves valid for Corona equilibrium.   The divergence of the non-LTE curves from the LTE curves at lower pressures and/or lower electron temperatures and densities shows how large the deviation from LTE may become in such parameter ranges.   Taking values for 1 atm. it can be seen that LTE is closely approached for electron temperatures in the interval $14,000 < T_e < 28,000°(K)$.

Deviations of this kind from LTE may be found, for example, in plasma regions adjacent to walls where the electron density drops appreciably, and in all types of low density plasmas of laboratory dimensions.   Well known examples of the latter are the positive column of glow discharges and the plasma generated in fluorescent lamps.

Radiation Emitted by a High Temperature Gas

In this section the different types of radiation which may be emitted by a plasma will be discussed with emphasis on the emission from plasmas which contain only atoms as the neutral component.

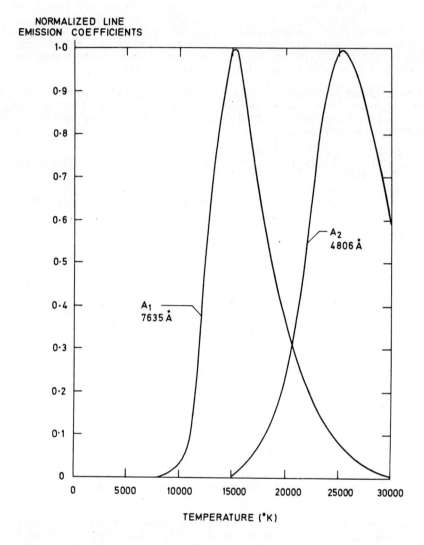

NORMALIZED LINE
EMISSION COEFFICIENTS

A_1
7635 Å

A_2
4806 Å

TEMPERATURE (°K)

Fig. 5-4   Relative emission coefficients of two argon lines

The pressure in the plasma shall be sufficiently high (>.1 atm), to make LTE feasible.

An analysis of the total emitted radiation of a plasma reveals a number of different radiation mechanisms. Their relative importance is a function of temperature and pressure and, in magnetized plasmas, also of the magnetic field. From a theoretical point of view, this radiation is useful for diagnostic purposes if its origin and temperature dependence is known. The experiment requires, in addition, that there is sufficient intensity of the spectrally resolved radiation and that this radiation is sensitive to temperature changes.

Line radiation (bound-bound transitions)

Excited neutral atoms or ions may return to the ground state in one or several steps. Because of the discrete nature of bound energy states the emitted radiation appears as spectral lines according to equations 5-20 and 5-20a. By combining equations 5-20a and 5-21 the line emission coefficient for an optically thin homogeneous plasma is found to be:

$$\epsilon_L = \frac{1}{4\pi} A_{r,t}^{r,s} n_{r,s} h\nu \qquad \text{(Eq. 5-40)}$$

The factor $\frac{1}{4\pi}$ represents the unit solid angle. Therefore, the dimension of the line emission coefficient is Watt/sterad cm^3. The line emission coefficient is already integrated over the natural width Δx of a spectral line:

$$\epsilon_L = \int_{\Delta x} \epsilon_\nu d\nu$$

ϵ_ν is the monochromatic emission coefficient (see Eq. 5-6). For the following considerations, it will be assumed that LTE prevails in the plasma, i.e. the number density of excited atoms or ions may be expressed by a Boltzmann distribution (see Eq. 5-31). Replacing $n_{r,s}$ in equation 5-40 by this Boltzmann distribution yields:

$$\epsilon_L = \frac{1}{4\pi} A_{r,t}^{r,s} n_r \frac{g_{r,s}}{Z_r} \exp(-\chi_{r,s}/kT) h\nu \qquad \text{(Eq. 5-41)}$$

In this equation the temperature appears explicitly only in the exponential term, but n_r also depends strongly on the temperature whereas the partition function $Z_r = \Sigma g_{r,s} \exp(-\chi_{r,s}/kT)$ is a rather weak function of the temperature. For constant pressure, $\epsilon_L(T)$ assumes a maximum at a certain temperature T^* because of the tendency of n_r to decrease owing to the depletion of particles of species r by increasing ionization to species r+1 and the effect of the perfect gas law ($n_e + \Sigma_r n_r = p/kT$, where p is the total pressure). As an example, Figure 5-4 illustrates the emission coefficients of two argon lines (r=0 and r=1) on a relative scale and according to this figure, the neutral line will show up in the spectrum only in the temperature interval $10^4\,°K < T < 3.10^4\,°K$. As the temperature increases, lines corresponding to higher ionization stages will appear in the spectrum and those of lower ionization stages will vanish entirely.

Recombination Radiation (free-bound transitions)

In the process of radiative recombination a free electron is captured by a positive ion into a certain bound energy state and the excess energy is converted into radiation according to the relation:

$$\frac{m_e v_e^2}{2} + \chi_{r,s} = h\nu \qquad \qquad \text{(Eq. 5-40)}$$

In this equation, m_e represents the electron mass, v_e the electron velocity and $\chi_{r,s}$ the energy level s of an r-times ionized atom to which the electron is trapped. Since the captured free electrons possess a continuous kinetic energy spectrum according to a Maxwellian distribution, the emitted radiation will also be continuously distributed, but with a threshold value (or series limit, λ_{max} due to the trapping of electrons with near zero velocity:

$$\lambda_{max} = \frac{hc}{\chi_{r,s}} \qquad \qquad \text{(Eq. 5-41)}$$

Recombinations may occur into all possible energy levels $\chi_{r,s}$ so that the number of continuous spectra will coincide with the number s of energy states of these particular ions of species r. The entire free-bound continuum will then consist of a super-position of all continuous spectra emitted from the different species r which are present in the plasma. An exact calculation of the total free-bound continuum over the entire wavelength range is only possible for hydrogen (2). Since the rate with which radiative recombination processes occur is proportional to the electron as well as the ion density, the emitted free-bound radiation intensity is proportional to the product of both. In the following part the contribution of free-bound radiation to the total continuum will be discussed.

Bremsstrahlung (free-free transitions)

Free electrons in a plasma may lose kinetic energy in the Coulomb field of positive ions and this energy is readily converted into radiation. Since the initial as well as the final states of the electrons are free states in which the electrons may assume arbitrary energies within the Maxwellian distribution, the emitted radiation is of the continuum type. Radiation in a frequency interval between ν and $\nu+d\nu$ will be emitted by free electrons which have a kinetic energy $m_e v_e^2/2 \geqslant h\nu$, i.e. the spectrum of the emitted radiation depends on the kinetic energy or temperature of the electrons. In the elementary process of bremsstrahlung, one electron and one ion are involved. Therefore, the intensity of this radiation is expected to be proportional to the product of electron and ion density. The actual emission coefficient of a free-free continuum is given by:

$$\epsilon_\nu = \overline{C(Z'+s)^2} \, \frac{n_e n_1}{(kT)^{\frac{1}{2}}} \, \exp\,(-h\nu/kT) \qquad \qquad \text{(Eq. 5-42)}$$

where:

$$C = \frac{32\pi^2 e^6}{3\sqrt{3}\,c^3\,(2\pi m_e)^{3/2}}$$

e designates the elementary charge, n_e and n_1 the electron and ion density, and $Z'e$ is the ion charge. The number s accounts for the fact that fast electrons may penetrate some of the outer electron shells of ions with higher nuclear charge (s=0 for hydrogen ions). Therefore, such electrons will be exposed to a higher positive charge than the ionic charge $Z'e$.

Considering the total radiation continuum consisting of free-free and free-bound radiation, the emission coefficient turns out to be independent of the frequency for $\nu \leqslant \nu_g$:

$$\epsilon_\nu = \overline{C(Z'+s)^2} \; \frac{n_e n_1}{\sqrt{kT}} \qquad\qquad\qquad (Eq.\ 5\text{-}43)$$

The energy $h\nu_g$ is taken between the ionization level and the energy level corresponding to the limiting frequency ν_g. Since equation 5-43 includes only free-bound radiation of closely neighboring energy levels (quasi-continuum), which are usually found in the vicinity of the ionization level, the validity of equation 5-43 breaks off for $\nu > \nu_g$. Free-bound radiation stemming from the trapping of electrons to lower energy levels which are farther separated from each other leads to pronounced series limits.

For a plasma in LTE the product $n_e n_1$ may be expressed by the Saha-Eggert equation, which assumes the following form in a singly ionized gas (Eq. 5-30) for $r = 0$:

$$\frac{n_e n_1}{n_o} = \frac{2Z_1}{Z_0} \; \frac{(2\pi m_e kT)^{3/2}}{h^3} \; \exp\,(-\chi_1/kT) \qquad\qquad (Eq.\ 5\text{-}44)$$

n_o designates the number density of neutral atoms, Z_1 and Z_0 the partition functions for ions and neutral atoms respectively, and χ_1 the ionization energy. With equation 5-44 the emission coefficient for the combined continuum radiation may be written as:

$$\epsilon_\nu = \frac{64\pi^2 \overline{(Z'+s)^2} e^6}{3\sqrt{3}\,h^3 c^3} \; \frac{Z_1}{Z_0} \; n_o kT \exp\,(-\chi_1/kT) \qquad\qquad (Eq.\ 5\text{-}45)$$

In this equation $n_o kT$ may be replaced by the total pressure p provided that the degree of ionization is small ($\zeta < 10\%$). For this particular situation the continuum emission coefficient is directly proportional to the pressure.

Blackbody radiation

The emission coefficients described in the previous three parts are all based on the assumption that the plasma is optically thin, or in other words, that there is no appreciable absorption of radiation in the plasma itself. This assumption may fail for line as well as for continuum radiation. Very strong absorption, for example, occurs for resonance lines where the absorption coefficient κ'_ν is so high that a layer thickness L of a fraction of a millimeter is already sufficient for complete absorption. In the immediate neighborhood of such a resonance line, the absorption coefficient may be a factor of 10^8 smaller so that layer thicknesses of 10^6 cm or more are required for complete absorption.

Finkelnburg and Peters (2) calculated the conditions for which the continuous radiation of a laboratory plasma would approach blackbody radiation ($I_\nu \geqslant 0.9 B_\nu$) in the visible range of the spectrum (5,000 Å). Figure 5-5 shows the result of their calculations for five different gases. By considering only singly ionized species of these gases, all curves merge into a common curve which corresponds to an ionization degree of 100%. Above this curve a laboratory plasma with a layer thickness of 2 mm or larger would be a cavity radiator at the plasma temperature. Argon for example, with an ionization potential of 15.8 volts, would fall between the curves for helium and hydrogen and become a blackbody radiator for temperatures $T > 2 \times 10°K$ and pressures $p \geqslant 200$ atm. Cesium, with the lowest ionization potential, would require a minimum pressure of about five atmospheres to become a cavity radiator at 5,000°K.

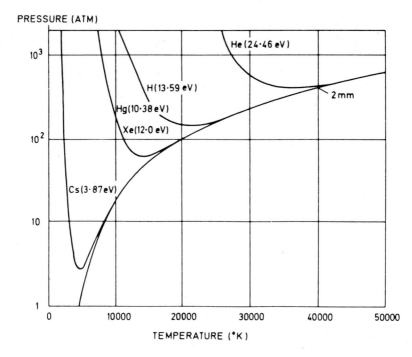

Fig. 5-5   Blackbody radiation of plamas for a layer thickness ≥ 2 mm; the
indicated plasmas emit blackbody radiation in the visible range of
the spectrum (2)

Conceivably, there are other physical processes in plasmas which also lead to the emission of continuous radiation. For example, neutral atoms or molecules of certain elements may have an affinity for electrons. This causes free-free and free-bound radiation by similar mechanisms as described for the interaction of positive ions with electrons. The recombination process corresponds in this case to the formation of negative ions.

Another process which may be responsible for the generation of continuous spectra is the chemical reaction between neutral particles in the plasma. Such a reaction may be considered as a 'recombination' process with a corresponding 'recombination' continuum. This type of chemical reaction plays an important role in re-entry plasmas as well as in plasmas emanating from rocket exhausts. In the latter case the situation may become rather complex because of the numerous combustion products involved.

Finally, with a magnetic field in the plasma, electrons which are forced into an orbital motion around the magnetic flux lines give rise to a continuous radiation called cyclotron radiation. However, the number of collisions which the electrons suffer in the plasma has to be small compared with the number of electron orbits. This requirement is usually expressed by the relation:

$$\omega_e \tau_e = \frac{\lambda_e}{r_L} \gg 1 \qquad \text{(Eq. 5-46)}$$

ω_e is the electron cyclotron frequency, τ_e the average time interval between two electron collisions, λ_e the mean free path length of the electrons, and r_L the average Larmor radius.

Since this review deals essentially with rather dense plasmas and moderate magnetic field intensities, cyclotron radiation will not be of importance.

Some facts about molecular radiation

Finally, some aspects of the radiation emitted by molecular gases will be discussed. Since molecular gases are dissociated at higher temperatures, appreciably lower temperature levels ($< 10^4 °K$) in conjunction with pressures in the order of 1 atm will be considered in this paragraph.

In contrast to atomic gases, molecular gases emit rather complex spectra. Excitation of vibrational and rotational energy states alone results in the emission of vibrational-rotational spectra, which consist of line sequences in the infrared range of the spectrum while simultaneous electronic and vibrational-rotational transitions result in band spectra extending into the visible or even ultraviolet range of the spectrum. Continuous radiation may be superimposed on these bands (recombination continuum, for example). Each single band of a molecular spectrum consists of a number of regularly arranged lines, the intensity distribution of which may be used to determine the gas temperature.

The energy eigenvalues of the rotational states of a diatomic molecule within a single band are given by:

$$X_s = \frac{h^2}{8\pi^2 \Theta} J(J+1) \qquad \text{(Eq. 5-47)}$$

disregarding the constant electronic excitation energy which has to be added to

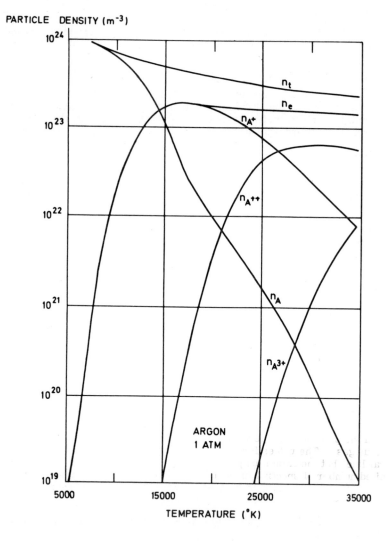

PARTICLE DENSITY (m⁻³)

Fig. 5-6   Composition of an argon plasma in T. E.

equation 5-47. Θ represents the moment of inertia of the molecule and J is the rotational quantum number (J=0, 1, 2, $\cdots$). An approximate expression for the temperature dependence of the line emission coefficients of the rotational lines within a band is obtained by inserting the rotational energy states χ_s into equation 5-39.

$$\epsilon_L \sim (2J + 1) \exp \left[- \frac{h^2}{8\pi^2 \Theta kT} \, J(J+1) \right] h\nu \qquad \text{(Eq. 5-48)}$$

In this equation the factor $2J+1 = g_s$ represents the statistical weight of rotational energy states.

Spectrometric Methods

The discussion of the spectrometric methods shall be subdivided into methods which allow the determination of the temperature directly, and indirect methods which determine the electron density as the unknown and then apply the Saha equation for a temperature evaluation.

Direct methods

Absolute emission coefficient of a spectral line - for the sake of simplicity this method will be discussed for lines emitted from neutral atoms (r=0). The method may be readily extended to ionic lines (r>0) by calculating the equilibrium composition of the plasma in question. As an example of such a calculation, Figure 5-6 shows the equilibrium composition of an argon plasma at atmospheric pressure.

The formula for the line emission coefficient (Eq. 5-41) has been derived assuming an optically thin plasma in which LTE prevails and one of the most accurate methods of determining the temperature field in a plasma is based on an absolute measurement of ϵ_L. In order to solve for the unknown temperature in equation 5-41, the temperature dependence of n_o and Z_0 must be known. As discussed in conjunction with equation 5-41 the partition function is only a weak function of the temperature and may, in a first approximation, be replaced by a constant. The number density n_o, which is the total number density of neutral atoms regardless of their excitation state, may be found from Dalton's law:

$$p = (2n_e + n_o) kT \qquad \text{(Eq. 5-49)}$$

where p is the known total pressure in the plasma. The Saha equation (see Eq. 5-32 for r = 0) provides the necessary relationship between electron density and temperature but equation 5-49 and the Saha equation may be applied in this simple form only if the plasma is not generated from a gas mixture but rather from a homogeneous gas. The values for ν, χ_s and g_s are tabulated for a large number of spectral lines but the transition probability, A_t^s, which is accurately known only for a limited number of spectral lines, constitutes a problem for this method. With the exception of hydrogen, these transition probabilities are experimental values.

In summary, the temperature may be derived from the following set of equations, assuming that the absolute line emission coefficient of a neutral line has been measured:

$$\epsilon_L = \frac{1}{4\pi} A_t^s \, n_o \, \frac{g_s}{Z_0} \exp\left(-\chi_s/kT\right) h\nu \, ,$$

$$p = (2n_e + n_o) kT \, ,$$

$$\frac{n_e^2}{n_o} = \frac{2Z_1}{Z_0} \left(\frac{2\pi m_e kT}{h^2} \right)^{3/2} \exp(-\chi_1/kT) \qquad \text{(Eq. 5-50)}$$

In the last two equations the plasma equation $n_e = n_1$ (quasi neutrality) for a singly ionized gas has been introduced. The ionization energy, χ_1, which appears in the exponential term of the Saha equation requires a correction frequently, especially if this equation is applied to high pressure plasmas. In such plasmas a lowering of the ionization potential is observed, e.g. the electron continuum appears already at longer wavelengths than those anticipated from the theoretical ionization limit. The originally discrete energy levels of the atoms split up in energy bands due to the disturbing influence of neighboring particles, the effect being known as pressure or collision broadening. By virtue of this broadening effect the upper energy levels of the atoms, which are very close to each other, begin to overlap and form a quasi-continuum. This quasi-continuum leads to a reduction of the ionization potential and has been already mentioned in connection with equation 5-43. For hydrogen plasmas Unsöld (7) calculated the lowering of the ionization potential to $\Delta\chi_H = 7 \times 10^{-7} n_e^{1/3}$. In fact, this relation may be used as an approximation for other elements as well because the arrangement of the upper energy levels of other elements is similar to that of hydrogen. (Broadening of hydrogenic energy levels due to the linear Stark effect will be further discussed under 'Stark Broadening').

For the measurement of absolute intensities the spectrometer and the associated optical components must be calibrated with a radiation standard (tungsten ribbon lamp or carbon arc).

Line intensity ratios (relative line emission coefficients) - for a simplification of the notation we will consider ratios of neutral line emission coefficients. The emission coefficients of two different neutral lines stemming from the same location in a plasma may be written as:

$$\epsilon_{L1} = \frac{1}{4\pi} (A_t^s)_1 \, n_o \frac{g_s}{Z_0} \exp\left[(-\chi_{s1}/kT) \right] \qquad h\nu_1$$

$$\qquad\qquad\qquad\qquad\qquad\qquad\qquad\qquad\qquad\qquad\qquad \text{(Eq. 5-51}$$

$$\epsilon_{L2} = \frac{1}{4\pi} (A_t^s)_2 \, n_o \frac{g_{s2}}{Z_0} \exp\left[(-\chi_{s2}/kT) \right] \qquad h\nu_2$$

The ratio of these two emission coefficients:

$$\frac{\epsilon_{L1}}{\epsilon_{L2}} = \frac{(A_t^s \nu g_s)_1}{(A_t^s \nu g_s)_2} \exp\left[\frac{-(\chi_{s1} - \chi_{s2})}{kT} \right] \qquad \text{(Eq. 5-52)}$$

does not contain the atom density n_o and the partition function Z_0. This method offers three advantages over the absolute intensity method:

(a)   a relative measurement of the emission coefficients is sufficient, which is much simpler experimentally than an absolute measurement

(b)   the transition probabilities are required on a relative scale only

(c)   the evaluation of the temperature is straightforward.

Unfortunately, the accuracy of this method is frequently rather poor because the energy eigenvalues of ions of the same ionization stage are very close to each other.

Considering errors of energy eigenvalues only, the relative error of this method is:

$$\frac{\Delta T}{T} = \frac{\Delta(\chi_{s1} - \chi_{s2})}{\chi_{s1} - \chi_{s2}} \qquad \text{(Eq. 5-53)}$$

An improvement of the accuracy may be achieved by extending this method to more than two lines. Rewriting one of equations 5-51 with $n_o h/4\pi Z_0 = C$ results in:

$$\log \left(\frac{\epsilon_L}{A_t^s \nu g_s} \right) = - \frac{\chi_s}{k} \frac{1}{T} + \log C \qquad \text{(Eq. 5-54)}$$

or

$$y = - x \frac{1}{T} + C' \qquad \text{(Eq. 5-54a)}$$

Plotting $y = \log (\epsilon_L/A_t^s \nu g_s)$ as a function of $x = \chi_s/k$ results in a straight line with slope $- 1/T$. Although the application of a large number of lines may reduce the error, the method as such is not very sensitive to the temperature.

The same method may be applied for the rotational lines within a single band of a molecular gas. From a logarithmic plot of $\epsilon_L/(2J+1)h\nu$ versus $h^2J(J+1)/8\pi^2 \Theta k$ (see Eq. 5-48) a straight line with slope of $- 1/T$ is obtained. In this way temperatures may be determined in plasmas which contain molecular species, existing only at lower temperature levels. Figure 5-7 shows, as an example, the variation of the equilibrium molecule concentration in a nitrogen plasma as a function of the temperature.

Intensity distribution of a spectral line (Larenz method) - the relative distribution of the line emission coefficient as a function of the temperature is determined by $n_r(T)$, $Z_r(T)$ and the exponential function in equation 5-41. Assuming that the temperature $T=T^*$ is known at a certain location $\rho=\rho^*$ in the plasma source, the ratio of the emission coefficients at an arbitrary location ρ to that at ρ^* is then:

$$\frac{\epsilon_L(T)}{\epsilon_L(T^*)} = \frac{n_r(T) Z_r(T^*)}{n_r(T^*) Z_r(T)} \exp \left[\frac{-\chi_{r,s}}{k} \left(\frac{1}{T} - \frac{1}{T^*} \right) \right] \qquad \text{(Eq. 5-55)}$$

Eq. 5-55 permits the determination of the entire temperature distribution in the source from the measured relative intensities $\epsilon_L(T)$. A modification of this method, known as the off-axis-peaking or Larenz method, makes use of the fact that the emission coefficient of a spectral line reaches a maximum at a certain temperature. By identifying this temperature with T^*, which can be accurately calculated, a calibration temperature within the source is obtained, provided that the maximum temperature in the source $T_m > T^*$. In rotationally symmetric plasmas, as for example in electric arcs, the temperature reaches a maximum in the axis so if this temperature $T_{axis} > T^*$, the line emission coefficient will show an off-axis peak. From the calculated relative distribution $(\epsilon_L)_{rel} = f_1(T)$ and the measured relative distribution $(\epsilon_L)_{rel} = f_2(\rho)$, the desired temperature distribution $T(\rho)$ may be derived. This may be done graphically as shown in Figure 5.8

Relative line emission coefficients of different ionization stages - a modification of the method discussed under 'Line intensity ratios' makes use of the fact that the energy levels of an atomic line and of an ionic line of the same element are much farther separated from each other than the levels of the same ionization stage. This method will be discussed for lines stemming from a neutral and a singly ionized atom in a plasma generated from a homogeneous gas. By indicating the neutral component by a subscript 0 and the singly ionized component by a subscript 1, the ratio of the emission coefficients is:

254

PARTICLE DENSITY (m^{-3})

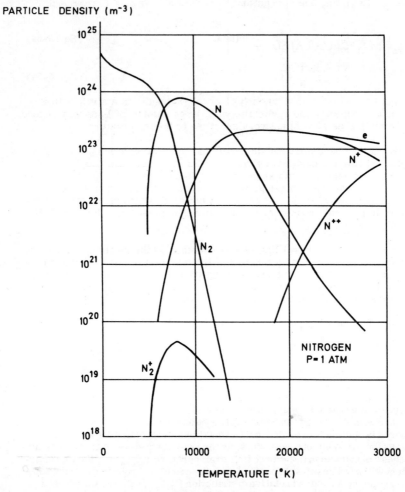

Fig. 5-7   Composition of a nitrogen plasma in T. E.

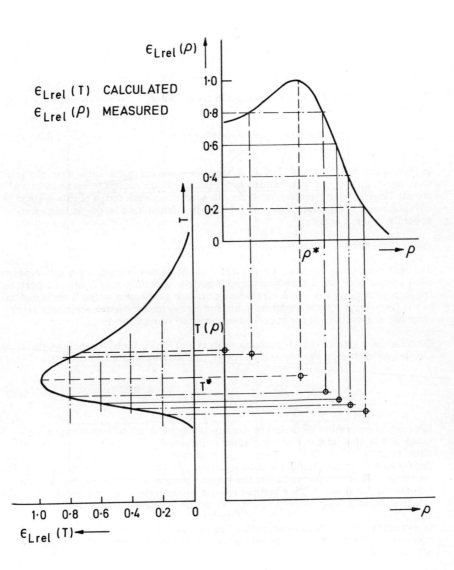

Fig. 5-8   Off-axis peaking method

$$\frac{\epsilon_{L1}}{\epsilon_{L0}} = \frac{n_1 Z_0}{n_0 Z_1} \frac{(A_t^s g_s \nu)_1}{(A_t^s g_s \nu)_0} \exp\left[\frac{-(\chi_{s1} - \chi_{s0})}{kT}\right] \qquad \text{(Eq. 5-56)}$$

Since the plasma is assumed to be in LTE, the Saha equation (Eq. 5-41) may be applied. Combining equation 5-41 for r=0 with equation 5-56 one finds:

$$\frac{\epsilon_{L1}}{\epsilon_{L0}} = \frac{2}{n_e(T)} \frac{(A_t^s g_s \nu)_1}{(A_t^s g_s \nu)_0} \left(\frac{2\pi m_e kT}{h^2}\right)^{3/2} \exp\left[\frac{-(\chi_1 + \chi_{s1} - \chi_{s0})}{kT}\right]$$

$$\text{(Eq. 5-57)}$$

The electron density $n_e(T)$ follows again from Dalton's law and from the Saha equation as:

$$n_e(T) = S(T) \left[1 + \frac{p}{kT} \frac{1}{S(T)}\right]^{\frac{1}{2}} - 1 \qquad \text{(Eq. 5-58)}$$

In this equation $S(T)$ is used as an abbreviation for the right hand side of the Saha equation. If the temperature in a plasma is high enough to make ionic and atomic lines appear simultaneously in the spectrum, application of this method is advantageous. A measurement of relative line intensities leads, in this case, to accurate temperatures.

Indirect methods

Absolute continuum emission coefficient - as discussed in connection with equation 5-43 a superposition of free-bound and free-free radiation may lead, in a certain frequency range $\nu \leqslant \nu$ to a continuum emission coefficient which is independent of the frequency. This condition holds for free-bound radiation stemming from trapping of electrons to the upper closely spaced energy levels.

Considering a plasma which contains neutral and singly ionized species only ($n_e = n_1$) the frequency independent emission coefficient may be written as (c.f. Eq. 5-43).

$$\epsilon_\nu = \overline{C(Z' + s)^2} \frac{n_e^2}{\sqrt{kT}} \qquad \text{(Eq. 5-59)}$$

In order to determine the electron density from the absolute measurement of ϵ_ν, a value of s is required. For the plasmas discussed in this review, s is always close to unity. For $\sqrt{kT}$ a rough estimate is made which may be, if necessary, improved by iteration using the Saha equation. Assuming LTE in the plasma, the temperature may be derived from the known electron density using the Saha equation and Dalton's law. This method results in accurate temperatures because the electron density depends very sensitively on the temperature.

In summary, the desired temperature may be derived from the following set of equations if the specified assumptions hold in a plasma generated from a homogeneous gas:

$$\epsilon_\nu = \overline{C(Z' + s)^2} \frac{n_e^2}{\sqrt{kT}}, \quad \nu \leqslant \nu_g,$$

$$\frac{n_e^2}{n_0} = \frac{2Z_1}{Z_0} \frac{2\pi m_e kT}{h^2}^{3/2} \exp(-\chi_1/kT),$$

$$p = (2n_e + n_0) kT.$$

The method may be extended directly to plasmas generated from gas mixtures if the number density ratios of the mixture are known. If these ratios are not known an additional measurement is required to determine the ratio of a neutral and an ionic line emission coefficient for two lines belonging to the same element (1).

Stark broadening - the last method to be discussed in this report is suitable for a direct measurement of electron densities in plasmas. It is unique in the sense that it does not require the existence of LTE in the plasma. Measurements based on this method may, therefore, be used for a check of the validity of LTE assumptions.

Broadening of a spectral line may be caused by a number of processes which are usually grouped under the term 'pressure or collision' and 'Doppler' broadening. The broadening mechanism which is especially of interest for the plasmas considered in this review is the linear Stark effect. Broadening of lines emitted by hydrogenic atoms or ions due to the linear Stark effect occurs as soon as these particles are exposed to strong electric fields. The electric field removes the degeneracy of hydrogenic energy levels, i.e. an originally discrete energy level is now split into a large number of very closely spaced levels (energy band). Electronic transitions between these energy bands result in more or less broadened lines. The half-width ($\Delta\lambda\frac{1}{2}$) of a broadened line depends on the Stark coefficient of an individual element and increases with increasing field strength. The hydrogen H_β-line is especially sensitive to the linear Stark effect as shown in the following table, which also demonstrates that the broadening is a strong function of the electron density and a rather weak function of the plasma temperature.

Table 5-1

Line	$T(°K)$	$n_e(cm^{-3})$	$\Delta\lambda\frac{1}{2}(\text{\AA})$
H_β	10^4	10^{14}	.42
	10^4	10^{17}	48
4,861 Å	4×10^4	10^{14}	.42
	4×10^4	10^{17}	50
He II	2×10^4	10^{15}	.27
3,203 Å	2×10^4	10^{18}	24
A II	2×10^4	10^{15}	.0014
4,806 Å	2×10^4	10^{18}	1.4

The magnitude of the electric field to which a radiating atom or ion is exposed depends on the electron density. Assuming that $n_1 (=n_e)$ is the number density of singly ionized atoms in a plasma, the average distance between two neighboring ions, z, is then proportional to $n_1^{-1/3}$. The Coulomb force between two ions separated by a distance z is $f = e^2/z^2 \sim e^2 n_1^{2/3}$ and the corresponding electric field strength is $E \sim e n_1^{2/3}$. Because of the random motion of the ions in the plasma this field strength assumes a statistical distribution. By introducing a normal field strength $E_0 = 2.61 e n_1^{2/3}$, the actual reduced microfield intensity may be

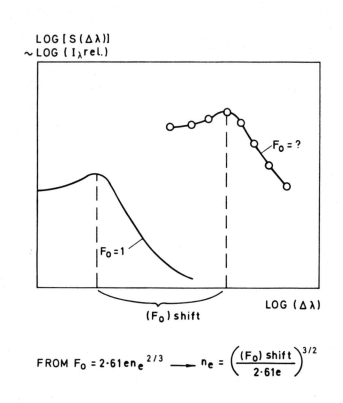

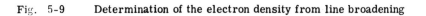

Fig. 5-9   Determination of the electron density from line broadening

written as $\beta = E/E_0$. Holtzmark calculated the distribution function $W(\beta)$ of the microfields and the resulting Stark broadened profiles. If $\Delta\lambda$ is the distance from the center of a broadened line, the shape of a line may be characterized by a function $S(\alpha)$ where $\alpha = \Delta\lambda/E_0$ which is normalized so that $\int_{-\infty}^{+\infty} S(\alpha)\,d\alpha = 1$. The original Holtzmark theory only takes positive ions into account and predicts reliable values of line broadening for electron densities $n_e \leqslant 10^{16} cm^{-3}$. For higher electron densities Griem and Kolb modified this theory to take into proper account the electrons neglected in the Holtzmark theory.

The procedure to be followed for measuring electron densities with this method in a plasma will be discussed for a specific example, namely, the H_β-line. The theoretical normalized profile $S(\alpha)$ is available from the literature.

(a)   Plot the theoretical profile $S(\alpha)$ for $E_o = 1$ choosing a logarithmic scale for both coordinates.

(b)   Enter the data points in relative intensity units in the same diagram. The resulting experimental curve contains the unknown value of E_o.

(c)   Shift the experimental curve to a best fit on the theoretical curve. The shift of the abscissa then yields the desired electron density:

$$n_e = \left[\frac{(E_o)_{shift}}{2.61e} \right]^{3/2} \qquad \text{(Eq. 5-61)}$$

The graphical procedure is shown schematically in Figure 5-9. According to equation 5-61 an error in the measurement of $\Delta\lambda$ causes an error in the electron density which is larger by a factor of 1.5.

As discussed before, if the plasma is in LTE the temperature may be derived by applying the Saha equation and Dalton's law. For the chosen example the corresponding set of equations is:

$$n_e = \left[\frac{(E_o)_{shift}}{2.61\,e} \right]^{3/2} ,$$

$$\frac{n_e^2}{n_0} = \frac{2Z_1}{Z_0} \left(\frac{2\pi m_e kT}{h^2} \right)^{3/2} \exp\,(-\chi_1/kT) ,$$

$$(\chi_1 = 13.59\ eV,\ 2Z_1/Z_0 \simeq 2), \qquad \text{(Eqs. 5-62)}$$

$$p = (2n_e + n_0)kT$$

Temperatures evaluated from equation 5-62 are accurate within a few percent even if the error of the measured electron density reaches 20%, because the temperature depends essentially on the logarithm of the electron density only.

Methods for Emitting-Absorbing Gases

The most popular method for determining temperatures in emitting-absorbing gases in a temperature range from approximately 1,000 to 8,000°K is the line reversal technique. This method has been suffcesfully applied for temperature measurements in flames, in internal combustion engines, in rocket exhausts, in shocks and in high temperature expansion flows (7-14). It may also be applied for high temperature plasmas. In fact, the upper temperature limit may be as high as 50,000°K depending on the availability of sufficiently strong and reliable radiation standards for these temperature levels (3). For temperatures below 1,000°K the luminosity of most gases in the visible range of the spectrum becomes too small for accurate measurements. Seeding of the gas with elements or salts of elements with low excitation potentials may appreciably enhance the luminosity, sodium being frequently used for this purpose.

The line reversal technique considers emission and absorption of the same spectral line within a hot, luminous gas volume. Since line emission and absorption are governed by the populations of the respective energy levels, the temperature obtained from the reversal technique will be the effective electronic excitation temperature of the particular element employed for the measurement. This excitation temperature is the same as the kinetic gas temperature only if the ratio of lower- and upper-state populations for the chosen spectral line is controlled by particle impact; in other words, LTE is required down to the lower energy level of the electronic transition considered. At the same time scattering should be insignificant when compared to the other radiation processes (absorption, spontaneous emission, induced emission). The latter requirement may be violated, for example, in flames which contain a large number of solid particles but other possible deviations from LTE should be carefully checked before this method is applied.

If the method is applicable, reversal temperatures are found by viewing radiation over a certain frequency interval, from a comparison source through the hot gas whose temperature is desired. Usually, the chosen frequency interval will cover a strong line (resonance line) emitted by the hot gas or the added seeding material. If the comparison light source (continuous emitter) is relatively weak, the chosen line will appear bright, due to net emission, on the background of the comparison source spectrum. If the radiation of the comparison source is sufficiently strong, the chosen line will appear dark due to net absorption in the hot gas. At the reversal point the intensity of the comparison source and of the hot gas is the same and therefore, the line is no longer discernible on the background spectrum of the comparison source. The brightness temperature of the comparison source and the blackbody temperature of the gas are now the same for the selected wavelength interval. The 'true' reversal method as well as a modification of this technique which makes it more versatile for many applications will be discussed in the following paragraphs.

These reversal methods permit a rather quick determination of the unknown gas temperature if the gas is essentially isothermal. If there are significant temperature gradients within the hot gas the required procedure for evaluating the temperature distribution becomes much more complex than that employed for optically thin gases using the Abel transform. This review will be restricted to a discussion of the isothermal case. · For non-isothermal situations the reader is referred to the literature (for example (15).

Basic equations - line reversal techniques to be discussed in this review are based on Kirchhoff's law which, in turn, requires the existence of TE in the gas. As pointed out before, this condition is never met rigorously in laboratory plasmas but it holds frequently for resonance lines which require small absorption lengths only. For a hot gas having a uniform temperature T_g Kirchhoff's law may be written for a resonance line as:

$$E_\nu (T_g) = \alpha_\nu (T_g)$$

(Eq. 5-63)

In this equation $E_\nu = I_\nu/B_\nu$ represents the monochromatic emittance and α_ν the monochromatic absorptance of the gas. Both quantities are functions of the gas temperature T_g and the dimensions of the emitting-absorbing gaseous volume. If t_ν is the monochromatic transmittance of a gas (no scattering) the monochromatic absorptance may be expressed by:

$$\alpha_\nu = 1 - t_\nu (T_g) \tag{Eq. 5-64}$$

$$= 1 - \exp(-\tau_\nu)$$

with τ_ν as the optical depth of a gas layer of thickness L. For very large optical depths ($\tau_\nu \gg 1$) the line being viewed appears black and the temperature can be directly determined from the measured absolute intensity $B_\nu(T_g)$. The determination of temperatures from optically thin radiation sources ($\tau_\nu \ll 1$) has already been discussed. The reversal method is applicable between these two extremes, i.e., for intermediate values of the optical depth.

The radiation intensity $I_{\nu g}$ emitted by an emitting-absorbing gas of uniform temperature T_g within a frequency interval from ν to $\nu + \Delta\nu$ is:

$$I_{\nu g} = E_\nu(T_g) \, B_\nu(T_g) \tag{Eq. 5-65}$$

By viewing a comparison source through the hot gas in the same frequency interval, a total intensity $I_{\nu t}$ is observed consisting of the radiation emitted by the gas plus a fraction of the radiation from the comparison source which is transmitted through the gas:

$$I_{\nu t} = I_{\nu g} + [\, 1 - \alpha_\nu (T_g)\,] \; I_{\nu c}$$

Applying Kirchhoff's law to this equation yields:

$$I_{\nu t} = I_{\nu g} + [\, 1 - E_\nu (T_g)\,] \; I_{\nu c} \tag{Eq. 5-66}$$

I_ν is the radiation intensity of the comparison source in the frequency interval from ν to $\nu + \Delta\nu$. Equations 5-63 to 5-66 constitute the working equations of the reversal technique.

'True' reversal technique - when the true reversal method is employed the radiation intensity of the comparison source is adjusted until it becomes equal to the total intensity $I_{\nu t}$ viewed through the gas. From equation 5-66 and 5-65 follows:

$$I_{\nu t} = I_{\nu c}(T_b) = E_\nu(T_g) \, B_\nu (T_g) + [\, 1 - E_\nu(T_g)\,] \; I_{\nu c}(T_b)$$

or:

$$I_{\nu c} (T_b) = B_\nu(T_g) \tag{Eq. 5-67}$$

The known brightness or 'black' temperature T_b obtained for the reversal point is then identical with the desired gas temperature T_g, because the brightness temperature T_b is defined as the temperature at which a black body would emit the same intensity $I_{\nu c}$ as the comparison source does in the specified frequency interval.

Optical pyrometers are usually calibrated for brightness temperatures. If another radiation standard is employed as a comparison source (for example, a tungsten ribbon lamp) with a known surface emittance $E_\nu(T_c)$ the comparison intensity becomes $I_{\nu c}(T_c) = E_\nu(T_c) \, B_\nu(T_c)$ and the desired gas temperature follows from the equation:

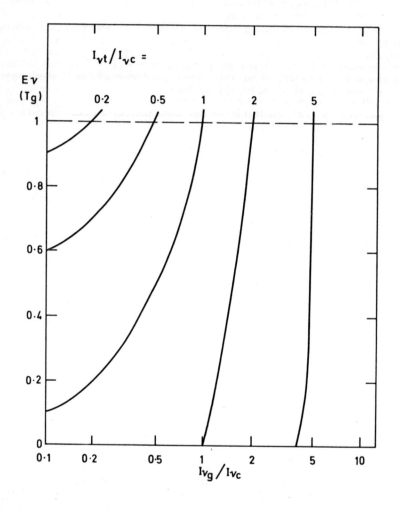

Fig. 5-10   Modified reversal technique

$$E_\nu(T_c) \; B_\nu(T_c) = B_\nu(T_g)$$

and equation 5-13 as:

$$T_g = \frac{h\nu}{k} \left[\log \left(1 + \frac{2h\nu^3}{c^2 E_\nu(T_c) B_\nu(T_c)} \right) \right]^{-1} \qquad \text{(Eq. 5-68)}$$

The application of the true reversal technique is limited by the brightness temperature range of available comparison sources. An extension beyond this range is provided by a modified reversal technique which will be discussed in the following paragraph.

Modified reversal technique - this method is frequently applied when true reversal cannot be obtained as in high temperature flames, for example, or in shock wave generated plasmas requiring high speed resolution. The basic equations will apply for this method but an independent measurement is now required of $I_{\nu g}$, $I_{\nu c}$ and $I_{\nu t}$. Equation 5-66 written in terms of these three measured quantities yields:

$$I_{\nu t} = I_{\nu g} + \left[1 - \frac{I_{\nu g}}{B_\nu(T_g)} \right] I_{\nu c}$$

or:

$$B_\nu(T_g) = \frac{I_{\nu c} \; I_{\nu g}}{I_{\nu c} + I_{\nu g} - I_{\nu t}} \qquad \text{(Eq. 5-69)}$$

The right-hand side of this equation contains measured values only; therefore, the desired temperature T_g may be derived from the experimentally determining value of $B_\nu(T_g)$. Although this method provides a wider range of applicability than the true reversal technique, a limitation is imposed by the increasing error as the ratio of gas to comparison source radiation intensity increases. This fact is illustrated in Figure 5-10 which represents a plot of equation 5-69 which may be rewritten in the form:

$$E_\nu(T_g) = \frac{I_{\nu g}}{B_\nu(T_g)} = 1 + \frac{I_{\nu g}}{I_{\nu c}} - \frac{I_{\nu t}}{I_{\nu c}}$$

The solid lines in this diagram represent possible operating conditions. For $I_{\nu t}/I_{\nu c} < 1$ the temperature of the comparison source is larger than the unknown gas temperature, whereas for $I_{\nu t}/I_{\nu c} > 1$ the opposite is true. The ratio $I_{\nu t}/I_{\nu c} = 1$ represents true reversal.

The steep slope of curves $I_{\nu t}/I_{\nu c} > 1$ indicates that the error of $E_\nu(T_g)$ increases rapidly with increasing values of $I_{\nu t}/I_{\nu c}$ for a given error in the latter and in $I_{\nu g}/I_{\nu c}$, and becomes intolerable for values of $I_{\nu t}/I_{\nu c} > 2$. It is, therefore, desirable to keep $I_{\nu t}/I_{\nu c}$ close to unity or even at values smaller than unity. In addition, the accuracy of measured line reversal temperatures depends on the sensitivity of the line intensity on temperature. The rising portion of the intensity distribution of a spectral line is essentially proportional to $\exp[-\chi_s/kT]$ (see also Fig. 5-4). By choosing a suitable seeding material (χ_s) for the estimated gas temperature the accuracy of reversal temperatures may be in the order of 1% or even better. For example, using the sodium D-lines for reversal measurements in a temperature interval from 1,800 to 2,500°K results in an error of approximately 1%. This error is caused mainly by the calibration error of the comparison source.

References

1. Finkelnburg, W., and Maecker, H., 'Elektrische Bögen und thermisches Plasma,' Encyclopedia of Physics, Vol. XXII, Springer-Verlag, Germany, 1956.

2. Finkelnburg, W., and Peters, Th., 'Kontinuierliche Spektren,' Encyclopedia of Physics, Vol. XXVIII, Spectroscopy II, Springer-Verlag, Germany, 1957.

3. Griem, H. R., 'Plasma Spectroscopy,' McGraw-Hill, New York, 1964.

4. Huddlestone, R. H., and Leonard, S. L., eds., 'Plasma Diagnostic Techniques,' Academic Press, New York, 1965.

5. Drawin, H. W., and Felenbok, P., 'Data for Plasmas in Local Thermodynamic Equilibrium,' Gauthier-Villars, Paris, 1965.

6. Dickerman, P. J., ed., 'Optical Spectrometric Measurements of High Temperatures,' Univ. of Chicago Press, 1961.

7. Unsöld, A., 'Physik der Sternatmosphären,' Springer-Verlag, Berlin, 2nd ed., 1955.

8. 'Temperature: Its Measurement and Control in Science and Industry,' Reinhold, Vol. I, 1941.

9. 'Temperature,' Vol. II, 1955.

10. 'Temperature,' Vol. III, Part 1, 1962.

11. Gaydon, A. G., 'Spectroscopy of Flames,' Wiley, New York, 1957.

12. Gaydon, A. G., and Wolfhard, H. G., 'Flames,' Chapman and Hall, London, 2nd ed., 1960.

13. Marrodimeann, R., and Bioteux, H., 'Flame Spectroscopy,' Wiley, New York, 1965.

14. Weinberg, F. J., 'Optics of Flames,' Butterworth Scientific Publications, Washington, 1963.

15. Penner, S. S., 'Quantitative Molecular Spectroscopy and Gas Emissivities,' Ch. 16, Addison-Wesley, Reading, Mass. 1959.

Nomenclature

$A_{r,t}^{r,s}$ probability for spontaneous transition within an r-times ionized atom from a quantum level s to a lower quantum level t

$B_{r,t}^{r,s}$ transition probability for induced emission

$B_{r,s}^{r,t}$ transition probability for absorption

B_ν intensity of blackbody radiation

C, C'	constants
c	light velocity (3×10^8 m/sec)
E	electric field strength, emittance
e	electronic charge (1.6×10^{-19} amp sec)
f	Coulomb force
g	statistical weight, constant
h	Planck's constant
I	total radiation intensity.
I_ν	monochromatic radiation intensity
$I_{\nu, o}$	initial spectral intensity
J	rotational quantum number
k	Boltzmann constant
L, l	length
m	mass of particles
n	number density of particles, principal quantum number
p	pressure
R	radius of plasma source
r_L	average Larmor radius
r, x, y	coordinates
S	ionization coefficient
S(T)	abbreviation for the right hand side of the Saha equation
$S(\alpha)$	normalized function
s	correction for the penetration of the outer electron shells by fast electrons
T	temperature
t, Δt	time, transmittance
u	total radiation density
u_ν	monochromatic radiation density
V, ΔV	volume
v	thermal velocity

$W(\beta)$	distribution function of microfields
Z	partition function
$Z'e$	ionic charge
z	average distance between two neighboring ions in a plasma
α	combined collisional-radiative recombination coefficient, Sommerfeld's fine structure constant, $\alpha = \Delta\lambda/E_o$, absorptance
$\beta = E/E_o$	dimensionless parameter
β_ν	monochromatic extinction coefficient
γ_ν	monochromatic scattering coefficient
Δa	element of area
Δx	natural width of a spectral line
$\Delta\lambda$	distance from center of a spectral line
$\Delta\omega$	unit solid angle
ϵ_ν	spontaneous spectral emission coefficient
ϵ_ν'	total spectral emission coefficient
ζ_n	number of valence electrons
θ	moment of inertia of a diatomic molecule
κ_ν'	volume absorption coefficient
$\kappa'_{\nu m}$	mass absorption coefficient
λ	wave length, mean free path length
$\nu, \Delta\nu$	frequency
ξ	degree of ionization
ρ	radial coordinate
τ_ν	optical depth
τ_e	average time interval between two electron collisions
Φ	radiation flux
$\chi, \Delta\chi$	energy
χ_i, χ_1	ionization energy
$\chi_{i, H}$	ionization energy of hydrogen
ω_e	electron cyclotron frequency

A	argon
a	heavy particle
b	brightness
c	comparison source
e	electron
g	limiting value, gas temperature
L	spectral line
m, max	maximum value
r	ionization stage, different species
s	energy state
t	energy state, total
ν	monochromatic
o	neutral particles, reference state
1	singly ionized particles
1, 2	different spectral lines (see text)

Superscripts

*	reference value

6

Probe Measurements in High-Temperature Gases and Dense Plasmas

JERRY GREY
Greyrad Corporation, Princeton, New Jersey.

Summary

Water-cooled or gas-cooled probes are capable of measuring a number of gas and flow properties continuously under conditions of extremely high heat transfer; e.g., in rocket motor interiors and nozzles, arcjet exhausts, hyperthermal wind tunnels, metal smelting furnaces, high-temperature chemical processing reactors, etc. These probes can measure, in various combinations, gas enthalpy, composition, velocity, Mach number, temperature (both atom or ion and electron temperatures in plasmas), electron density, degree of ionization, heat transfer rate, high frequency pressure oscillations, scale and intensity of turbulence (in plasmas), and steady-state static and impact pressures. Typical conditions under which these steady-state measurements may be made are: gas temperatures over $17,000°K$; heat flux levels up to 50 Btu/in^2-sec (~ 8 kw/cm^2); Mach numbers up to 25; stagnation pressures up to 150 atmospheres; temperature gradients up to $20,000°K$/cm, etc. Accuracy levels as high as ± 1 percent have been achieved in this type of environment.

Introduction

The study of high temperature gases and plasmas has received great attention in the past decade. Much of this effort stemmed from the practical problems associated with plasma confinement, the anticipated possibility of controlled thermonuclear reactions, and various forms of electric propulsion devices for space application.

Most of the early plasma research was performed at relatively low pressures. A reasonably comprehensive bibliography of much of the work through the nineteenth century and the first half of the twentieth century appears in Ref. (1). An important recent trend has been the study of higher pressures; i.e., 'dense' plasmas characteristic of hyperthermal wind tunnels, reentry material test facilities, and high-temperature chemical processing operations. For the purposes of this section, a dense plasma may be defined as a partly or fully ionized gas, in which the relevant mean free path for elastic collisions is much smaller (e.g., at least one order of magnitude) than the characteristic length associated with the hardware (e.g., probe radius).

In the study of dense plasmas, one of the first problems encountered by the investigator is that of measurement: how does one measure the properties of a fluid whose enthalpy and density are such that heat transfer rates to immersed diagnostic probes are measured in terms of kW/cm^2 or whose optical characteristics are such as to render the fluid opaque even to microwaves, or whose gradients are so steep as to invalidate spectroscopic, microwave, or laser-beam diagnostic approaches.

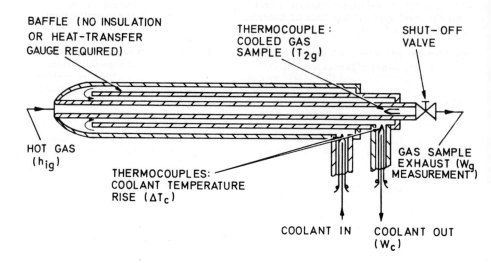

BAFFLE (NO INSULATION OR HEAT-TRANSFER GAUGE REQUIRED)

THERMOCOUPLE: COOLED GAS SAMPLE (T_{2g})

SHUT-OFF VALVE

HOT GAS (h_{ig})

THERMOCOUPLES: COOLANT TEMPERATURE RISE (ΔT_c)

GAS SAMPLE EXHAUST (W_g MEASUREMENT)

COOLANT IN

COOLANT OUT (W_c)

Fig. 6-1   Calorimetric probe used with tare-measurement technique

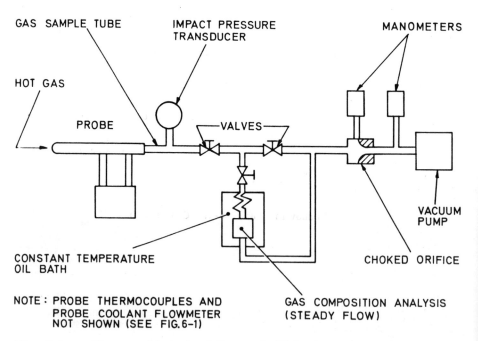

GAS SAMPLE TUBE

IMPACT PRESSURE TRANSDUCER

MANOMETERS

HOT GAS

PROBE

VALVES

VACUUM PUMP

CONSTANT TEMPERATURE OIL BATH

CHOKED ORIFICE

NOTE: PROBE THERMOCOUPLES AND PROBE COOLANT FLOWMETER NOT SHOWN (SEE FIG. 6-1)

GAS COMPOSITION ANALYSIS (STEADY FLOW)

Fig. 6-2   Diagram of instrumentation used with tare-measurement calorimetric probe to measure enthalpy, velocity and gas composition

These notes describe a family of probe-type diagnostic instruments designed specifically for the dense plasma environment, and the included references illustrate their use both in relatively classical problems such as stream mixing and in entirely novel applications such as determination of the degree of nonequilibrium in partly ionized plasmas.

The high temperature, of course, leads to a number of difficult measurement problems; e.g., dense plasmas are characterized by many forms of nonequilibrium radiation, metastable excited electronic states, collisional nonequilibrium such as electron-heavy-particle energy differences, chemical nonequilibrium represented by different dissociation/reassociation and ionization/recombination rates, and the thermodynamic nonequilibria of vibrational and sometimes rotational relaxation. Thus, even when measurements can be made, interpretation is often subject to some question. This uncertainty is illustrated by some of the examples described in the cited references, and often represents one of the principal limitations on correlations between experiment and theory.

Historical development of probe techniques in high-temperature gases began, of course, with Langmuir's classical studies (2) in ionized gases of very low density and therefore low heat flux to the probes. The first example of a relatively sophisticated diagnostic probe utilizing forced cooling methods was the double-sonic-orifice temperature probe developed in the late 1940's, and described in some detail, with the proper literature citations, in (3). Subsequent developments during the past decade have led to the evolution of sophisticated cooled-probe techniques capable of measuring virtually every property of flowing hot gases and plasmas. These techniques are described in detail in subsequent parts of these notes.

Techniques

Calorimetric Probes

The concept of calorimetric enthalpy and heat flux measurements is not new, but the technology required for their useful application in high-temperature, high-density gases and plasmas was not developed until the middle 1950's.

Early calorimetric probes attempted, unsuccessfully, to isolate the calorimeter completely from the exterior cooling jacket required for high heat-flux environments. The first successful approach avoided the problem by utilizing a 'tare' measurement (4). In this probe concept, the energy required to cool the probe without aspiration of a gas sample is subtracted from the energy required to cool the probe with the aspirated gas sample flowing, thereby permitting determination of the gas sample enthalpy.

This probe configuration is shown in Figure 6-1. Construction of the probe itself is generally of copper, with stainless-steel supports. Cooling water from a high-pressure source - up to 55 atm - enters through the mounting block, passes up the front stainless-steel support, and through the outermost coolant channel to the probe tip, returning via the inner coolant channel. Sheathed, ungrounded thermocouple junctions are located precisely at the probe coolant channel inlet and outlet.

The central tube carries a steady flow of sample gas from the probe tip past a thermocouple junction located precisely opposite the 'water out' thermocouple, and then through a gas sample tube to one or more instruments as described later.

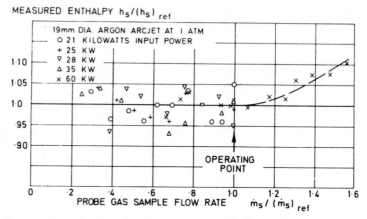
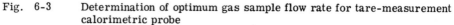

Fig. 6-3   Determination of optimum gas sample flow rate for tare-measurement
calorimetric probe

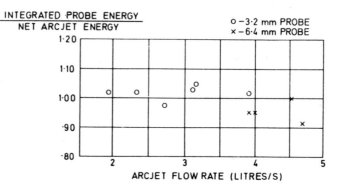

Fig. 6-4   Energy calibration of tare-measurement calorimetric probe

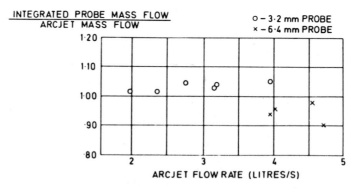

Fig. 6-5   Mass flow calibration of tare-measurement calorimetric probe

In the unique 'tare' measurement, which effectively eliminates errors due to external cooling requirements, a valve in the gas sample line is closed, thus preventing gas from entering the probe, and observations of coolant temperature rise and flow rate are made. The valve is then opened, allowing a gas sample to flow through the probe, and the same measurements are repeated, together with those of the steady gas sample temperature at the probe exit and steady gas sample flow rate. The rate of heat removal from the gas sample is thus given by the difference between the two coolant rates:

$$\omega_g (h_{1g} - h_{2g}) = (\dot{\omega}_c C_{pc} \Delta T_c)_{flow} - (\dot{\omega}_c C_{pc} \Delta T_c)_{no\ flow}$$

where $\dot{\omega}_g$ = gas sample mass flow rate, $\dot{\omega}_c$ = coolant water mass flow rate, h_{1g} = unknown gas enthalpy at probe entrance, h_{2g} = gas enthalpy at probe exit thermocouple, C_{pc} = coolant specific heat, and ΔT_c = coolant temperature rise = $(T_c)_{out} - (T_c)_{in}$.

The technique was found to be quite successful, since the 'tare' measurement not only eliminates the error due to heat transfer from the outer portion of the jacket, but also the error due to radiation heating of the probe. Further, fabrication is comparatively simple compared to double-jacketed or tip-thermocouple designs, and models with outer diameters as small as 1.6 mm have been run successfully in atmospheric-pressure arcjet exhausts at temperatures over $13,900°K$. Further, the probe may be used to measure impact pressure when the gas sample flow is shut off during the tare measurement (and thereby the velocity or Mach number), and when the gas sample is extracted it may be analyzed for chemical composition. A typical experimental configuration for such determinations is shown in Figure 6-2.

The two disadvantages of the tare-measurement technique are (a) the necessity for intermittent probe operation, requiring either a steady-state environment or duplication of the test conditions for the flow and no-flow data points, and (b) the selection of a sufficiently small gas sample flow rate so that approximate flow conditions near the probe tip with no gas sample flowing are closely duplicated when the gas sample is being extracted.

The latter condition is readily established in a steady-state environment by simply making the tare measurement, and then taking a series of data at increasingly larger and larger gas sample flow rates. Calculation of gas enthalpy by the above equation for each sample flow rate should give the same value until the sample flow rate becomes large enough to violate the tip-flow duplication requirement, at which point an increasingly large error will be noted. A typical determination of this type, showing the resulting optimum gas sample flow rate to be used, appears in Figure 6-3. Note that the highest error-free gas sample rate should be used in order to obtain maximum probe sensitivity.

One consideration in any calorimetric probe analysis is the conversion of measured enthalpy to temperature, which requires a knowledge of the thermodynamic state of the unknown gas. In the case of nonreacting gases this is no problem. However, for partly dissociated or ionized media it is necessary either to establish that the unknown gas flow is in equilibrium, so that an equation of state may be used (e.g., the Saha equation) or else to measure independently the electron or dissociated radical concentration. This requirement does not, however, prejudice the enthalpy measurement. A second consideration, as discussed previously, is that these probes measure only stagnation enthalpy, and therefore require either very low subsonic flow ($M \ll 1$) or, in the case of supersonic or high subsonic Mach numbers, a separate determination of Mach number or velocity in order to determine the free-stream temperature T. In the case of the tare-measurement probe, this measurement is readily made while the tare measurement is being taken.

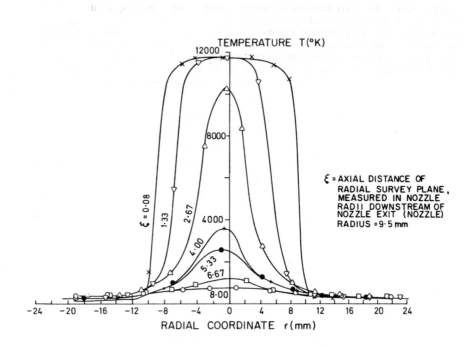

Fig. 6-6 Temperature surveys of axisymmetric subsonic turbulent arcjet exhausts using the tare measurement calorimetric probe of Figure 6-1

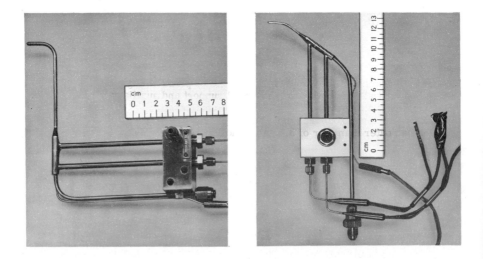

Fig. 6-7 Bent configurations of tare-measurement calorimetric probes of Figure 6-1

Furthermore, as in all high-temperature measurement devices, calibration of the calorimetric probe at operating temperatures presents something of a problem, since some sort of calibration standard is required. This was done for the probe of Figure 6-1 by utilizing an arcjet as a calorimeter; i.e., the total power of the jet issuing from the exit plane of an arcjet nozzle was computed from carefully-measured input power and arcjet-cooling-jacket power. The calorimetric probe of Figure 6-1 was then used to survey the nozzle exit plane (about 15 points on the diameter of an axisymmetric 19.1 mm diameter jet), and the resulting enthalpy, density, and velocity distributions were integrated to give the total power in the jet at the nozzle exit-plane. The departure from unity of the ratio of probe-measured power to arcjet-measured power:

$$\frac{\int_o^r 2\pi r \, (\rho V h) \, dr}{EI - \dot{m}_{ca} c_{ca} \Delta T_{ca}}$$

then provided a direct indication of the measurement error. Typical results are shown here in Figure 6-4.

It is illustrated that the good agreement of this figure was not fortuitous or the result of compensating errors, by the equally good agreement between the ratio of integrated probe-measured mass flow rate to arcjet input mass flow rate. The measured mass flow rate ratio:

$$\int_o^r 2\pi r \, (\rho V) \, dr \, / \, \dot{m}_a$$

is plotted in Figure 6-5, illustrating the same degree of precision as did the power ratio of Figure 6-4.

Each experimental point shown in Figures 6-4 and 6-5 represents a 15-data-point integration, illustrating the excellent resolution of the small-diameter probe. This characteristic, essential for making local measurements in a gas stream having high gradients, is more clearly brought out in Figure 6-6, which shows a series of temperature profiles at different axial locations in a turbulent subsonic arcjet (5).

An additional feature of the simple single-jacketed probe of Figure 6-1 is that it may be bent up to 90° in order to remove all support and auxiliary hardware from the hot region. Two commercially-available configurations used extensively in high-temperature environments are shown in Figure 6-7. The 90° probe in this figure has an outer diameter of 3.6 mm, and the 30° probe an outer diameter of 1.9 mm.

A final advantage of the tare-measurement probe is the comparatively modest requirement for auxiliary equipment. A 115 litre capacity 55 atm pressurized-water source provides both a one-hour controlled coolant supply and the necessary flow and pressure instrumentation, and a rack-mounted gas sample analysis system embodying the equipment of Figure 6-2 can be assembled from standard components.

In applying tare-measurement calorimetric probes to environments other than the one-atmosphere argon arcjet described by Grey, Jacobs, and Sherman, an important consideration in determining attainable accuracy levels is the so-called probe sensitivity. This has been defined as:

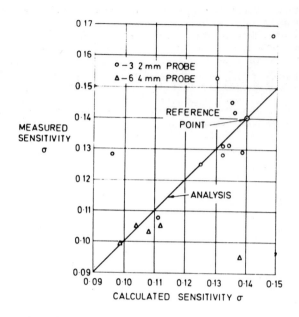

Fig. 6-8   Correlation of tare-measurement calorimetric probe sensitivity analysis with experimental results

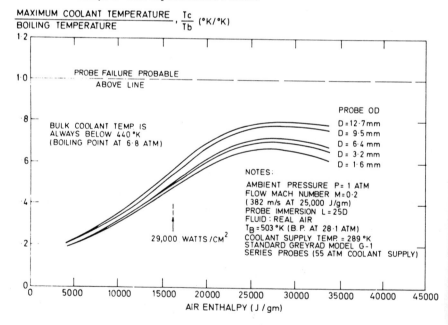

Fig. 6-9   Typical heat transfer capability of simple tare-measurement probe

$$\sigma = \frac{(\Delta T_c)_f - (\Delta T_c)_{\text{no flow}}}{(\Delta T_c)_f}$$

The sensitivity σ, which must be at least 0.05 in order that conventional thermo-couples provide adequate accuracy, depends not only on the hot-gas environment but also on the characteristics of the probe itself. An approximate analysis of this dependence has been performed by Grey (6) for a straight probe of the configuration shown in Figure 6-1. The analysis for the general case of a partly-dissociated, partly-ionized gas as given by Grey requires numerical integration and cannot be expressed in closed form; however, for small degrees of dissociation and/or ionization the sensitivity is given (6) by the approximate expression:

$$\frac{\sigma}{\sigma_{ref}} \approx \frac{(\dot{m}/A)_{ref}}{(\dot{m}/A)} \frac{(di/do)}{(di/do)_{ref}} \frac{di}{di_{ref}}^2 \frac{L_{ref}}{L} \frac{P}{P_{ref}} \frac{\Delta P}{\Delta P_{ref}} \frac{T_{ref}}{T}^{3/2}$$

where $()_{ref}$ indicates any reference set of values. This result was compared with experimental measurements for probes of two sizes for the following set of reference conditions:

P_{ref}	1 atm
σ_{ref}	0.14
T_{ref}	11,900°K
$(\dot{m}/A)_{ref}$	6.4 $\frac{Kg}{m^2 S}$
L_{ref}	98.3mm
$(d_i)_{ref}$	0.91mm
$(d_o)_{ref}$	3.58mm
$(\Delta P)_{ref}$	48.5mm Hg
Gas:	Argon

The result is shown here in Figure 6-8, which plots measured sensitivity σ against the sensitivity computed from the above equation. The ranges of conditions covered by these tests were:

T	6,700 to 13,300°K
ΔP	2.54 to 50.8mm Hg
$\dot{m}/A$	7 to 70 $\frac{Kg}{m^2 S}$
d_i	0.91 to 1.78mm
d_o	3.58 to 6.4

Despite the apparently unexplainable wide scatter of four of the data points, the first-order sensitivity formulation given above appears adequate, at least for estimation of the behavior of the tare-measurement probe of Figure 6-1 under different operating conditions.

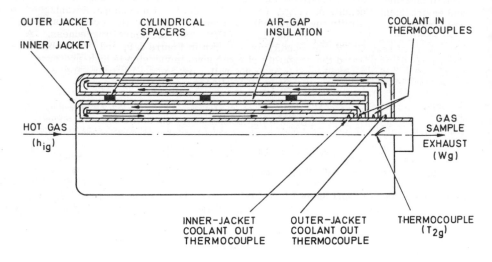

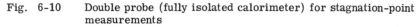

Fig. 6-10   Double probe (fully isolated calorimeter) for stagnation-point measurements

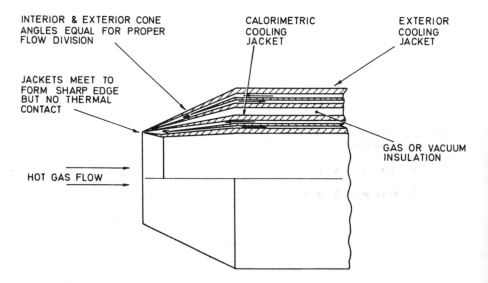

Fig. 6-11   Shock-swallowing double probe for enthalpy and mass flux measuremen in supersonic/hypersonic flows

This simple probe concept has been extremely successful in making rather sophisticated measurements at relatively high temperatures over a wide range of flow and environmental conditions (e.g., (5), (7-13) etc.). Its principal advantages are simplicity, capability for withstanding extremely high heat flux conditions in very small-diameter configurations (1.6mm OD), and mechanical ruggedness. A typical set of heat-flux design conditions is shown in Figure 6-9, and this probe design has demonstrated the capability of continuous immersion in high-pressure (100 atm) arc-heated wind tunnels at probe wall-surface heat transfer rates exceeding 8.2 Kw/cm^2.

Principal disadvantages of the simple tare-measurement probe are (a) the need to ensure sufficiently repeatable flow duplication at the tip between the tare and actual calorimetric measurements, as discussed above, (b) the decrease in sensitivity which occurs as the energy extracted from the gas sample flow becomes small relative to the total energy absorbed by the probe coolant; e.g., at low pressures and (c) the restriction to stagnation-point measurements in supersonic flows, imposed by both the blunt tip (needed for high heat flux capability) and the tare measurement requirement.

The first of these problems is readily accounted for by the calibration technique discussed earlier. The second and third disadvantages however, represent true limitations on the capability of the tare-measurement probe technique, and therefore, should test conditions be such as to introduce problems of low sensitivity or probe bow-shock interactions, different probe designs are required as will be discussed later. Parameters governing probe sensitivity are summarized in (6). Comparisons of blunt and shock-swallowing probes are made in (14) and (15), demonstrating the inconclusive nature of the current state of knowledge on probe shock effects ((14) indicates a major difference; (15) demonstrates none at all).

The real problem of reduced sensitivity at lower test pressures however, needs to be approached by returning to the old idea of completely isolating the calorimetric portion of the probe from the cooling jackets. This concept, now practical in probe dimensions as small as 4.8mm O.D. is shown in Figure 6-10 (other possible configurations being suggested in (16). Thermal isolation of the calorimeter, whose coolant flow may now be decreased to obtain any desired temperature rise, is achieved by (a) gas or vacuum space between the calorimetric (inner) jacket and exterior cooling jacket (b) silvering of the opposing jacket surfaces, and (c) regulation of flow passage dimensions so that with the prescribed coolant temperature rise in each jacket, there is no temperature difference between opposite points on the inner and outer jackets, thus eliminating interjacket heat flux.

The double-probe configuration of Figure 6-10 has been quite successful in reducing the error due to low sensitivity of the original tare-measurement concept described in (4). One interim method which proved unsuccessful because of unknown interjacket heat transfer was the 'split-flow' probe, described in (17 - 20).

A logical extension of the blunt double-probe configuration shown in Figure 6-10 is the sharp-inlet design of Figure 6-11. Operating on the same isolated-calorimeter principle as the blunt double-probe, this shock-swallowing probe concept provides two additional advantageous features: (a) ingestion of a much higher gas sample mass flow, particularly at hypersonic Mach numbers, thus improving sensitivity considerably (14), and (b) provision of mass-flux-measurement capability. Because of the large material concentration at the sharp edge, however, this probe cannot meet the heat-flux capability of either the simple tare-measurement probe, (Fig. 6-1) or the blunt double-probe configuration of Figure 6-10. Furthermore, the fabrication problems associated with this geometry have limited minimum probe diameters to the order of one inch. However, for large very low density (hypersonic) applications, the sharp-inlet probe has proven to be quite useful (for example, (14),(15),(21), (22).

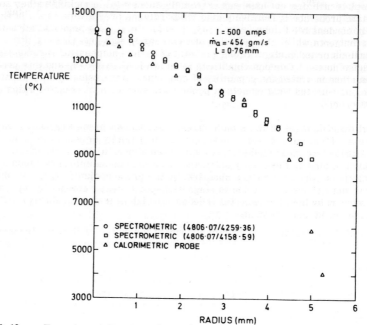

Fig. 6-12   Experimental comparison of calorimetric and spectrometric methods
of temperature determination

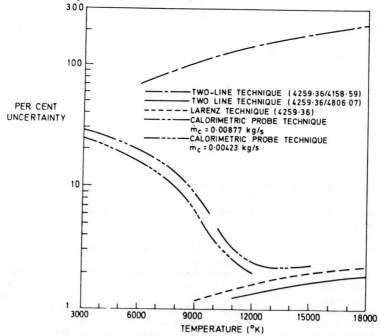

Fig. 6-13   Experimental uncertainty of plasma jet temperature-measurement
techniques

The concept of utilizing gaseous rather than liquid coolants with the above-described calorimetric probe configurations makes them extremely useful for measurement on enthalpy in condensible fluids; e.g., iodine vapor, lithium or other metal vapors, or in environments where the presence of water might be hazardous; e.g., nuclear rocket plenums or exhausts. Other gas-cooled probe applications are described later in these notes. One possible application of probe gas cooling has appeared in the literature in a number of instances (23), (24), (25) but without much practical development: the transpiration-cooled probe. To date, no truly effective transpiration-cooled probes have evolved.

One serious problem with any probe designed for extreme-temperature measurements is that of calibration. The only methods utilized to date are comparison methods, rather than true calibrations, but nevertheless these provide a basis for rather high confidence levels in these probes. Arcjet energy balances have demonstrated accuracies (standard deviation) within 2 percent, as described earlier (3), (4); comparisons with spectroscopic methods in regions where these comparisons were possible have demonstrated agreement within the same level (8), as illustrated in Figures 6-12 and 6-13, and comparisons with electrostatic-probe electron temperature measurements in equilibrium gases have shown better than 2 percent agreement (26), as will be discussed in detail later.

Cooled Electrostatic Probe

Although electrostatic probes have been applied to the measurement of electron and ion temperatures and densities for decades (1), (2), their utilization for so-called dense plasmas has been quite limited. Despite an enormous growth in the recent literature on cooled or diffusion controlled electrostatic probe theory, only a handful of experimental papers have appeared.

In principle, however, the use of a few relatively nonrestrictive assumptions makes possible the measurement of electron and ion characteristics in dense plasmas with surprisingly high accuracy, within the specific conditions required by the necessary assumptions. One excellent example of this simplified approach is indicated in (26), in which rather sophisticated nonequilibrium measurements in argon plasmas were achieved, without requiring theoretical treatment of any greater complexity than Langmuir's original concept. A detailed presentation of the analytical background leading to these measurements of electron temperature and density appears in (27), and an illustration of the simple theory which predicts the experimentally observed difference between electron and heavy-particle temperatures is described in (28). Subsequent applications of the cooled-probe technique have been utilized in measuring electron, positive ion and negative ion densities in rocket exhaust plasmas.

The fundamental difficulty in the application of cooled-probe techniques to electrostatic-probe measurements is the analysis of the effect of a cooled probe surface on observed current-voltage traces, in order that proper interpretation of the data be made possible.

Because the detailed theoretical probe problem is still largely a matter of conjecture, a somewhat simplified approach has been used, principally for the purpose of establishing direct comparisons with experimental data. The approximate theory does, however, deal with all the problems encountered by the application of a cooled probe, i.e., the presence of temperature and velocity boundary layers, distortion of charged and neutral particle densities in the region near the probe, and the mechanisms of ionization and recombination in the probe neighborhood. The sole purpose of this analysis is, of course, to relate the information obtained from the probe to the conditions in the undisturbed plasma. The approximate analysis is directed at a determination of the freestream electron temperature and,

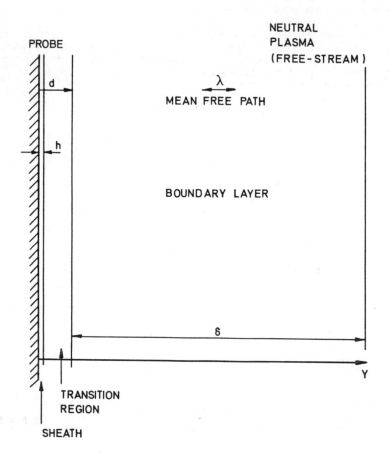

Fig. 6-14   Schematic diagram of four regions near a cooled electrostatic probe

if possible, the freestream electron density, based on characteristics that can be measured by a cooled probe.

In order to demonstrate that these measurements are valid, it is also of interest to determine the ratio of saturated electron current (high positive probe voltage) to saturated ion current (high negative probe voltage) and the floating potential (voltage at which electron and ion currents are equal). Since the electron temperature is the critical parameter to be measured, it is essential that knowledge of the probe's effect on this quantity be established. The saturation current ratio and the floating potential can be directly measured experimentally and therefore provide a satisfactory check on the assumptions used in the analysis once the electron temperature has been determined.

We begin by separating the over-all problem into four regions as shown in Figure 6-14, a sheath, in which the electric field effects are dominant, a transition region, in which electric field effects may still exist but in which the effects of collisions become important, a boundary layer in which there are no field effects and finally the freestream conditions, which extend to infinity. Note that we may characterize the probe by a flat plate as in Figure 6-14, since for the proposed environment the probe dimension will be thousands of times greater than a mean free path or the sheath thickness.

Establishing the relative dimensions of the three bounded regions in Figure 6-14, we first assume that the sheath thickness is of the order of the Debye length. Using Bohm's criterion (29) for the transition region thickness d, that the field beyond d is smaller than the variation in thermal energy over an electron-ion mean free path, we find (for the typical set of environmental conditions in Table 6-1) that d is of the order of 20 Debye lengths but still less than the order of a mean free path (30-32). It is thus concluded that all electric-field effects are confined to a region within one pertinent mean free path from the probe. Further discussion of this conclusion appears later.

Table 6-1: Typical Conditions for Cooled-Electrostatic Probe Evaluation

Properties		Speeds, cm/sec		Lengths, cm	
T_∞	$= 12,000°K$ $(21,500°R)$	C_e	$= 7 \times 10^7$	$L/2$	$= 10^{-1}$
T_w	$= 300°K$ $(540°R)$	C_A	$= 2.5 \times 10^5$	δ	$=. 1.0 \times 10^{-2}$
P	$= 1$ atm	U_∞	$= 3 \times 10^4$	λ_{e-A}	$= 1.43 \times 10^{-3}$
$N_{A\infty}$	$= 6 \times 10^{17} cm^{-3}$		$\cdots$	λ_{e-I}	$= 1.5 \times 10^{-4}$
N_{AW}	$= 2.7 \times 10^{19} cm^{-3}$		$\cdots$	h	$= 2.87 \times 10^{-6}$
$N_{e\infty}$	$= 6.3 \times 10^{16} cm^{-3}$		$\cdots$		$\cdots$
α_∞	$= 0.105$		$\cdots$		$\cdots$

Consider the specific case of a positive cooled probe of dimension $L \gg \lambda$ immersed in a subsonic plasma flow, the electrons of which are in a Maxwellian distribution around a temperature no lower than the heavy-particle temperature. The foregoing arguments permit us to assume that (a) the boundary-layer thickness δ is much greater than that of the sheath ($\delta \gg h$), and (b) electrons are captured by the probe when they reach the sheath boundary. Furthermore, the heavy-particle temperature in the boundary layer is assumed to decrease from its freestream value to the cooled-probe wall temperature in accordance with usual boundary-layer behavior. Finally, we assume for the moment that although the electrons may lose energy to the ions or atoms by elastic collisions, they do not suffer recombination, i.e., the boundary layer is chemically frozen.

The fraction of energy lost by an electron to a heavy particle in a single elastic collision may be written as:

$$\frac{\overline{\Delta E}}{E_o} = \overline{F(\chi)} \; \frac{4 \, m_e \, m_H}{(m_e + m_H)^2}$$

where $\overline{F(\chi)}$ is the average steric factor over all possible deflection angles χ and has the value $\frac{1}{2}$.

Thus, for $m_e \ll m_H$:

$$\overline{\Delta E}/E_o \approx 2(m_e/m_H)$$

For argon:

$$\overline{\Delta E}/E_o \approx 1/36,600$$

so that after n collisions, where $n \ll 36,600$:

$$E_n/E_o \approx [1 - (n/36,600)]$$

We may now approximate the number of heavy-particle collisions which an electron will experience in traversing the boundary layer by:

$$n = (6)^{\frac{1}{2}} \; (\delta/\overline{\lambda}) \; (Re_L)^{\frac{1}{2}}$$

where the factor $(6)^{\frac{1}{2}}$ accounts for the three-dimensional movement of the electron, δ is the Schlichting stagnation-point boundary-layer thickness (33), $\overline{\lambda}$ is the mean value of the pertinent mean free path, and $(Re_L)^{\frac{1}{2}}$ (Reynolds number based on probe radius L) accounts for the effective increase in δ due to the potential flow around the stagnation point.

Values of n for various temperatures in the 1-atm subsonic argon plasma flow under consideration are shown in Table 6-2, using actual Ramsauer cross-sectional data for argon (σ_{e-A} and σ_{e-I} based on electron energy).

It is clear that in the medium temperature range the electrons suffer so few collisions across the boundary layer (~ 0.010 cm thick) that they lose very little energy: e.g., when $T = 10,500°K$ ($19,000°R$), $n = 370$, and the final electron energy is ~ 99 percent E_o. Clearly in this range it may be assumed that the electron temperature change across the probe boundary layer will be negligible. This conclusion is in excellent agreement with the work of Talbot (34), Kumura and Kanzawa (35), and Pytte and Williams (36). Calculations were also performed to determine the effects of variable heavy-particle temperature profiles, electron and atom densities, and mean free paths through the boundary layer which showed essentially no difference from the results in Table 6-2.

At higher temperatures, however, the reduction in ion-electron mean free path causes n to increase, so that at $13,500°K$ ($24,000°R$) the electrons suffer an energy loss of about 5 percent. Although this effect levels off when the plasma becomes fully ionized (i. e., over 15, 000 °K or 27, 000 °R), electron temperature corrections will then be of the order of 10 or 20 percent and clearly represent a limitation of the cooled-probe technique.

Table 2: Calculation of Number of Electron Collisions n in 0.01-cm Boundary Layer on 0.095-cm (radius) Probe in Argon at 1 atm

T_∞, °K	T_∞, °R	α_∞	$N_{e\ \infty}$, cm^{-3}	$N_{A\ \infty}$, cm^{-3}	λ_∞, cm	n
13, 500	24, 300	0.300	1.5×10^{17}	4.5×10^{17}	6.7×10^{-5}	2, 000
12, 000	21, 500	0.100	6.3×10^{16}	6.0×10^{17}	1.5×10^{-4}	840
10, 500	18, 900	0.035	2.5×10^{16}	7.1×10^{17}	4.6×10^{-4}	370
8, 500	15, 300	0.003	2.4×10^{14}	8.0×10^{17}	1.0×10^{-4}	175
7, 200	13, 000	10^{-4}	1.0×10^{14}	1.0×10^{18}	1.0×10^{-3}	175
6, 100	11, 000	10^{-5}	1.3×10^{13}	1.3×10^{18}	1.0×10^{-3}	175
5, 200	9, 400	10^{-6}	1.5×10^{12}	1.5×10^{18}	1.0×10^{-3}	175
1, 000	1, 800	10^{-13}	10^6	7.2×10^{18}	7.3×10^{-4}	220
300	540	10^{-13}	10^6	2.7×10^{19}	1.8×10^{-4}	1, 000

It has been established that under the proper plasma conditions, the electron temperature in the freestream plasma will be preserved throughout the boundary layer, so that $T_e \approx T_{e\infty}$ and $T_I \approx T_w$, and it is assumed that as before, $(h/L)^2 << 1$, y $\geqslant \lambda \geqslant h$, and $\delta << L$. One further assumption is required in order to utilize these expressions to evaluate the performance of the cooled electrostatic probe. Since it has already been shown that most of the probe potential drop has occurred at y = λ, the effective potential φ_λ is approximated by $\varphi_\lambda \approx V - V$ plasma. If it is now assumed that V plasma $\approx$ constant for slightly negative applied voltages V, the classical Langmuir electron-current expression can be differentiated:

$$je \approx \tfrac{1}{4} Ne_\lambda \ \overline{Ce}_\lambda \ \exp[-e\varphi_\lambda/kTe],$$

replacing $d\varphi_\lambda$ by dV, obtaining the familiar result:

$$\frac{d(\log_e je)}{dV} = -\frac{e}{kTe_\lambda} \approx -\frac{e}{kTe_\infty}$$

This result could be subject to some doubt on two counts: firstly the plasma potential may change appreciably in the range $-\varphi_F < V < O$, and secondly, the conclusion $T_{e_\lambda} \approx T_{e\infty}$ is valid only in the neighborhood of (V - V plasma). Experimental data have shown however, as will be discussed later, that the indicated proportionality of log je to V is valid over a sufficiently wide range of applied negative voltages to be useful in determining the electron temperature.

It can also be concluded that, if this expression is used to calculate the electron temperature $T_{e\infty}$ from measured current-voltage characteristics, the comparable first-order (Langmuir) expressions for saturation current ratio and floating potential may be experimentally evaluated by direct measurement. It is, of course, first necessary to validate the all-important electron temperature determination by some independent calibration measurement, which is performed as described later.

It must be carefully noted that the preceding estimates are not presented in the guise of a theory of the operation of an electrostatic probe in a dense plasma, but

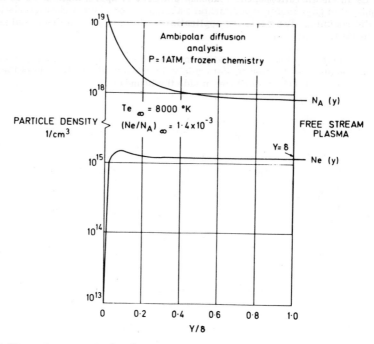

Fig. 6-15   Argon neutral and electron particle density boundary-layer profiles

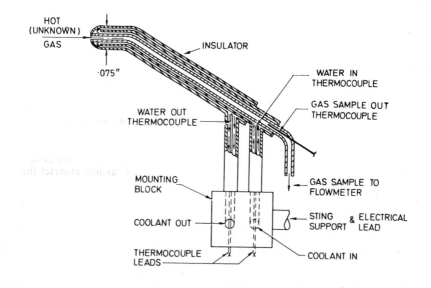

Fig. 6-16   Calorimetric-electrostatic probe

rather as an identification of the reasonable degree of approximation which may be employed to gain useful experimental information on plasma characteristics in a specific regime. The basis for application of this analysis is discussed at length in (26).

In one final problem, that of estimating the freestream electron density by cooled-probe measurements, it must be determined in detail what the effect is of the cooled boundary layer on electron densities inside the boundary layer, i.e., between the freestream and a location one mean free path from the probe surface. This involves the solution of the ambipolar diffusion equation in the neighborhood of the probe which has been performed by Brundin and Talbot (37). They assumed steady, one-dimensional, weakly ionized, constant-pressure flow in a stagnation-point boundary layer in which the plasma was quasi-neutral (outside the sheath), with frozen electron temperature ($T_{e_\infty} = T_e = T_{e_\lambda}$), equal ion and atom temperatures ($T_I = T_A$) and frozen chemistry (no recombination). Their analysis allowed for variable heavy-particle temperature, density, viscosity, diffusion coefficient, and thermal conductivity within the boundary layer. A similar analysis for full constant-pressure equilibrium chemistry (27) produced similar results for N_e/N_A, except that large differences were observed near the wall.

The very useful result of this numerical calculation (Fig. 6-15) i.e., that $N_{e_\infty} \approx N_e$, appears to be fortuitous rather than general and cannot be applied indiscriminately. However, the breadth of application of this result can be determined by measuring the random electron current $(j_e)_r$ at the plasma potential and calculating N_{e_λ} for known $T_{e_\lambda} \approx T_{e_\infty}$. Then, since N_{e_∞} is known from electron Saha equilibrium about T_{e_∞}, a direct comparison may be made. Conversely, we may assume, based on the result of Figure 6-15, that $N_{e_\infty} \approx N_{e_\lambda}$ and deduce T_{e_∞} from measurements of $(j_e)_r$ under the previous approximations $T_{e_\lambda} \approx T_{e_\infty}$ and $(j_e) \approx (j_e)_r$. These values of T_{e_∞} may then be compared with values obtained by other measurements, as will be discussed later.

One further consideration that deserves some comment is the assumption implicit in the foregoing analysis, that electron-ion recombination was negligible in the probe boundary layer. This has been checked (27) by the detailed consideration of all possible recombination mechanisms, i.e., radiative, dielectronic, dissociative, and three-body. It was concluded that the characteristic recombination times for a 1-atm argon plasma were considerably greater than the electron or ion transit times in the boundary layer for all temperatures below $11,000°K$ ($20,000°R$), but that the two times become comparable at about $12,000°K$ ($21,500°R$). This contribution becomes increasingly more important up to about $15,000°K$ ($27,000°R$), where the recombination time is about an order of magnitude smaller than the transit time. Above $15,000°K$ ($27,000°R$), the plasma is virtually fully ionized, and the probe boundary layer may be assumed to be in chemical equilibrium. Thus, the assumption of frozen chemistry is valid in the same range as is the earlier approximation that $T_{e_\infty} \approx T_{e_\lambda}$ and thereby does not further restrict the useful regime of the cooled-probe technique.

The primary purpose of the experiments was to evaluate the cooled-probe method for measuring electron temperature and if possible, electron density, in a dense plasma. A secondary purpose was to examine the validity of the rough analytical approach in the dense plasma regime by comparing predicted and measured values of saturation current ratio and floating potential.

Tests were run by inserting the cooled calorimetric-electrostatic probe of Figure 6-16 into the 1 cm diam exhaust of the laminar atmospheric-pressure argon arcjet and making measurements at different axial locations on the jet centerline. The probe consisted of a 1.9mm diam calorimetric probe (4) insulated with a zirconium

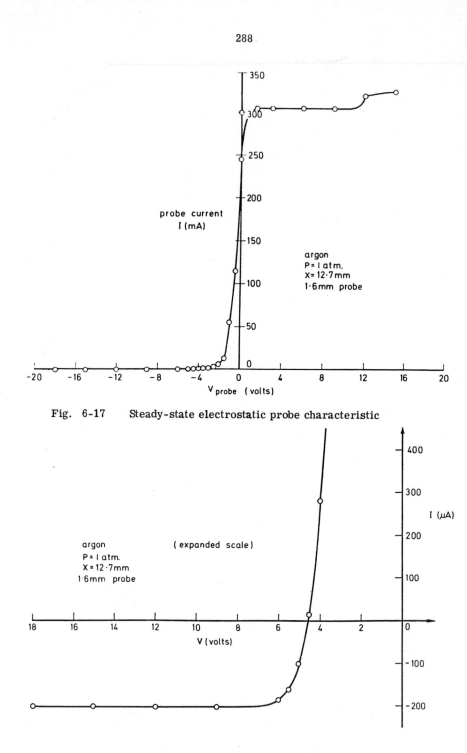

Fig. 6-17   Steady-state electrostatic probe characteristic

Fig. 6-18   Steady-state electrostatic probe characteristic

oxide/boron nitride composition over all but a small known area (1.6mm diam) on the probe tip. The measurements were of total enthalpy, velocity, and chemical composition (to verify that the argon was undiluted by traces of air in the jet environment), as measured by the calorimetric portion of the probe (4), as well as the current-voltage trace of the electrostatic portion. The latter measurement was performed when gas flow through the probe was shut off so that the probe gas sample tube mouth was at stagnation conditions, and the effective collecting area therefore did not include the heavily cooled interior of the gas sample tube. Both d.c. and sweep techniques were used i.e., using a d.c. battery at different voltages to power the probe, reading the resulting direct current output on a Keithley electrometer; or using an x-y oscilloscope both to drive the probe (x axis) and to display the current output (y axis). Oscilloscope sweep frequencies used were 60 Hz and revealed excellent reproducibility of the probe current-voltage trace in laminar arcjet flows.

Typical d.c. test data of the electrostatic probe appear in Figure 6-17, and Figure 6-18 amplifies the negative portion of Figure 6-4. These figures clearly show the expected ion-current saturation, as predicted for the high values of L/λ and L/h, and indicate the degree of precision obtainable in the measurement of saturation current ratio $(j_e/j_I)_{sat}$ and floating potential φ_F for comparison with first-order theory.

Determination of the electron temperature was performed by the previously-discussed classical method as illustrated in Figure 6-19, which by its appreciable range of linearity, clearly illustrates the validity of the assumption that for the range of conditions tested, the probe electric field effects do not penetrate very far into the boundary layer. Note also the clear definition of the plasma potential.

A final measurement extracted from the cooled electrostatic probe data was the electron current at the plasma potential ($\varphi_\lambda = O$). Because the saturation ion current is so low, we can assume that at $\varphi_\lambda = O$, the total current is that due to the electrons and will be the random electron current:

$$j_e \, (\varphi_\lambda = O) = \tfrac{1}{4} N_{e\lambda} \, \overline{C}_{e\lambda}$$

Taking $T_{e\lambda} \approx T_{e\infty}$, therefore, we may now evaluate the range of validity of the results of Figure 6-15, i.e., the observation that for one particular numerical condition, $N_{e\lambda} \approx N_{e\infty}$. The measurement of j_e at $\varphi_\lambda = O$ is thus used, with the assumption that $N_{e\lambda} = N_{e\infty}$, to determine $T_{e\infty}$ and the result is compared with $T_{e\infty}$ as determined by two other methods. Agreement within ± 2 percent on values of $T_{e\infty}$ implies that the assumption $N_{e\lambda} \approx N_{e\infty}$ is valid to within about ± 10 percent.

The principal experimental problem was the evaluation of electron temperature measurements by the cooled electrostatic probe. This was done by utilizing as a calibration measurement the enthalpy measured by the calorimetric portion of the probe, which was then used to determine the average gas temperature (very close to the heavy-particle temperature T_H for the low degrees of ionization of these tests). Electron temperatures were determined by the classical method shown in Figure 6-19, from current-voltage characteristics of the electrostatic portion of the probe. Also, the random electric current (at the plasma potential) was used to calculate electron temperature in order to evaluate the postulate that $N_{e\lambda} = N_{e\infty}$, as was discussed previously.

The foregoing measurements were made at a number of axial stations along the centerline of a laminar argon jet as mentioned earlier, the jet cooling thereby providing a suitable temperature range. Results of the axial survey of 1 atm

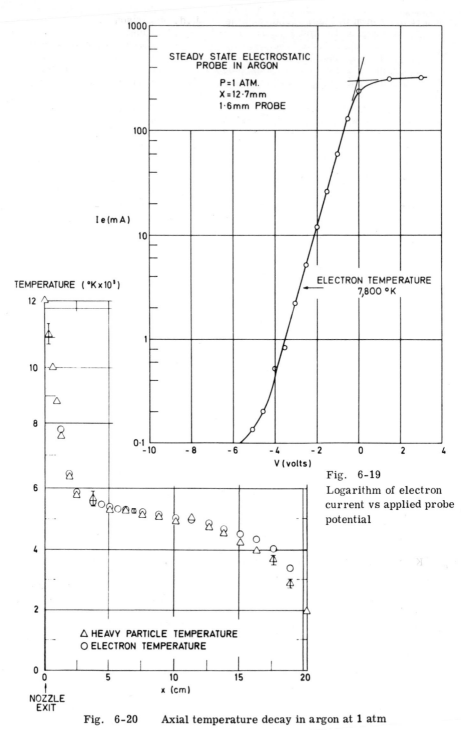

Fig. 6-19

Logarithm of electron current vs applied probe potential

Fig. 6-20   Axial temperature decay in argon at 1 atm

pressure are shown in Figure 6-20, and the detailed comparison between T_H, $T_{e\infty}$, from Figure 6-19, and $T_{e\infty}$, from random-current measurements (assuming $N_{e\lambda} = N_{e\infty}$) is shown in Table 6-3. Agreement at the higher temperatures between $T_{H\infty}$ and $T_{e\infty}$ by both methods is quite good, indicating an accuracy level for the electrostatic probe which is at least as good as that of the calorimetric probe, i.e., better than 3 percent for $T_{e\infty}$, and thus of the order of 10 percent for $N_{e\infty}$.

Table 6-3: Calibration of Electron Temperature and Density Measurements in Argon Plasma at 1 atm

Location X, cm	Electron temperature T_e Electrostatic probe, °K		Heavy particle temperature T_H Calorimetric probe, °K
	In I_e vs V	Random current at $\varphi = 0$ (assuming $N_e \approx N_{e\infty}$)	
1.27	7,840	7,840	7,840
2.54	5,890	5,890	5,780
3.81	5,550	5,560	5,660
5.08	5,390	5,360	5,290

Finally, the probe data used to prepare Figure 6-20 and Table 6-3 were applied as a check on the saturation current ratio and floating potential estimates of the first-order (Langmuir) theory. Results are presented in Table 6-4 and indicate that the first-order approximations are reasonably valid, with no greater than about 10 percent error within the region studied. However, note that there is a consistent variation between experiment and theory in both of these properties, indicating the likelihood of a systematic contribution by the higher-order terms in both expressions.

Table 6-4: Saturation Current Ratio and Floating Potential in Argon Plasma at 1 atm

T_e, °K	$(j_e/j_i)_{sat}$		$\varphi_F - \varphi_{plasma}$, V	
	Experiment	Theory	Experiment (a)	Theory
7,840	1450	1380	-5.0	-4.72
5,890	1300	1200	-4.0	-3.70
5,550	1200	1170	-3.5	-3.45
5.390	1100	1150	-3.0	-3.25
5,220	1000	1130	-2.6	-2.95

(a) $\pm \frac{1}{2}$ v uncertainty in plasma potential.

Having established the validity of the cooled-probe method for electron temperature

292

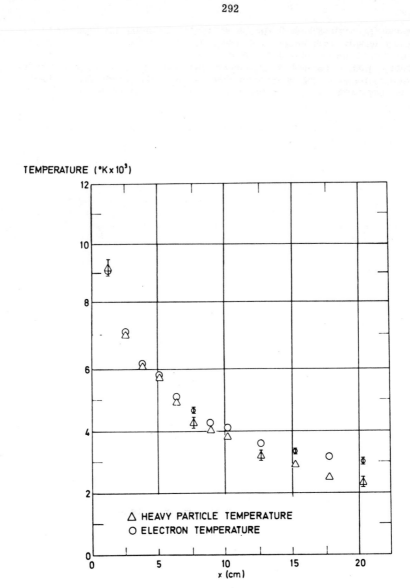

Fig. 6-21   Axial temperature decay in argon at 380 mm Hg

measurements, a series of tests was run at reduced pressure ($\frac{1}{2}$ atm) in order to detect any departure from equilibrium by simultaneous measurement of heavy-particle temperatures (calorimetric probe) and electron temperatures (electrostatic probe). Results are shown in Figure 6-21, clearly indicating a divergence in the two temperatures starting at about 5000°K (9000°R) and increasing rapidly at lower temperatures, a trend predicted by Jacobs and Grey (28). Applying the electron temperature'freezing'criterion established in (28) to these $\frac{1}{2}$-atm tests, the first recognizable difference between electron and heavy-particle temperatures should appear at about 5500°K (9900°R), which is in reasonable agreement with the experimental observation of Figure 6-21.

A final observation, in confirmation of those reported by Demetriades and Doughman, (38) (39) was that, when the electrostatic probe was driven by 60 Hz a.c., an excellent semi-qualitative indication of turbulence was observed. That is, in laminar flows, the current-voltage characteristic of the probe, as observed on an oscilloscope screen, was reproducible. However, as soon as the probe was moved to a transition region in the subsonic jet, the current-voltage trace was slightly different on each sweep, giving the appearance, on a retentive oscilloscope screen, of a line-broadening effect. This broadening was observed to increase qualitatively with intensity of turbulence and is most likely to be caused by fluctuations in local electron density.

For the general conditions appropriate to these experiments, e.g., for dense arcjet environments, it was concluded that many of the factors that result in highly complicated plasma behavior near the probe become relatively insignificant, permitting the use of surprisingly simple probe trace analyses. Although these simple approximations are certainly limited in their applicability as compared with the multitude of elaborate theoretical studies prevalent in the literature, they appear to be reasonably valid over a surprisingly wide range of practical conditions.

Radiation Probe

Measurement of total thermal radiation from arcjets and other difficult environments has often been complicated, or even precluded, by the cool absorbing gas layer which generally surrounds the hot-gas region of interest. At plasma temperatures and pressures for which enthalpy or other probe measurements are useful, the radiated energy can often constitute a significant fraction, and its determination can be quite important. A simple water-cooled collimator (Fig. 6-22) is thus used to penetrate the cool outer regions (which can often absorb as much as 90 percent of the total energy radiated from a dense, partly-ionized gas), and observe the hot core flow directly. This technique is described in detail in (40).

Cyclic Probe

An approach to the measurement of high gas temperatures using an intermittently-cooled thermocouple was developed in the early sixties, but it has not seen extensive application. It nevertheless represents an attractive technique for the determination of temperatures in gases whose pressure-enthalpy product is too low for proper sensitivity of the simple tare-measurement calorimetric probe, and yet at temperatures too high for thermocouples or other conventional immersion instruments.

The cyclic probe (41) consists of a cooled tube through which a thermocouple junction is alternately injected out into the hot gas stream and retracted inside the cooled tube (see Fig. 6-23). The thermocouple output is thus an oscillating voltage, which alternately increases to some never-attained high asymptotic value

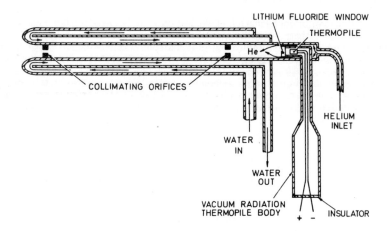

Fig. 6-22   Cooled probe used for radiation measurements inside optically inaccessible plasma regions

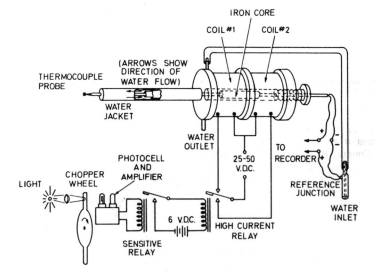

Fig. 6-23   Intermittent (cyclic) thermocouple probe and cycling circuit

while in the hot gas, whose temperature is often well above the thermocouple's melting point, and decreases to a never-attained low asymptotic value while in the cooled tube. The average voltage, as is shown in (41), is a direct function of the cyclic frequency, the ratio of dwell times inside the tube and exposed to the hot gas, and the gas temperature. Since the frequency and dwell-time ratio are known, the temperature can be determined. Calibration of this device may be achieved by simple varying the frequency which, incidentally, can also be adjusted to provide maximum sensitivity without probe failure.

Transient Pressure Probe

This is a unique cooled-probe technique developed for a difficult measurement in an extremely high heat-flux environment. In the measurement of transient deto-nation wave characteristics inside rocket thrust chambers which are experiencing high-frequency combustion instability, it is necessary to mount a very high-fre-quency response transducer within the chamber (not at the wall). The only suitable transducer element (in terms of frequency response) is a piezo-electric crystal; unfortunately, however, crystals are subject to severe temperature drift, and therefore require highly effective cooling in the expected 8.2 Kw/cm^2 environ-ment.

The solution, shown in Figure 6-24, was to employ a cooled probe with a commer-cial 5.6mm diameter crystal transducer mounted in its tip (natural frequency approximately 400,000 Hz). The transducer diaphragm was splash-cooled by a ring of tiny re-entrant jets directed at different angles so as to completely cover the transducer face. An ablative coating provided short-term protection during passage of the detonation wave (in case the resulting coolant-jet interruption would have caused damage to the transducer). This design provides effective cooling of the transducer, with no sacrifice in frequency response, and full protection against drift-producing temperature changes.

Heat Flux Probe

As indicated in (3), one method for deducing gas enthalpy in the high-density environment of interest is the measurement of heat transfer rate. In fact, the local heat flux itself is often an extremely important measurement for engineering design purposes. Unfortunately, however, most heat-flux gauges distort the very heat flux pattern they are attempting to measure. That is, unless the heat flux to, say, a cooled body is not distorted by the installation of a gauge, the gauge will measure the wrong heat transfer rate, even though the gauge itself may be calibrated to very high accuracy.

One recent development of considerable interest is the use of an old principle in a new form to measure high heat transfer rates without distorting the heat flux to be measured. Illustrated in Figure 6-25, this concept utilizes the one-dimen-sional Fourier heat conduction equation to measure heat flux. The gauge itself consists of three thin, flat wafers selected from the many pairs of thermocouple materials. For example, the outer wafers could be copper and the inner one constantan. Electrical lead wires, insulated and sealed in copper tubing for ruggedness, are brought out of the back of the gauge. If the front of the gauge is now exposed to a high-temperature region and the back is at a lower temperature (e.g., by water cooling), the heat flux through the gauge will produce a tempera-ture difference across the center wafer. Since the wafer thickness, which has been measured to the nearest 0.00013mm is much smaller than its diameter, the heat flux is very nearly one-dimensional in nature. The measured temperature drop ΔT, the known wafer thickness Δx, and the mean thermal conductivity $\bar{k}$ of the center wafer (known exactly because the maximum and minimum temperatures

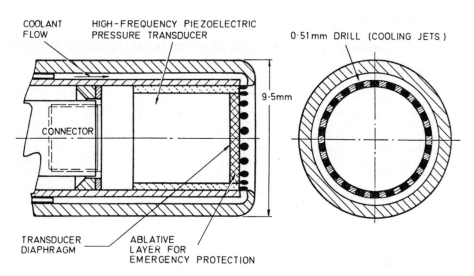

Fig. 6-24   Water-cooled high-frequency transient pressure probe

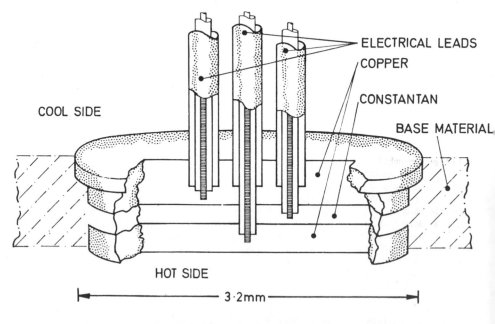

Fig. 6-25   View of cooled thin-wafer heat flux gauge showing its construction
and operating principle

of the wafer are known), may then be used in the simple integrated form of the one-dimensional Fourier equation to calculate the heat flux q /A:

$$q\ /A\ =\ -\bar{k}\ \frac{\Delta T}{\Delta x}$$

This basic principle, of course, is not at all new in the field of heat flux measurement. However, this heat transfer gauge possesses several unique features which provide major improvements in accuracy over prior applications of the principle. Firstly, relative thicknesses of the three wafers can be varied to match exactly the conductance of the base material in which the gauge is mounted. Thus, lateral heat conduction (in directions other than along the gauge axis) is minimized. For example, the copper-constantan gauge can match the conductance of any base material whose mean thermal conductivity falls between those of copper and constantan. Other base materials can be matched by using different thermocouple materials; e.g., chrome alumel, tungsten-tungsten/rhenium, platinum-platinum/rhodium, etc.

Secondly, by using relatively fine electrical leads (0.25mm maximum), and by using appropriate insulation material and thicknesses so that the overall conductance of the wire installation is identical to that of the center wafer, it is possible to reduce the distortion from true one-dimensional heat flux to very small values.

Thirdly, the "hot-side" surface of the gauge can be coated or plated with the same material and finish as the base material, so that its radiation absorption characteristics will be identical with those of the base material. Thus, the gauge installation produces no effect on base material heat transfer due to radiation or convection in addition to conduction.

This thin-wafer heat flux gauge can be used in a stagnation-point probe (Fig. 6-26) for heat transfer rates as high as 5 Kw/cm^2 or incorporated into a cooled-skin structure such as a hyperthermal wind-tunnel model (Fig. 6-27). In either application, its unique combination of high heat flux capability, ruggedness of construction, small diameter and thickness, and most important, virtually exact simulation of the one-dimensional heat transfer equation, make it one of the most useful techniques for heat flux measurement in any range.

Conclusion

In the somewhat more familiar temperature range (1000-2200°K) the utilization of water or gas-cooled probe techniques (calorimetric, heat flux, etc.) for measurement and control of gas temperatures offers several advantages over the more conventional thermocouples and resistance thermometers generally utilized in this range. Most important is their life expectancy: because a cooled probe operates at maximum surface temperatures well below those at which strength and corrosion characteristics begin to deteriorate (e.g., 370° - 480°K), a cooled calorimetric or heat flux probe will far outlast even a high temperature thermocouple, which must, by its very nature, always operate at the gas temperature to be measured. Further, for control purposes, both calorimetric and heat-flux probes sense the product of density and enthalpy (or density and temperature, for nondissociated gases), and therefore lend themselves to utilization as fundamental input-energy control-function sensors for virtually any energy-producing system (e.g., jet engines, furnaces, arcjets or other plasma generators, etc.). Moreover cooled probes can be used even for the measurement of condensible flows by simply using a gaseous coolant (e.g., hydrogen or helium) to maintain the probe surface temperature above the boiling point of the fluid to be measured.

WATER COOLED COPPER TUBE   MODEL G-15 GAUGE

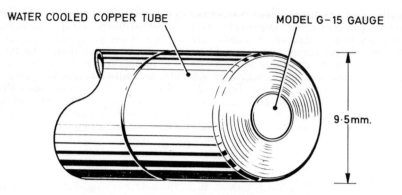

9·5mm.

Fig. 6-26   Wafer-type heat flux gauge installed in cooled stagnation-point heat
flux probe suitable for measurement up to 5 kW/cm^2

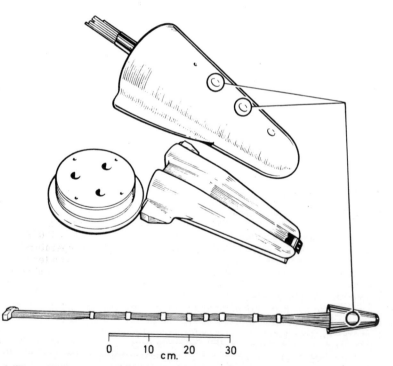

0   10   20   30
cm.

Fig. 6-27   Wafer-type heat flux gauge installed in a water cooled hypersonic
wind-tunnel model. Heat transfer rates to this 9° half-angle blunted
cone model range from 24 to 350 watts/cm^2

Finally, probe techniques lend themselves to many areas not suitable for optical methods (spectroscopic, microwave, laser, electron-beam, etc.). Disturbance of the flow to be measured, a definite disadvantage of any probe technique, is minimized by the recent advances achieved in probe miniaturization. On the plus side, they have the capability for accurate local measurement of steady-stage or transient characteristics in opaque or otherwise optically inaccessible gases having high property gradients, (e.g., $20,000°K/cm$). When combined with the relatively low cost and complexity associated with auxiliary equipment, and the ruggedness, simplicity, and low cost of the probes themselves, this often tends to make probe measurements more palatable than the optical methods.

References

1. **Finkelnburg, W., and Maecker, H.** 'Electric Arcs and Thermal Plasma,' Handbuch der Physik, Vol. 22, Springer-Verlag, Heidelberg, Germany.

2. **Langmuir, I.** 'The Pressure Effect and Other Phenomena in Gaseous Discharges,' J. of the Franklin Institute Vol. 196, 1923, pp. 751-762.

3. **Grey, J.** 'Thermodynamic Methods of High-Temperature Measurement,' ISA Transactions, Vol. 4, April, 1965, pp. 102-115.

4. **Grey, J., Jacobs, P. F. and Sherman, M. P.** 'Calorimetric Probe for the Measurement of Extremely High Temperatures,' Review of Scientific Instruments, Vol. 33, July, 1962, pp. 738-741.

5. **Grey, J. and Jacobs, P. F.** 'Experiments on Turbulent Mixing in a Partially Ionized Gas,' AIAA Journal, Vol. 2, March, 1964, pp. 433-438.

6. **Grey, J.** 'Sensitivity Analysis for the Calorimetric Probe,' Review of Scientific Inst. Vol. 34, Aug. 1963, pp. 857-859.

7. **Grey, J., Sherman, M. P., Williams, P. M. and Fradkin, D. B.** 'Laminar Arcjet Mixing and Heat Transfer: Theory and Experiments,' AIAA Journal Vol. 4, June, 1966, pp. 986-993.

8. **Incropera, F. P. and Leppert, G.** 'Investigation of Arc Jet Temperature-Measurement Techniques,' ISA Transactions Vol. 6, Jan. 1967, pp. 35-41.

9. **Au, G. G. and Sprengel, U.** 'Kalorimetrische Messungen von Ortlichen Temperaturen und Geschwindigkeiten in einem Stickstoff-Plasmastrahl,' Zeitschrift fur Flugwissenschaften Vol. 14, April, 1966, pp. 188-194.

10. **Williams, P. M. and Grey, J.** 'Simulation of Gaseous Core Nuclear Rocket Characteristics Using Cold and Arc Heated Flows,' NASA Contractor Report No. CR-690, June, 1967.

11. **Grey, J.** 'Cooled Probe Diagnostics of Dense Plasma Mixing and Heat Transfer Processes,' American Inst. of Chem. Eng. Preprint 9C, Nov. 26-30, 1967.

12. **Massier, P. F., Back, L. H. and Roschke, E. J.** 'Heat Transfer and Laminar Boundary Layer Distributions to an Internal Subsonic Gas Stream at Temperatures up to $13,900°R$,' NASA Contract NAS-7-100, Jet Prop. Lab. 1968.

13. O'Connor, T. J., Comfort, E. G. and Cass, L. A. 'Turbulent Mixing of an Axisymmetric Jet of Partially Dissociated Nitrogen with Ambient Air,' AIAA Journal Vol. 4, Nov. 1966, pp. 2026-2032.

14. Anderson, L. A. and Sheldahl, R. E. 'Flow-Swallowing Enthalpy Probes in Low-Density Plasma Streams,' AIAA Paper No. 68-390, April 8-10, 1968.

15. Folck, J. L. and Heck, R. R. 'Operational Experiences and Preliminary Results of Total Enthalpy Probe Measurements in the AFFDL 50-Megawatt Electrogasdynamics Facility,' USAF Report No. FDM-TM-68-2, April, 1968.

16. Huber, F. J. A. 'Probes for Measuring Mass Flux, Stagnation Point Heating and Total Enthalpy of High-Temperature Hypersonic Flows,' AIAA Preprint No. 66-750, Sept. 21-23, 1966.

17. Halbach, C. R. and Freeman, L. 'The Enthalpy Sensor - A High Gas Temperature Measuring Probe,' Report MR 20, 331, The Marquardt Corporation, June, 1965.

18. Haas, F. C. and Vassallo, F. A. 'Measurement of Stagnation Enthalpy in a High Energy Gas Stream,' published in Chem. Eng. Prog. Symposium Series 41, Vol. 59, AICHE, 1963.

19. Malliaris, A. C. et al 'Optical and Radar Observables of Ablative Materials,' AFML TR 66-331, Pt. 1, Air Force Systems Command, Oct. 1966.

20. Grey, J. 'Enthalpy Probes for Arc Plasmas - First Status Review,' Report to Committee E-21, ASTM, April 12, 1966.

21. Esker, D. W. 'A Probe for Total-Enthalpy Measurements in Arcjet Exhausts,' AIAA Journal, Vol. 5, Aug. 1967, pp. 1504-1506.

22. Grey, J. 'Enthalpy Probes for Arc Plasmas — Third Status Review,' Report to Committee E-21, ASTM, May 22, 1968.

23. Haas, F. C. 'An Evaporating Film Calorimetric Enthalpy Probe,' Report No. AD-1651-Y-1, Cornell Aeronautical Lab. Feb. 1963.

24. Cheng, D. Y. and Blackshear, P. L. 'Factors Influencing the Performance of a Fast-Response, Transpiration-Cooled, High-Temperature Probe,' AIAA Paper No. 65-359, July 26-29, 1965.

25. Schneider, P. J. and Maurer, R. E. 'Coolant Starvation in a Transpiration - Cooled Hemispherical Shell,' Journal of Spacecraft and Rockets Vol. 5, June, 1968, pp. 751-752.

26. Grey, J. and Jacobs, P. F. 'Cooled Electrostatic Probe,' AIAA Journal Vol. 5, Jan. 1967, pp. 84-90.

27. Jacobs, P. F. and Grey, J. 'Electron-Heavy Particle Nonequilibrium in a Dense Argon Plasma,' Report No. ARL 66-0143, OAR, U. S. Air Force, July, 1966.

28. Jacobs, P. F. and Grey, J. 'A Criterion for Electron-Heavy-Particle Nonequilibrium in a Partly-Ionized Gas,' AIAA Preprint 66-192, March 2-4, 1966.

29. **Bohm, D.** 'The Characteristics of Electrical Discharges in Magnetic Fields,' McGraw-Hill, New York, 1949, Chap. III, pp. 77-86.

30. **Cohen, I. M.** 'Asymptotic Theory of Spherical Electrostatic Probes in a Slightly-Ionized, Collision-Dominated Gas,' Phys. Fluids Vol. 6, 1963, pp. 1492-1499.

31. **Waymouth, J. F.** 'Perturbation of a Plasma by a Probe,' Phys. Fluids Vol. 7, 1964, pp. 1843-1854.

32. **Schlichting, H.** 'Boundary Layer Theory,' Pergamon Press, New York, pp. 282-288.

33. **Hall, L. S.** 'Probes and Magnetic Pumping in Plasma,' Lawrence Radiation Lab., UCRL 6535.

34. **Talbot, L.** 'Theory of the Stagnation-Point Langmuir Probe,' Phys. Fluids Vol. 3, 1960, pp. 289-297.

35. **Kumura, I. and Kanzawa, A.** 'Experiments on Heat Transfer to Wires in a Partially Ionized Argon Plasma,' AIAA Journal Vol. 3, 1965, pp. 476-481.

36. **Pytte, A. and Williams, A. R.** 'On Electrical Conduction in a Nonuniform Helium Plasma,' U.S.A.F. Aeronautical Research Lab. Report 1963, pp. 63-166.

37. **Brundin, C. L. and Talbot, L.** 'The Application of Langmuir Probes to Flowing Ionized Gases,' AGARD Report 478, Sept. 1964.

38. **Demetriades, A. and Doughman, E. L.** 'Langmuir-Probe-Measurement Method for Turbulent Plasmas,' Phys. Fluids Vol. 8, 1965, pp. 1001-1002.

39. **Demetriades, A. and Doughman, E. L.** 'Langmuir Probe Diagnosis of Turbulent Plasmas,' AIAA Journal Vol. 4, 1966, pp. 451-459.

40. **Grey, J., Sherman, M. P. and Jacobs, P. F.** 'A Collimated Total Radiation Probe for Arcjet Measurements,' IEEE Transactions on Nuclear Science, Vol. NS-11, Jan. 1964, pp. 176-186.

41. **Raezer, S. D. and Olsen, H. L.** 'Temperature - Its Measurement and Control in Science and Industry,' Vol. 3, Pt. 2, Paper No. 83, Reinhold, N.Y., 1962.

Bibliography

Vassallo, F. A. 'Miniature Enthalpy Probes for High-Temperature Gas Streams,' Report No. ARL 66-0115, USAF, June, 1966.

Carden, W. H. 'Heat Transfer in Nonequilibrium Dissociated Hypersonic Flow with Surface Catalysis and Second-Order Effects,' AIAA Journal Vol. 4, No. 10, 1966, pp. 1704-1711.

Christensen, D. and Buhler, R. D. 'Arcjet Tunnel Development and Calibration for Parabolic Reentry Simulation,' Final Summary Report IFR011-1872, Plasmadyne Corp., June, 1961.

'Thirty Kilowatt Plasmajet Rocket Development — Third Year Development Program,' NASA CR-54079, 2 July 1964.

Sprengel, U. 'Kalorimetrische Messunger von Ortlichen Temperaturen in einem Stickstoff-Plasmastrahl,' Raumfahrtforschung und – Technik, Beilage zur Atompraxis, Jan, 1966.

Incropera, F.P. 'Temperature Measurement and Internal Flow Heat Transfer Analysis for Partially Ionized Argon,' Tech. Report No. SU 247-11, Dept. of Mech. Eng. Stanford Univ. Aug. 1966.

Meyer, N. 'Investigation of Greyrad Calorimetric Probe,' BSE Thesis, Coll. of Eng. Univ. of Cincinnati, 1966.

Potter, J.L., Arney, G.D., Kinslow, M. and Carden, W.H. 'Gasdynamic Diagnosis of High-Speed Flows Expanded from Plasma States,' IEEE Transactions on Nuclear Science, Vol. NS-11, Jan, 1964, pp. 145-157.

Cookson, T.S., Dunham, P.G. and Kilham, J.K. 'Stagnation Point Heat Flow Meter,' J. of Scientific Instruments, Vol. 42, April, 1965, pp. 260-262.

Blackshear, P.L. and Dorman, F.D. 'Heat-Sensing Probe and Process,' U.S. Patent No. 3,296,865, Jan. 10, 1967. (Diluent Probe).

Kubanek, G.R. and Gauvin, W.H. 'Plasma Jet Research Facility for Solids-Gas Heat Transfer Studies,' Tech. Report No. 466, Pulp and Paper Research Inst. of Canada, 1966.

Krause, L.N., Glawe, G.E. and Johnson, R.C. 'Temperature – Its Measurement and Control in Science and Industry,' Vol. 3, Part 2, Paper No. 54. Reinhold, New York, 1962.

Rosner, D.E. 'Sensitivity of a Downstream Langmuir Probe to Rocket Motor Chamber Conditions,' Report No. TP-109, AeroChem Research Lab, Jan. 1965.

Bryon, S. and Spongberg, R.M. 'Gasdynamic Instrumentation of High Enthalpy Flows,' IEEE Transactions on Nuclear Science, Vol. NS-11, pp. 381-387.

Rosner, D.E. 'Catalytic Probes for the Determination of Atom Concentrations in High Speed Gas Streams,' ARS Journal 32, July, 1962, pp. 1065-1073.

Rosner, E.E. 'Diffusion and Chemical Surface Catalysis in a Low-Temperature Plasmajet,' J. of Heat Transfer, Nov. 1962, pp. 386-394.

Rosner, D.E., Fontijn, A. and Kurzius, S.C. 'Chemical Scavenger Probes in Nonequilibrium Gasdynamics,' AIAA Journ, 2, 1964, p. 779.

Fontijn, A., Rosner, D.E. and Kurzius, S.C. 'Chemical Scavenger Probe Studies of Atom and Excited Molecule Reactivity in Active Nitrogen from a Supersonic Stream,' Candaian J. of Chemistry, Vol. 42, 1964, pp. 2440-2450.

Fingerson, L.M. 'Research on the Development and Evaluation of a Two-Sensor Enthalpy Probe,' Report No. ARL 64-161, USAF Oct. 1964.

Moore, D.W., Jr. 'A Pneumatic Method for Measuring High-Temperature Gases,' Aeronautical Eng. Review, Vol. 7, No. 5, May, 1948, pp. 30-34.

Wildhack, W. A. 'A Versatile Pneumatic Instrument Based on Critical Flow,' Review of Scientific Inst. Vol. 21, No. 1, Jan. 1950, pp. 25-30.

Blackshear, P. J., Jr. 'Sonic Flow Orifice Temperature Probe for High Gas Temperature Measurements,' NACA TN 2167, Sept. 1950.

Simmons, F. S. and Glawe, G. E. 'Theory and Design of a Pneumatic Temperature Probe and Experimental Results Obtained in a High-Temperature Gas Stream,' NACA TN 3893, Jan. 1957.

Edmonson, R. B., Thompson, W. R. and Hines, A. L. 'Thermodynamic Temperature Probe,' American Rocket Sockety Preprint No. 1431-60, December 5-8, 1960.

Fay, J. A. and Riddell, F. R. 'Theory of Stagnation-Point Heat Transfer in Dissociated Air,' Journal of the Aero/Space Sciences, Vol. 25, No. 2, Feb, 1958.

Rosner, D. E. 'Similitude Treatment of Hypersonic Stagnation Heat Transfer,' American Rocket Society Journal, Vol. 29, No. 2, Feb. 1959, pp. 215-216.

Cordero, J., Diederich, F. W. and Hurwicz, H. 'Aerothermodynamic Test Techniques for Reentry Structures and Materials,' Aerospace Eng. Vol. 22, No. 1, Jan. 1963, pp. 166-191.

Fay, J. A. and Kemp, N. H. 'Theory of Stagnation Point Heat Transfer in a Partially Ionized Diatomic Gas,' presented at IAS Annual Meeting, New York, Jan. 21-23, 1963.

Rosner, D. E. 'On the Effects of Diffusion and Chemical Reaction in Convective Heat Transfer,' Report No. TM-13, AeroChem Research Lab. June 8, 1959.

Wethern, R. J. 'Method of Analyzing Laminar Air Arc-Tunnel Heat Transfer Data,' AIAA Journal, Vol. 1, No. 7, July 1963, pp. 1665-1666.

Rosner, D. E. 'Application of Heat Flux Potentials to the Calculation of Convective Heat Transfer in Chemically Reacting Gases,' Report No. TP-20, AeroChem Research Lab, Dec. 14, 1960.

Fruchtman, I. 'Temperature Measurement of Hot Gas Streams,' AIAA Journal, Vol. 1, No. 8, August, 1963, pp. 1909-1910.

Freeman, M. P. 'Temperature — Its Measurement and Control in Science and Industry,' Vol. 3, Part 2, Plasma Jet Diagnosis Utilizing the Ablating Probe, Reinhold, N. Y., 1962, pp. 969-975.

Sherman, M. P. and Grey, J. 'Calculation of Transport Properties for Mixtures of Helium and Partly-Ionized Argon,' Princeton Univ. Aeronautical Eng. Lab. Report No. 673, Dec. 1963.

Sherman, M. P. and Grey, J. 'Interactions Between a Partly-Ionized Laminar Subsonic Jet and a Cool Stagnant Gas,' Princeton Univ. Aeronautical Eng. Lab. Report No. 707, Sept. 1964.

Su, C. H. and Lam, S. H. 'Continuous Theory of Spherical Electrostatic Probes,' Phys. Fluids Vol. 6, Oct. 1963, pp. 1479-1491.

Lam, S. H. 'A General Theory for the Flow of Weakly Ionized Gases, AIAA Journal Vol. 2, Feb. 1964, pp. 256-262.

Petschek, H. and Bryon, S. 'Approach to Equilibrium Ionization Behind Strong Shock Waves in Argon,' Annals of Phys. Vol. 1, 1957, p. 270

Massey, H. S. W. and Burhop, E. H. S. 'Electronic and Ionic Impact Phenomena,' Oxford Univ. Pres 1951.

Blythe, P. A. 'Nonequilibrium Flow Through a Nozzle,' J. of Fluid Mech, Vol. 17, 1963, p. 126

Grey, J. 'Enthalpy Probes for Arc Plasmas — Second Status Review,' Prelim. Report to ASTM, Toronto, May 3, 1967.

Johnson, D. H., 'Nonequilibrium Electron Temperature Measurements in a Supersonic Arc Jet Using a Cooled Langmuir Probe,' 26th Supersonic Tunnel Assoc. Meeting, Ames Research Center, May 16-18, 1967.

Staats, G. E., McGregor, W. K. and Frolich, J. P. 'Magnetogasdynamic Experiments Conducted in a Supersonic Plasma Arc Tunnel,' AEDC TR-67-266, Feb, 1968.

Krause, L. N., Buchele, D. R. and Warshawsky, I. 'Measurement Technique for Hypersonic Propulsion,' NASA TM X-52299, May 16-18, 1967.

Softley, E. J. 'Use of a Pulse Heated Fine Wire Probe for the Measurement of Total Temperature in Shock Driven Facilities,' AIAA Paper No. 68-393, April 8-10, 1968.

McCroskey, W. J. 'Density and Velocity Measurements in High Speed Flows,' AIAA Paper No. 68-392, April, 8-10, 1968.

Crites, R. C. and Cysz, P. 'Inlet and Test Section Diagnostics Using a Miniature Mass Flow Probe in Hypersonic Impulse Tunnel,' AIAA Paper No. 68-398, April 8-10, 1968.

Boatright, W. V., Sebacher, D. I. and Guy, R. W. 'Review of Testing Techniques and Flow Calibration Results for Hypersonic Arc Tunnels,' AIAA Paper No. 68-379, April 8-10, 1968.

Kilburg, R. F. 'A High Response Probe for Measurement of Total Temperature and Total Pressure Profiles Through a Turbulent Boundary Layer with High Heat Transfer in Supersonic Flow,' AIAA Paper No. 68-374, April 8-10, 1968.

Vassallo, F. A. 'A Fast Acting Miniature Enthalpy Probe,' AIAA Paper No. 68-391, April 8-10, 1968.

Nomenclature

English Symbols

C_{ca} -   Coolant air specific heat

C_e -   Speed of electron

C_{pc} -   Specific heat at constant pressure of coolant

d -   Distance from wall to edge of transition region

d_i -   Inside diameter of probe

d_o -   Outside diameter of probe

E -   Free stream electron energy

E_o -   Energy of heavy particle

EI -   Electrical power input to arc jet

e -   Elementary charge

$F(\chi)$ -   Average steric factor

h -   Enthalpy, thickness of sheath region

h_{1g} -   Unknown gas enthalpy at probe entrance

h_{2g} -   Gas enthalpy at probe exit

J_e -   Electron current

J_I -   Ion current

k -   Boltzmann's constant

$\bar{k}$ -   Mean thermal conductivity

L -   Probe radius

$\dot{m}_a$ -   Input mass flow rate of arc jet

$\dot{m}_{ca}$ -   Mass flow rate of coolant air

m_e -   Mass of electron

m_H -   Mass of heavy particle

$\dot{m}/A$ -   Mass flux (Kg/sm^2)

N_A -   Atom density

N_e -   Electron density

n -   Number of collisions

q/A   – heat flux (watts/m^2)

Re_L – Reynolds number based on probe radius

r   – Radial direction

T_A – Temperature of atoms

T_e – Temperature of electron

T_I – Temperature of ions

$(T_c)_{in}$ – Coolant temperature entering probe

$(T_c)_{out}$ – Coolant temperature leaving probe

V   – Velocity

$\dot{w}_c$ – Coolant water mass flow rate

$\dot{w}_g$ – Gas sample mass flow rate

Greek Symbols

δ   – Boundary layer thickness

ΔE   – Energy lost by an electron to a heavy particle

ΔT   – Temperature drop across a heat flux probe

ΔT_c – Coolant temperature rise

ΔT_{ca} – Coolant air temperature rise

$(\Delta T_c)_f$ – Coolant temperature change with gas sample flow

$(\Delta T_c)_{no\ flow}$ Coolant temperature change with no gas sample flow

ΔX   – Thickness of heat flux probe wafer

$\bar{\lambda}$ – Mean free path

ρ   – Density

σ   – Probe sensitivity

σ_{e-A} – Collision cross section for an electron atom collision.

σ_{e-I} Collision cross section for an electron ion collision.

φ_F – Floating potential of probe

φ_λ – Effective potential of probe

χ   – Deflection angle

Subscripts

r – Random

λ – Condition one mean free path from probe

∞ – Free stream condition

7

Transient Experimental Techniques for Surface Heat Flux Rates

C. J. SCOTT.

University of Minnesota, Minneapolis.

Summary

The available techniques for measuring surface heat flux rates are described. For micro-second duration experiments the thin-film thermometer and thick-film calorimeter are attached to the surface under investigation. For longer testing times, the heat capacity of the surface itself is employed as the calorimeter.

For simplicity the discussion is restricted to infinite and infinite plates. A few of the exact solutions are given along with graphed time-temperature curves which may be used to infer heat flux rates from transient temperature measurements.

Introduction

In order to calculate the thermal performance of bodies undergoing temperature changes it is necessary to accurately know the boundary conditions. An energy balance equates the energy increase within a body to the heat added at the boundaries so that knowledge of the surface heat flux (q_w) is of importance. The specification of q_w is generally complicated by the fact that a convective or radiative heat flux is a function of the surface temperature.

Suppose a surface is gaining heat Q_w by a combination of convective, conductive, and radiative processes, i.e., $Q_w = Q_{conv} + Q_{cond} + Q_{rad}$. Q_w is related to the wall temperature by Newton's law of cooling $d^2Q_w = h(T_f - T_w) dA_w d\tau$ where h is the heat transfer coefficient, T_f is the ambient fluid temperature; A_w is the surface area; and τ is the time. At the wall of a solid the convective velocity is zero, while the radiative transmissivity is close to zero, such that within the body the energy transport is by conduction only. Fourier's hypothesis governs the internal heat conduction and is written $d^2Q_w = -k \left.\dfrac{\partial T}{\partial n}\right]_w dA_w d\tau$. Continuity of heat flow at the surface yields $h(T_f - T_w) = -k \left.\dfrac{\partial T}{\partial n}\right]_w$. The quantity h is sometimes referred to as the specific surface conductance while the value $1/h = r_s$ is called the specific surface thermal resistance. For combined exchange processes the sum of the individual resistances if the thermal resistance of the overall heat transfer process.

In a transient heating process the heat gained by a body is determined by the resistance to the flow of heat at the surface as well as the internal resistance of the body itself. Whenever the internal conduction is of importance, a dimensionless conduction Nusselt number, given by $Nu_{cond} = L/k_w = Bi$ (usually referred to as the Biot number), enters as a parameter. The Biot number may be thought of as the ratio of internal r_i to surface r_s specific resistances since:

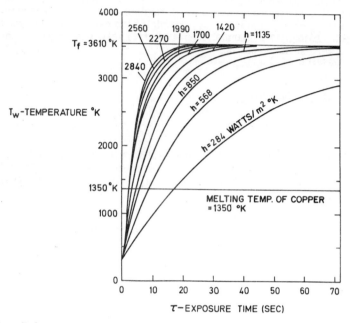

Fig. 7-1   Theoretical convective heat transfer performance of an ideal calorimeter based on a 3.18 mm copper slug

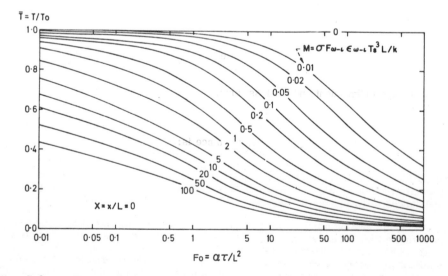

Fig. 7-2   Temperature response of a plate $0 \leqslant x \leqslant L$ with insulated face $X = L$ after sudden exposure to a constant-temperature radiation heat source T_s at $x = 0$

$$Bi = \frac{h\,L}{k_w} = \frac{L/k_w}{1/h} = \frac{r_i}{r_s} \qquad \qquad \text{Eq. 7-1}$$

It is of primary importance to estimate the value of the Biot number in a given heat flux transducer design, in order to justify any assumptions used to simplify the design. One limiting case is represented by $Bi = 0$ which implies zero internal resistance. This condition is approached in practice by minimizing the calorimeter thickness L and maximizing the calorimeter thermal conductivity k_w while the other extreme, $Bi \to \infty$ implies a zero surface resistance. Since the purpose of the present paper is to discuss the possibilities for experimentally determining the surface resistance, the limiting case of zero surface resistance will not be considered at length. Of course exact solutions exist for the case of transient, one-dimensional heat conduction in bodies of basic geometric shape (1). Graphs of solutions, (2) which assume constant material density, specific heat and thermal conductivity, are available and may be used for reference when examining the limiting conditions.

Case A – r_i = 0, Negligible Internal Resistance

When a 'thin' body is constructed of material possessing a 'large' thermal conductivity, its internal resistance may be ignored such that the overall heat transfer process is controlled by the surface resistance. No temperature differences can exist under these conditions – the body is isothermal and $T = T(\tau) = T_w(\tau)$. Consider a body having an initial temperature T_i ($\tau=0$) that is suddenly exposed to a fluid at constant temperature T_f (or the fluid temperature undergoes a step change at $\tau=0$ from T_i to T_f). The specific rate of energy transfer from the surroundings for $\tau > 0$ is governed by:

$$q_w = \frac{Q_w}{A_w} = \frac{d^2Q_w}{dA_w d\tau} = \rho_w V_w C_{pw} \frac{dT_w}{d\tau} + q_L \qquad \text{Eq. 7-2}$$

where ρ_w, V_w, C_{pw}, and A_w are the density, volume, specific heat capacity, and area of the wall material and q_L is the rate of heat gain/loss from the calorimeter due to internal heat sources or sinks, internal conduction, and backside conduction, convection and radiation.

The Ideal Calorimeter

In order to discuss a variety of calorimeter applications the concept of an 'ideal calorimeter' is introduced. An ideal calorimeter is constructed of an infinite thermal conductivity material. In addition the parameters ρ_w, C_{pw}, V_w and A_w are temperature independent and the loss term, q_L, is zero.

Example (a) Convection Boundary Condition

In convective heating, the basic energy balance is:

$$Q_w = \rho_w C_{pw} V_w \frac{dT_w}{d\tau} = hA_w (T_f - T_w) \qquad \text{Eq. 7-3}$$

Equation 7-3 illustrates a commonly used transient method for determining heat flux rates by experimentally measuring the temperature-time slope. Normally the wall temperature is measured as a function of time and the data differentiated, an inherently inaccurate technique. The heat transfer coefficient h is determined using the right side of Equation 7-3. Since the convective heat flux is transmitted by wall heat conduction, an energy balance at the wall surface yields $h(T_f - T_w) = -k \frac{\partial}{\partial x}$ $\left[T(o, \tau)\right]$ - or after normalizing with $Bi = hL/k$, $\bar{T} = (T - T_i)/(T_f - T_i)$, $Fo = \alpha\tau/L^2$:

$$\text{Bi} \left[1 - \bar{T} \, (0, \text{Fo}) \right] = - \frac{\partial}{\partial (x/_L)} \left[\bar{T} \, (o, \text{Fo}) \right] \qquad \text{Eq. 7-4}$$

If h is not a function of temperature, Equation 7-3 may be integrated to yield:

$$\frac{T - T_f}{T_i - T_f} = e^{-\left(\frac{hA_w}{\rho_w C_{pw} V_w} \right) \tau} = e^{-\frac{\tau}{\theta}} \qquad \text{Eq. 7-5}$$

The constant $(\rho_w C_{pw} V_w / hA_w)$ has the units of time and may be considered as a time constant θ. Once the time constant is obtained the heat flux may be obtained from Equation 7-3. For a uniform slab, $(V_w/A_w) = L$ and the spatially uniform temperature of the object changes exponentially with time. Figure 7-1 illustrates theoretical convective heating temperature - time curves of an ideal calorimeter based on a L = 3.18 mm thick copper slab suddenly exposed to a fluid temperature of $T_f = 3610°K$ and several values of h. Note the difficulty in determining the different slopes $(dT_w/d\tau)$ for large values of h. Since copper melts at 1360°K, the times for $T_w = 1360°K$ maximum operating times for the calorimeter. Copper calorimeters actually deviate from these curves at temperature above 700°K because of the variations of C_{pw} with T.

The heat transfer coefficient is obtained explicitly by taking the natural logarithm of both sides of Equation 7-5:

$$\left(\frac{h}{\rho_w C_{pw} L} \right) \tau = \frac{\tau}{\theta} = \ln \left(\frac{T - T_f}{T_i - T_f} \right) \qquad \text{Eq. 7-6}$$

It is convenient to plot $(T - T_f)/(T_i - T_f)$ vs. τ on semi-log paper. The slope of this curve (a straight line) is the reciprocal time constant θ^{-1} and it is possible to use arbitrary initial conditions. Writing Equation 7-6 at two separate locations, i.e., (T_{w1}, τ_1), (T_{w2}, τ_2) yields:

$$\theta \doteq (\tau_2 - \tau_1) \ \ln \left(\frac{T_{w1} - T_f}{T_{w2} - T_f} \right) \qquad \text{Eq. 7-7}$$

Example (b) Radiation

If no convection is present, or the convective component is small, the following equation is applicable:

$$q_w = \frac{d^2 Q_w}{d\tau \, dA_w} = F_{w-s} \ \epsilon_{w-s} \ \sigma(T_s^4 - T_w^4) = \rho_w C_{pw} L \ \frac{dT_w}{d\tau} = -k \frac{\partial}{\partial x} [T(o, \tau)]_\omega \qquad \text{Eq. 7-8}$$

Consider again an ideal calorimeter which has no heat losses, temperature independent parameters ρ_w, C_{pw}, t_w and a emissivity ϵ_w that is independent of temperature. Assume that the radiation source is a conical cavity whose emissivity is unity (blackbody). If the calorimeter is aligned with the mouth of the cavity, centered and normal to the axis of the cone, the shape factor F_{w-s} is unity and the interchange factor ϵ_{w-s} is the product of the emissivity of the calorimeter surface and the emissivity of the conical source. According to Euqation 7-8, the experimental determination of q_w requires records of the rate of change of calorimeter temperature. Normalizing Equation 7-8 yields a characteristic radiation equation, (with $\bar{T} = T/T_o$)

$$M(\bar{T}_s^4 - \bar{T}_w^4) = - \frac{\partial}{\partial (x/_L)} \left[\bar{T}(0, \text{Fo}) \right] \qquad \text{Eq. 7-9}$$

The parameter $M - \sigma F_{w-s} \epsilon_{w-s} T_o^3 L/k$ is analogous to the Biot number for the convection boundary condition. Figure 7-2 presents a typical surface response curve of a plate of thickness L with insulated back face after sudden exposure to a constant temperature radiation source. For constant properties Equation 7-8 integrates to, (4):

$$\left(\frac{2\sigma\epsilon_w T_s^3}{\rho_w C_{pw}L}\right) \tau = \tan^{-1}\left(\frac{T}{T_s}\right) - \tan^{-1}\left(\frac{T_i}{T_s}\right) \qquad \text{Eq. 7-10}$$

$$+ \frac{1}{2}\ln\left[\frac{1 + \dfrac{T}{T_s}}{1 - \dfrac{T}{T_s}}\right] - \frac{1}{2}\ln\left[\frac{1 + \dfrac{T_i}{T_s}}{1 - \dfrac{T_i}{T_s}}\right]$$

The reciprocal of the quantity in the brackets on the left side of Equation 7-10 may be considered as a radiation time constant and used to determine ϵ_w. Figure 7-3 presents theoretical radiant heating temperature-time curves for $t_w = 3.18$ mm thick copper calorimeter with an emissivity $\epsilon_w = 0.8$ viewing several radiation source temperatures T_s.

Example (c) Convection with variable fluid temperature

For several special cases involving variable fluid temperatures, Equation 7-3 may be rewritten:

$$\frac{dT_w}{d\tau} + \frac{1}{\theta} T_w = \frac{1}{\theta} T_f (\tau) \qquad \text{Eq. 7-11}$$

where T_f is now considered to be a function of time τ.

Integrating Equation 7-11 yields:

$$\theta = \frac{\int_0^\tau T_f d\tau - \int_0^\tau T_w d\tau}{T_w(\tau) - T_i} \qquad \text{Eq. 7-12}$$

The integrals in Equation 7-12 may be evaluated numerically from the measured traces of $T_f(\tau)$ and $T_w(\tau)$, otherwise the solution of Equation 7-11 is given in terms of an integrating factor, (3):

$$T_w = e^{\int \frac{d\tau}{\theta}}\left[\int \frac{T_f}{\theta} e^{+\int \frac{d\tau}{\theta}} d\tau\right] + \text{Const } e^{-\int \frac{d\tau}{\theta}} \qquad \text{Eq. 7-13}$$

If the time const $\theta = \rho_w C_{pw}L/h$ is constant and the initial wall temperature $T_w(o) = T_i$, general solution of Equation 7-11 is:

$$T_w = e^{-\frac{\tau}{\theta}}\left[\frac{1}{\theta}\int_0^\tau T_f e^{-\frac{\tau}{\theta}} d\tau + T_{wi}\right] \qquad \text{Eq. 7-14}$$

Example (c-i) The fluid temperature varies linearly such that:

$$T_f = T_{f_o} + \frac{dT_f}{d\tau}\tau \qquad \text{Eq. 7-15}$$

and Equation 7-14 integrates (5) to:

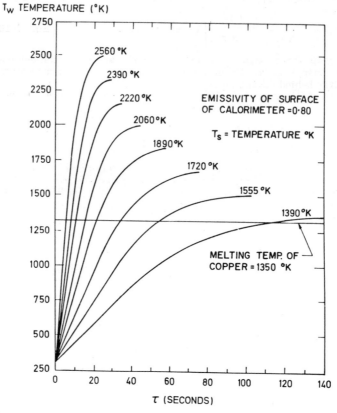

Fig. 7-3   Theoretical thermal history of an ideal calorimeter exposed to a black body heat source based on a 3.18 mm copper slug

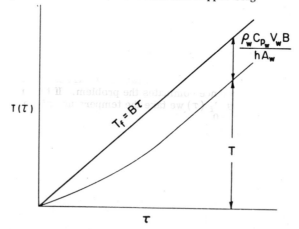

Fig. 7-4   Time temperature history of a plate $0 \leqslant x \leqslant L$ subjected to a ramp fluid temperature

$$T_w = T_{f_o} - \theta \frac{dT_f}{d\tau} \left[1 - e^{-\frac{\tau}{\theta}} \right] \qquad \text{Eq. 7-16}$$

The thermal response is exponential and the methods for the explicit determination of θ given for Case A apply. From Equation 7-16 it is clear that the wall temperature always lags behind the fluid temperature. After the initial transient ($e^{-\tau/\theta} \to 0$) the lag becomes $\theta \frac{dT_f}{d\tau}$ and this feature may be used to determine θ. Figure 7-4 illustrates the response predicted by Equation 7-16.

Example (c-ii) Sinusoidal fluid temperature variation

If the fluid temperature is oscillated sinusoidally with a frequency ω and an amplitude ΔT_f such that $T_f = \bar{T}_f + \Delta T_f \sin \omega\tau$, Equation 7-14 integrates (6) to give, with $\dfrac{\rho_w C_{pw} V_w}{h A_w} = \theta$:

$$\frac{T_w - \bar{T}_f + \dfrac{\Delta T_f}{\sqrt{1+\omega^2\theta^2}} \left[\sin\left\{ \tan^{-1}(\omega\theta) - \omega\tau \right\} \right]}{T_{w_i} - \bar{T}_f + \dfrac{\Delta T_f}{\sqrt{1+\omega^2\theta^2}} \left\{ \sin\,\tan^{-1}(\omega\theta) \right\}} = e^{-\frac{\tau}{\theta}} \qquad \text{Eq. 7-17}$$

For large times $e^{-\tau/\theta} \to 0$ and we obtain the steady periodic solution:

$$T_w = \bar{T}_f + \frac{\Delta T_f}{\sqrt{1+\omega^2\theta^2}} \left[\sin(\omega\tau - \tan^{-1}\omega\theta) \right] \qquad \text{Eq. 7-18}$$

As the gas temperature is oscillated the wall temperature lags the gas temperature by an angle $\tan^{-1}(\omega\theta)$ (see Figure 7-5). This phase lag angle is the product of the forcing frequency ω and the time constant θ. The heat transfer coefficient is obtained by measuring the phase lag from simultaneous measurements of the gas temperature and wall temperature. The experiments are conducted with small temperature oscillations ($\pm 6° <$), generating essentially isothermal conditions. The method avoids the inherently inaccurate determination of a temperature-time slope; avoids the requirements of inducing a sharp step change in the gas temperature and yields data with nearly uniform surface temperatures.

Case B — $r_s = 0$, Negligible Surface Resistance

A class of problems exist in which the surface thermal resistance is negligible and the internal thermal resistance dominates the problem. If the ambient temperature of the surrounding fluid is $T_f(\tau)$ we take the temperature of the surface of the object to be $T_f(\tau)$ for $\tau > 0$.

(a) $T_f = $ constant, $T_i = T_i(x)$

Consider an infinite slab of thickness t_w with the initial temperature distribution $T_i(x)$. The temperature of the surface $T(o, \tau)$ is suddenly changed to $T_f = $ const for all $\tau > 0$. The solution must satisfy the system:

$$\frac{\partial^2 T}{\partial x^2} = \frac{\rho_w C_{pw}}{k_w} \frac{\partial T}{\partial \tau} \qquad \text{Eq. 7-19}$$

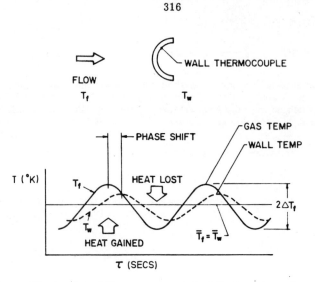

Fig. 7-5   Illustration of the measurement of the heat transfer coefficient by means of sinusoidal temperature oscillations

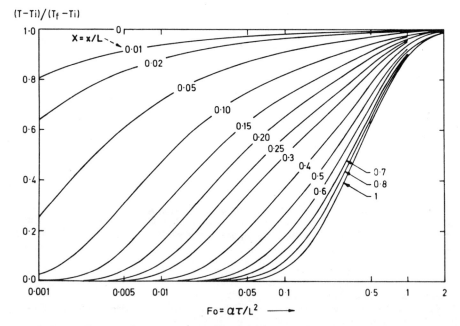

Fig. 7-6   Temperature response of a plate $0 \leqslant x \leqslant L$ with insulated back face $x = L$ after sudden change in external fluid temperature from T_i when $\tau < 0$ T_F when $\tau \geqslant 0$.

$$T = T_i \, (x) \qquad\qquad \text{at} \quad \tau = 0; \quad 0 \le x \le t_w$$

$$T(o, \tau) = T_f = \text{const} \qquad\qquad \text{at} \quad x = 0; \quad \tau > 0 \qquad \text{Eq. } 7\text{-}20$$

$$\frac{\partial T}{\partial x} (L, T) = 0 \qquad\qquad \text{at} \quad x = L; \quad \tau > 0$$

For the special case of a uniform initial temperature $T_i \, (x) = T_i$ the general solution of the system (Eq. 7-19, 20) presented in (1) and plotted in Figure 7-6 is presented in (1) and plotted in Figure 7-6. Figure 7-6 illustrates the use of Schneider's time-temperature charts.

Case C — Exact Solutions and the Time—Temperature Charts
(Finite Internal and Surface Resistance)

The most realistic heat flux measurements require consideration of both internal and surface resistances. In this discussion we consider the ambient fluid temperature T_f to be uniform as well as the heat transfer coefficient. Consider the convective heating of a large plate of uniform thickness L which again is initially at a uniform temperature T_i. The plate is suddenly exposed to a fluid temperature T_f for $\tau > 0$ while the back face at x=L is insulated. The general solution is, (7):

$$\frac{T - T_f}{T_i - T_f} = 4 \sum_{n=1}^{\infty} \left(\frac{\sin M_n}{2M_n + \sin 2M_n} \right) e^{-M_n^2 F_o} \, \text{Cos} \, 2M_n \left(1 - \frac{x}{L} \right)$$

$$\text{Eq. } 7\text{-}22$$

where M_n are the eigenvalues given by the characteristic equation:

$$M_n \tan M_n = B_i \qquad\qquad \text{Eq. } 7\text{-}23$$

Note that the solution is a function of two parameters, Fo and Bi rather than just one as in the case of negligible surface resistance.

Schneider presents a large (120) number of time-temperature charts covering a variety of body shapes for a wide range of Fourier and Biot numbers. These charts are convenient for thermal engineers who need to deduce heat flux rates from transient temperature response measurements while not having sufficient computational experience or direct use of a computer.

Figures 7-7 and 7-8 presents the plotted results of Equations 7-22, 7-23 for the locations x/L = 0, 1.0 and these curves apply to the case of large Biot and Fourier numbers. To use the curves one can plot the experimental temperature difference ratio versus the Fourier number and examine the theoretical Biot number curve which best fits the data. One must remember that to obtain surface heat flux values in this way accurate values of the thermal conductivity, density, heat capacity and thickness must be available.

The temperature difference that exists across the thickness of the surface may be obtained by a superposition of Figures 7-7 and 7-8, and in this way an estimate of the errors involved in assuming negligible internal resistance are readily made.

Case D — Rapid Response Measurements

The development of heat transfer gauges has always been directed to some particular application. Earlier work focused on determination of cylinder wall temperature

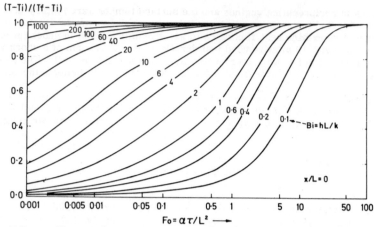

Fig. 7-7   Temperature response of a plate $0 \leqslant x \leqslant L$ with insulated back face $x = L$ after sudden exposure to a uniform convective environment at $x = 0$

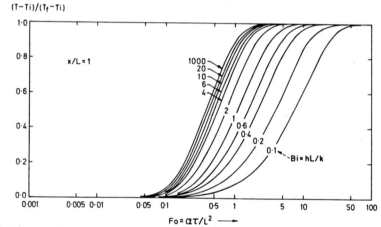

Fig. 7-8   Temperature response of a plate $0 \leqslant x \leqslant L$ with insulated back face $x = L$ after sudden exposure to a uniform convective environment at $x = 0$

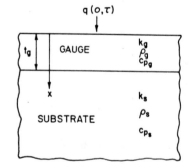

Fig. 7-9   Gage notation for thick and thin films

variations in reciprocating engines and the surface temperature history in gun barrels subjected to continuous firing. Later it was necessary to develop instrumentation to determine heat flux rates to aerodynamic models in shock tubes and shock tunnels with 10 microsecond test duration. An early form of a shock wave detector consisted of a thin film mounted flush in a shock tube wall. The gauge provided a very fast electrical pulse for trigger purposes to indicate the passage of the shock wave.

Two basic techniques have evolved for such measurement techniques, (8) which are: thin - film surface thermometry and thick - film calorimetry. The first method records instantaneous surface temperature from which instantaneous heat flux rates are deduced using classical heat conduction theory. In the second method the gauge absorbs the total heat input to the surface, and the instantaneous heat flux rate is determined by the time rate of change of temperature of the gauge.

It is clear that most heat flux gauges are based on approximations. It is necessary for the experimentalist to arm himself with a variety of exact solutions; i.e. those tabulated in (1). In dealing with the heat conduction equation, the property, sensor thermal diffusivity ($\alpha_g = k_g/\rho_g C_{pg}$), is fundamental. Recall (9) that for metals the thermal diffusivity is about 400 times that of thermal (and electrical) insulators. The thermal diffusion depth ($\delta_g = \alpha_g \tau$) is a measure of the extreme depth to which a surface heat flux has penetrated in time $\sqrt{\tau}$. Therefore, thermal diffusion depths of metals are 20 times those of insulators.

Thin-Film Gauges

When a film thickness t_g is much less than the thermal diffusion depth ($t_g << \delta_g$), temperature gradients in the film may be neglected (see Fig. 7-9 for notation). The film senses the instantaneous surface temperature of the substrate (subscripts) but there exists a response lag relative to zero film thickness because of the small but finite gauge heat capacity. As an example of this response lag consider a suddenly applied heat flux rate varying inversely with the square root of time. With zero gauge thickness the substrate temperature jumps to a new constant value. For a finite gauge thickness, the substrate surface temperature attains 94 percent of the ideal temperature change in a time $\tau = 100 \, \tau_r$ where:

$$\tau_r = \frac{\rho_g^2 \, C_{pg}^2 \, t_g^2}{\rho_s \, C_{ps} \, k_s}$$

Eq. 7-24

and τ_r is the characteristic time of the gauge-substrate combination.

In most applications the heat flux rate into the gauge is one-dimensional. The required relation between the surface heat flux rate and the measured gauge temperature is obtained by solving the one-dimensional, constant-property, heat conduction equation in a semi-infinite slab:

$$\frac{\partial T}{\partial \tau} = \frac{k_g}{\rho_g C_{pg}} \left(\frac{\partial^2 T}{\partial x^2} \right) \quad \begin{array}{l} x>0 \\ \tau>0 \end{array}$$

Eq. 7-25

Where $T(x, \tau)$ is the difference between the instantaneous and initial temperatures. The boundary conditions are $q(0, \tau) = -k \frac{\partial T}{\partial x}(0, \tau)$; $T(x, 0) = 0$. The general solution (10):

$$T(x, \tau) = \frac{1}{\sqrt{\pi \, \rho_s \, C_{pg} k_s}} \int_0^\tau \frac{q(0, t)}{\sqrt{\tau - t}} \, e^{-\dfrac{x^2}{4 k_s \rho_s C_{pg}} (\tau - t)} \, dt$$

Eq. 7-26

is obtained by use of the convolution integral of the Laplace transform. At the substrate surface x=0, the relations between the wall temperature $T(0, \tau)$ and the impressed heat flux $\phi(\tau)$ are:

$$T(0, \tau) = \frac{1}{\sqrt{\pi \rho_s C_{ps} k_s}} \int_0^\tau \frac{q(0, t)}{\sqrt{\tau - t}} \, dt \qquad \text{Eq. 7-27}$$

$$q(0, \tau) = \frac{\sqrt{\rho_s C_{ps} k_s}}{\sqrt{\pi}} \int_0^\tau \frac{dT(0, t)}{dt} \frac{1}{\sqrt{\tau - t}} \, dt \qquad \text{Eq. 7-28}$$

Equation 7-28 is not suited for numerical evaluation since it involves derivatives of temperature integrals. Equation 7-28 can also be written:

$$q(0, \tau) = \sqrt{\frac{\rho_s C_{ps} k_s}{\pi}} \left[\frac{T(\tau)}{\sqrt{\tau}} + \frac{1}{2} \int_0^\tau \frac{T(\tau) - T(t)}{(\tau - t)^{3/2}} \, dt \right] \qquad \text{Eq. 7-29}$$

Numerical difficulties encountered in evaluating the integral as $t \to \tau$ are the subject of several recent papers. The integrand evaluated at τ takes the form $0/0$ and application of L'Hôpital's rule yields an infinite integrand at τ. It is necessary to evaluate the terms enclosed in the square brackets by numerical procedures.

For constant heat flux $q(0, \tau) = q_o = \text{const}$,

Equations 7-27 and 7-28 integrate to:

$$q(x, \tau) = q_o \, \text{erfc} \left(\frac{x}{2 \sqrt{\dfrac{k_s}{\rho_s C_{ps}}} \, \tau} \right) \qquad \text{Eq. 7-30}$$

$$T(0, \tau) = 2 \, q_o \, \frac{\sqrt{\tau}}{\sqrt{\pi} \sqrt{\rho_s C_{ps} k_s}} \qquad \text{Eq. 7-31}$$

For a heat flux gauge several possibilities exist for determining the gauge temperature. For example either a thermocouple or a resistance thermometer may be used for measuring the time-temperature trace. The greater sensitivity of the resistance thermometer gives it an advantage over the thermocouple. For example sensitivities of resistance thermometers are as great as 1 mv/°C while the sensitivities of conventional thermocouples range from 0.005-0.05 mv/°C. Evaporated thermocouples require two overlapping films and ceramic films (thermistors) are sometimes considered (vs metallic films) because their temperature coefficient of resistance (dR/dT) is much larger, but is constant only over a narrow range. Other techniques (10) employ a variable reluctance gauge (a copper mass used to vary reluctance in a magnetic circuit), or a dielectric material as a temperature sensor. When a dielectric material such as barium titanate is heated an electric charge is generated which is proportional to the temperature change. If the gauge is connected to a resistor the circuit is directly proportional to the time rate of change of gauge temperature.

Some normal operating conditions of thin-film thermometers are listed below, (10):

Film material - platinum evaporated or painted on pyrex substrate

Film thickness - 0.025 microns

Film response time - 10^{-7} second

Film current - 10^{-2} amp

Film resistance - 100 ± 25 ohms

Film dimensions - 6.35×0.635 mm

Film allowable temperature change - $^1/_4$ to $280°K$

Film $\rho_g C_{p_g} k_g$ - $1520 \pm 5\%$ $\dfrac{\text{watts}}{\text{m}^2°K}$

If the temperature changes are not too large ($\Delta T < 30°K$) the resistance of the film varies liniearly with temperature $R_g = R_{g_o} (1 + \alpha T)$ or:

$$T = \frac{\Delta R}{R_o \alpha} \qquad \qquad \text{Eq. 7-32}$$

The resistance change ΔR is related to the voltage drop across the film voltage $\Delta V(\tau)$ and the constant film current, I_o, by the relation $\Delta R = \Delta V / I_o$ so that the operating equation for constant heat flux (11) is:

$$q_o = \left(\frac{\sqrt{\pi \rho_s C_{p_s} k_s}}{2\alpha R_o I_o} \right) \frac{\Delta V}{\sqrt{\tau}} \qquad \qquad \text{Eq. 7-33}$$

Gauge calibration consists of determining the quantity $\sqrt{\rho_s C_{p_s} k_s} / \alpha$ at room temperature plus variations of this parameter with temperature. The bulk material properties cannot be relied upon.

An electrical pulse resulting from the discharge of a charged capacitor across the metal film provides a simple means of generating a known, constant heat flux if the time constant of the discharge circuit is large compared to the calibration test time. A severe limitation of Equation 7-33 arises from the required knowledge of the gauge area ($q_s = Q_s / A_s$). Early experience showed calibrations accurate to $\pm 15\%$, primarily due to errors in film dimensions. Recent accuracies are about $\pm 5\%$. The thin-film boundaries are often irregular and difficult to define. Skinner (12) devised a technique for determining $\sqrt{\rho_s C_{p_s} k_s}$ that eliminates the necessity of a film area measurement. If the film is calibrated electrically in a thermally conducting fluid i.e. (distilled water), the heat generated will diffuse into both the substrate and the fluid (f) according to the relation:

$$T(\tau) = \frac{2}{\sqrt{\pi}} q_o \frac{\sqrt{\tau}}{\sqrt{\rho_s C_{p_s} k_s} + \rho_f C_{p_f} k_f} \qquad \qquad \text{Eq. 7-34}$$

The film dimensions are removed from the problem if the identical calibration is made in both a fluid with known thermal properties and in air, where all of the heat is absorbed by the substrate material.

A platinum film is electrically active and subject to short circuiting when submerged in an ionized or conducting medium. Electrical insulation is accomplished by depositing a thin coating (i.e., magnesium fluoride) over the gauge. This coating—usually several microinches thick—introduces a negligible thermal lag in most circumstances.

For constant impressed heat flux, the error in temperature or heat transfer rate due to neglecting the gauge heat capacity, is proportional to the ratio of heat stored in the gauge to that stored in the substrate such that:

$$\frac{\Delta q}{q} = \frac{\Delta T}{T} \approx \frac{\sqrt{\pi}}{2} \sqrt{\frac{\rho_s C_{ps}}{k_s \tau}} \frac{\rho_g C_{pg}}{\rho_s C_{ps}} \qquad \qquad \text{Eq. 7-35}$$

Effect of Temperature Variation on Thermal Properties

The established data reduction techniques are based on constant gauge properties - restricted to small temperature changes (50°C). Recent investigations have been made on the effect of temperature-dependent thermal properties on the classical solution for heat conduction. The variable property diffusion equation:

$$\rho \, C_p \frac{\partial T}{\partial \tau} = \frac{\partial}{\partial x} \left[k \, \frac{\partial T}{\partial x} \right]$$

Eq. 7-36

is solved using the integral-conductivity function $\phi(T) = \int_0^T k_s dT$.

For common substrate materials the temperature variation of the thermal conductivity dominates while the temperature effect on thermal diffusivity is small. Two cases were considered (10), assuming $k = A + B \log_{10} T$. The zeroth-order solutions are:

For $q_o = $ const:
$$T \{ \ \} = \frac{2q_o \sqrt{\tau}}{\sqrt{\pi \rho_s Cp_s k_s}}$$

Eq. 7-37

For $q_o = \dfrac{D}{\sqrt{\tau}}$:
$$T \{ \ \} = D \sqrt{\frac{\pi}{\rho_s C_{p_s}}}$$

Eq. 7-38

where $\{ \ \} = 1 + \dfrac{B}{k_{s_o}} \left[\dfrac{T_o}{T} (1 + \dfrac{T}{T_o}) \log_{10} (1 + \dfrac{T}{T_o}) -0.434 \right]$ Eq. 7-39

The zeroth-order effect of temperature on the thermal properties is to increase the surface temperature.

Advantage of thin-film thermometer (10)

    (a)   rapid response

    (b)   sensitivity for measuring low levels of heat transfer

    (c)   output can be numerically evaluated to accurately determine the instantaneous heat flux rate

Limitations of thin-film thermometer (10)

    (a)   numerical evaluation of heat flux is laborious (requires temperature history be read, tabulated, and programmed)

    (b)   measurement accuracy fixed by calibration of substrate properties $\rho_s C_{p_s} k_s$

    (c)   sensor electrically active $\therefore$ Cannot be used in a conducting media

    (d)   thin-film sensitive to erosion by foreign particles.

Thick Film Gauges

For the thick film case, the heat received by the gauge is largely stored within the gauge while only a negligibile portion is transferred to the substrate. Thin film sensors are not successful under conditions of very high heat flux rates and/or long test durations giving excessive temperature rises. For thick films the gauge thickness t_g is comparable to or much larger than the thermal diffusion depth δ_g. In reality the gauge is a calorimeter in which the governing relation

$$q = q_s + \frac{d}{d\tau}\left[\rho_g\, C_{pg}\, t_g\, \bar{T}(\tau)\right] \; ; \; \bar{T}(\tau) = \frac{1}{t_g}\int_o^{t_g} T(x,\tau)\,dx \qquad \text{Eq. 7-40}$$

where q_s is the heat transferred to the substrate materials and for constant heat flux is found to be:

$$q_s = q_o \left(\frac{2a}{a+1}\right)\sum_{n=1}^{\infty} \text{erfc}\left[\frac{(2n+1)}{2\sqrt{\dfrac{k_g}{\rho_g C_{pg}}}}\frac{t_g}{\tau}\right] \qquad \text{Eq. 7-41}$$

and:

$$a = \sqrt{\frac{\rho_s C_{ps} k_s}{\rho_g C_{pg} k_g}} \qquad \text{Eq. 7-42}$$

With $t_g = \delta_g$ the thick film may be thin by usual standards.

Using platinum and a test duration of 100 microseconds, δ_g is 0.0013 mm. Typical thicknesses for shock tube operation are 0.025 mm of platinum for test times of 5×10^{-5} second.

Many of the techniques used for thin-film gauges apply directly to thick film sensors including calibration and temperature sensing techniques. One method of measuring $\bar{T}$ is to use the film as a resistance thermometer. For thick-film calibration, an electrical scheme similar to that developed for thin-film gauges is sometimes used; i.e., a pulse of electrical current is passed through the gauge causing Joule heating of the resistor. Because the resistance of the gauge is quite low (10^{-3} ohms) electrical currents of 500-700 amperes are required. In operation 5 to 10 amperes are required to develop sufficient voltage differences across the resistance element so that resistance change measurements can be made.

The instantaneous heat flux is proportional to the local slope of $\bar{T}$ vs τ. Although the data reduction is much simpler for the thick rather than the thin-film, the measurement of slopes is inherently inaccurate.

Advantages of the thick film resistor (10)

(a)   rapid response - response time may be defined as the time for the rear surface temperature-time derivative to equal $d\bar{T}/d\tau$

(b)   large thermal capacity - can sense larger q without surface melting at higher temperatures

(c)   insensitive to erosion due to large thickness

Limitations

(a)   Smallest heat flux rate is 110 $\frac{\text{watts}}{\text{cm}^2}$ or 2 orders of magnitude greater than thin-film thermometer

(b)   Calibration necessary to determine film properties

(c)   Large thickness => small resistance => large electrical current passing through film

(d)   It is always difficult to infer instantaneous heat flux rates from data that must be time-differentiated.

324

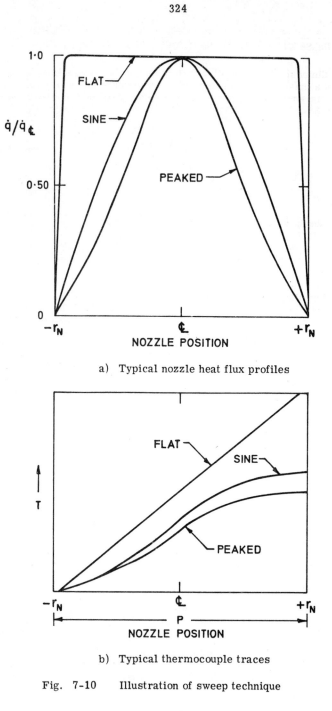

a) Typical nozzle heat flux profiles

b) Typical thermocouple traces

Fig. 7-10   Illustration of sweep technique

The use of thick-film calorimeter gauges simultaneously with thin-film resistance thermometers at intermediate heat flux rates gives a possibility for experimental comparison of the two techniques. In the ranges where both types of gauges have been used good agreement was found (9).

Sweep Operation

The discussion of the preceding apply most generally to a step input of heat flux such as obtained by the use of a shutter, a removable probe cover, or rapid insertion of a probe into a high energy gas flow. In the sweep technique (13), the probe is traversed across a gas flow in a continuous motion-thus a zero dwell time is considered. During sweep operation, the calorimeter response must be sufficient to give a true $dT/d\tau$ in order that a transverse heat flux profile may be obtained. It has been found (13) that for many cases of a small probe sweeping across a large jet flow, adequate response is obtained when $.5 \dfrac{t^2}{\alpha} = \tau_r < 0.10P$ where P is the sweep

period. If this response time requirement is met, the $dT/d\tau$ ($\sim dt/dP$) is proportional to the local flux at any time during the sweep. Calorimeters of this type have a potential application for measurement of heat flux levels to 11,000 $\dfrac{watts}{cm^2}$ with test times ranging for 10 - 300 milliseconds.

Some typical thermocouple traces are plotted in Figure 7-10 for a series of nozzle temperature profiles. The heat flux rate profiles developed from these profiles developed from these profiles are also shown in the lower half of the figure.

References

1. Carslaw, H. S., and Jaeger, J. C., 'Conduction of Heat in Solids', Clarendon Press, Oxford, 1947.

2. Schneider, P. J., 'Temperature Response Charts', John Wiley, New York, 1963.

3. Kudryavtsev, Y. V., 'Unsteady State Heat Transfer', English translation Scripta Technica Ltd., Iliffe, London, 1966.

4. Brookley, C. E., 'Measurement of Heat Flux in Solid Propellant Rocketry', Presented at Inst. Soc. of America, 18th Conf, Chicago, Sept. 1963.

5. Eckert, E. R. G., and Drake, R. M., 'Heat and Mass Transfer', McGraw-Hill, New York, 2nd Ed. 1959.

6. Bell, J. C., and Katz E. R., 'A Method of Measuring Heat Transfer Using Cyclic Temperature Variation', Heat Transfer and Fluid Mech. Inst. (1949).

7. Schneider, P. J., 'Conduction Heat Transfer', Addison-Wesley, Reading, Mass. Sept. 1957.

8. Hall, J. G., and Hertzbert, A., 'Recent Advances in Transient Surface Temperature Thermometry', Jet Prop. Jour. Vol. 28, No. 11, Nov. 1958, pp. 719-723.

9. Rose, P. H., 'Development of the Calorimeter Heat Transfer Gauge for Use in Shock Tubes', AVCO Research Rep. 17, Feb. 1958.

10. Vidal, R. J., 'Transient Surface Temperature Measurements', Symposium: 'Measurement in Unsteady Flow', ASME Hydraulic Div. Conf., New York, May 1962.

11. Bogdan, L., 'High Temperature Thin-Film Resistance Thermometers for Heat Transfer Measurement', Cornell Aeronautical Lab. Rep. No. HM-1510-Y-5, Feb., 1963.

12. Skinner, G. T., 'Calibration of Thin-Film Backing Materials', ARS Jour. Vol. 31, No. 5, May 1961.

13. Starner, K. E., 'Use of Thin-Skinned Calorimeters for High Heat Flux Jet Measurements', Aerospace Corp. Rep. TR-0158 (3240-10)-4, July, 1967.

14. Sparrow, E. M., and Gregg, J. L., 'Prandtl Number Effects on Unsteady Forced Convection Heat Transfer', NACA TN 4311, June, 1958.

Nomenclature

English

Bi $\quad$ = Biot number = hL/k

C_{pw} $\quad$ = specific heat of body material, $\dfrac{J}{Kg\,°K}$

c $\quad$ = constant

∂ $\quad$ = partial derivative

d $\quad$ = total derivative

e $\quad$ = constant = 2.71828

Fo $\quad$ = Fourier number = $\alpha\tau/t_w^2$

F_{w-s} $\quad$ = radiation surface configuration factor

h $\quad$ = convective unit surface conductance, $\dfrac{watts}{m^2\,°K}$

k_w $\quad$ = thermal conductivity of body material, $\dfrac{watts}{m\,°K}$

L $\quad$ = body thickness, m

Q $\quad$ - total heat input = qA, watts

q $\quad$ = rate of heat input, $\dfrac{watts}{cm^2}$

T $\quad$ = temperature - $°K$

$\bar{T}$ $\quad$ = dimensionless temperature

t $\quad$ = thickness, m

x $\quad$ = depth, m

∞ $\quad$ = infinitely large

Greek

α $\quad$ = thermal diffusivity of body material = $k/\rho C_p$, $\dfrac{cm^2}{s}$

δ $\quad$ = diffusion depth - m

ϵ_{w-s} $\quad$ = emissivity interchange factor

π $\quad$ = constant = 3.14159

ρ $\quad$ = density of body material, kg/m^3

σ $\quad$ = Stefan-Boltzmann radiation constant = 17.3×10^{-10}, $\dfrac{watts}{m^2\,°K^4}$

τ $\quad$ = time, s

ω $\quad$ = frequency - cycles/sec

Subscript

f — ambient fluid

max — maximum

o — initial $(\tau=0)$

w — wall

Appendix A Effect of Non-Uniform Surface Temperature

Transient measurements obtained from calorimeters are often in gross error due to improper simulation of the test surface. The calorimeter should not disturb the thermal conditions which occur when it is not present. Proper simulation of the contour, smoothness, surface emissivity and time constant $\dfrac{\rho_m V_m C_{pm}}{A_m}$ are necessary or deviations of the surface temperature history may occur. For example if a slab calorimeter $\dfrac{V_m}{A_m} = t$ has an improper time constant, a non-uniform wall temperature distribution will be set up. An insulated plug-type calorimeter sometimes generates a step in the wall temperature. For laminar flat plate flow, this effect alters the to be measured heat flux.

If a plate exposed to a steady flow has a temperature T_f up to $x = x_o$ and a temperature T_w downstream of x_o, the ratio of heat transfer coefficient with (c) step wall temperature (h) to the heat transfer coefficient with constant wall temp h_{iso} is (5):

$$\frac{h}{h_{iso}} = \left[1 - \left(\frac{x_o}{x} \right)^{3/4} \right]^{-1/3} \qquad\qquad \text{Eq. 7-43}$$

Appendix B The Quasi-Steady Assumption

It is often interesting to compare the heat flux results of experiments using transient techniques with analytically predicted values. In general the theoretical analyses apply to the steady state case only and any comparison is only approximate. The comparison is facilitated if the quasi-steady assumption is adopted which supposes that the thermal layer passes through a succession of instantaneous steady states. Truly there is a difference between the actual instantaneous heat transfer and the quasi-steady value. Sparrow and Gregg (14) examined this problem for the case of laminar flow over a flat plate and obtained the approximate result for Pr = 0.72:

$$\frac{q_{inst}}{q_{qs}} = 1 + \frac{x}{U_\infty} \left\{ 2.39 \frac{\frac{dT_w}{d\tau}}{\left(T_w - T_f\right)_{qs}} - 0.801 \frac{\frac{d^2 T_w}{d\tau^2}}{\left(T_w - T_f\right)_{qs}} \frac{x}{U_\infty} + \ldots \right\}$$

In most forced-convection situations the term in the brackets is small compared to the first. For example if $T_w - T_f = 55.5^\circ$ K, $dT_w/d\tau = 55.5^\circ$ K/s, $x = 0.0305$m, and $U_\infty = 30.5$ m/s, $q_{inst}/q_{qs} \simeq 1.02$. In nearly all situations the small values of x/U_∞ assure quasi-steady heat transfer.

8

Analogies to Heat Transfer Processes

E. R. G. ECKERT
School of Mechanical and Aerospace Engineering University of Minnesota,
Minneapolis, Minnesota.

Summary

In this paper, analogies will be discussed which have been conceived and utilized
to study various heat transfer processes. After a short discussion of analogies
to conductive and radiative heat transfer, the main body of the paper will be
devoted to analogies describing convective heat transfer situations. The literature
listed at the end of this paper will be useful for those wanting to obtain more
information on the various analogies.

Conduction Heat Transfer

Fourier's equation describing steady heat conduction in a constant property medium
has mathematically the form of Laplace's equation in the absence of internal heat
sources or of Poisson's equation in the presence of internal heat sources. These
equations also describe various other physical processes which consequently can
be used to set up analogs. The flow of electricity according to Ohm's law is
described by Laplace's equation and provides the possibility of electric analogs.
These are constructed using a conducting paper or an electrolytic trough; the
latter device has the advantage that it can easily be adjusted to the solution of
rotationally symmetric problems or to general 3-dimensional situations.

In fluid mechanics, Laplace's equation describes the flow of an inviscid fluid. Flow
of a viscous fluid between two parallel plates at a small Reynolds number generates
the same streamlines as flow of an inviscid fluid and can, therefore, also be used
as an analog (Hele-Shaw flow). Ludwig Prandtl was the first one to point out the
fact that Laplace's or Poisson's equation describes the shape of a thin membrane
and that this can again be used for a very useful analog to flow or heat conduction
processes.

A hydraulic analog can be constructed to an unsteady heat conduction process in
which the thermal capacity is replaced by the capacity of stand pipes and the conductive resistance by capillary tubes which interconnect the stand pipes. The
liquid level in the stand pipes is then an analog to the temperature in the heat
conduction process. This analog can easily be modified to study the effect of
change of phase as it occurs, for example in a freezing or melting process (1).

The usefulness of these analogs has recently diminished because of the availability
of digital electronic computers. Such a computer can actually be considered as
an analog which has the advantage that all conductive situations can be studied
including complicating features like variation of the properties involved. For
this reason, the analogies mentioned above will not be discussed in any detail
and the reader is referred to the referenced literature.

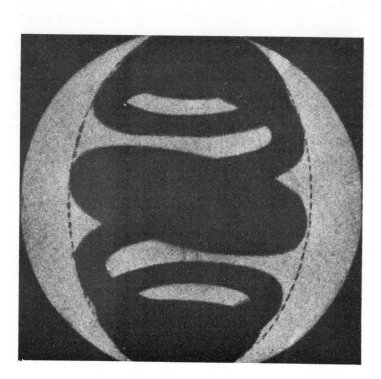

Fig. 8-1   Optical determination of the angle factor of a coil (2)

Radiative Heat Transfer

Electric networks have been proposed to describe radiative heat transfer in engineering systems. In these analogs Ohm's resistances are interconnected in parallel and in series and various electric potentials are applied to the external node points. Such an analog is very useful for demonstration because engineers are often more acquainted with electric networks than with radiative exchange processes. To solve radiative energy processes, again today one prefers the digital electronic computer, especially since the Monte Carlo method offers a procedure by which, in principle, any radiative exchange can be calculated.

Mechanical and optical analogs have been developed to obtain shape or angle factors needed in the analysis of radiative exchange. These are useful for intricate geometries for which the analysis is often extremely involved and an example is shown in Figure 8-1. The photo is obtained by the optical analogy (2). The ratio of the areas of the dark shadow to the illuminated disk is the shape factor describing the radiative energy exchange between a hot coil and its cold surroundings, assuming the coil surfaces to be black, diffuse radiators. Similar analogs can also be conceived which describe the energy exchange between specularly reflecting surfaces.

Convective Heat Transfer

Mass Transfer Analogy for a Constant Property Fluid

Basic Considerations

The flow of a constant property fluid is described by the continuity equation and the Navier-Stokes equations. These will be presented here for a Cartesian coordinate system in tensor notation and with dimensionless parameters. Accordingly, the three coordinates will be indicated by x_1', x_2', x_3', respectively, or generally by x_i' or x_j' with i or j having values from 1 to 3. In the same way, the three velocity components will be denoted by v_i' or v_j'. Length dimensions will be made non-dimensional, dividing them by a reference length, L_o', velocities are made dimensionless by an arbitrarily chosen reference velocity v_o'. The time τ is made dimensionless by a reference time L_o'/v_o' and pressures p' are made dimensionless with a reference pressure $\rho'v_o'^2$ with ρ' indicating the fluid density:

$$x_i = \frac{x_i'}{L_o'} \;,\quad v_i = \frac{v_i'}{v_o'} \;,\quad \tau = \frac{\tau'}{L_o'/v_o'} \;,\quad p = \frac{p'}{\rho'v_o'^2} \qquad \text{(Eq. 8-1)}$$

With this notation, the continuity and momentum equations take on the following form:

$$\frac{\partial}{\partial x_i}(v_i) = 0 \qquad \text{(Eq. 8-2)}$$

$$\frac{Dv_i}{d\tau} = -\frac{\partial p}{\partial x_i} + \frac{1}{Re_o}\frac{\partial}{\partial x_j}\left[\left(1+\frac{\epsilon}{\nu}\right)\left(\frac{\partial v_i}{\partial x_j}+\frac{\partial v_j}{\partial x_i}\right)\right] \qquad \text{(Eq. 8-3)}$$

In reading these equations, it has to be recalled that any term in which a subscript i or j is repeated stands for the sum of three terms with the subscript replaced alternatively by 1, 2, and 3. The operator $\frac{D}{d\tau}$ stands for the substantial derivative towards time, τ. The index i in Equation 8-3 indicates that this equation represents three equations in which the index i is again alternatively replaced by 1, 2, 3. The Reynolds number, Re_o, is based on the reference parameters ($Re_o = v'_o L'_o / \nu$, with ν indicating the kinematic viscosity), ϵ denotes the turbulent diffusivity of momentum. The following relation can be derived from similarity considerations or from experiments.

$$\frac{\epsilon}{\nu} = f(Re_o, x_i) \qquad \text{(Eq. 8-4)}$$

It may in addition be influenced by the turbulence characteristics of the flow entering the system under consideration or by the roughness of the surfaces involved. Dimensional analysis, which will not be pursued here, leads to the result that for objects of similar shape any dimensionless parameter characterizing the flow is a function of Reynolds number and of dimensionless location only. This holds, for instance, for friction factors, drag coefficients, dimensionless pressure, velocity distribution and so on.

It should also be pointed out that for a constant property fluid, the flow process is completely described by equations 8-2 and 8-3 and by the corresponding boundary conditions. This means, for instance, that the flow process is completely independent of the fact whether heat or mass transfer is present or not. An experimentally determined flow field in an isothermal one-component fluid therefore remains unaltered when heat or mass transfer is superimposed on the flow process.

We will now consider a heat transfer process which is superimposed on the velocity field and described by the following equation written again in dimensionless parameters:

$$\frac{Dt}{d\tau} = \frac{1}{Re_o Pr} \frac{\partial}{\partial x_i} \left[\left(1 + \frac{\epsilon}{\nu} \frac{Pr}{Pr_t}\right) \frac{\partial t}{\partial x_i} \right] \qquad \text{(Eq. 8-5)}$$

The parameter, Pr, indicates the Prandtl number of the fluid ($Pr = \nu/\alpha$, where α denotes the thermal diffusivity of the fluid) and the turbulent Prandtl number, Pr_t, is, in a similar way, defined as the ratio of the turbulent diffusivity ϵ for momentum to the turbulent diffusivity ϵ_H for heat, $Pr_t = \epsilon / \epsilon_H$. t, indicating a dimensionless temperature, stands for the ratio of a temperature difference Δt divided by a reference temperature difference Δt_o where both temperature differences are counted from an arbitrary reference temperature. Δt_o, for instance, can denote the difference between the surface temperature of an object exposed to the flow to the fluid upstream temperature. The turbulent Prandtl number is given by a relation:

$$Pr_t = f(Re_o, Pr, x_i) \qquad \text{(Eq. 8-6)}$$

This follows again from similarity considerations and from experimental evidence. In addition, it is again influenced by the upstream turbulence and by surface roughness. From equations 8-2 to 8-6 it follows that local Nusselt numbers as dimensionless expressions for the local heat transfer coefficients will be described by a functional relationship of the following form:

$$Nu = f(Re_o, Pr, x_i) \qquad \text{(Eq. 8-7)}$$

We consider now a mass transfer process in a two-component single-phase medium superimposed on the velocity field. This process is described by the equation:

$$\frac{Dw}{d\tau} = \frac{1}{Re_o Sc} \frac{\partial}{\partial x_i} \left[\left(1 + \frac{\epsilon}{\nu} \frac{Sc}{Sc_t}\right) \frac{\partial t}{\partial x_i} \right] \tag{Eq. 8-8}$$

in which w, a dimensionless mass fraction of one of the components, stands again for the ratio of a mass fraction difference to a reference mass fraction difference defined in the same way as the dimensionless temperature t in Equation 8-5. $Sc = \nu/D$ is the Schmidt number with D denoting the binary mass diffusion coefficient and $Sc_t = \epsilon/\epsilon_M$ is the turbulent Schmidt number with ϵ_M indicating the turbulent diffusivity for mass negligible variation of properties is assumed.

Dimensional analysis requires that local Sherwood numbers, defined as the product of the mass transfer coefficient h_M and a reference length L_o divided by the mass diffusion coefficient D, can be expressed in the following way:

$$Sh = f(Re_o, Sc, x_i) \tag{Eq. 8-9}$$

The fact that Equations 8-5 and 8-8 are of the same form, however, allows an additional important conclusion to be drawn. For this purpose it is useful to realize that all available experimental evidence points to the fact that:

$$Sc_t = Pr_t \tag{Eq. 8-10}$$

or in other words, that Equation 8-6 describes the turbulent Schmidt number, Sc_t, as well as the turbulent Prandtl number, Pr_t. With this in mind, Equation 8-8 can be changed to Equation 8-5 by replacing w with t and Sc with Pr. From this it follows that for any geometrically similar configuration and for similar boundary conditions an equation of the form of Equation 8-9 can be obtained from the corresponding Equation 8-7 if one replaces in that equation the Nusselt number by the Sherwood number and the Prandtl number by the Schmidt number.

Dimensional analysis can also be performed on the equations which describe natural convection heat transfer of a fluid with slightly varying properties, on the one hand, and natural convection mass transfer in an isothermal two-component fluid where the properties of the two components differ little. The result is again that a simple relation exists between the Sherwood number describing the mass transfer process and the Nusselt number describing the heat transfer process. The local Sherwood number, Sh, can be presented as a function of a Grashof number, Gr_{oM} based on reference parameters, a Schmidt number, Sc, and dimensionless coordinates x_i fixing the location under consideration on the surface of the object at which mass transfer occurs:

$$Sh = f(Gr_{oM} \ Sc, \ x_i) \quad \text{or} \quad Sh = f(Ra_{oM}, \ Sc, \ x_i) \tag{Eq. 8-11}$$

More recently, the Rayleigh Number, $Ra_{oM} = Gr_{oM}$, Sc, is used instead of the Grashof number because the Sherwood number, and also transition to turbulence, depends much less on the Schmidt number when it is expressed by a Rayleigh number, than when it is expressed by a Grashof number. The analogy between heat and mass transfer leads again to the result that, for any fixed geometry and for similar boundary conditions, an equation describing heat transfer can be obtained from Equation 8-11 when the Sherwood number is replaced by the Nusselt number, the Grashof number or Rayleigh number for mass transfer by a Grashof number or Rayleigh number respectively for heat transfer and the Schmidt number by the Prandtl number. This is indicated in the following lines:

$$\overset{Nu}{\underset{}{Sh}} = f(\overset{Gr_o}{\underset{}{Gr_{oM}}} \ \overset{Pr}{\underset{}{Sc}}, \ x_i) \quad \text{or} \quad \overset{Nu}{\underset{}{Sh}} = f(\overset{Ra_o}{\underset{}{Ra_{oM}}} \ \overset{Pr}{\underset{}{Sc}}, \ x_i) \tag{Eq. 8-12}$$

(For the definition of the dimensionless parameters, see the list of symbols.)

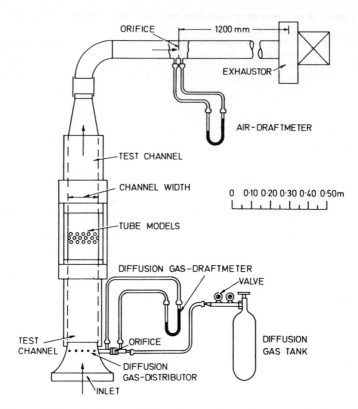

Fig. 8-2   Test setup for mass transfer analog using ammonia absorption (4)

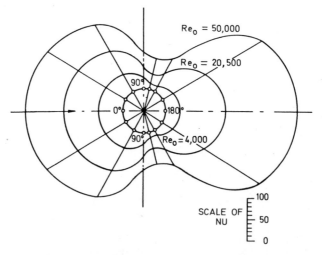

Fig. 8-3   Local nusselt numbers on a tube in crossflow of air determined by mass transfer analogy (4)

In the derivation of the mass transfer analogy, one can also consider Equations 8-2, 8-3, 8-5 and 8-8 as describing turbulent heat and mass transfer processes, even when the turbulent contributions expressed by the turbulent diffusivity ϵ are disregarded. In this case, the equations describe in principle the time-varying turbulent velocity, temperature, and composition fields when the proper boundary conditions are applied. Our knowledge today is insufficient to solve these equations; however, the similarity considerations can be based on them and the conclusions are the same as presented in the preceding paragraphs. They express the content of the mass transfer analogy. Its value lies in the fact that any heat transfer relation provides also a mass transfer relation for a similar problem but the similarity in the boundary conditions has to be carefully considered. A mass transfer process, for instance, frequently causes a mass release or mass absorption on the solid surfaces involved. This creates a finite velocity normal to the wall surfaces and if these velocities are sufficiently large to effect the mass transfer process, then the corresponding heat transfer relation must be for a process with similar velocities at the surface.

The mass transfer analogy can also be utilized in reverse to obtain heat transfer information through mass transfer experiments because there are situations in which a mass transfer process can be set up with cleaner boundary conditions and can be studied more easily and more accurately than the corresponding heat transfer process. Examples of such experiments are discussed in the following paragraphs.

Mass transfer experiments have been performed in gases as well as in liquids using absorption, condensation, or evaporation of a gaseous component at a surface. The analogy has also been used in liquids with solution or absorption of a substance at the surface. In the latter case, use of an electrolyte offers special advantages and the corresponding electro-chemical method has been used to a considerable degree.

Mass Transfer Analogy in Gases

The first one to make use of the mass transfer analogy in 1921 to study heat transfer was H. Thoma. The results of his study are contained in a book called "High Performance Steam Boilers" (3). Thoma used models of tube banks made out of filter paper and soaked with phosphoric acid. An air-ammonia mixture was directed through the tube bank. The ammonia is absorbed so readily on the surface of the tubes that its concentration there was negligible. The amount of ammonia transferred to the surface was determined by titration of the acid in the filter paper. Thoma obtained, in this way, heat transfer coefficients which were, in the main, well verified by later heat transfer measurements.

The same method was used on an enlarged scale by W. Lohrisch (4) in a wind tunnel shown in Figure 8-2. He verified essentially the results obtained by Thoma and determined also local heat transfer coefficients in the way that the filter paper covering the tube surface was subdivided into a number of longitudinal strips. Figure 8-3 presents results obtained in this way. Both Thoma and Lohrisch also used mass transfer experiments for flow visualization. In this case the model surfaces were soaked with chloric acid and the developing ammonia chloride clouds were photographed, as in Figures 8-4 and 8-5. The Schmidt number for diffusion of ammonia into air at $0°C$ has a value Sc = 0.634. Experiments performed at this temperature result, therefore, in Nusselt numbers at a Prandtl number 0.634.

Evaporation of water vapor in measured quantities from surfaces covered by a water film into an air stream have also been used as a mass transfer analogy. R. Hilpert (5) studied, in this way, combined heat and mass transfer in free

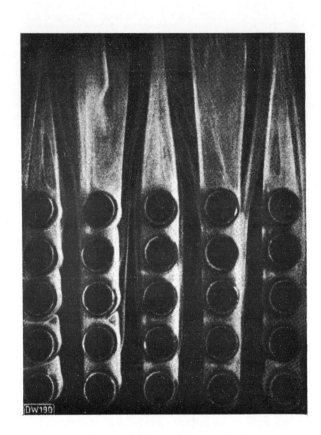

Fig. 8-4   Visualization of mass transfer in flow of air through a bundle of
tubes in line (4)

Fig. 8-5   Visualization of mass transfer in flow of air through a bundle of
staggered tubes (4)

Table 8-1: Physical Properties of Naphthalene Vapor at One Atmosphere Pressure (8), ν = kinematic viscosity; ρ_{so} density of solid naphthalene; p_v = vapor pressure of solid naphthalene; * = 1 b = 1.0197 Rgf/cm^2.

t	ν	Sc	ρ_{so}	p_v
(°F)	cm^2/s	---	g/cm^3	b*
70	546	2.38	1.139	0.0111
75	556	2.39	1.127	0.0148
80	565	2.40	1.114	0.0194
85	575	2.40	1.101	0.0254
90	584	2.41	1.088	0.0331
95	533	2.41	1.075	0.0429

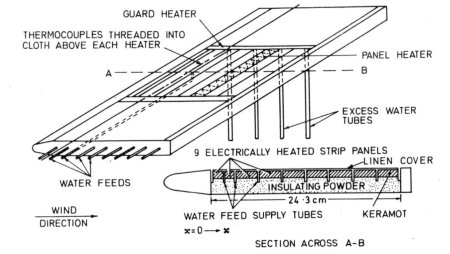

Fig. 8-6   Mass transfer analog to measure heat transfer on an isothermal flat plate by evaporation of water vapor (6)

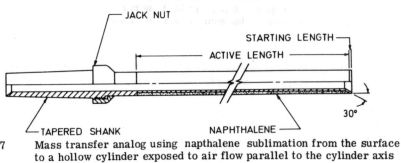

Fig. 8-7   Mass transfer analog using napthalene sublimation from the surface to a hollow cylinder exposed to air flow parallel to the cylinder axis (8)

convection from a vertical plate. Powell and Griffith (6) used the same method to obtain local heat transfer coefficients on a flat plate with forced flow over its surface. Figure 8-6 shows the experimental arrangement for these studies. The rate of evaporation from the strips of linen covering the surface of the plate was determined in two ways: directly by measuring the amount of water fed through the individual supply tubes and indirectly by measuring the electric energy needed to keep the surface temperature uniform and at the same value for a wet and dry surface. The Schmidt number for diffusion of water vapor into air at $8°C$ is 0.615. Experiments at this temperature lead to Nusselt numbers for fluids with a Prandtl number of the same magnitude.

Evaporation of naphthalene has frequently been used in mass transfer analogy studies. The method appears to have been introduced by Jakob and Kezios in 1953 and has been used in a variety of experimental investigations since that time (7) to (13). The naphthalene used is usually of crystal grade, having the chemical symbol $C_{10}H_8$, a molecular weight of 128.2, a melting point between 79 and $80°C$, and 0.001 per cent residue after ignition. In (8), the method was used to obtain information on local heat transfer coefficients along the surface of a cylinder exposed to an axial flow of air.

Figure 8-7 presents a sketch of the cylinder showing that the cylinder was hollow with air flowing through the interior as well as along the outside, minimizing in this way starting effects. The cylinder model was manufactured from steel and had a thin layer of naphthalene along its outer surface. The naphthalene was cast onto the steel model in a mold made of dental plaster consisting of two parts to facilitate the removal of the model. The surface of the mold was coated with epoxy resin to make it impermeable to molten naphthalene and was covered with a thin layer of silicone grease to prevent adhesion of the model. The model and the mold were preheated by steam passed through the interior of the metal tube, the molten naphthalene was poured at a temperature of approximately $100°C$ into the vertical mold, and then cooled by gradually pouring water into the interior of the cylinder, raising the water level slowly so that the cooling proceeded from the lower end upward. In this way a dense layer of naphthalene could be obtained which had an outer diameter of 25 mm, with a tolerance of one-tenth of a millimeter. The model was exposed to an air stream in a wind tunnel and after completion of a run, removed and the change in diameter measured by a profilometer graduated to 2.5μ. In this way the local evaporation rate could be determined. To avoid a mass loss by evaporation, the measurements with the profilometer were made in an air tight enclosure in which the air was saturated with naphthalene vapor. The cylinder radius changed during an experiment by up to 40μ.

The experiments were evaluated in the following way: The local evaporation rate was obtained by the profilometer measurements; the concentration of naphthalene at the cylinder surface was obtained from the partial pressure of the naphthalene gas, through the ideal gas equation in which the partial pressure was obtained from the surface temperature, using equilibrium data listed in Table 8-1. The surface temperature itself was not measured and it was assumed that it was within the accuracy of the measurements equal to the temperature in the air stream. The density of the solid naphthalene which enters the weight loss calculation was obtained by weighing a small naphthalene cylinder which was cast in the same way as the model.

The mass transfer analogy proved especially advantageous in the study of heat transfer at the surface of a rotating disk, because the analogy avoided temperature and heat flux measurements which are difficult to perform on a rotating part. Reference 11 reports on these measurements and Figure 8-8 is a sketch of the test equipment. The rotating horizontal disk, with 205 mm diameter has on its upper

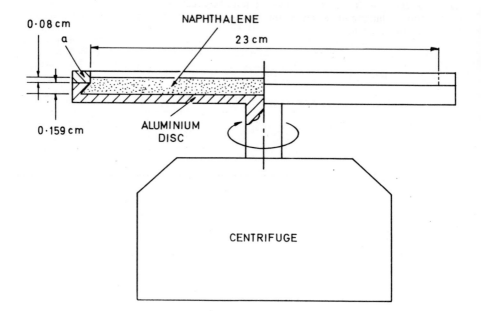

Fig. 8-8   Mass transfer analog to determine heat transfer characteristics of a disk rotating in air using naphthalene evaporation (11)

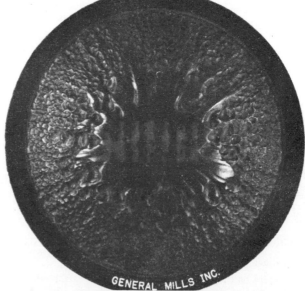

Fig. 8-9   Plaster cast of a blunt model of naphthalene exposed to a supersonic airstream (experiments at General Mills, Inc.)

surface a layer of naphthalene which was cast onto the surface in a molten condition. After cooling in air, the ring a, which was necessary for casting, was removed and the upper surface of the naphthalene layer was machined on a lathe. The disk was rotated for 6 to 20 min at speeds up to 10000 RPM and the mass loss was measured by weighing. The average mass transfer coefficient h_M was then obtained with the following relation:

$$h_M = \frac{mR_v T_s}{p_{vs}A} \qquad \text{(Eq. 8-13)}$$

in which m denotes the mass loss per unit time, R_v the gas constant of the naphthalene vapor, T_s the surface temperature of the naphthalene, p_{vs} the vapor pressure of naphthalene at the surface temperature and A the surface area. The difference between the surface temperature and the measured temperature in the air surrounding the disk was again neglected. It was estimated that the temperature depression of the surface due to evaporation was approximately $0.05°C$ and the temperature change due to the recovery effect was approximately $0.5°C$. Properties in Table 8-1 were again used for the evaluation. The accuracy in the determination of the mass transfer coefficient was estimated to be approximately 6 per cent. Nusselt numbers were obtained through the mass transfer analogy.

Another situation for which the mass transfer analogy proved useful is laminar or turbulent heat transfer in forced convection on a flat plate with span-wise strips which are alternately unheated and heated to a uniform temperature (12) (13). The step-wise temperature variation connected with this situation is practically impossible to obtain in a heat transfer experiment because of heat conduction within the plate but it presents no difficulty at all in a mass transfer study. The experimental procedures used in these studies and in (7), (9) and (10) were essentially the same as discussed above.

Mass transfer studies using naphthalene evaporation can also be made to simulate conditions as they occur in ablation cooling. For this purpose, the rate of evaporation is increased by operation of the wind tunnel into which the model is placed at elevated temperatures. Such studies were performed some years ago at the Research Laboratory of General Mills, Inc. and Figure 8-9 shows the plaster cast of a blunt object of naphthalene which has been exposed for some time to a high temperature air stream. The ablation pattern shown resembles closely the pattern on a reentering satellite or space ship with protection by a plastic ablating material.

Electro-Chemical Method

Mass transfer studies which simulate heat transfer in liquids can be done very effectively by the electro-chemical method. This method was introduced for the measurement of average mass transfer coefficients by C. Wagner in 1949 (14), and by C.R. Wilke, C.W. Tobias, and M. Eisenberg in 1954 (15). P. Grassmann and N. Ibl extended it to the measurement of local mass transfer coefficients in 1961 and T.H. Hanratty and associates used it for turbulence measurements in the immediate neighborhood of a surface in 1962.

The liquid used in such experiments is an electrolyte so when two electrodes are inserted into it, the negatively charged ions move to the anode, the positively charged ions to the cathode. At a sufficiently large potential difference between the two electrodes, the ions react there releasing or binding one or more electrons. The movement of the ions towards the electrodes is caused by diffusion, by convection if the electrolyte is in motion, and by ion movement in the electric field. The number $ṅ$ of moles of ions moving toward an electrode per unit time and area is then described by the following equation:

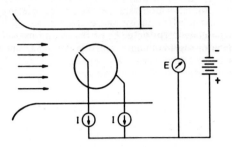

Fig. 8-10   Sketch of the electro-chemical method applied to study local heat transfer on a circular cylinder exposed to a transverse liquid flow

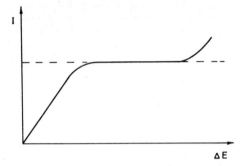

Fig. 8-11   Determination of the saturation current in the electro-chemical method

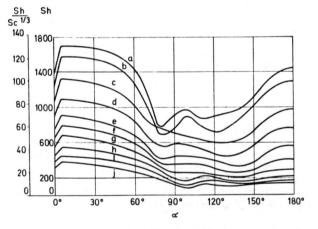

(a) Re = 11 730, (b) Re = 10 200, (c) Re = 7000, (d) Re = 4820,
(e) Re = 3080, (f) Re = 2220, (g) Re = 1485, (h) Re = 1020,
(i) Re = 656, (j) Re = 458.

Fig. 8-12   Local Sherwood numbers around the periphery of a cylinder exposed to a transverse liquid flow measured by the electro-chemical method (16)

$$\dot{n} = v_y c - D \frac{dc}{dy} - cB_i \frac{dE}{dy} \qquad \text{(Eq. 8-14)}$$

in which v_y indicates the convective velocity of the electrolyte toward the electrode, c the mole concentration of the ions under consideration, D the mass diffusion coefficient of the ions in the electrolyte, B_i the ion mobility, E the electric potential, and y the direction normal to the electrode surface.

In a normal mass transfer process, an electric field is absent and the last term in the above equation has therefore to be made vanishingly small in order to use the ion transport as an analog to a normal mass transfer process. This can be done in the following way: A second strong electrolyte - the so-called supporting electrolyte - is added to the liquid, selected so that its ions do not react at the electrodes at the potential difference used in the experiment. If such an electrolyte were to be present alone, then the electric current between the electrodes, which flows when the electric circuit is closed, diminishes rapidly toward zero because layers of ions accumulating near the electrodes create strong space charges. The gradients of the electric field are then concentrated in these thin layers with a thickness of order 10^{-9} m, whereas in the main body of the electrolyte the electric potential is constant. This situation is practically maintained when the supporting electrolyte is added to the active electrolyte simulating the mass transfer process. In this way the last term in Equation 8-14 can be disregarded and a transport of ions of the active electrolyte occurs by diffusion and convection only. The number $\dot{n}$ of moles can easily be obtained by a measurement of the electric current I flowing into or out of the electrode with the equation:

$$I = \dot{n}zF \qquad \text{(Eq. 8-15)}$$

in which z denotes the valence of the ion and F Faraday's constant, which equals $(0.965 \times 10^8 \ \frac{As}{kg\ Aeq.})$.

In the use of the electro-chemical method to study a mass transfer process, and through the analogy also a heat transfer process, one of the electrodes is the model on which mass transfer or heat transfer respectively occurs. The other electrode can be the wall of the flow channel or of the container. Provision should be made that the second electrode is large in area compared to the model so that the resistance for mass transfer is large on the model surface alone. Under normal conditions, the concentration field is concentrated in a boundary layer surrounding the model, whereas concentration differences are minimized in the main body of the electrolyte by convection, which can either be enforced or created by the concentration differences themselves (natural convection).

Figure 8-10 is a sketch of an arrangement to measure local heat transfer coefficients around the periphery of a cylinder exposed to the flow of an electrolyte normal to its axis. The model is in this case the anode, and the channel wall the cathode. A thin strip on the cylinder surface is electrically insulated so that the current into this strip can be measured separately. From the measurement of this current, a local mass transfer coefficient h_M is obtained through the equation:

$$n = h_M (c_\infty - c_s) \qquad \text{(Eq. 8-16)}$$

The ion mole concentration c_∞ is readily measured in the bulk of the fluid. The difficulty of measuring the ion concentration c_s at the model surface is circumvented by adjustment of the electric potential difference ΔE between the two electrodes in such a way that the saturation current is obtained. This is indicated in a diagram as shown in Figure 8-11 by the fact that the current i becomes independent of the magnitude of the electric potential ΔE (by the horizontal portion of the current-potential curve). In this case, the ion concentration c_s at the model surface is zero.

An electrolyte which has frequently been used in this method is the system Ferrocyanid/Ferricyanid $[K_3Fe(CN)_6/K_4Fe(CN)_6]$. The reactions of the ions on the electrodes are described by the following equation:

$$Fe(CN)_6^{-3} + e^- \rightleftarrows Fe(CN)_6^{-4} \qquad \text{(Eq. 8-17)}$$

The reaction goes from left to right at the cathode and from right to left at the anode. In (16) a 0.025 normal solution in water was used for the two chemicals and sodium-hydroxide [NaOH 2 normal] was added as the supporting electrolyte to equalize the electric potential in the main body of the fluid.

Figure 8-12 presents the results obtained in (16). The ordinate can be interpreted either as the Sherwood number or the Nusselt number. In the first case, the Schmidt number is $Sc = 2,170$; in the second case the Prandtl number has this value. It is of interest to observe the dip in the two numbers close to the stagnation point as such a dip has also been observed in other mass transfer measurements. The cylinder used in these measurements was manufactured of nickel with a diameter of 50 mm and the insulated nickel strip in the cylinder wall used for the local mass transfer measurements had 0.5 mm width and was separated from the rest of the surface by a Teflon strip 0.05 mm thick. This demonstrates one advantage of this method as very local measurements can be made because sensitive instruments exist to measure an electric current.

The accuracy of the mass transfer measurements is claimed to be ± 2 to 3 per cent and time-wise fluctuations can also be readily recorded. Some precautions have to be taken, on the other hand, to obtain accurate results as the electrolyte disintegrates when exposed to light and the concentration of the electrolyte has therefore to be checked continuously and the model surface frequently cleaned; otherwise a layer with high electrical resistance is deposited on it. The test setup was manufactured of nickel and rubber-coated steel.

In (17) copper sulphate $(CuSO_4)$ was used with sulphuric acid (H_2SO_4) as the strong electrolyte to study free convection on a horizontal cylinder and on a sphere. Similar studies are also reported in (18) and (19).

The electro-chemical method was also used for measurements of wall shear and of turbulence parameters in boundary layers (20) (21). The reading of a small electrode (of the order of 1 mm^2) in an electrically neutral wall can be interpreted as the velocity gradient at the surface. The time mean signal then determines the time-averaged velocity gradient, while the time variation of the signal describes instantaneous velocity gradients. A probe in a larger electrode surface reads the local mass flux as has been discussed in the preceding paragraph. It can also be used to obtain the limiting law of the turbulent diffusivity at the wall surface. In (21), it was found that the turbulent diffusivity is proportional to the fourth power of the wall distance. In these turbulence measurements, the test setup and the models were manufactured out of plexiglass with platinum foil serving an electrodes.

Electro-chemiluminescence

A variation of the electro-chemical method (22) to (25) can be used for flow visualization and for an optical measurement of mass fluxes. To the active electrolyte and the supporting electrolyte is added a chemiluminescent substance which produces a glow at the anode. In this way, the flow close to the anode surface becomes visible and flow separation, for instance, can be detected very clearly. The intensity of the glow is proportional to the mass transfer rate so that optical measurements can also be used for quantitative determination of mass fluxes.

In (22) hydrogen peroxide (H_2O_2) is used as the active electrolyte and potassium chloride (KCL) as supporting electrolyte. Luminol (Eastman Kodak Luminol = 5-amino-2, 3-dihydro-1, 4 phthalazinedione) is the chemiluminescent substance. Finally, potassium hydroxide (KOH) is added to adjust the pH value of the solution since Luminol only exhibits chemiluminescence in an alkaline solution of pH larger than approximately 8. Table 8-2 gives the composition of the solution as it was used in (22).

The test setup and the model were again made of plexiglass and the electrodes of platinum. The intensity of the chemiluminescence was measured with a photo multiplier. Best conditions for luminescence were obtained at a potential difference of 0. 41 V between anode and electrolyte. The relation between the measured intensity and the mass flux was obtained by calibration, using a flat plate and the stagnation region of a cylinder in cross flow for which the mass flux was known from laminar boundary layer analysis.

Related to the above method is a study (26) in which fluorescence was used to determine the thickness of the layer on the surface of a liquid film into which a gas penetrates. Accurate measurements could be obtained regardless of the fact that this layer was only 0. 1 mm thick. Figure 8-13 shows that the light intensity J, emitted when exposed to ultra-violet light of the two substances A and B changes quite suddenly at a certain pH value. Substance B was used to measure the thickness of the alkaline absorption layer. The method also served for flow visualization and demonstrated clearly the Marangoni effect. This name describes local flows which arise in liquids when the absorbed substance creates local variations of surface tension.

Mass Transfer Analogy for a Variable Property Fluid

The mass transfer analogy has been used to a much smaller degree for a study of heat transfer in a variable property fluid. The only paper on this subject appears to be (27). Local ablation rates and temperatures were measured on a flat plate with a naphthalene coating exposed to subsonic and supersonic air flow and the results, together with a turbulent boundary layer analysis by R. G. Deissler, were used to obtain information on local friction coefficients.

In the following lines, the basic considerations will be presented for a mass transfer analogy in a variable property fluid, for steady flow with a velocity small enough so that energy dissipation can be neglected (or for a gas with a Prandtl number equal one). For this purpose we consider two cases: Case 1, in which a one-component fluid undergoes a heat transfer process at large temperature differences and Case 2, in which a two-component fluid mixture undergoes a mass transfer process at large concentration differences but for the isothermal condition. The conservation equations are in this case written in the dimensioned parameters. They express for Case 1 conservation of mass, of momentum, and of energy respectively:

$$\frac{\partial}{\partial x_i} (\rho v_i) = 0 \qquad \text{(Eq. 8-18)}$$

$$\rho v_i \frac{\partial v_i}{\partial x_i} = - \frac{\partial p}{\partial x_j} + \frac{\partial}{\partial x_i} \left[(\mu + \rho\epsilon) (\frac{\partial v_i}{\partial x_j} + \frac{\partial v_j}{\partial x_i}) - (\mu' + \rho\epsilon') \frac{\partial v_i}{\partial x_i} \delta_{ij} \right]$$

$$\text{(Eq. 8-19)}$$

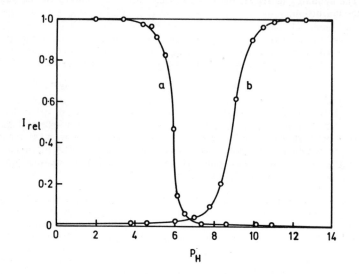

Fig. 8-13   Relative intensity I_{rel} of fluorescence as a function of the p_H value
for two chemical substances

(a) 2-Naphthochinolin
(b) Natrium-2-naphthol-6-sulfonat (26)

Table 8-2: Composition of a chemiluminescent solution (22)

Substance	g/l of solution	Remarks
H_2O	–	solvent should be distilled
KCl	74.56	supporting electrolyte
KOH	1.68	adjust pH. Luminol exhibits chemiluminescence in alkaline solution only
H_2O_2 *	0.0976	oxidizing agent, concentraion strongly affects light intensity. *corresponds to 0.3 ml of H_2O_2 (30% solution)
Luminol	0.15	chemiluminescent substance soluble in alkaline solutins only

$$\rho v_i \frac{\partial i}{\partial x_i} = \frac{\partial}{\partial x_i} \left[\left(\frac{\mu}{Pr} + \rho \frac{\epsilon}{Pr_t} \right) \frac{\partial i}{\partial x_i} \right]$$ (Eq. 8-20)

The fluid is assumed Newtonian and the equations are again written in tensor notation. The symbol i indicates the fluid enthalpy and δ_{ij} denotes the Kronneker Delta with the definition:

$\delta_{ij} = 1$ for $i = j$

$\delta_{ij} = 0$ for $i \neq j$

A mass transfer process according to Case 2 is described by the system of Equations 8-18, 8-19 and 8-21:

$$\rho v_i \frac{\partial w}{\partial x_i} = \frac{\partial}{\partial w_i} \left[\left(\frac{\mu}{Sc} + \rho \frac{\epsilon}{Sc_t} \right) \frac{\partial w}{\partial x_i} \right]$$ (Eq. 8-21)

where Equation 8-21 expresses conservation of mass of one of the components, the mass fraction of which is denoted by w.

Similarity exists between the two cases when the variation of the properties ρ and μ as a function of temperature in Case 1 is similar to the variation of the same properties with mass fraction, w, in Case 2. In addition, the dependance of Pr on temperature must be similar to the dependance of Sc on mass-fraction. The turbulent parameters Pr_t and Sc_t are equal to each other as was pointed out before. The similarity of the properties has to exist only in the parameter range which occurs in a specific problem, a condition which is found to be well approximated in various situations. For gases, the Prandtl and Schmidt numbers can usually be considered constant. The dependance of the density on temperature and on mass fraction respectively can be expressed according to the ideal gas laws through the following equations:

$$\rho = \frac{pM}{R(t + T_o)}$$ (Eq. 8-22)

$$\rho = \frac{p}{RT} \frac{M_1 M_2 / (M_2 - M_1)}{w + M_1 / (M_2 - M_1)}$$ (Eq. 8-23)

It can be observed that the similarity requirement is fulfilled. For the viscosity, this is not exactly the case; however, the variation is often expressible by a linear relation in certain ranges of temperature or mass fraction respectively. In this case, then, the similarity requirement is again fulfilled and Sherwood numbers obtained for a mass transfer situation can be readily interpreted as Nusselt numbers for a heat transfer situation with similar boundary conditions, by replacement of the Sherwood number in the dimensionless expressions by the Nusselt number and the Schmidt number by the Prandtl number.

References

1. Gershun, T., 'A Study of Conductive Heat Transfer with Change of Phase-Mathematical and Analogue Solutions.' Ph.D. Thesis, Univ. of Minnesota. 1955.

2. Eckert, E., Z. Ver. deut. Ingr., 79, 1955 1495.

3.   **Thoma, H.**, 'Hochleistungskessel,' Julius Springer, Berlin 1921.

4.   **Lohrisch, W.**, Forschungsarb. a. d. Geb. d. Ingenieurwes. No. 322. 1929.

5.   **Hilpert, R.**, VDI-Forschungsheft No. 355. 1932.

6.   **Powell, R. W.** and **Griffiths, E.**, Trans. Institution Chem. Engrs. (Brit.)
     13 1935 175.

7.   **Sogin, H. H.**, and **Jakob, M.**, 'Heat and Mass Transfer from Slender Cylin-
     ders to Air Streams in Axisymmetrical Flow,' Heat Transfer and Fluid
     Mechanics Inst. Preprint of Papers, Stanford Univ. Press, 5 1953.

8.   **Christian, W. J.**, and **Kezios, S. P.**, 'Experimental Investigation of Mass
     Transfer by Sublimation from Sharp-Edged Cylinders in Axisymmetric Flow
     with Laminar Boundary Layer.' 1957 Heat Transfer and Fluid Mechanics
     Inst. Stanford Univ. Press, 359 1957.

9.   **Ko, Shao-Yen** and **Sogin, H. H.**, 'Laminar Mass and Heat Transfer from
     Ellipsoidal Surfaces of Fineness Ratio 4 in Axisymmetric Flow.' Trans.
     Amer. Soc. Mech. Eng. 80, 1958 387.

10. **Sogin, H. H.**, 'Sublimation from Disks to Air Streams Flowing Normal to
     Their Surface.' Trans. Amer. Soc. Mech. Eng. 80, 1958, 593.

11. **Kreith, K.**, **Taylor, J. H.**, and **Chong, J. P.**, 'Heat and Mass Transfer from
     a Rotating Disk.' J. of Heat Transfer, 81, 1959, 95.

12. **Sogin, H. H.**, 'Laminar Transfer from Isothermal Spanwise Strips on a Flat
     Plate.' J. of Heat Transfer, 82, 1960, 53.

13. **Sogin, H. H.**, and **Goldstein, R. J.**, 'Turbulent Transfer from Isothermal
     Spanwise Strips on a Flat Plate.' Proceedings of the 1961-62 Heat Transfer
     Conf. Amer. Soc. of Mech. Eng. 447, 1963.

14. **Wagner, C.**, 'Theorie und Experiment in der elektrochemischen Verfah-
     renstechnik.' Chemie-Ingenieur-Technik, 32, 1 1960.

15. **Wilke, C. R.**, **Tobias, C. W.**, and **Eisenberg, M.**, 'Free-Convection Mass
     Transfer at Vertical Plates.' Chem. Eng. Prog. 49, 663 1953.

16. **Grassmann, P.**, **Ibl, N.**, and **Trüb, J.**, 'Elektrochemische Messung von
     Stoffübergangszahlen.' Chemie-Ingenieure-Technik, 33, 529, 1961.

17. **Schutz, G.**, 'Untersuchung des Stoffaustausch-Anlaufgebietes in einem Rohr
     bei vollausgebildeter hydrodynamischer Strömung mit einer elektrochemischen
     Methode.' Int. J. Heat Mass Transfer, 7, 1077 1964.

18. **Kozdoba, L. A.**, and **Zagoruiko, V. A.**, 'Solution of Heat and Mass Transfer
     Problems by the Electrical Analogy Method.' Int. Chem. Engng. 7, 202
     1967.

19. **Newman, J.**, The Effect of Migration in Laminar Diffusion Layers.
     Int. J. Heat Mass Transfer, 10, 983 1967.

20. **Hanratty, T. J.**, 'Study of Turbulence Close to a Solid Wall.' Phys. of
     Fluids Supplement,' S126 1967.

21. **Son, J. S.**, and **Hanratty, T. J.**, 'Limiting Relation for the Eddy Diffusivity Close to a Wall.' A. I. Ch. E. J. 13, 689, 1967.

22. **Colello, R. G.**, and **Springer, G. S.**, 'Mass-Transfer Measurements with the Technique of Electrochemiluminescence.' Int. J. Heat Mass Transfer, 9, 1391, 1966.

23. **Springer, G. S.**, 'Use of Electrochemiluminescence in the Measurement of Mass-Transfer Rates.' Rev. Scient. Instrum. 35, 1277, 1964.

24. **Howland, B.**, **Springer, G. S.**, and **Hill, M. G.**, 'Use of Electrochemilumin-escence in Visualizing Separated Flows.' J. Fluid Mech. 24, 697, 1966.

25. **Luikov, A. V.**, **Shulman, Z. P.**, and **Puris, B. I.**, 'Mass Transfer of a Cylinder in Forced Non-Newtonian Liquid Flow.' Preprints of the Third All-Union Heat and Mass Transfer Conf. May 14-18th, Minsk, 1968.

26. **Hiby, J. W.**, **Braun, D.**, and **Eickel, K. H.**, 'Eine Fluoreszenzmethode zur Untersuchung des Stoffübergangs bei der Gasabsorption im Rieselfilm.' Chemi-Ingenieur-Technik, 39, 297, 1967.

27. **Sherwood, T. K.**, and **Träss, O.**, 'Sublimation Mass Transfer Through Compressible Boundary Layers on a Flat Plate.' J. of Heat Transfer 82, 313, 1960.

Bibliography

Conduction:

Eckert, E., 'Introduction to Heat and Mass Transfer,' (trans. J. F. Gross). McGraw-Hill, New York, 1963.

Jakob, M., 'Heat Transfer, vol. I', John Wiley, New York, 1949.

Schneider, P. J., 'Conduction Heat Transfer,' Addison-Wesley, Reading, Mass. 1955.

Radiation:

Eckert, E., and **Drake, R. M. Jr.**, 'Heat and Mass Transfer,' McGraw-Hill, New York, 1959.

Jakob, M., 'Heat Transfer, vol. II', John Wiley, New York, 1967.

Convection:

Jakob, M., 'Heat Transfer, vols. I and II', John Wiley, New York.

Nomenclature

A - area

c - mole concentration

D - mass diffusion coefficient

E - electric potential

F	-	Faraday's constant
g	-	gravitational acceleration
h	-	heat transfer coefficient
I	-	electric current per unit area
i	-	enthalpy
L_o	-	reference length
M	-	molecular weight
m	-	mass flow per unit area and time
ṅ	-	mole flow per unit area and time
p	-	pressure
R	-	gas constant
T	-	absolute temperature
t	-	temperature
v_o	-	reference velocity
v_i, v_j	-	velocity components
w	-	mass fraction
x_i, x_j	-	Cartesian coordinates
z	-	valence
α	-	thermal diffusivity
β	-	thermal expansion coefficient
ϵ	-	turbulent diffusivity of momentum
ϵ_H	-	turbulent diffusivity of heat
ϵ_M	-	turbulent diffusivity of mass
μ	-	viscosity
ν	-	kinematic viscosity
ρ	-	density
τ	-	time

$$Re_o = \frac{\rho v_o L_o}{\mu} \qquad \text{Reynolds number}$$

$$Pr = \frac{\nu}{\alpha} \qquad \text{Prandtl number}$$

$$Pr_t = \frac{\epsilon}{\epsilon_H} \qquad \text{turbulent Prandtl number}$$

$$Nu = \frac{hL_o}{k} \qquad \text{Nusselt number}$$

$$Sc = \frac{\nu}{D} \qquad \text{Schmidt number}$$

$Sc_t = \dfrac{\epsilon}{\epsilon_M}$ turbulent Schmidt number

$Sh = \dfrac{k_m L_o}{D}$ Sherwood number

$Gr_o = \dfrac{g\beta L_o^3 (t_\infty - t_s)}{\nu^2}$ Grashof number for heat transfer

$Gr_{oM} = \dfrac{g L_o (\rho_\infty - \rho_s)}{\nu^2 \rho}$ Grashof number for mass transfer

$Ra_o = \dfrac{g\beta L_o^3 (t_\infty - t_s)}{\nu\alpha}$ Rayleigh number for heat transfer

$Ra_{oM} = \dfrac{g L_o^3 (\rho_\infty - \rho_s)}{\nu\alpha\rho}$ Rayleigh number for heat transfer

Subscripts:

o   reference state

H   heat

M   mass

s   surface

v   vapor

∞ in main stream

9

Thermal Radiation Measurements

D. K. EDWARDS
University of California, Los Angeles.

Summary

Measurement techniques for determining radiant energy fluxes and radiation characteristics of materials are reviewed. A convenient operator and matrix notation
together with a consistent nomenclature is set forth to facilitate understanding of
what an instrument really measures. Radiometry, surface characteristic measurements, and gas property measurements are considered. Attention is focused on
spectral directional reflectance measurements with heated cavity, integrating
sphere, and 2π-steradian mirror reciprocal reflectometers. Problems encountered in radiation measurements are shown to be largely avoidable by careful
formulation of the measured quantity using the notation propounded.

Introduction

Man cannot yet calculate from "first principles" the radiation received from the
sun. But one can measure without great difficulty the heat radiation received
within a few percent. One cannot predict with any confidence from first principles
the infrared reflectance of sandblasted aluminium. But one can measure the
reflectance rather easily to within a few percent. With knowledge gained from
such measurements engineers can predict and can arrange to use or provide for
radiant energy transfers. Measurements together with a careful assessment of
their probable accuracy are essential to the applied worker.

Thermal radiation measurements fall into two main catagories; measurement of
the radiant energy received from some source, and measurement of the radiation
characteristics of materials, often expressed as a ratio of power reflected, absorbed, or transmitted to power incident. Some aspects of problems in both catagories will be reviewed briefly in what follows, but the entire field of thermal
radiation measurements is too broad to be reviewed in a short work. A worker
in the field must have knowledge of applications, radiative transfer theory, the
physics of interactions between radiation and matter, optics, and, by no means
least important, hardware.

In what follows there is first a review of the concept of radiant intensity which is
basic to the subject of radiation heat transfer and measurement techniques.
Included in this first section is a brief treatment of coherency and polarisation,
which is usually neglected in discussions of thermal radiation. While such
phenomena are absent at thermodynamic equilibrium, they arise naturally as soon
as the departures from strict equilibrium necessary for net energy transfer occur,
and these phenomena often play a role in radiation instruments. There is then a
short review of radiation characteristics which affect instrument performance and
which themselves are often the object of a measurement. Brief reviews of the

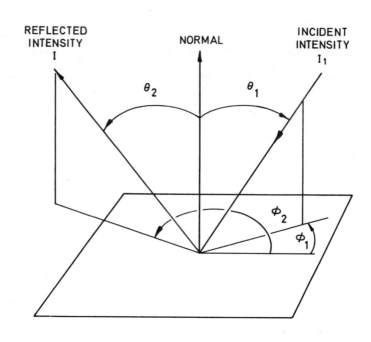

REFLECTED
INTENSITY
I

NORMAL

INCIDENT
INTENSITY
I_1

θ_2

θ_1

ϕ_2

ϕ_1

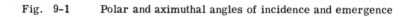

Fig. 9-1   Polar and aximuthal angles of incidence and emergence

fields of radiometry and radiation property measurement are then given.   In these reviews the reader may note a recurring theme, an admonition to formulate the measured quantity and to consider at least the first-order departures from the elementary concept forming the basis for the measurement technique.

Thermal Radiation

Black Body Radiation

Thermal agitations of particles with charge give rise to electromagnetic radiation within matter in the gaseous, liquid, or solid state.   Bose-Einstein statistics (1) indicate that the number of photon wave packets per unit volume with energies between ϵ' and $\epsilon' + d\epsilon'$ is, at thermodynamic equilibrium:

$$\frac{dN}{d\epsilon'} = \frac{8\pi\epsilon'^2/h^3c^3}{e^{\epsilon'/kT} - 1} \tag{Eq. 9-1}$$

where k is Boltzmann's constant (1.38054×10^{-23} joule/°K) and c is the velocity of the radiation (2.997925×10^8 m/sec in vacuum).   At equilibrium the directions of propagation are uniformly distributed over a sphere of 4π steradians.   The number of photons crossing a small area dA within a small pencil of solid angle $d\Omega$ around a direction θ, ϕ (See Fig. 9-1) is then:

$$dn = \frac{dN}{d\epsilon'} \ d\epsilon' \ \frac{d\Omega}{4\pi} cdA\cos\theta \tag{Eq. 9-2}$$

Each photon carries energy ϵ' which is related to wavenumber ν or wavelength λ by Einstein's photoelectric law:

$$\epsilon' = hc\nu = hc/\lambda \ ;$$
$$hcd\nu = \left|d\epsilon'\right| = (hc/\lambda^2)d\lambda \tag{Eq. 9-3}$$

where h is Planck's constant (6.6256×10^{-34} joule-sec).   The power per unit projected area per unit solid angle per unit spectral band width is then:

$$I_b(\lambda, T) = \frac{\epsilon'dn}{\cos\theta dAd\Omega \, d\lambda} = \frac{2hc^2\lambda^{-5}}{e^{hc/\lambda kT} - 1} \tag{Eq. 9-4a}$$

$$I_b(\nu, T) = \frac{\epsilon'dn}{\cos\theta dAd\Omega \, d\nu} = \frac{2hc^2\nu^3}{e^{hc\nu/kT} - 1} \tag{Eq. 9-4b}$$

This quantity is referred to in engineering literature as the Planck black body spectral radiant intensity (2).

A particularly useful relation is the fraction of Planckian radiation having wavelengths between 0 and λ:

$$f_b(\lambda \ T) = f_b(\lambda T) = \frac{\int_0^\lambda I_b(\lambda', T)d\lambda'}{\int_0^\infty I_b(\lambda', T)d\lambda'} \tag{Eq. 9-5}$$

That the external Planck fraction f_b is a function of only the product λT may be seen readily by making a change of variable from ν or λ to $hc\nu/kT$ or $k\lambda T/hc$ and noting that:

$$\int_0^\infty \frac{x^3 dx}{e^{ax}-1} = \frac{\pi^4}{15a^4}$$

(Eq. 9-6)

For engineering purposes the dimensional variable λT used by Dunkle (3) usually serves best (The reader may consult Ch. 2 of (4) for another view). Czerny and Walther (5) term f_b the fractional function of the first kind. The notation $f_b(\lambda T)$ makes it possible to write the black body intensity as:

$$I_b(\lambda, T) = \frac{1}{\pi} \sigma T^5 f_b' (\lambda T)$$

(Eq. 9-7)

where the prime denotes differentiation with respect to the argument λT, and the quantity σ is the Stefan-Boltzmann constant:

$$\sigma = \pi \left(\frac{2hc^2}{15}\right) \left(\frac{\pi k}{hc}\right)^4$$

(Eq. 9-8)

Laboratory black body or hohlraum sources are used to approach Planckian radiation. Such sources are often a heated tube with a dark specularly reflecting wall and a grooved dark back end. Sometimes the front of the tube is covered with a plate having a small orifice. A number of commercial models are available (e.g. Table 3-3 of (4)). A good source should be made with a thick wall of highly conducting material and be heated so as to minimize temperature gradients. Errors due to a slightly cold front end may be partially mitigated by not viewing that portion of the cavity directly and giving it a low emittance. Of course, the temperature of the high emissivity zone viewed must be determined in an accurate manner.

Radiant Intensity

A geometrical optics viewpoint is most often taken, because of its practicality and simplicity. The photons are imagined to travel in straight lines along paths from one area of concern to another, the path lengths being much greater than the photon wavelength being considered. The optical elements themselves may have films or particles small compared to wavelength or features regular even in terms of wavelengths, but the behavior of these elements is described in terms of radiation characteristics. In addition the state of the matter in the optical elements is taken to be that characterized by a temperature T describing an equilibrium condition. Heat conduction (through collisions) is often sufficiently large to make such a characterization reasonable.

From this viewpoint, the quantity most often desired by a worker interested in calculating radiation heat transfer rates is the spectral radiant intensity I, the power per unit projected area, per unit solid angle, per unit band width. If this quantity is known, power transfer rates can easily be found by integration (usually numerical integration). One integration is made over the spectrum of photon wavelengths (or wave numbers of energies), and a second is made over the hemisphere over an area. Denote the first by a total transfer operator operating upon a spectral intensity I:

$$\mathcal{T}\{I(\theta, \phi, \lambda)\} = \int_0^\infty I(\theta, \phi, \lambda) d\lambda$$

(Eq. 9-9)

Denote the second integration by a hemispherical transfer operator operating upon I:

$$\overline{\mathcal{H}}\{I(\theta, \phi, \lambda)\} = \int_0^{2\pi} \int_0^{\pi/2} I(\theta, \phi, \lambda) \sin\theta \cos\theta \, d\theta \, d\phi$$

(Eq. 9-10)

where θ and ϕ are polar and azimuthal angles as shown in Figure 9-1. The radiant power per unit area leaving one side of a plane is then:

$$q_R^+ = \overline{\tau} \; \overline{H} \; \{ I^+(\theta, \phi, \lambda) \} \quad \text{watts/m}^2 \qquad\qquad \text{(Eq. 9-11)}$$

The order of the two operators may be reversed, of course. The operators operating on the black body intensity give the Stefan-Boltzmann relation:

$$\overline{\tau} \; \overline{H} \; \{ I_b \,(\lambda, T) \} \; = \; \sigma \, T^4 \qquad\qquad \text{(Eq. 9-12)}$$

A superscript + or - is used to distinguish whether or not the photons are travelling away from or toward the surface for which the θ, ϕ angles are defined. The quantity q_R^+ is often termed the radiosity (symbol J or B) and q_R^- the irradiation (symbol G or H). The net radiation heat flux across a control surface is then:

$$q_R = q_+ - q_- \qquad\qquad \text{(Eq. 9-13)}$$

Two such control surfaces may be taken in the vicinity of an interface between two media. Spalding (6) has named these the S-surface just inside the considered medium and the L-surface just within the second one. Since the volume between the S and L surfaces is arbitrarily small, the net flux q_R across one surface is the same as that across the other. The q_+ crossing the S-surface is referred to as the emissive power when the irradiation q_- at the S-surface is zero, since it is the result of non-externally induced emission within the second medium. For a strongly absorbing second medium it is possible to consider an M surface somewhat below the L surface where the net radiative flux is not distinguished from the conductive flux. For quasi-steady state conditions the conductive heat flux crossing the M-surface will be the same as the sum of the radiation and conduction, if any, crossing the L-surface (and the S-surface, when no mass transfers occur).

Coherence and Polarization

In the classical limit, the stream of photon wave-packets forms a continuous propagating electromagnetic wave whose intensity I is proportional to the square of the magnitude of the electric field vector e, which oscillates perpendicular to the direction of propagation. The electric vector e can be resolved into a set of mutually perpendicular components, e_p and e_s. Let those components (and the square root of the constant of proportionality giving I) be represented by the real parts of the following complex numbers (7):

$$z_p \; = \; M_p \exp \left\{ i[2\pi \nu(ct\text{-}S) \; + \; \delta_p] \right\} \qquad\qquad \text{(Eq. 9-14a)}$$

$$z_s \; = \; M_s \exp \left\{ i[2\pi \nu(ct\text{-}S) \; + \; \delta_s] \right\} \qquad\qquad \text{(Eq. 9-14b)}$$

where ν is the wavenumber, t time, S path length, δ the instantaneous phase angle, and i the unit imaginary number $+ \sqrt{-1}$. The radiant intensity I is the sum of the intensities of the components:

$$I = I_p + I_s \qquad\qquad \text{(Eq. 9-15)}$$

where:

$$I_p \; = \; \langle z_p z_p^* \rangle \qquad\qquad I_s \; = \; \langle z_p z_p^* \rangle \qquad\qquad \text{(Eq. 9-16)}$$

The asterisk denotes the complex conjugate, and the angular brackets denote a time and wavelength average over a short time period around time t, and a narrow wavelength band around wavelength λ. The brackets are a tacit admission that the experimenter can never measure an instantaneous power flux or an infinitely narrow spectral band, since a detector responds only to a finite amount of energy.

Planckian radiation has a random character; there is no fixed relation between δ_p and δ_s, and I_p equals I_s. Such radiation is said to be "incoherent" in phase, "unpolarized", or "natural". However, reflection of Planckian radiation from a plane surface at an angle from the normal, or transmission of Planckian radiation through an optical element, may alter the ratio of M_p to M_s and/or cause a fixed shift in δ_p or δ_s for a particular set of s and p directions. The fact that such modifications occur means that the spectral radiant intensity alone is not sufficient to describe the nature of the radiant flux and the way that it interacts with matter.

Suppose one considers, say, transmission of a beam of radiant intensity I through a retardation plate, causing a shift in δ_s of Δ_s and a shift in δ_p of Δ_p, followed by reflection from a glossy black paint at an angle of 55° or so, an angle near the Brewster angle. One finds that, in order to predict the amount of radiation absorbed by the black paint, one must know not only $<z_p z_p^*>$ and $<z_s z_s^*>$ but also the real and imaginary parts of $<2z_p z_s^*>$. These latter quantities are the third and fourth Stokes coefficients (8) I_u and I_v. One must know a four-component vector then in order to describe properly the radiant intensity:

$$[I] = \begin{bmatrix} I_p \\ I_s \\ I_u \\ I_v \end{bmatrix} = \begin{bmatrix} z_p z_p^* \\ z_s z_s^* \\ R(2z_p z_s^*) \\ I(2z_p z_s^*) \end{bmatrix} \qquad \text{(Eq. 9-17)}$$

The intensity I is the sum of the first two components:

$$I = [E]^t \cdot [I], \quad [E]^t = [1\ 1\ 0\ 0] \qquad \text{(Eq. 9-18)}$$

and the black body intensity vector has only two non-zero components:

$$[I_b] = [x_b] I_b, \quad [x_b] = \begin{bmatrix} 1/2 \\ 1/2 \\ 0 \\ 0 \end{bmatrix} \qquad \text{(Eq. 9-19)}$$

Reference (7) shows also how a transformation from one set of p_1, s_1 directions to a second set p_2, s_2 rotated by angle β from the first. Resolving the z_{p1} and z_{s1} vectors into new components and applying Equation 9-17 shows that the transformation can be represented compactly by matrix multiplication:

$$\begin{bmatrix} I_{p2} \\ I_{s2} \\ I_{u2} \\ I_{v2} \end{bmatrix} = \begin{bmatrix} \cos^2\beta & \sin^2\beta & \frac{1}{2}\sin 2\beta & 0 \\ \sin^2\beta & \cos^2\beta & -\frac{1}{2}\sin 2\beta & 0 \\ -\sin 2\beta & \sin 2\beta & \cos 2\beta & 0 \\ 0 & 0 & 0 & 1 \end{bmatrix} \cdot \begin{bmatrix} I_{p1} \\ I_{s1} \\ I_{u1} \\ I_{v1} \end{bmatrix} \qquad \text{(Eq. 9-20)}$$

$$[I_2] = [D_{1-2}] \cdot [I_1] \qquad \text{(Eq. 9-20a)}$$

Polarization arises incidentally or inadvertently in many radiation instruments. Reflection from a mirror at an angle from the normal, or transmission through a prism when the beam enters or emerges at an off-normal angle, introduces such polarization. One might insert other polarizing elements deliberately into such an instrument to counteract the incidental polarization or to cause complete polarization so that the measurement will be more precisely defined. Analysis of the effect of such elements can be made using the radiant intensity vector just introduced and radiation characteristics defined below.

Thermal Radiation Characteristics

Specular Surface of an Isotropic Material

An isotropic material with a plane surface reflects specularly, that is, the radiant intensity incident at θ_1 ϕ_1 causes a reflected beam at $\theta_2 = \theta_1$ and $\phi_2 = \phi_1 + \pi$. The magnitudes of the reflected components parallel and perpendicular to the plane of incidence are changed and the phases are changed so that:

$$
\begin{bmatrix} I_{p2} \\ I_{s2} \\ I_{u2} \\ I_{v2} \end{bmatrix} = \begin{bmatrix} \rho_{pp} & 0 & 0 & 0 \\ 0 & \rho_{ss} & 0 & 0 \\ 0 & 0 & \rho_{uu} & \rho_{uv} \\ 0 & 0 & \rho_{vu} & \rho_{vv} \end{bmatrix} \begin{bmatrix} I_{p1} \\ I_{s1} \\ I_{u1} \\ I_{v1} \end{bmatrix}
\tag{Eq. 9-21}
$$

where the reflectivity matrix elements are given by the Fresnel relations (See also Sect. 8.5, of (4):

$$
\rho_{ss} = \frac{(\cos\theta - a)^2 + b^2}{(\cos\theta + a)^2 + b^2}
\tag{Eq. 9-22a}
$$

$$
\rho_{pp} = \frac{[(n^2-k^2)\cos\theta - a]^2 + [2nk\cos\theta - b]^2}{[(n^2-k^2)\cos\theta + a]^2 + [2nk\cos\theta + b]^2}
\tag{Eq. 9-22b}
$$

$$
\rho_{uu} = \rho_{vv} = \sqrt{\rho_{ss}\rho_{pp}}\ \cos\delta
\tag{Eq. 9-22c}
$$

$$
\rho_{vu} = -\rho_{uv} = \sqrt{\rho_{ss}\rho_{pp}}\ \sin\delta
\tag{Eq. 9-22d}
$$

$$
\delta = 2\pi + (\Delta_p - \Delta_s)
\tag{Eq. 9-22e}
$$

$$
\tan\Delta_p = \frac{2\cos\theta[(n^2-k^2)b - (2nk)a]}{(n^2+k^2)^2\cos^2\theta - (a^2+b^2)}
\tag{Eq. 9-22f}
$$

$$
\tan\Delta_s = 2b\cos\theta / [\cos^2\theta - a^2 - b^2]
\tag{Eq. 9-22g}
$$

$$
a^2 = \tfrac{1}{2}[\sqrt{(n^2-k^2-\sin^2\theta)^2 + 4n^2k^2} + (n^2-k^2) - \sin^2\theta]
\tag{Eq. 9-22h}
$$

$$
b^2 = \tfrac{1}{2}[\sqrt{(n^2-k^2-\sin^2\theta)^2 + 4n^2k^2} - (n^2-k^2) + \sin^2\theta]
\tag{Eq. 9-22i}
$$

The above relations are written for a medium of $n=1$, $k=0$ (a vacuum) above a material of refractive index n and absorptive index k. The subscript p denotes a direction parallel to the plane of incidence, and s designates one perpendicular to that plane, fixed by the surface normal and incident ray.

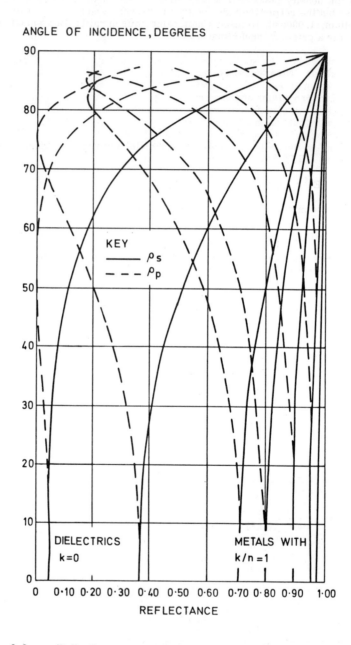

ANGLE OF INCIDENCE, DEGREES

KEY

—— ρ_s

--- ρ_p

DIELECTRICS
k = 0

METALS WITH
k/n = 1

REFLECTANCE

Fig. 9-2   Reflection components for a plane interface between isotropic
media (7)

For dielectrics k is much smaller than n, and for metals k is generally greater than n, but when the Hagen-Ruebens reflection law holds at long wavelengths, k equals n. Most low density gases have n very close to unity and k zero away from absorption bands, but the refractive index of air, 1.000293, is sufficiently different from that of helium, 1.000036, to make a noticeable shift in calibration when helium is used to purge a prism monochromator.

Figure 9-2 shows how the specular reflectance elements ρ_{pp} and ρ_{ss} vary with angle from the normal. Note that at an angle of $\theta_B = \sin^{-1}n$ reflection is strongly polarizing. One can note also that the reflectivity of poor reflectors like glossy paint resins rises to high values at large angles from the normal. For metals the ρ_{pp} reflectance drops at high angles from the normal and then increases to unity just at completely grazing incidence.

The directional reflectivity of a material irradiated by (partly) polarized radiation is $[\rho_V]$ where:

$$[\rho_V]^t = [E]^t \cdot [\rho_M] \tag{Eq. 9-23}$$

For an isotropic material:

$$[\rho_V]^t = [\rho_{pp} \, \rho_{ss} \, 0 \, 0] \tag{Eq. 9-23a}$$

The superscript t denotes a row matrix, that is, the transpose of the column matrix. The quantity $[\rho_M]$ is the matrix in Equation 9-20, and $[E]^t$ was defined in Equation 9-18. The intensity reflected is:

$$I_2 = [\rho_V]^t [I_1] \tag{Eq. 9-24}$$

If I_1 is incoherent, we can write:

$$I_2 = [\rho_V]^t [x_b] \, I_1 = \rho(\theta_1, \phi_1) \, I_1 \tag{Eq. 9-25}$$

so that the directional reflectivity $\rho(\theta, \phi)$ is:

$$\rho(\theta, \phi) = [\rho_V]^t [x_b] \tag{Eq. 9-26}$$

For the isotropic solid:

$$\rho(\theta) = \tfrac{1}{2}[\rho_{pp} + \rho_{ss}] \tag{Eq. 9-26a}$$

The directional absorptivity of a material sufficiently thick to be opaque is, by conservation of energy:

$$\alpha(\theta, \phi) = 1 - \rho(\theta, \phi) \tag{Eq. 9-27}$$

If the irradiation is polarized, we must use the directional absorptivity vector:

$$[\alpha_V]^t = [E]^t - [\rho_V]^t \tag{Eq. 9-28}$$

The heat flux absorbed is then:

$$q_{ABS} = \overline{\overline{7}} \, \overline{H} \, \{[\alpha_V]^t \cdot [I_s^-]\} \tag{Eq. 9-29}$$

At thermodynamic equilibrium the principle of detailed balancing (1) requires among other things that photons absorbed from a certain direction and of a certain energy be re-emitted back to their source. This aspect of the principle of detailed balancing is called Kirchoff's law, which has several forms:

$$[\epsilon_V]^t = [\alpha_V]^t \tag{Eq. 9-30}$$

$$\epsilon(\theta, \phi, \lambda, T) = [\epsilon_V]^t \cdot [x_b] = [\alpha_V]^t \cdot [x_b] = \alpha(\theta, \phi, \lambda, T) \tag{Eq. 9-30a}$$

$$\overline{7}\{\epsilon(\theta, \phi, \lambda, T)I_b(\lambda, T)\} = \overline{7}\{\alpha(\theta, \phi, \lambda, T)I_b(\lambda, T)\}$$

$$\epsilon_T(\theta, \phi, T)(\sigma T^4/\pi) = \alpha_T(\theta, \phi, T, T)(\sigma T^4/\pi) \tag{Eq. 9-30b}$$

$$\epsilon_T(\theta, \phi, T) = \alpha_T(\theta, \phi, T, T)$$

$$\overline{H}\,\overline{7}\{\epsilon(\theta, \phi, \lambda, T)I_b(\lambda, T)\} = \overline{H}\,\overline{7}\{\alpha(\theta, \phi, \lambda, T)I_b(\lambda, T)\} \tag{Eq. 9-30c}$$

$$\epsilon_{TH}(T) = \alpha_{TH}(T, T)$$

The quantities with subscript T are the total emissivity and absorptivity. Those with subscript H are the hemispherical emissivity and absorptivity. The double subscript TH indicates total hemispherical emissivity and absorptivity. These are defined as indicated in equations 9-30b and 9-30c. The total absorptivity is:

$$\alpha_T(\theta, \phi, T, T_S) = \overline{7}_{T_S}\{\alpha(\theta, \phi, \lambda, T)\} \tag{Eq. 9-31}$$

where the operator is the total property operator for black body radiation with source temperature T_S.

$$\overline{7}_{T_S}\{\alpha(\theta, \phi, \lambda, T)\} = \int_0^\infty \alpha(\theta, \phi, \lambda, T)f_b'(\lambda T_S)d(\lambda T_S) \tag{Eq. 9-32}$$

The hemispherical absorptivity is:

$$\alpha_H(\lambda, T) = H\{\alpha(\theta, \phi, \lambda, T)\} \tag{Eq. 9-33}$$

where the hemispherical property operator is:

$$H\{\alpha(\theta, \phi, \lambda, T)\} = \frac{1}{\pi}\int_0^{2\pi}\int_0^{\pi/2}\alpha(\theta, \phi, \lambda, T)\sin\theta\cos\theta\,d\theta\,d\phi \tag{Eq. 9-34}$$

In this convenient notation the total hemispherical absorptivity is then:

$$\alpha_{TH}(T, T_S) = H\,\overline{7}_{T_S}\{[\alpha_V]^t \cdot [x_b]\} \tag{Eq. 9-35}$$

In many engineering problems involving radiation transfer within an enclosure a second kind of total average is desired. This total net quantity may be defined by:

$$\epsilon_{T_n}(T, T_S) = \frac{\epsilon_T(T)\sigma T^4 - \alpha_T(T, T_S)\sigma T_S^4}{\sigma T^4 - \sigma T_S^4} \tag{Eq. 9-36}$$

Often the limit of $\epsilon_{T_n}(T, T_S)$ as T_S approaches T is desired. In our operator notation this internal total emissivity is $\epsilon_{T_i}(T)$:

$$\epsilon_{T_i}(\theta, \phi, T) = \overline{7}_{T_i}\{\alpha(\theta, \phi, \lambda, T)\} \tag{Eq. 9-37}$$

where:

$$\overline{7}_{T_i}\{\alpha(\theta, \phi, \lambda, T)\} = \int_0^\infty \alpha(\theta, \phi, \lambda, T)f_i'(\lambda T)d(\lambda T) \tag{Eq. 9-38}$$

where, from Eq. 9-5 and 9-7, the internal fraction f_i is given by:

$$f_i'(\lambda T) = \frac{5}{4}f_b'(\lambda T) + \frac{1}{4}(\lambda T)f_b''(\lambda T) \qquad \text{(Eq. 9-39)}$$

As in Equation 9-7 the prime represents differentiation with respect to the argument. As before this internal total operator may be combined with the hemispherical operator to obtain an internal total hemispherical emissivity. The quantity in Equation 9-30c can be referred to as the external total hemispherical emissivity. The adjectives internal and external are used by this writer because the internal characteristic is usually appropriate for internal surfaces in a space vehicle, and the external characteristic is appropriate for external surfaces. Confusion of the total net emittance with the total external emittance has been referred to as the nongray error (9). The internal fraction f_i is tabulated in (5). There it is called the fractional function of the second kind (symbol B*).

Specular Surfaces of Anisotropic Materials

In general it is possible that all 16 terms in the four-by-four reflectance matrix in Equation 9-21 could be non-zero. Equations 9-23 and 9-26 to 9-30 would still hold. In general it is also possible to have a thin isothermal slab which transmits. In this case a transmittance matrix similar to the reflectance matrix exists to describe the transmitted intensity. Equation 9-28 is then replaced with:

$$[E]^t = [\alpha_V]^t + [\rho_V]^t + [\tau_V]^t \qquad \text{(Eq. 9-40)}$$

Diffuse Surfaces

If the surface is rough or if the material below the surface contains scattering particles, the surface is said to be imperfectly diffuse. In this case the reflected radiant intensity in any direction θ_2, ϕ_2, not necessarily the specular direction but not excluding it, is given by the bidirectional reflectance matrix:

$$d[I_2] = \frac{1}{\pi}[\rho_{BM}][I_1] \cos\theta_1 d\Omega_1 \qquad \text{(Eq. 9-41)}$$

The bidirectional reflectance (scalar) is the value that results when the irradiation is incoherent. In this case the reflected intensity is:

$$dI_2 = \frac{1}{\pi} \rho_B(\theta_1, \phi_1, \theta_2, \phi_2, \lambda, T)I_1 \cos\theta_1 d\Omega \qquad \text{(Eq. 9-42)}$$

where:

$$\rho_B = [E]^t [\rho_{BM}][x_b] \qquad \text{(Eq. 9-43)}$$

Apparatuses to measure ρ_B are called bidirectional reflectometers or goniospectrophotometers. Early apparatus (10) was used for total measurements in illumination engineering.

The principle of detailed balancing requires that there be no net exchange between two radiators via the surface when equilibrium exists. This requirement is expressed by:

$$[\rho_{BM}(\theta_1, \phi_1, \theta_2, \phi_2, \lambda, T)] = [\rho_{BM}(\theta_2, \phi_1, \theta_1, \phi_2, \lambda T)] \qquad \text{(Eq. 9-44)}$$

$$\rho_B(\theta_1, \phi_1, \theta_2, \phi_2, \lambda, T) = \rho_B(\theta_2, \phi_1, \theta_1, \phi_2, \lambda, T) \qquad \text{(Eq. 9-44a)}$$

This requirement is often called the Helmholtz reciprocity principle (e.g. 11) and is, unfortunately, not well understood by some workers. This principle has had a profound influence upon the design of directional reflectometers and emittance inspection devices as will be shown.

If it is desired to know all the radiation reflected regardless of its directional distribution, one integrates the bidirectional reflectance over the hemisphere:

$$[\rho_V(\theta_1, \phi_1, \lambda, T)]^t = \mathcal{H}_2\{[E]^t \cdot [\rho_{BM}(\theta_1, \phi_1, \theta_2, \phi_2, \lambda, T)]\} \qquad \text{(Eq. 9-45)}$$

For incoherent irradiation the directional reflectance is:

$$\rho(\theta_1, \phi_1, \lambda, T) = \mathcal{H}_2\{[E]^t \cdot [\rho_{BM}] \cdot [x_b]\} \qquad \text{(Eq. 9-46)}$$

As a result of the Helmholtz reciprocity Equation 9-46 can just as well be written:

$$\rho(\theta_2, \phi_2, \lambda, T) = \mathcal{H}_1\{\rho_B(\theta_1, \phi_1, \theta_2, \phi_2, \lambda, T)\} \qquad \text{(Eq. 9-46a)}$$

But the experimental arrangement implied is quite different. For the case described by Equation 9-46, a beam of radiation is brought onto the specimen, and all radiation reflected is detected. For the case described by Equation 9-46a, the specimen is perfectly diffusely irradiated, and the reflected intensity in direction θ_2, ϕ_2 is compared to the intensity of the irradiation. Because of the completely different experimental arrangements the quantity in Equation 9-46 has been called the angular-hemispherical or directional-hemispherical reflectance and that in Equation 9-46a called the hemispherical-angular or hemispherical-directional reflectance (12). The quantities are, of course, equal except for errors in measurement or for departures from thermodynamic equilibrium populations. While the redundance in the double-adjective has the desirable effect of calling the attention of the reader to the measurement technique, it has the undesirable side effect of confusing some as to whether the quantity obtained by subtraction from unity (for an opaque surface) is the directional or hemispherical absorptance (it is the directional absorptance).

Total and hemispherical characteristics of imperfectly diffuse specimens are defined as was previously done for the isotropic solid. One simply applies the total and hemispherical operators to the directional characteristics. Note that the word 'characteristic' is used in preference to 'property' when a complex 'surface system' is involved. Note also the use of the 'ance' ending in preference to the 'ivity' ending for such systems. Finally one should keep in mind that all the characteristics are defined for the nearly isothermal system in the near equilibrium state. Transmittances are defined only for thin slabs in which lateral photon movement is negligible.

Radiometry

Detectors, Signals, and Noise

Two broad classes of detectors are in common usage, photo-electric and thermal. The first broad class depends upon a photon-electron interaction. In the photomultiplier vacuum tube, a photon causes emission of an electron which is accelerated by an electric field to collide with a second emitter and so release a cascade of electrons which are detected. In a barrier layer photovoltaic cell a photon causes an electron to be elevated from the semiconductor's valence band into a conduction band. When the electrical charge carrier diffuses across the barrier, power is delivered to an external circuit. In a photoconductor the creation of a hole-electron pair in a solid or an ion-electron pair in a gas allows current to flow under an imposed field caused by an external bias. In film or in the eye photochemical reactions occur due to photon-electron interactions.

These photon-electron detectors tend to be spectrally selective to a high degree. At photon energies below that necessary to overcome the surface work function of a photo-emitter or to enable an electron to cross the band gap in a semiconductor, the chances of a detectable photon-electron interaction are quite small. At photon energies above this threshold value, the excess energy causes no increase in detector signal, so that the relative sensitivity of the detector tends to decrease directly proportional to wavelength, as λ becomes shorter. On the other hand these detectors have a high sensitivity and a fast response time (1-1000 microseconds). Photomultipliers can be used from the ultraviolet to approximately one micron; a room temperature lead sulphide photo-conductor can be used to approximately 3 microns; cooled photoconductors such as doped germanium can be used as far as 100 microns in the infrared. Chapter 11 of (4) shows typical detector characteristics.

A thermal detector is one in which the photons are merely absorbed to create a heat effect, an increase in the thermal motions of the constituents of matter. The heat effect then has to be detected in some manner. In the thermistor the effect is an increase in electrical resistance; in the thermocouple the effect is generation of thermoelectric power; in the Golay cell the effect is a pressure rise and expansion in a gas causing the deflection of a small mirror which in turn sweeps a light beam over a photocell. These thermal detectors are relatively insensitive and slow in response (0.1 to 10 sec. time constant). Their advantage is that they can be made to be linear and relatively nonselective over a wide spectral range.

Table 9-1 lists some characteristics which must be considered in selecting a detector. It may be seen that noise equivalent power, that is, the radiant power just sufficient to give a signal of the same order as the noise, is just one of many considerations. Spectral, directional, and spatial selectivity, stability, ruggedness, and many other considerations must be given weight.

The Ideal Radiometer

From the foregoing it is evident that the energy received between time t_1 and t_2, wavelengths λ_1 and λ_2, within a solid angle defined by some θ, ϕ limits, and within an area element specified by some x-y limits is:

$$Q = \int_{t_1}^{t_2} \int_{\lambda_1}^{\lambda_2} \int_{\phi_1}^{\phi_2} \int_{\theta_1}^{\theta_2} \int_{y_1}^{y_2} \int_{x_1}^{x_2} [\alpha_V]^t \cdot [I]\cos\theta \, dxdy \, \theta \, d\phi d\lambda dt \quad \text{(Eq. 9-47)}$$

It would be ideal to have a radiometer which would respond to this power only, which could have y_1 and y_2 varied arbitrarily as a function of x; ϕ_1 and θ_2 similarly varied arbitrarily as a function of θ, the values of λ_1, λ_2, t_1, and t_2 chosen at will, and $[\alpha_V]^t$ variable at will to find the nature of $[I]$. In actuality we obtain a signal $V-V_0$ (subject to uncertainty $+\Delta V$). The quantity V_0 results when a shutter is viewed and V results when the source is viewed,

$$V = \int_{-\infty}^{0} \int_{0}^{\infty} \int_{0}^{2\pi} \int_{0}^{\pi/2} \int_{y_1}^{y_2} \int_{x_1}^{x_2} [R]^t \{[I]-[x_b]I_b\} \cos\theta \, dxdyd\theta \, d\phi d\lambda dt \quad \text{(Eq. 9-48)}$$

where $[R]$ is a four-component response function, each component of which is a function of time, wavelength, direction, and position on the detector. Its vector nature arises from the fact that it contains a product of 4 by 4 transmittance or reflectance matrices and the 4 component detector absorptivity vector. It is impossible to give $[R]$ a sharp step-function characteristic which would give equation 9-47. The quantity I_b in equation 9-48 is the Planck spectral intensity for the detector temperature.

One obtains a defined measurement (a "clean" measurement) in certain limiting cases. Consider for example the field of view. If the object viewed entirely fills

Table 9-1: Characteristics Influencing Detector Selection

CHARACTERISTIC	COMMENTS
1. Noise equivalent power	This quantity is the radiant power sufficient to give a signal of the same order as the noise.
2. Time response	Photon detectors are fast. Thermal detectors are slow.
3. Spectral selectivity	Photo detectors are spectrally selective. Thermal detectors can be quite non-selective.
4. Directional selectivity	Exposing the edges of a photoconductor cell or using a diffusing cover can improve omnidirectional characteristics.
5. Spatial selectivity	Photoconductors are more sensitive near their electrodes. Thermocouple detectors are more sensitive near their junctions. Time responses may differ spatially over thermocouple detectors so that response may be quite sensitive to phasing in chopped systems.
6. Linearity	Photodetectors saturate.
7. Stability	For example, photomultipliers may suffer a permanent loss of sensitivity by exposure to too large a flux. Plated thermopiles may slowly change over a period of months or years due to diffusion and chemical changes. Short term there may be reversible changes due to, say, sensitivity to temperature level. Thermal detectors are susceptible to zero drift when used in the D.C. mode.
8. Ease of operation and maintenance of detector and auxiliary equipment. Ruggedness and reliability.	Golay cells used to have a very limited useful life, but may now last as long as vacuum thermocouples. Both eventually fatigue and are somewhat delicate.
9. Size, cost, weight, volume.	These factors seldom influence laboratory equipment, but do influence field or flight instruments.

the field of view, and the intensity [I] is constant over the field of view, then the significant instrument characteristic is an integral of [R]. On the other hand if the object viewed falls well within the field of view, where [R] is essentially constant, then the significant source characteristic is an integral of [I], and the significant instrument characteristic is the central value of [R]. Similar considerations hold for the other parameters. It is interesting to note, however, that one never knows that [I] is constant over the field of view. One must infer that it is. To aid in drawing such inferences, it is well to be able to vary or sweep the solid angle field and spectral band.

Spectral, Band-Pass, and Total Radiometers

The ideal radiometer doesn't exist, and certainly for many applications a relatively crude characterization of the irradiation is adequate. In those cases where spectral measurements are necessary, a spectral radiometer is used. In this case the instrument is essentially a spectrometer with an optics system for viewing the source. In the infrared, first surface aluminized mirrors are usually used in the optics train, and an infrared transmitting prism such as LiF, NaCl, KBr, or CsBr or an aluminized blazed grating is used to disperse the radiation, so that the spectrometer entrance slit image coincides with the exit slit image only for a certain wavelength. With equal exit and entrance slits the spectral slit function (transmittance) is triangular in shape.

Since a grating has higher orders of shorter wavelengths superposed on the first order either a fore-prism or reflection or transmission filters must be used to eliminate unwanted short wavelength radiation. Such filters may be selective absorbers such as black polyethylene; selective scatterers such as aluminized glass or powders embedded in polyethylene, or selective reflectors such as rest-strahlen crystals. Photon detectors are desirable for spectral measurements because of their sensitivity and fast response time, but thermocouples or thermistors are often used to obtain a wide spectral range without the need for detector changes. Table 19-3 of (4) gives a summary of some commercially available spectrometers. Recently Fourier transform interferometers and rapid scan spectrometers have come on to the market (13).

In those cases where a wide band or a total measurement is desired, a thermal detector is almost invariably used (14). Filters may be inserted in the optics intentionally to limit the spectral response, or the filter may be in the optics by virtue of a requirement for a window or by the convenience introduced through use of a lens. Figures 7-24 to 7-27 of (4) show the spectral transmittance of some of the older commercially available filters. Due to advances in thin film technology quite a variety of reflection and transmission filters can now be obtained.

Radiometers with Thermal Detectors

The thermal radiometer consists of a housing to provide an isothermal environment for the detector, the detector itself, and field or filter optics. In a directional radiometer a field stop, or a field-stopped mirror or lens, limits the detector to a view in a relatively small solid angle. In a hemispherical radiometer the detector is given a view of the entire hemisphere. In this latter case the radiometer case may take the degenerate form of a jet of air over a mirror as in the case of the aspirated hemispherical radiometer used in meteorology.

Of concern in the design and use of total radiometers is the thermal resistance from the detector to the case R and the thermal capacity of the detector C. The RC-product is the time constant of the instrument; the value of R fixes the D.C. sensitivity, and the nature of R determines the conditions of use. If R is small, the time constant is fast but the D.C. signal is also small. If C is large, the time constant is large, but the detector may be rugged and inexpensive. The thermal resistance is the net effect of conduction, convection, and radiation from the detector to the housing. A conduction-coupled radiometer is one with a large thermal conductance from the detector to the housing so that convection and radiation transfer has a negligible effect in the detector heat balance. Such a radiometer is desirable because it is not too sensitive to atmospheric pressure, radiometer temperature level, and radiometer orientation with respect to gravity. A heat balance on the detector can be formulated using the principles set forth in any good heat transfer text [15]. A fin type of analysis is often applicable.

In addition to radiation coupling, factors causing calibration shift with temperature level are a nonlinear thermocouple or thermistor response. With thermistors it is possible to arrange for compensation either by using two different ones in series or by arranging for compensation in the external bridge circuit. In the first case two thermistors having opposite signs for the second derivative of the resistivity versus temperature are combined to give a second derivative of zero in the total resistance versus temperature. In the latter case the bridge resistors R_e are chosen with a resistivity temperature coefficient such that the quantity $(R_e + R_d)^{-1}$ (dR_d/dt) is independent of temperature, where R_d is the thermistor resistance.

Radiometers with thermal detectors are notorious for zero drift. For this reason an automatic internal chopper is often used, and two identical detectors coupled in the same way to the case, one exposed and one unexposed, are often employed. One can cite Coblentz's cryptic observation regarding zero drift, "Moll's surface thermopile made of thin sheets of copper-constantan had the defect that the 'cold junctions' were soldered to relatively heavy posts" (15). When working with small values of $Id\Omega$, frequent zero readings should be taken using a highly reflecting shutter at the radiometer temperature. A chopper, i.e., a rotating internal shutter, if used, should be highly reflecting and located on the source side of the main field stop. Because of the term I_b in equation 9-48, the detector housing temperature must be well defined and accurately known, and the specular shutter and chopper should be viewed at an angle so that the detector does not look itself in the eye, i.e., does not view a mirror image of itself.

Calibration of Radiometers

Calibration of radiometers is usually accomplished by viewing a Planckian cavity source, as mentioned in the text following equation 9-8. Secondary standard lamps which are calibrated against other standard lamps calibrated with a cavity source are also used (17). Heated gases in which the temperature is obtained spectroscopically and for which the absorption coefficient has been measured have also been used to calibrate spectral radiometers. Radiometer detectors equivalent to "microcalorimeters" have been calibrated by "absolute" methods, for example, by replacing the radiant heating with electrical heating as in the Callendar and Angstrom radiometers or by knowing the heat of fusion of melting ice, the heat capacity of a silver disk, etc. (18) (19).

Surface Radiation Measurements

The Surface-System Concept

Radiation is of course not emitted or absorbed by a surface but by a volume. In some cases this volume is a thin layer along a surface of a strongly absorbing medium, that is, the volume between the Spalding S-surface and M-surface already mentioned in the discussion following equation 5-13. Such a layer is referred to as an opaque surface system or for short, an opaque surface. In other cases the material of concern is a thin slab, such as a thin pane of glass, or a thin plastic film. Such a slab is termed a transmitting surface system, or for short, a

transmitting surface. When such 'surfaces' (surface systems) have their energy
level populations characterized by a temperature T corresponding to a thermodynamic equilibrium population distribution, we can speak of surface thermal radiation characteristics (20) as reviewed under 'Thermal Radiation Characteristics'.
Such characteristics facilitate engineering heat transfer accountings.

Types of Measurements

As noted earlier there is an extensive array of characteristics which can be
measured. There are two characteristics, reflectance and transmittance, to which
can be applied the four direction adjectives (bidirectional, specular, directional,
and hemispherical) and the three spectrum adjectives (spectral, internal total, and
external total) for a subtotal of 24 possible combinations. In addition there is the
spectral emittance or absorptance (which are equal), the external total emittance
and absorptance (not equal) and the internal total emittance for which the
adjectives directional and hemispherical apply, for a subtotal of 8 more. The total
of 32 by no means exhausts the possibilities, for one sometimes desires to use
moments or integrals of the spectral, bidirectional, or directional characteristics
over some portion of the spectrum or some portion of the incident or emergent
hemispheres. And of course a spectral measurement must have the wavelength
specified, a bidirectional measurement must have two directions (4 angles) specified, a directional measurement one direction (2 angles) specified, and one can
even measure specular (regular) reflectance or transmittance at off-specular
directions, for example, the back direction in the case of a corner reflector.

If polarization enters the problem, one then can multiply some of the first 24 quantities by the 16 elements needed for the four-by-four polarization matrix, and
measurements of the last 8 quantities would have to be increased four-fold to
obtain the four components of the polarization vector. There is no particular point
in trying to catalog all of these quantities. The reader would do bett er to spend
his time rereading the previous parts on 'Thermal Radiation' and 'Thermal Radiation Characteristics'.

The engineer must consider what surface characteristics he really needs. For
surfaces inside an enclosure the internal total hemispherical emittance is usually
adequate. For surfaces outside, say, a space vehicle, the total hemispherical
emittance and short wavelength spectral directional absorptance will usually
suffice. Sometimes an indication is useful that the surface is, from a power transfer point of view, specular or not specular. The engineer must consider the cost
of making the measurements and the cost of making use of the measurements. It
should not be overlooked that a quantity can be measured either directly or by
making a more primitive measurement and making the appropriate integration.
Often, because of instrumental errors, it is desirable to obtain a quantity with a
direct measurement, and by integration of the more primitive measurements. For
example total hemispherical emissivity can be measured directly or obtained from
integrations of easily-made measurements of spectral directional reflectivity and
transmissivity.

Bidirectional Characteristics

Bidirectional reflectance or transmittance is measured by irradiating a specimen
in a small solid angle with radiation from a source, and viewing the specimen in
a small solid angle with a radiometer as shown schematically in Figure 9-3.
Schmidt and Eckert (21), Eckert (22), Münch (23), and others have made total
measurements and Birkebak and Eckert (12) have reported spectral measurements.
It is best to introduce chopping on the source side and measure the A.C. detector
signal so that D.C. sample emission is not detected. After experimenting with
monochromatic irradiation (24) and total irradiation schemes, this writer believes

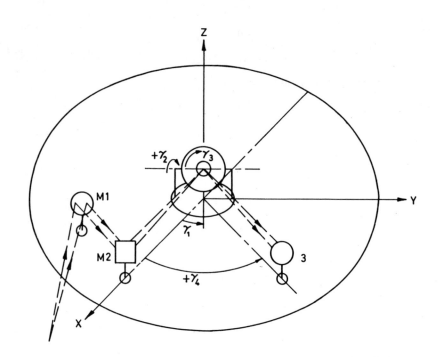

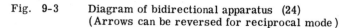

Fig. 9-3   Diagram of bidirectional apparatus (24)
(Arrows can be reversed for reciprocal mode)

it best to have no optics on the source side, and to use a black body source of a well-defined area, so that the solid angle of irradiation is known from simple geometric considerations, and to use a spectrometer detector.

Specular reflection or transmission may occur, and such behaviour amounts to a delta-function bidirectional characteristic. It is important for the experimenter to try to establish whether or not the measured quantity appears to have a limit in the mathematical sense as the solid angle of irradiation approaches zero (25). The fact that both the solid angle of irradiation and that of detection are desired to be small means that the amount of energy for detection is small. These factors make accurate spectral measurements in the infrared very difficult and time-consuming. There have been claims made that the Fourier-transform interferometer is a panacea for these difficulties and it is true that the information theory aspects of making bidirectional measurements deserve careful consideration. To this writer's knowledge the Fourier-transform interferometers have not been subjected to a thoughtful error analysis, but the various dispersion spectrometers have been.

Directional Absorptance and Emittance

Directional absorptance is usually measured indirectly, by making directional reflectance plus transmittance measurements and subtracting from unity, or measuring directional emittance and utilizing Kirchoff's laws. In the integrating sphere to be described in more detail below, the sum of reflectance and transmittance can be measured simultaneously. Direct measurement of directional absorptance, by coating a detector or calorimeter, is sometimes attempted for the total characteristic but never to this writer's knowledge for the spectral characteristic.

Directional emittance can be measured at moderate temperatures (usually above room temperature) by viewing a heated specimen with a directional radiometer (26) - (29). Both total and spectral determinations are made. Spectral measurements usually require temperatures considerably above room temperature, so that spectral directional reflectance and transmittance are usually measured instead for low sample temperatures, to give spectral directional absorptance and, from Kirchoff's law, spectral directional emittance. In other cases where sample temperature is difficult or inconvenient to measure, reflectance and transmittance measurements are preferable.

Direct and Reciprocal Measurements of Directional Reflectance

Directional reflectance (or transmittance) can be attempted in a direct manner by irradiating a sample from a particular direction, then attempting to detect all reflected (or transmitted) radiation regardless of its directional distribution. A more successful approach in many instances is to attempt to irradiate the specimen perfectly diffusely and detect the reflected intensity in a small solid angle. This mode of measurement is referred to as a reciprocal determination, as it rests on the Helmholtz reciprocity principle, that is, the principle of the detailed balance from thermodynamics.

The practical advantage of the reciprocal mode is that it is much easier to make a large area uniform source than a large area uniform response detector. Measurements can be made single-beam by observing a 100 per cent reference signal when the sphere wall is irradiated (direct mode) or observed (reciprocal mode), a zero when the beam is blocked, and a sample signal when the sample is irradiated out of the view of the detector. In a ratio-recording instrument the chopper is replaced by a nutating mirror which alternately switches the beam from the sample to the reference spot on the wall. It is best to arrange the geometry so that the reference spot on the wall is that spot fixed by the specular ray to or from the sample.

Spectral Directional Reflectance in the 0.3 to 2.5 Micron Region

A device which works equally well in the direct or reciprocal mode is the integrating sphere (30) to (34). Figures 9-4, 9-5, 9-6 and the top of Figure 9-7 show diagrams of these instruments. The shape factor from any receiver element on a sphere to any source element on a sphere is simply the source element area divided by the total area of the sphere. It follows that, if the sphere wall is perfectly diffuse and if the detector views all parts of the sphere equally well (a diffuse plane detector on the wall or a spherical one in the center), the sphere can act as a 2π-steradian detector for a specimen anywhere within the sphere. In the reciprocal mode the sphere wall can be uniformly irradiated (from a plane perfectly diffuse source on the wall or a spherical source in the center) so that a specimen anywhere within the sphere receives perfectly diffuse irradiation. It is essential in the direct mode that the detector does not see the sample or in the reciprocal mode that the sample does not see the source. In the direct mode, with a directional detector viewing a small area of the sphere wall, for purposes of analysis the detector should be regarded as the viewed area on the wall. Chopping should be done on the source side so as to eliminate sample emission from the measurement, but unless high temperature specimens are used, sample emission is not too consequential in the short wavelengths. Highly reflecting highly diffuse sphere coatings such as magnesium oxide or barium sulphate work well only in the short wavelengths, and the sphere is relatively inefficient and therefore requires an efficient photon detector. Thus the integrating sphere is not usually employed outside the 0.3 to 2.5 micron region.

A reciprocal mode short wavelength reflectometer is the McNicholas milk glass sphere (10), (30) shown at the top of Figure 9-7, In this device a cavity is made uniformly radiating by transmission through a diffusing wall. This instrument has been largely supplanted by the integrating sphere.

Directional Reflectance in the 2 to 20 Micron Region

The reciprocal mode heated cavity is made uniformily radiating by thermal emission (35), (36), (37). If, in either the heated cavity or integrating sphere, the sample is on the wall, as it was on most early devices, only one polar angle of view is convenient. Mounting the sample at the end of a rotatable rod within the cavity or sphere permits the polar angle to be varied at will (36), (37). Figures 9-8 and 9-9 show diagrams of a single beam heated cavity reflectometer with a rotatable sample (37) and figures 9-10 and 9-11 show two sample spectra (38) measured with the instrument. Another observation that can be made with the directional heated cavity with rotatable sample is shown schematically in Figure 9-12. A quick crude measure of 'diffuseness' is obtained by rotating the specimen to normal incidence so that specularly reflected radiation is not detected.

Except for an ingenious modification by K. E. Nelson (39), the heated cavity is used with chopping on the detector side, so that it is subject to sample emission errors. In the Nelson scheme a cylinder split into halves, one heated and one cooled, is rotated above the specimen which is viewed through a slot in the cylinder as shown in Figure 9-13. As it has not proved too convenient to have a large temperature difference between the halves, the device is used only for total measurements. The internal total reflectance is measured, unless a filter such as that indicated in Figure 9-14 is used to correct the integral weighting factor. Black polyethylene serves well. The device is limited to one angle of view.

The heated cavity works best in the intermediate wavelength range from 2 to 20 microns where there is ample thermal radiation from, say, a 1000°K source and not too much sample emission error, if the sample temperature and chopper surrounds temperature are kept within a few degrees of each other.

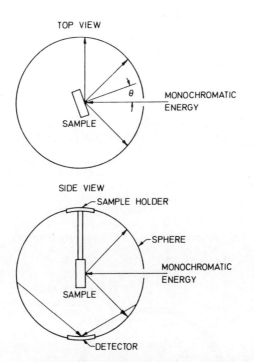

TOP VIEW

θ

MONOCHROMATIC
ENERGY

SAMPLE

SIDE VIEW

SAMPLE HOLDER

SPHERE

MONOCHROMATIC
ENERGY

SAMPLE

DETECTOR

Fig. 9-4 Diagram of integrating sphere with rotatable specimen

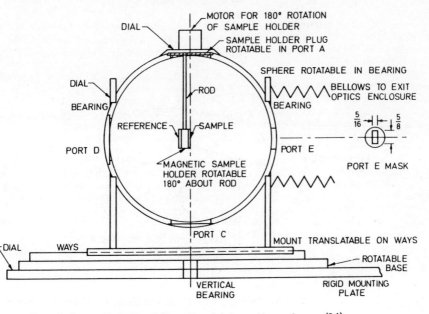

DIAL

MOTOR FOR 180° ROTATION
OF SAMPLE HOLDER

SAMPLE HOLDER PLUG
ROTATABLE IN PORT A

SPHERE ROTATABLE IN BEARING

DIAL

BELLOWS TO EXIT
OPTICS ENCLOSURE

BEARING

ROD

BEARING

REFERENCE

SAMPLE

$\frac{5}{16}$ $\frac{5}{8}$

PORT D

PORT E

MAGNETIC SAMPLE
HOLDER ROTATABLE
180° ABOUT ROD

PORT E MASK

PORT C

MOUNT TRANSLATABLE ON WAYS

DIAL

WAYS

ROTATABLE
BASE

VERTICAL
BEARING

RIGID MOUNTING
PLATE

Fig. 9-5   Details of directional integrating sphere   (34)

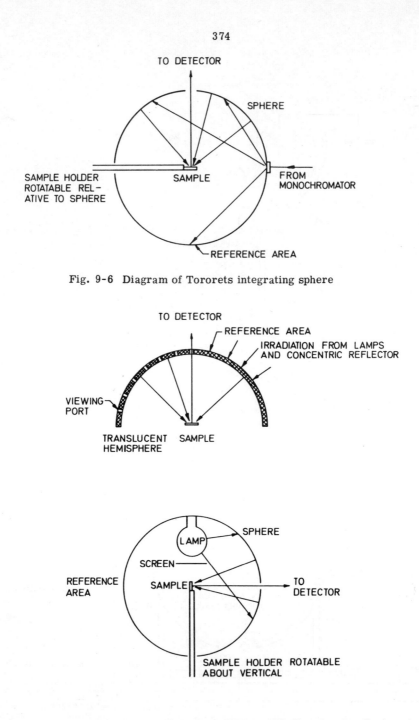

Fig. 9-6 Diagram of Tororets integrating sphere

Fig. 9-7 Diagram of McNicholas and Tingwaldt directional reflectometers

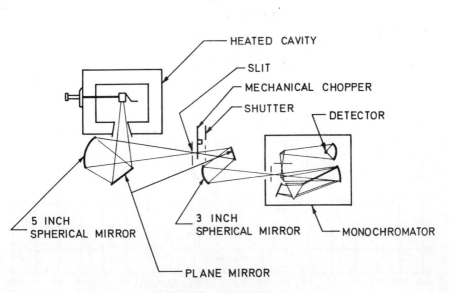

HEATED CAVITY

SLIT

MECHANICAL CHOPPER

SHUTTER

DETECTOR

5 INCH
SPHERICAL MIRROR

3 INCH
SPHERICAL MIRROR

MONOCHROMATOR

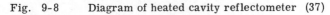

PLANE MIRROR

Fig. 9-8   Diagram of heated cavity reflectometer (37)

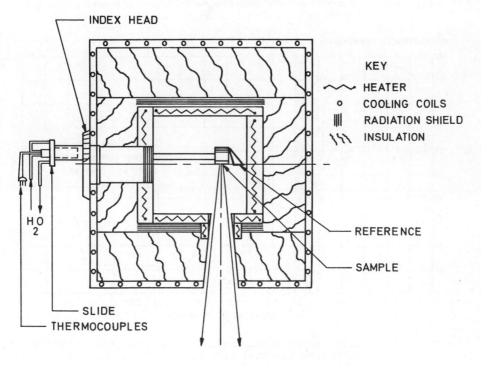

INDEX HEAD

KEY

〜〜 HEATER
o   COOLING COILS
‖‖‖ RADIATION SHIELD
〟〟〟 INSULATION

REFERENCE

SAMPLE

H O
 2

SLIDE
THERMOCOUPLES

Fig. 9-9   Details of heated cavity reflectometer (37)

REFLECTANCE (PERCENT)

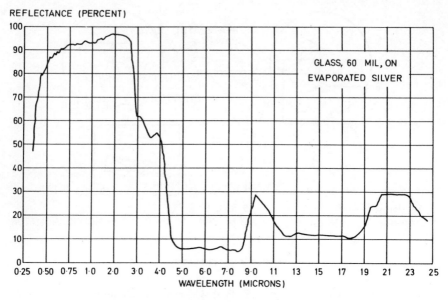

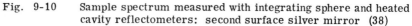

Fig. 9-10   Sample spectrum measured with integrating sphere and heated
cavity reflectometers: second surface silver mirror (38)

REFLECTANCE (PERCENT)

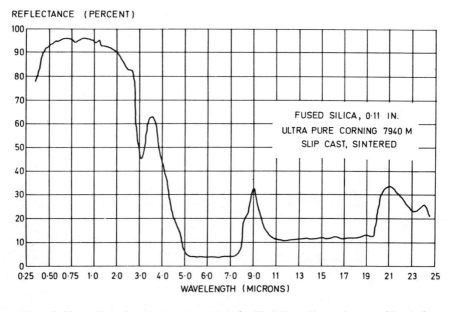

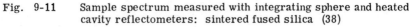

Fig. 9-11   Sample spectrum measured with integrating sphere and heated
cavity reflectometers: sintered fused silica (38)

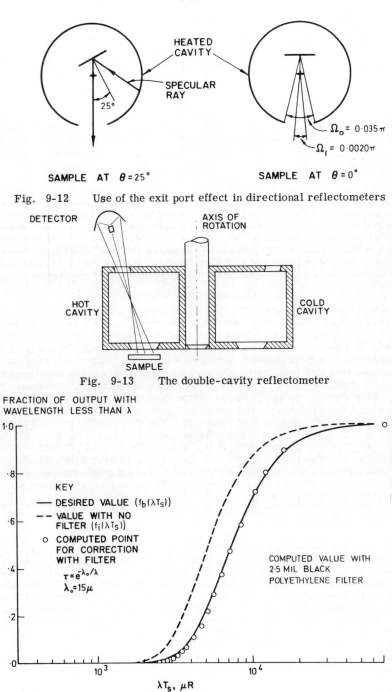

Fig. 9-12   Use of the exit port effect in directional reflectometers

Fig. 9-13   The double-cavity reflectometer

Fig. 9-14   Ogive $f(\lambda T_S)$ for the double-cavity reflectometer

Directional Reflectance in the Far Infrared

A device which works equally well in the long and short wavelengths (but not as well as the ones just mentioned in their respective spectral ranges) is the 2π-steradian mirror. Paschen and Coblentz used hemispheres at the turn of this century and Eckert and coworkers (28) and others have likewise used a hemisphere in the direct mode. Gier, Dunkle and Bevans (40) used two identical opposed 2π-steradian paraboloids, and Dunn, Richmond, and Wiebelt (41) used an ellipsoid in the direct mode. In the direct mode, radiation is brought onto the sample directionally through a hold in the mirror or via a reflection from a spot on the mirror, collected by the 2π-steradian mirror or mirrors, and somewhat focused on a detector. Errors occur from optical aberrations and more importantly, nonuniformly sensitive detectors.

This writer has been an advocate (42), (43) of the McNicholas (30) reciprocal mode for the 2π-steradian mirror. Those 2π-steradian mirror instruments used in the reciprocal mode, (44)-(47) have displayed superior performance particularly when the interreflection error is minimized (46). A special advantage of the 2π-steradian mirror is that it lends itself to source-side chopping in either mode of operation. For this reason it is preferable to the heated cavity at wavelengths beyond 20 microns; it is more easily used with specimens which are difficult to cool; and it permits measurements with specimen temperatures at either elevated or cryogenic levels.

Figure 9-15 shows a schematic diagram of the apparatus described in (46, 47) and Figure 9-16 shows a photograph. Visible in the foreground is a surface source which radiates upward to an inclined water cooled roughened and sooted mirror. Above the mirror a mechanical chopper exists to interrupt radiation going from the mirror to the off-axis paraboloid, whose edge is visible at the right of the source. Radiation is reflected from the highly-off-axis paraboloid onto the slightly off axis one (47). Radiation reflected from this paraboloid is focused somewhat on a specimen holder which is shown turned toward the camera out of its natural position. If one were able to put an infrared eye at the specimen location, one would see only the source via reflection in the mirrors. The sample is therefore diffusely irradiated except for the square observation port, visible near the center of the mirror just above the chopper blade hub. The sample is viewed through this port by a grating monochromator, shown with cover removed behind the reflectometer. A vacuum thermocouple with diamond window is used for a detector (A Golay cell would extend the spectral range). Figure 9-17 shows some data obtained with the instrument (46).

Hemispherical Characteristics

Total hemispherical emittance is measured rather easily calorimetrically at temperatures above room temperature, particularly when the specimen is a coating which can be applied to a ribbon, cylinder, or sphere. At temperatures significantly below room temperature such factors as lead conduction, the possibility of phase changes, temperature drift, and edge effects cause difficulties, as pointed out by Nelson and Bevans (48). Geometries tending to be focusing such as concentric spheres or cylinders are troublesome also. The measurement made is said to be a calorimetric one, because a heat balance is made on a specimen suspended within a blackened and baffled evacuated enclosure.

A radiometric measurement of hemispherical emittance can be made, if a hemispherical radiometer is used with a plane specimen. However, except at high fluxes hemispherical radiometers are rather difficult to use. Eichhorn (49) has pointed out that a directional radiometer can be used for hemispherical emittance when a spherical specimen lies entirely within the radiometer's field of view or,

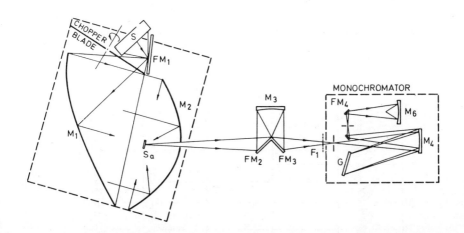

Fig. 9-15   Diagram of reciprocal paraboloid reflectometer (46)

Fig. 9-16   Photograph of reciprocal paraboloid reflectometer (46)

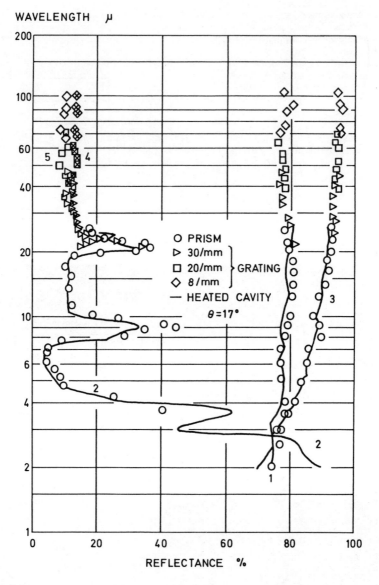

Fig. 9-17   Sample far infrared spectra measured with reciprocal
paraboloid reflectometer (46)
Curve 1: Vacuum evaporated gold on wire mesh bonded to
mylar; wire spacing, .24 mm; wire dia. .080 mm.
Curve 2: Sintered fused silica Corning 7940 M 2.8 mm thick
Curve 3: Polished 17-7 PH stainless steel
Curve 4: Alundum heater cement; Norton RA1161 3 mm thick

perhaps more conveniently, when a cylindrical specimen has a triangular a, masked off within the radiometer's field of view.

In the short wavelength region hemispherical reflectance can be measured using a single integrating sphere. In this case the sample is neither irradiated by the source nor viewed by the detector, but rather the efficiency of the sphere is observed as the sample is substituted for a portion of the sphere wall, a portion masked from view of the source and detector. Hemispherical transmittance can be measured with a double integrating sphere scheme, one for the source and one for the detector. Again neither the source nor detector should directly view the specimen.

Error Analyses

No measurement is useful without an accompanying estimate of its uncertainty. After the basic principle on which an instrument functions is recognized, the first step is to reject all idealizations made. Common idealizations are some of the following:

The specimen is perfectly diffuse

The specimen is perfectly specular

The specimen is in a near thermodynamic equilibrium state

All energy transfer into the specimen is by radiation

All energy storage within the specimen is negligible or accounted for with a constant specific heat

The surrounds are isothermal

The surrounds are diffuse

Interreflections are negligible or accounted for perfectly

The irradiation is unidirectional

The irradiation is incoherent

The irradiation all has the same chopping phase

The detector is at steady state

The detector is linear

The detector is insensitive to the state of polarization of the irradiation

The detector is uniformly sensitive independent of direction, image location, and phase

The optics are isothermal

The sample and reference optics are identical

The optics are nonpolarizing

The optics are nonscattering

The optics focus perfectly

The spectral slit width is small

The source is steady

The source, optics, and detector are nonselective over the spectral slit region

Usually a perturbation analysis is adequate, that is, the effect of rejecting an idealization can usually be analyzed without rejecting all of them at once. Errors can then be added with account taken of their sign, and uncertainties with nonskewed distributions can be combined in a root mean square (50). For example, consider an integrating sphere. Some spheres used for relative measurements have the sample in clear view of the detector. In this case the intensity of the sample I_S in the direction toward the detector is given by, (assuming incoherent irradiation):

$$\pi I_S A_S = P \rho_B (\theta, \phi, \theta_S, \phi_S) \qquad \text{(Eq. 9-49)}$$

where θ, ϕ is the direction of incidence and θ_S, ϕ_S gives the direction toward the sample, P is the power incident on the sample and A_S is the irradiated area. We define:

$$p_{DS} = \int_{A_D} \frac{\rho_B (\theta, \phi, \theta_S, \phi_S)}{\rho (\theta, \phi)} \left[\frac{\cos \theta_S \cos \theta_D}{\pi r_{DS}^2} \right] dA_D \qquad \text{(Eq. 9-50)}$$

so that the quantity $p_{DS} \rho_S P$ is the power reflected directly to the detector with area A_D when sample S is irradiated. The signal put out by a linear detector with response independent of angle of incidence is then:

$$V_S = K\{p_{DS}\rho_S P + \rho_S (1-p_{DS}) P \eta\} \qquad \text{(Eq. 9-51)}$$

where η is the sphere efficiency, which for a small detector in a large sphere is:

$$\eta = \frac{A_D}{A_W} \frac{\rho_W}{1-\rho_W} \qquad \text{(Eq. 9-52)}$$

The quantity ρ_W is the average reflectance of the sphere wall including the detector, openings, sample, etc. The reference signal is:

$$V_R = K \{ p_{DR} \rho_R P + \rho_R (1-p_R) P \eta\} \qquad \text{(Eq. 9-53)}$$

so that the ratio is:

$$\frac{V_S}{V_R} = \frac{p_{DS} + \eta (1-p_S)}{p_{DR} + \eta (1-p_R)} \frac{\rho_S}{\rho_R} \qquad \text{(Eq. 9-54)}$$

The error in taking $V_S / V_R = \rho_S / \rho$ is then:

$$\delta (\rho_S / \rho_R) = \frac{(\rho_S / \rho_R) - (V_S / V_R)}{(\rho_S / \rho_R)} = \frac{(p_R - p_S)(1-\eta)}{p_R + (1-p_R)} \qquad \text{(Eq. 9-55)}$$

If the reference is diffuse, p_{DR} may be of the order of one or two percent, and η is typically of this order. The quantity p_{DS} may have any value from zero to unity. Large errors are seen to be possible and have in fact been detected, but not always understood (51)(52).

As a second example consider entrance port error in an integrating sphere. The power lost out of the entrance port E is $p_{ES} P$ so that the signal, when the sample is not viewed by the detector, is:

$$V_S = K(1-p_{ES})\rho_S (\theta, \phi) \eta P \qquad \text{(Eq. 9-56)}$$

The reference signal when a portion of the wall viewed by the detector is:

$$V_R = K \eta P \qquad \text{(Eq. 9-57)}$$

The ratio is then:

$$\frac{V_S}{V_R} = (1-p_{ES}) \rho(\theta, \phi) \qquad \text{(Eq. 9-58)}$$

For a specular sample irradiated somewhat off normal p_{ES} is zero. However, if the sample is slightly diffusing p_{ES} may be appreciable. Some manufacturers have used two entrance ports both just slightly away from the specularly reflected ray. Needless to say, such irrational design is pure folly. It is best to be able to vary the angle of incidence appreciably as in the directional integrating sphere with suspended sample (34).

As a final example, we can consider an easily understood error in a directional heated cavity. In what was otherwise a nice design Tingwaldt (36) suspended a cooled specimen at the center of a jacketed pyrex glass sphere which was heated by condensing sulphur. With the center position there is an appreciable interreflection error caused by specular reflection from the sphere wall back to the cold specimen. Glass reflects fairly well in the 9 to 11 and 18 to 22 rest-strahlen bands, and anomalous results were in fact observed in the rest-strahlen region.

For further details of error analyses of sample emission error in heated cavities; substitution, shadowing (or interreflection) errors in integrating spheres; stray light and polarization errors; the interested reader should see References (30)(31) (37)(43)(46)(47)(51)(53)(54). Table 9-2 summarizes some of the more significant errors to be considered when using directional reflectometers.

Gas Radiation Measurements

Types of Measurements

In the case of a gas volume in a state defined by temperature T, that is, in a state of local thermodynamic equilibrium (56), it is desired to know the absorption and scattering mass coefficients k_a and k_s. For an isotropic gas, perhaps with entrained particles, the quantity k_a will not depend upon direction, but the distribution of scattered radiation will depend upon the angle between the scattered ray and original one. The absorbed power in path dS is:

$$dId\Omega_1 = -\rho_m k_a dS\, I_1\, d\Omega_1 \qquad \text{(Eq. 9-59)}$$

and the scattered intensity emerging is:

$$dI(\theta_2) = \frac{1}{4\pi}\rho_m k_s(\theta_2-\theta_1) dS\, I_1\, d\Omega_1 \qquad \text{(Eq. 9-60)}$$

where ρ_m is the mass density of the absorbing-scattering species. If the gas contains scatterers one has a problem akin to that of measuring the bidirectional reflectance to find $k_s(\theta_2-\theta_1)$, and the determination of the forward scattering or backward scattering coefficient:

$$k_f = \frac{1}{2\pi}\int_0^{\pi/2} k_s(\theta_2-\theta_1)d(\theta_2-\theta_1) \qquad \text{(Eq. 9-61)}$$

$$k_b = \frac{1}{2\pi}\int_{\pi/2}^{\pi} k_s(\theta_2-\theta_1)d(\theta_2-\theta_1) \qquad \text{(Eq. 9-62)}$$

is akin to the determination of the directional transmittance or reflectance. Further, one has polarization to account for. In the interests of keeping this survey of thermal radiation measurements within the bounds of a short work, only a few observations are made in what follows on the problem of making measurements for equilibrium gases containing no scattering particles.

For no scattering particles Equation 9-59 can be integrated over a path of length L to yield:

$$I = I_0 e^{-\int_0^L \rho_m k_a dS} \qquad\qquad \text{(Eq. 9-63)}$$

and for constant pressure and temperature:

$$I = I_0 e^{-k_a w} \qquad\qquad \text{(Eq. 9-64)}$$

where w is the mass path length:

$$w = \rho_m L \qquad\qquad \text{(Eq. 9-65)}$$

From a conceptual point of view the measurement problem is then very simple. One simply views a chopped source through a gas cell length L with a spectrometer to measure $e^{-k_a w}$ or views a cold black target through the hot gas with detector side chopping to measure $(1-e^{-k_a w})I_b$. However, there are problems with the gas containment system and with the interpretation of the measurement.

The types of measurements which are made are consequently characterized by adjectives describing the gas containment system and the spectral response of the detector. The gas systems fall into the following catagories:

  Hot window cell

  Cold window cell

  Nozzle seal cell

  Free jet

The spectral nature of the measurement is described in the following ways:

  Narrow band measurement

  Band absorption measurement

  Total measurement

Gas Containment Systems

The hot window cell contains the gas within a container having two windows (or a window and a mirror) heated to the cell temperature, so that the gas and cell are essentially in equilibrium. Such cells have been used by Tingwaldt, Penner, and many others (57)-(60). Troubles arise from lack of suitable windows for particular combinations of temperature, pressure, and desired spectral range. There may be chemical attack and gas adsorption on the window and it has been this writer's experience that polycrystalline windows should be avoided at elevated temperatures. But even with crystal windows high temperatures and long wavelengths are unobtainable.

Cold window cells are cells in which the windows are cooled. Shock tubes are a good example (61)(62). Tien and Giedt (63) used a heated cell with moveable cooled windows. Cold window cells introduce inhomogeneities into the gas temperature and density. Under some circumstances these inhomogeneities are not too serious and, of course, in high temperature shock tube studies they have to be accepted. The cold window cell does lend itself to studies of nonhomogeneous gases (64)(65).

Nozzle seal cells are open flow cells in which absorbing gas meets nonabsorbing gas in the throat of a nozzle containing a slot, through which the gas mixture is withdrawn. Such a cell makes it possible to contain an infrared absorbing emitting

TABLE 9-2: Directional Reflectometers and Principal Errors

INSTRUMENT	TYPICAL ERRORS	REF.	COMMENTS
Integrating Sphere	1. Direct Irradiation Error	(34)	1. Sample should not see detector in a direct mode or source in reciprocal mode. See (51) and (52) for bad examples.
	2. Port Error*	(34)	
	3. Directional Sensitivity Error	(34)	3. Detector should have cosine response in direct mode or wall source should be perfectly diffuse in reciprocal mode.
	4. Polarization*	(34)	
	5. Stray Radiation*	(35)	
	6. Nondiffuseness of Sphere Wall	(34)	
	7. Shadowing	(34)	
	8. Interreflections (substitution)	(34)	
	9. Nonlinearity of Detection System*	(34)	
Heated Cavity	1. Sample Emission	(51)	1. Common to all instruments with no source side chopping.
	2. Port Error*	(37)	
	3. Temperature Gradients	(37)	3. Use of reference fin reduces error.
	4. Shadowing by retainer	(37)	
	5. Interreflections	(37)	5. See (36) for a bad example.
	6. Stray Radiation*	(55)	
	7. Nonlinearity*	(55)	
	8. Polarization*	(55)	
Two-pi Mirror	1. Optical Aberrations	(46)	1. Optical quality images may be sacrificed to obtain hemispherical irradiation or detection. See (46).
	2. Directional Sensitivity of Detector or Source	(46)	2. Source should not be viewed at high angles from the normal.

TABLE 9-2 Continued

INSTRUMENT	TYPICAL ERRORS	REF.	COMMENTS
	3. Spatial Sensitivity of Detector or Source (phase and amplitude)	(46)	3. Strongly favors reciprocal mode operation.
	4. Port Error* and Shadowing	(47)	4. See (46) for a bad example.
	5. Interreflections	(46)	
	6. Variation of Mirror reflectances with angle and position.	(46)	
	7. Stray radiation*	(46)	7. See also (55).
	8. Nonlinearity*	(46)	
	9. Polarization*	(46)	

* Common to all instruments.

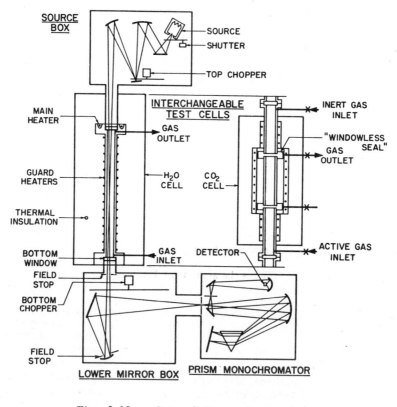

Fig. 9-18   Gas radiation apparatus (65)

gas, that is, a gas with an asymmetric diatomic or polyatomic molecule having infrared vibration-rotation bands, between two layers of an infrared nonabsorbing gas, that is, a nonabsorbing symmetric diatomic or monatomic gas. Hottel and Mangelsdorf (66), Eckert (67) and other early workers used such cells to make total radiation measurements for H_2O and CO_2. Edwards and coworkers used a nozzle seal cell to make band absorption measurements of CO_2, CH_4, and H_2O (68) and figure 9-18 shows the cells used in these studies. The nozzle seal system eliminates some of the problems with windows, but does cause some inhomogeneities in composition at the ends of the cell (and temperature also, unless the seal gases are preheated, which is strongly recommended). In addition some degree of scattering is introduced from the turbulent eddies of differing indices of refraction in the nozzle throats. This problem has not been serious for spectral measurements where the incident energy is tagged by source-side chopping, but it led to significant problems in the older total measurements. Figure 9-19 shows a typical low resolution spectrum used to obtain band absorption.

Jet and burner measurements are those used to obtain high temperature spectra. Schmidt (69) used a nozzle for his early investigation of radiation from water vapor. Recently there have been a number of measurements reported using, in essence, a small rocket engine. For example, Ferriso and Ludwig used a 3.12 cm diameter jet at one atmosphere (70) and they show a shadowgraph of the image of the monochromator exit slit upon the jet. Scattering from the turbulent eddies and nonhomogeneities on the jet boundaries are evident in the shadowgraph, but just at the beginning of the jet the mixing layer between the jet and surrounding atmosphere is reasonably thin.

Interpretation of Measurements

A major difficulty in gas radiation measurements is that unless the pressure and/or temperature are high the spectral lines of the gas are narrow, on the order of 0.1 wavenumbers (cm^{-1}). A band may have hundreds of thousands of lines in a region of a few hundred wavenumbers in extent, and a given species may have one to ten or more important bands distributed throughout the infrared. As the temperature is increased above room temperature the lines which were important become weaker and new ones become stronger. The fact that the lines are narrow and that there are many of them dictates that the measured quantity usually is not the absorption coefficient k_a but rather an effective or mean absorptivity or emissivity. The mean absorptivity may be written:

$$\bar{\alpha}(\nu_0) = \frac{1}{\Delta\nu} \int_{\Delta\nu} (1-e^{-k_a w}) S(\nu-\nu_0) d\nu \qquad \text{(Eq. 9-66)}$$

where $S(\nu-\nu_0)$ is the spectral response function.

In the late thirties and early forties the approach taken was to measure total emissivity and absorptivity versus temperature, pressure and path-length-pressure-product, as mentioned in the preceeding section. Charts (71) reasonably accurate at one atmosphere, were developed for the total emissivity of CO_2 and H_2O, and approximate (in some cases very approximate) corrections were developed to account for pressure, composition, and the difference absorptivity and emissivity. The quantity measured was:

$$\alpha_T(w, P, T, T_s) = \int_0^\infty (1-e^{-k_a w}) \frac{\pi I_b(\nu, T_s)}{\sigma T_s^4} d\nu \qquad \text{(Eq. 9-67)}$$

The more recent works cited in the preceeding section have measured band absorption:

ABSORPTIVITY (PERCENT)

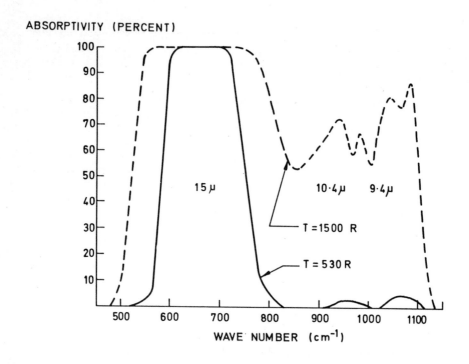

15 μ 10·4 μ 9·4 μ

T = 1500 R

T = 530 R

WAVE NUMBER (cm⁻¹)

Fig. 9-19   Sample gas radiation spectra: The 9.4, 10.4, and 15 micron CO_2 bands. The high temperature curve is 100% CO_2 at 10 atmospheres with a 39 cm path. The room temperature curve is 10% CO_2 in N_2 with a 129 cm path, 10 atmosphere pressure.

$$A(w, P, T) \equiv \int_{\nu_1}^{\nu_2} (1 - e^{-k_a w}) d\nu = \int_{\nu_1}^{\nu_2} \bar{\alpha}(\nu_0) d\nu_0 \qquad \text{(Eq. 9-68)}$$

and narrow band absorptivity $\bar{\alpha}(\nu_0, w, P, T)$. In order for the measurements of A or $\bar{\alpha}$ to be useful it is necessary to have band model correlations which can represent at least the pressure and mass path dependency of the quantities. It is highly desirable to be able to represent the temperature and wavenumber dependency as well. Models capable of correlating measurements of A are termed wide band models, and models capable of correlating $\bar{\alpha}$ are narrow band models.

Progress in the ability to make measurements has been accompanied by progress in models to represent the data. Plass (72)(73) has contributed much to the understanding of narrow band representations which were pioneered by Elsasser (74) and Goody (75). Reardon and Huffaker (76) have used narrow band correlations in predicting liquid fuel rocket engine exhaust radiation. Dudley Williams and coworkers used linear, square-root, and logarithmic relations to fit the w-dependency of wide band absorption (77), and Edwards and Menard (78) developed a wide band model which has been put into a form more convenient for some applications by Tien and Lowder (79). A somewhat sophisticated band model (80) gives a reasonable representation of the temperature and wavenumber dependencies of $\bar{\alpha}$, and the temperature dependency of A, in addition to approximately predicting the mass path length and pressure dependencies of both quantities.

Factors to be Considered in Error Analyses

It should be clear from the preceeding remarks that some factors to be considered are the following:

Reflection and scattering by windows when transmission is measured and reflection, scattering, and emission by windows when emission is measured.

Scattering by mixing zones in nozzle seals or in free jets.

Inhomogeneities in temperature, pressure, and composition.

Adsorption on windows.

In addition to these experimental problems there are problems in data interpretation or correlation:

Insufficient overlapping of lines when attempting to measure integrated intensity.

Pressure-induced changes in dipole moment.

Improper correlation model.

Insufficiently low pressure when attempting to measure line-width-to-line-spacing parameters.

The measured quantity should be formulated taking into account all the factors which can be treated theoretically. On the first list items 1 and 3 are easily treated, and on the second list items 1 and 4 can be treated theoretically. The remaining items on the list must be at least investigated experimentally.

Concluding Remarks

In this short section an attempt has been made to survey techniques used to measure radiant energy fluxes and thermal radiation characteristics. The references cited were selected to get the interested reader off to a good start. They are by no means exhaustive. The very old works of Paschen, Ulbricht, Coblentz and others have not been cited specifically, because this note is not intended to be a history. Nor have many of the very modern ones in symposia and reports been cited, because many of these papers are concerned with the objects or properties being measured and use standard techniques. An attempt has been made to mention most of the works regarded as important by this writer, for example, (30)-(37), (39) and (45) -(48). It should not be inferred that all the works cited are meant to be models. Table 9-2 indicates some cases of improper experimental arrangements.

A convenient notation and nomenclature has been propounded. Key adjectives are the ones describing the directions, namely, bidirectional, directional, and hemispherical and the ones describing the spectrum, namely, spectral, internal total, and external total. The reader should be cautioned that the words total, diffuse, and hemispherical are frequently garbled elsewhere. The reader should also be warned that there are Committees and Editors who enforce other schemes of notation and nomenclature. In regard to this latter point, it doesn't make a great deal of difference whether one uses or is forced to use emissivity, emittance, or emissance; intensity, radiance, or steradiance; radiosity or emittance. What is important is whether or not one's thinking is clear. One must know, for example, that there is both an internal and an external total emittance characteristic; that the radiant intensity (as used here) of a perfectly diffuse surface doesn't vary with $\cos\theta$ but is constant; that diffuse reflection may be far from perfectly diffuse and may, in fact, be essentially specular as far as computing power transfer is concerned.

In summary, there has been reviewed in 'Thermal Radiation' the concept of a radiant intensity vector used to describe the state of polarization of the radiant intensity, and relations between the radiant intensity and the radiant flux. In 'Thermal Radiation Characteristics' there was presented the concept of radiation characteristics to describe reflection, transmission, absorption, and emission from an external accounting viewpoint. Polarization and spectral and directional dependencies were provided for. 'Radiometry' considered the problem of measuring radiant intensity and radiant flux and key features of spectral and total radiometers were briefly stated. Measurement techniques for the radiation surface-system characteristics were reviewed in 'Surface Radiation Measurements'. It was shown that the major problem faced by the experimentalist is contriving to measure directional reflectance, regardless of the bidirectional reflectance characteristic of the specimen. Instruments suitably contrived were shown to be integrating spheres, heated cavities, and 2π-steradian mirrors. The advantages of reciprocal measurement arrangements over direct ones were described and examples of perturbation error analyses were presented. Last was a short review of gas radiation measurements where the concept of band absorption and the use of band models were reviewed. It was shown that the major problem faced by the experimentalist in the gas radiation property measurement area is accounting for discrete line structure in gas spectra.

References

1 Knuth, E. L., 'Introduction to Statistical Thermodynamics', McGraw-Hill, New York, 1966.
Davidson, N., 'Statistical Mechanics', McGraw-Hill, New York, pp 230-235. 1962.

2 Sparrow, E. M., and Cess, R. D., 'Radiation Heat Transfer', Brooks Cole, Belmont, Calif., 1966.

3 Dunkle, R. V., 'Thermal Radiation Tables and Applications', Trans. Am. Soc. Mech. Engrs., Vol 76, 549-552, 1954.

4 Wolfe, W. L., Ed., 'Handbook of Military Infrared Technology', U. S. Gov. Print. Office., Wash. D. C.

5 Czerny, M., and Walther, A., 'Tables of the Fractional Functions for the Planck Distribution Law', Springer Verlag, Berlin, 1961.

6 Spalding, D. B., 'Heat Transfer from Chemically Reacting Gases', in 'Modern Developments in Heat Transfer,' W. Ibele, Ed., Academic Press, New York, 1963, pp 19-64.

7 Edwards, D. K., and Bevans, J. T., 'Effect of Polarization on Spacecraft Radiation Heat Transfer', AIAA Journal, Vol 3, 1323-1329, 1965.

8 Chandrasekhar, S., 'Radiative Transfer', Dover, New York, 1960, p 27.

9 Edwards, D. K., and Nelson, K. E., 'Maximum Error (Discrepancy) in Total Emissivity Measurements Due to Non-Grayness of Samples', ARS Journal, Vol 31, 1021-1022, 1961.

10 McNicholas, H. J., 'Equipment for Measuring the Reflective and Transmissive Properties of Diffusing Media', Nat. Bur. Stds. J. of Res., Vol 13, 211-236, 1934.

11 Nicodemus, F. E., 'Directional Reflectance and Emissivity of an Opaque Surface', Applied Optics, Vol 4, 767-773, 1965.

12 Birkebak, R. C., and Eckert, E. R. G., 'Effects of Roughness of Metal Surfaces on Angular Distribution of Monochromatic Reflected Radiation', J. of Heat Transfer, Vol 87, 85-94, 1965.

13 Dolin, S. A., Kruegle, H. A., and Penzias, G. J., 'A Rapid Scan Spectrometer That Sweeps Corner Mirrors Through the Spectrum', Applied Optics, Vol 6, 267-274, 1967.

14 Drummond, A. J., Hickey, J. R., Scholes, W. J., and Laue, E. G., 'Multichannel Radiometer Measurement of Solar Irradiance', J. Spacecraft and Rockets, Vol 4, 1200-1206, 1967.

15 Eckert, E. R. G., and Drake, R. M., 'Heat and Mass Transfer', McGraw-Hill, New York, 1959.

16 Coblentz, W. W., 'Thermopile Construction and Use', in 'Measurement of Radiant Energy', Forsythe, W. E., ed., McGraw-Hill, New York, 1937, pp 191-198.

392

17   Stair, R., Schneider, W.E., and Fussell, W.B., 'The New Tungsten-Fila-
ment Lamp Standards of Total Irradiance', Applied Optics, Vol 6, 101-105,
1967.

18   Guild, J., 'Investigations in Absolute Radiometry', Proc. Roy. Soc. London,
Vol 161, 1, 1937.

19   Abbot, C.G., 'Studying the Sun's Heat on Mountain Peaks in Desert Land',
Ann. Rep. Smithstonian Inst., 1920, p145, See also p. 319, 1910, p. 153,
1912.

20   Dunkle, R.V., 'Thermal Radiation Characteristics of Surfaces', 'Fundamental Research in Heat Transfer,' J.A. Clark, ed., Macmillan, New York,
pp 1-31, 1963.

21   Schmidt, E., and Eckert, E.R.G., 'Uber die Richtungs-verteilung der
Warmestrahlung von Oberflachen', Forsch. a.d. Geb. d. Ingenieurw., Vol 6,
175, 1935.

22   Eckert, E.R.G., 'Messung der Reflexion von Warmestrahlen an Technischen
Oberflachen', Forsch. a.d. Geb. d. Ingenieurw., Vol 7, 265-270, 1936.

23   Munch, B., 'Die Richtungsverteilung bei der Reflexion von Warmestrahlung
und ihr Einfluss auf die Warmeubertragung', Mitteilungen a.d. Institut fur
Thermodynamik und Verbrennungsmotorenbau, No. 16, Verlag Leeman,
Zurich, 1955.

24   Herold, L.M., and Edwards, D.K., 'Bidirectional Characteristics of Rough,
Sintered-Metal, and Wire-Screen Systems', AIAA Journal, Vol 4, 1802-1810,
1966.

25   Moon, P. and Laurence, J. 'Construction and Test of a Goniophotometer',
J. Opt. Soc. Am., Vol 31, 130,1941.

26   Jakob, M., 'Heat Transfer', Vol. II, John Wiley, New York, 1957, pp 87-
89.

27   Snyder, N.W., Gier, J.T., and Dunkle, R.V., 'Total Normal Emissivity
Measurements on Aircraft Materials Between 100 and 800 F', Trans. Am.
Soc. Mech. Engrs., Vol 77, 1011-1019, 1955.

28   Birkebak, R.C., Hartnett, J.P., and Eckert, E.R.G., 'Measurement of
Radiation Properties of Solid Materials', in 'Prog. in Internal Res. on
Thermo. and Transport Properties,' Am. Soc. Mech. Engrs., 1962, pp 563-
574.

29   Richmond, J.C., Harrison, W.N., and Shorten, F.J., 'An Approach to
Thermal Emittance Standards', 'Measurement of Thermal Radiation Properties of Solids', NASA SP-31, 1963, pp. 403-423.

30   McNicholas, H.J., 'Absolute Methods in Reflectometry' Nat. Bur. of Stds.
J. of Res., 1, 29-73, 1928.

31   Karrer, E., 'Use of the Ulbricht Sphere in Measuring Reflection and
Transmission Factors', Bur. Stds. Sci. Papers, Vol 17, 203-225, 1922.

32   Tingwaldt, C.P., 'Uber die Messung von Reflexion, Durchlassigkeit und
Absorption an Prufkorpern beliebiger Form in der Ulbrichtschen Kugel',
Optik, Vol 9, 323-332, 1952.

33   Toporets, A. S.,   'Study of Diffuse Reflection from Powders under Diffuse
Illumination', Optics and Spectroscopy, Vol 7, 471-473, 1959.

34   Edwards, D. K., Gier, J. T., Nelson, K. E., and Roddick, R. D.,   'Integrating
Sphere for Imperfectly Diffuse Samples', J. Opt. Soc. Am., Vol 51, 1279-
1288, 1961.

35   Gier, J. T., Dunkle, R. V., and Bevans, J. T.,   'Measurement of Absolute
Spectral Reflectivity from 1.0 to 15 Microns', J. Opt. Soc. Am., Vol 44,
558-562, 1954.

36   Tingwaldt, C. P.,   'Measurement of Spectral Sensitivity in the Infrared',
Trans. of the Conference on the Use of Solar Energy, Vol. II, 1, Sec. A, 1955
p. 57.

37   Dunkle, R. V., Edwards, D. K., Gier, J. T., Nelson, K. E., and Roddick,
R. D.,   'Heated Cavity Reflectometer for Angular Reflectance Measurements',
in 'Prog. in Internat. Res. on Thermo. and Transport Properties,' Am. Soc.
Mech. Engrs., 1962, pp 541-562.

38   Edwards, D. K., and Roddick, R. D.,   'Spectral and Directional Thermal
Radiation Characteristics of Surfaces for Heat Rejection by Radiation',
Progress in Aeronautics and Astronautics, Vol 11, 427-446, 1963.

39   Nelson, K. E., Luedke, E. E., and Bevans, J. T.,   'A Device for the Rapid
Measurement of Total Emittance (sic)', J. Spacecraft and Rockets, Vol 3,
758-760, 1966.

40   Gier, J. T., Dunkle, R. V., and Bevans, J. T.,   Final Progress Report,
Snow Characteristics Project, Inst. Engin. Res., Univ. of Calif., Berkeley
1955.

41   Dunn, S. T., Richmond, J. C., and Wiebelt, J. A.,   'Ellipsoidal Mirror
Reflectometer', J. Opt. Soc. Am., Vol 55, 604, 1965, abstract of paper
TB15 presented at the Spring 1965 meeting of the Opt. Soc. Am.   See also
J. of Spacecraft and Rockets, Vol 3, 961-975, 1966.

42   Edwards, D. K.,   'Thermal Radiation Characteristics of Solids', Lecture at
The Princeton Univ. Conf. Heat Transfer in Major Technologies, April 6,
1961.

43   Edwards, D. K.,   'Measurement of Thermal Radiation Characteristics',
1963 Proceedings, Inst. of Environmental Sciences, Mt. Prospect, Illinois,
1963, pp. 417-424.

44   Janssen, J. E., and Torberg, R. H.,   'Measurement of Spectral Reflectance
Using an Integrating Hemisphere', in 'Measurement of Thermal Radiation
Properties of Solids', NASA SP-31, pp 169-182, 1963.

45   White, J. U.,   'New Method for Measuring Diffuse Reflectance in the Infrared', J. Opt. Sco. Am., Vol 54, 1332-1337, 1964.

46   Neher, R. T., and Edwards, D. K.,   'Far Infrared Reflectometer for Imperfectly Diffuse Specimens', Applied Optics, Vol 4, 775-780, 1965.

47   Edwards, D. K.,   'Comments on Reciprocal-Mode 2π-Steradian Reflectometers', Applied Optics, Vol 5, 175-176, 1966.

48   Nelson, K.E., and Bevans, J.T., 'Errors of the Calorimetric Method of
      Total Emittance Measurement', in 'Measurement of Thermal Radiation
      Properties of Solids,' NASA SP-31, 1963, pp. 55-63.

49   Eichhorn, R., Lect. at the Princeton Univ. Conf., 'Heat Transfer in Major
      Technologies', April 6, 1961.

50   Kline, S.J., and McClintock, F.A., 'Describing Uncertainties in Single-
      Sample Experiments', Mech. Eng. Vol 75, 3-8, 1953.

51   Dunkle, R.V., 'Spectral Reflectance Measurements', in 'Surface Effects on
      Spacecraft Materials,' F.J. Clauss, ed., John Wiley, New York, 1960, pp.
      117-136.

52   Olson, O.H., and Pontarelli, D.A., 'Asymmetry of an Integrating Sphere',
      Applied Optics, Vol 2, 631-633, 1963.

53   Dunkle, R.V., Ehrenburg, F., and Gier, J.T., 'Spectral Characteristics
      of Fabrics from 1 to 23 Microns', J. of Heat Transfer, Vol 82, 64-70, 1960.

54   Brandenberg, W.M., 'Focusing Properties of Hemispherical and Ellipsoidal
      Mirror Reflectometers', J. Opt. Soc. Am., Vol 54, 1235-1237, 1964.

55   Edwards, D.K., and Bayard de Volo, N., 'Useful Approximations for the
      Spectral and Total Emissivity of Smooth Bare Metals', in 'Advances in
      Thermophysical Properties at Extreme Temperatures and Pressures', Am.
      Soc. Mech. Engrs., 1965, pp. 174-188.

56   Goody, R.M., 'Atmospheric Radiation', Oxford Clarendon Press, London,
      1964, pp. 29-39.

57   Tingwaldt, C.V., 'Die Absorption der Kohlensaure in Gebeit der Bande
      $\lambda=2.7\mu$ zwischen 300° und 1100° absolut (°K)', Physik. Zeits., Vol 35, 715,
      1934. For 4.3 μ see Ibid., 39, 1,1938.

58   Penner, S.S., 'Quantitative Molecular Spectroscopy and Gas Emissivities',
      Addison-Wesley, Chap. 6, 1959.

59   Goldstein, R., 'Measurements of Infrared Absorption by Water Vapor at
      Temperatures to 1000°K', J. Quant. Spectroscopy and Rad. Trans., Vol 4,
      343-352, 1964.

60   Oppenheim, U.P., and Goldman, A., 'Spectral Emissivity of Water Vapor
      at 1200°K', 10th Symp. (Int.) on Combustion, The Combustion Inst.,
      Pittsburgh, 1965, pp. 185-188.

61   Sulzmann, K.G.P., 'High Temperature, Shock Tube CO_2 Transmission
      Measurements at 4.25μ', J. Quant. Spectroscopy and Rad. Trans., Vol 4,
      375-413, 1964.

62   Menard, W.A., Thomas, G.M., Helliwell, T.M., 'Experimental and
      Theoretical Study of Molecular, Continuum, and Line Radiation from
      Planetary Atmospheres', AIAA Journal, Vol 6, 655-664, 1968.

63   Tien, C.L., and Giedt, W.H., 'Experimental Determination of Infrared
      Absorption of High Temperature Gases', 'Advances in Thermophysical
      Properties at Extreme Temps. and Press.,' Am. Soc. Mech. Engrs., 1965,
      pp. 167-173.

Abu Romia, M.M. and **Tien, C.L.**, 'Measurements and Correlations of Infrared Radiation of Carbon Monoxide at Elevated Temperatures', J. Quantitative Spectroscopy and Rad. Trans., Vol. 6, 1966, pp. 143-167.

(64) **Simmons, F.S.**, 'An Analytical and Experimental Study of Molecular Radiative Transfer in Nonisothermal Gases', 10th Symp. (Int.) on Combustion, The Combustion Inst., Pittsburgh, 1965, pp. 177-184.

(65) **Edwards, D.K.**, **Glassen, L.K.**, **Hauser, W.C.**, and **Tuchscher, J.S.**, 'Radiation Heat Transfer in Nonisothermal Nongray Gases', J. Heat Transfer, Vol. 89, 219-229, 1967.
Weiner, M.M., and **Edwards, D.K.**, 'Nonisothermal Gas Radiation in Superposed Vibration-Rotation Bands' accepted for publication by J. Quant. Spectroscopy and Rad. Trans.

(66) **Hottel, H.C.**, and **Mangelsdorf, H.G.**, 'Heat Transmission from Non-Luminous Gases II. Experimental Study of CO_2 and H_2O', Trans. A. I. Ch. E., Vol 31, 517, 1935.

(67) **Eckert, E.R.G.**, 'Messung der Gesamtstrahlung von Wasserdampf und Kohlensaure in Mischung mit nichtstrahlenden Gazen bei Temperaturen bis 1300^0C', VDI Forschungsheft, 387, 1-20, 1937.

(68) **Edwards, D.K.**, 'Absorption by Infrared Bands of Carbon Dioxide Gas at Elevated Pressures and Temperatures', J. Opt. Soc. Am., Vol 50, 617-626 1960, also Applied Optics, Vol 3,847-852, 1964, Vol 3, 1501-1502, 1964, Vol 4, 715-721, 1965, 'Studies of Infrared Radiation in Gases', UCLA Dept. of Engin. Report 62-65, Jan. 1963; Chemical Engineering Progress Symposium Series, Vol 64, 173-180, 1968.

(69) **Schmidt, E.**, 'Messung der Gesamtstrahlung des Wasserdampf bei Temperaturen bis zu 1000^0C', Forsch. a.d. Geb. d. Ingenieurw., Vol 3, 57, 1932.

(70) **Ferriso, C.C.**, and **Ludwig, C.B.**, 'Spectral Emissivities and Integrated Intensities of the $2.7\ \mu\ H_2O$ Band Between 530 and $2200°K$', J. Quant. Spectroscopy and Rad. Trans., Vol 4, 215-227, 1964.

(71) **Hottel, H.C.**, and **Sarofim, A.F.**, 'Radiative Transfer', McGraw-Hill, New York, Ch. 6. 1967.

(72) **Plass, G.N.**, 'Useful Representations for Measurements of Spectral Band Absorption', J. Opt. Soc. Am., Vol 50, 868-875, 1960.

(73) **Plass, G.N.**, 'The Influence of Numerous Low-Intensity Spectral Lines on Band Absorptance' Applied Optics, Vol 3, 859-866, 1964.

(74) **Elsasser, W.M.**, 'Heat Transfer by Infrared Radiation in the Atmosphere', Harvard Meteorological Studies, No. 6, Harvard U. Press, 1942.

(75) **Goody, R.M.**, 'A Statistical Model for Water Vapour Absorption', Quart. J. Royal Meteor. Soc., Vol 78, 165, 1952.

(76) **Reardon, J.E.**, and **Huffaker, R.M.**, 'Radiative Heat Transfer Calculations for Saturn Exhaust Plumes', Mol. Rad. and its Appl. to Diagnostic Techniques, NASA TMX-53711, 1967, pp. 184-218.

(77) **Howard, J.N.**, **Burch, D.L.**, and **Williams, D.**, 'Near Infrared Transmission Through Synthetic Atmospheres', Geophysical Res. Paper, No. 40,

Air Force Cambridge Res. Cent., 1953. Also J. Opt. Soc. Am., Vol 46, 186, 237, 334.

78   **Edwards, D.K.**, and **Menard, W.A.**, 'Comparison of Models for Correlation of Total Band Absorption', Applied Optics, Vol 3, 621-625, 1964.
Edwards, D.K., 'Studies of Infrared Radiation in Gases', UCLA Dept. of Eng. Report 62-65, Jan. 1963.

79   **Tien, C.L.**, and **Lowder, J.E.**, 'A Correlation for Total Band Absorptance of Radiating Gases', Int. J. Heat and Mass Transfer Vol 9, 698-701, 1966.

80   **Weiner, M.M.**, and **Edwards, D.K.**, 'Theoretical Expression of Water Vapor Spectral Emissivity with Allowance for Line Structure', Internatal J. Heat and Mass Transfer, Vol 11, 55-65, Jan., 1968.

10

Measurement of Thermophysical Properties

W. LEIDENFROST
School of Mechanical Engineering, Purdue University, Lafayette, Ind.

Summary

The present paper describes many techniques which have been used in the measurements of the thermophysical properties; viscosity, thermal conductivity, thermal diffusivity and specific heat. From the many publications which have appeared describing such work a selection was made of those which appear to provide the most detailed and clear descriptions. An attempt was also made to cite the original publications, where possible.

No attempt is made to describe work at the extremes of pressure and/or temperature, such as above several thousand atmospheres or degrees or very low pressures or temperatures. In addition not all three phases (solid, liquid and gas) are discussed for all properties but the usual selection is made, e.g., viscosity of solids is not discussed, likewise non-Newtonian flow is not considered.

Introduction

Rapid technological developments during the last decades have generated an increasing effort in expanding our knowledge of properties of materials. This seems to be especially true for these property values needed whenever heat transfer must be evaluated, and whenever the proper design of heat transfer elements is vital, as in nuclear engineering, rocketry, space travel and in many other areas of our modern technology.

In addition to direct application of the property values in engineering computation and design, there is the need of scientists who try to predict property values by statistical mechanics, and who require basic information in the form of accurate property values to verify and check their models. The theoretical prediction of properties is of great importance when property data are needed at conditions where measurements are as yet impossible.

Experimental work on viscosity, thermal conductivity and specific heats has now been in progress for well over a century, and a comprehensive and detailed review of the numerious experimental arrangements which have been used for this purpose cannot be given in a single paper. We will only discuss, therefore, some general methods used for the determination of each of the three properties of interest and will illustrate some of the most commonly used apparatus and, in addition, try to demonstrate the approaches necessary to achieve reliable data.

General Remarks

Determination of properties, especially transport properties, is difficult and time consuming and requires painstaking attention to detail, great skill and much patience. These facts will be experienced by everyone who sets out to measure properties. The reasons for the difficulties can be summarized with Kestin (1) as follows. In order to produce a measureable effect due to any one of the transport properties of a sample, it is necessary to subject it to an irreversible thermodynamic process in the course of which it inevitably departs from thermodynamic equilibrium. Thus the state at which the property is measured is only an intermediate one which is averaged over a range of states existing in the apparatus. Consequently every effort must be made to disturb the system as little as possible from an equilibrium state, which implies that the effect to be measured is inherently very small. The smaller the departure from equilibrium the smaller the effect to be measured and the greater the difficulty in determining it precisely. Under actual experimental conditions it is always and unavoidably necessary to work at the threshold of sensitivity with respect to the measured effect,. in order to preserve a near equilibrium state. Actually in all measurements it is desirable to be in a position to extrapolate to a state of equilibrium and to perform experiments over a decreasing range of the effect which is being measured. The lower end of this series is naturally set by the resolution of the detectors used in the investigation.

Every one who sets out to determine a property should select a method for which an exact theory exists and which can be applied in an instrument with the least number of corrections and possibly only those corrections for which proper account can be made. This point will be discussed in detail later, for each investigation whenever necessary.

Determination of Viscosity

As the present paper is related especially to heat transfer, only the viscosity of fluids is of interest and will be discussed. The effects of viscosity on a macro.-scopic scale manifest themselves in the presence of shear and it is clear that the measurements of viscosity must involve a state of motion. It is of course, practically impossible to measure local shear stress and it is necessary to base the measurements on some effect of the motion, which must be very slow, i.e., laminar and at very low Reynolds numbers - since it is only for this condition that exact solutions of the governing equations are known.

For example we can measure the pressure drop in a fluid flowing through a tube, or the drag on a body falling through or rotating or oscillating in a stagnant fluid.

The Use of Poiseuille Flow

The use of Poiseuille flow seems at a first glance the simplest arrangement from the theoretical point of view. The laminar flow through a straight tube seems to be stable and the principal solution is elementary. For fully developed parabolic velocity profile the volumetric rate of flow $\dot{V}$ of the incompressible fluid is given by Hagen-Poiseuille equation:

$$\dot{V} = \frac{\pi D^4 \Delta p}{124 \mu L} \qquad \text{Eq. 10-1}$$

where Δp is the pressure drop over a length L of the tube whose diameter is D. Hence the viscosity μ can be calculated if V and Δp are measured.

Completely stable laminar flow will exist if the Reynolds number-based on the average velocity-satisfies the condition that Re is below some critical value, usually taken as 2300. This condition together with the requirement of a small but still measureable pressure drop, is the cause of the difficulties of the method especially when gases are the test fluids. The pipe diameter must be small and L must be large. D enters into Equation 10-1 raised to the fourth power and must therefore be determined extremely accurately, which becomes increasingly difficult with decreasing diameter of the bore. Therefore proper selection of diameter to length ratio must be made, which normally can be proper only for a certain value or small range of viscosity. In addition it must be kept in mind that a tube of a given bore can be manufactured precisely only for a certain length.

Operating the capillary viscometer makes it necessary to consider several corrections for reasons that the actual flow departs from that assumed in Equation 10-1. When a gas flows through the capillary it will expand slightly due to its pressure having decreased by Δp. This means that the volume rate of flow increases along the capillary. The gas is accelerated slightly and requires a larger pressure drop, and a compressibility correction must be introduced. In many instances it is necessary to use very narrow capillaries. The mean free path of a gas molecule may become comparable with the diameter of the tube, and a slip correction may be necessary. (i.e., 2). The formula holds true only for a parabolic velocity profile which develops asymptotically, theorectically for $L = \infty$ from the inlet. The shear stress in the undeveloped flow is larger, and inlet corrections must be applied for which an exact solution is still needed. The most extensive treatment of the influence was done by Schiller (3), also by others (Couette (4) Goldstein (5)). If the capillary is curved further corrections are needed (6) due to the change in flow pattern and vortices. Coiled capillaries have been used by Vasilesco (7), Hawkins, Solberg and Potter (8) and others to achieve a uniform temperature control which otherwise could not be done in capillaries of large length, chosen for the sake of obtaining an appreciable pressure drop in fluids of low viscosity. For the same reason flow in narrow annulus was used. Due to the curvature centrifical forces are acting on the fluid, secondary motion is introduced, and the velocity profile ceases to be parabolic so Equation 10-1 is not valid anymore. Since these vortices are unstable the correction proves to be extremely difficult.

Capillary viscometers have been used extensively by many researchers, (9) (10) (11) and others, in a variety of constructional forms. Consideration of all of these is beyond the scope of this paper and therefore only two principal arrangements will be described. The first one, developed by Ross and Hanks (12) is a steady state instrument applying Equation 10-1 directly and the layout of the instrument is shown in Fig. 10-1. The capillary a is accomodated in a solid membrane which divides the thermostated pressure vessel b into two compartments. The vessel is pressurized with the aid of a pressure balance c which maintains a constant pressure in the downstream chamber of the pressure vessel. The test fluid is made to circulate with the aid of two precision pumps d and e driven by a synchronous motor f through precision gear boxes. In this manner gas is exhausted from one compartment of the pressure vessel and an equal volume is forced into the other. The resulting pressure drop is measured with a differential manometer g. The flow rate $\dot{V}$ is determined from the displacement of the plunger of the pumps and from the speed of the synchronous motor. Another steady flow type instrument utilizes radial flow between disks. Normally, inward flow is used because the flow tends to be more stable. Apparatus of this kind appears recently to be capable of producing satisfactory results.

A quasi-steady viscometer was first proposed by Rankine (13). Figure 10-2 shows an instrument of this type and as it was designed by Michels and Gibson (14). The Rankine viscometer is shaped in the form of a loop consisting of the capillary a and a wider tube b, both connected at the lower end to a common branch c. The glass viscometer filled with the gas is placed in the steel vessel d containing mercury and the open end of c is immersed in the mercury. In order to bring the instrument into operational condition the pressure in d is increased and as a result of it mercury rises compressing the gas before it. When the mercury level has

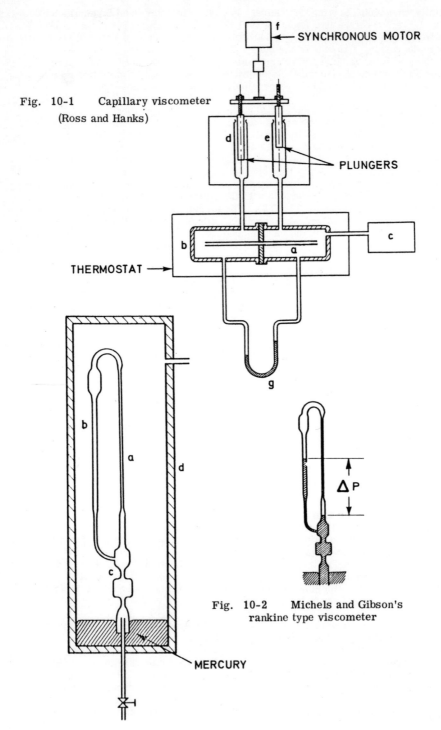

Fig. 10-1 Capillary viscometer
(Ross and Hanks)

SYNCHRONOUS MOTOR

PLUNGERS

THERMOSTAT

ΔP

Fig. 10-2 Michels and Gibson's
rankine type viscometer

MERCURY

reached the junction of the wider tube b to the common branch c, it will rise in b faster than in a due to the higher resistance of the gas flow in the capillary. An initial driving pressure drop is thereby established as shown in the insert of Fig. 10-2. The pressure in the pressure vessel is now maintained constant, and gas is forced through the capillary under the action of Δp falling gradually. The volume forced through is measured by timing the motion of the mercury meniscus rising in the wider tube of well known diameter connected to the lower end of the capillary. This volume must be identical to the one evaluated by integrating Equation 10-1 over the range of Δp observed.

The Rankine type viscometer was modified by Ubbelohde (15) and Cannon, Manning and Bell (16) resulting in an instrument in which the test liquid runs through the capillary due to its own hydrostatic head. The kinematic viscosity is evaluated by observing the time required for the liquid to run out of a reservoir of well known volume attached to the upper end of the capillary.

The Use of Falling Bodies

Stokes equation is, like the Hagen-Poiseuille equation, an exact solution of the Navier-Stokes equations and relates the drag W on a sphere to the viscosity μ, the radius of the sphere, and the velocity u.

$$W = 3 \pi \mu Du \qquad \text{Eq. 10-2}$$

Equation 10-2 is valid only for unaccelerated motion. This means that u must be the terminal velocity u_t which is reached whenever the drag equals the weight of the sphere. Equation 10-2 in addition is applicable only for Reynolds numbers of the order of unity.

The requirements of $u = u_t$ and $Re \leq 1$ can be fulfilled only with very small spheres, or larger but hollow ones of uniform and thin walls. Spheres of these two kinds are almost impossible to fabricate. The permissible radius may be increased by creating an upward force on the sphere by an electrical or a magnetic field - however, those fields may affect the viscosity of fluids to a certain degree. Other variations of the method had been proposed and are in use i.e., the fall of a sphere through a vertical or inclined tube of only slightly larger diameter. The idea is to ensure laminar friction on the small annulus in the hope that it will constitute almost all of the drag, but in reality wakes and vortices are formed behind the body, causing an increase in drag and departure from the theory due to Stoke. For the inclined tube there exists in addition the influence of the excentricity. All these facts cannot be properly accounted for and for this reason at the present time the otherwise very attractive falling body viscometer is not used as a primary instrument, but largely applied to relative measurements.

The Use of Rotating Bodies

The rotating cylinder method is in principle one very accurate way to obtain absolute viscosity measurements, and has been used frequently to establish standard values. The arrangement consists of two concentric cylinders one of which is suspended while the other rotates at a constant speed. For slow speeds the angular deflection of the stationary cylinder of infinite length, produced by the viscous torque is directly proportional to the viscosity as seen in the equation:

$$M = \pi \mu h \frac{D^2 d^2}{D^2 - d^2} \omega \qquad \text{Eq. 10-3}$$

where h is the height of either the outside or inside cylinder, M D and d their respective radii and ω the angular velocity. Equation 10-3 is valid only for infinite cylinders. For finite cylinders corrections must be made for end effects,

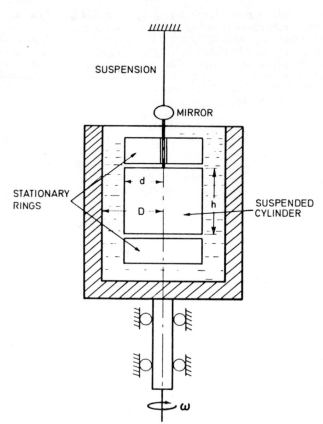

Fig. 10-3   Rotating cylinder viscometer

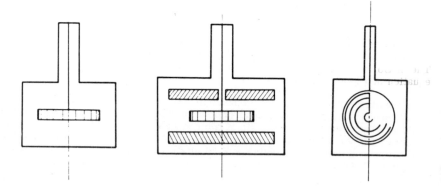

Fig. 10-4   Some oscillating systems for the measurements of viscosity

which can be minimized to a large degree by the use of guard rings. A typical instrumental arrangement is shown schematically in Fig. 10-3. There the outer cylinder is rotated (see also Gilchrist (17) and Kellstrom (18)) at a constant rpm while the inner cylinder is stationary, consisting of a middle part guarded either end by two rings fixed in position. The suspension system might be represented by an elastic wire as shown in Fig. 10-5 and an optical system for measurements of the angular deflection i.e., the torque. Another quite common arrangement is to suspend the cylinder by a rigid rod held in balance by a known electromagnetic torque. Bearden (19) rotated the inside cylinder to establish very accurate and reliable viscosity values of air. Rotating bodies of other geometries have also been used but with less satisfaction.

The rotating cylinder arrangements have many advantages - first of all that the cylinders can be relatively large in size and their precision machining can be done easily - furthermore present day technology can keep the angular velocity extremely accurately constant over a long period of time. A disadvantage is that the rotating mechanism, together with the need of using a calibrated wire or electromagnetic coils for torque measurements rule this system out as far as high temperature and high pressure applications are concerned.

The Use of Oscillating Bodies

This method makes use of the observation of the decay of slow torsional oscillations. The use of a torsional pendulum for viscosity measurements was suggested by Coulomb as early as 1784. Maxwell (20) used a pile of disks and since then many other researchers applied different systems but for many years only with limited success. Kestin and Leidenfrost (21) finally succeeded in developing this method for absolute and very accurate viscosity determinations. The achievement was made possible by the development of a precise theory of the instrument initiated first by Kestin and Persen (22) and completed by Newell (23). The theory is some-what involved and here we will discuss only its principle. The reader is referred to the works by Kestin and Newell. Figure 10-4 shows the most common arrangement. The disks or spheres axially suspended by an elastic wire are initially deflected slightly and then released. They oscillate with very slow motion in the test fluid surrounding the bodies either in an infinite space or in a narrow gap.

The period of the oscillation T and the damping decrement:

$$\Delta = \frac{1}{2\pi} \ell n \frac{\alpha_n}{\alpha_{n+1}}$$

Eq. 10-4

are measured. With the vacuum values of T_o and Δ_o enough information is available to describe the isochronous harmonically damped motion of the system.

The motion in the fluid due to shear on a disk is described by the Navier-Stokes equation in a cylindrical and symetrical coordinate system.

$$\frac{\partial u}{\partial t} = \nu \left(\frac{\partial^2 u}{\partial r^2} + \frac{1}{r} \frac{\partial u}{\partial r} - \frac{u}{r^2} \frac{\partial^2 u}{\partial z^2} \right)$$

Eq. 10-5

under the assumption that only circular motion exists, where u is the tangential velocity, ν the Kinematic viscosity and t the time.

Introducing:

$$\xi = \frac{r}{\delta}, \eta = \frac{z}{\delta}, \tau = \omega_o t$$

with:
$$\delta = \sqrt{\frac{\overline{\mu T_o}}{2\pi \rho}} = \sqrt{\frac{\nu}{\omega_o}}$$

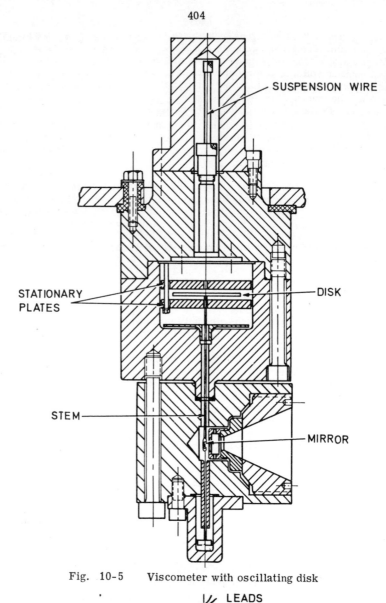

Fig. 10-5   Viscometer with oscillating disk

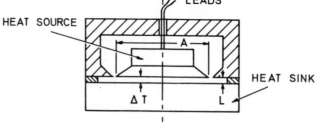

Fig. 10-6   Thermal conductivity apparatus: Linear Heat Flow

δ represents the average distance in the fluid at right angles to the body over which most of the shearing takes place and is referred to as boundary layer thickness or depth of penetration.

$\omega_o = 2\pi/T_o$ is the circular frequency in vacuum. Introducing furthermore $\phi = \dfrac{u}{r}$ the local angular velocity yields the Navier-Stokes equation in dimensionless form:

$$\frac{\partial \phi}{\partial \tau} = \frac{\partial^2 \phi}{\partial \xi^2} + \frac{3}{\xi} \frac{\partial \phi}{\partial \xi} + \frac{\partial^2 \phi}{\partial \eta^2} \qquad \text{Eq. 10-6}$$

The motion of the body is described by the ordinary differential equation:

$$M_f = I\ddot{\alpha} + I\omega_o^2 \alpha \qquad \text{Eq. 10-7}$$

where I is the moment of inertia of the body and M_f is the moment due to viscous forces depending on the velocity gradient of the solution of the Navier-Stokes equation.

For very slow motion observed at a sufficiently large value of time t, and when the motion can be regarded as isochronous and uniformly damped the principal solution is given in the form:

$$\alpha = A_1 \exp \sigma_1 t + A_2 \exp \sigma_2 t \qquad \text{Eq. 10-8}$$

where A_1 and A_2 are constants and:

$$\sigma_1; \sigma_2 = -\frac{(\Delta \pm i)}{\theta} \qquad \theta = \frac{T}{T_o} \qquad \text{Eq. 10-9}$$

are two complex conjugate roots (with negative real parts) of a transcendental characteristic equation of the type:

$$\sigma^2 + 1 + \sigma^{3/2} F(\rho_i M_k) = 0 \qquad \text{Eq. 10-10}$$

The function $F(\rho_i M_k)$ depends on the geometrical arrangements and contains one or several similarity parameters m_k. These in turn depend on the viscosity μ and on the density ρ of the fluid.

The determination of the precise form of the characteristic equation constitutes the theoretical problem of the measurements with oscillating bodies. The equations are very complex and can be solved only by iteration processes and high speed computers are necessary. This is the reason why this method of measurement only became successful recently.

For measurement it is of advantage to select in accordance with Fig. 10-4 the systems with infinite spacing much less than boundary layer thickness as only the viscosity enters the characteristic equation. For infinite spacing the density also must be known - which in many cases necessitates a separate measurement of this property.

Viscometers using oscillating bodies have been applied very successfully for determination of high pressure data, also for wide ranges of temperature (but this range is limited by the increase of internal damping of the suspension wire with temperature). The apparatus used by Kestin and Leidenfrost is shown in Fig. 10-5. The oscillating system consists of a thin plane parallel and highly polished disk suspended by an elastic wire. A long stem is attached to the bottom of the disk holding a mirror at its lower end. The oscillating system is housed in a high pressure chamber positioning also two stationary plates on either side of the disk. The system is deflected by means of a rod lifted and engaged to the stem and turned with the aid of a magnet. The motion of the system and its decay is observed by optical means through the window in front of the mirror. Kearsley

(24) successfully used a hollow sphere filled with the test fluid and oscillating in a vacuum chamber.

Determination of Thermal Conductivity

In the viscosity case we only have to consider the measurements of fluids. With respect to thermal conductivity all materials are important to heat transfer and the measurement of solids therefore must be included. Thermal conductivity can be measured in any apparatus which supplies the required boundary condition to a particular solution of the Fourier equation of heat conduction, without heat source or sink in cartesian coordinates and for k dependent on location.

$$\rho c \, \frac{dT}{dt} = \frac{\partial}{\partial x} \left(k_x \frac{\partial T}{\partial x}\right) + \frac{\partial}{\partial y} \left(k_y \frac{\partial T}{\partial y}\right) + \frac{\partial}{\partial z} \left(k_z \frac{\partial T}{\partial z}\right) \qquad \text{Eq. 10-11}$$

for an isotropic medium Equation 10-11 simplifies to:

$$\frac{\partial T}{\partial t} = a \, \nabla^2 T \qquad \text{Eq. 10-12}$$

This equation normally is applied to a one dimensional geometry and the thermal diffusivity a can readily be evaluated from the measured temperature distribution T as a function of time t. The thermal conductivity may then be determined with the heat capacity $c\rho$.

In the one dimensional case of steady state and k ≠ f (T) Equation 10-12 becomes:

$$\frac{d^2 T}{dx^2} = 0 \qquad \text{Eq. 10-13}$$

which is identical to:

$$q_k = - kA \, \frac{dT}{dx} \quad \text{for } q_k = \text{constant} \qquad \text{Eq. 10-13a}$$

and the thermal conductivity can be determined directly.

Practically all measurements of the thermal conductivity are based on Equations 11-13a, however, the boundary conditions established in various instruments and the corrections necessary differ from material to material. For this reason it seems to be more convenient to discuss the measurements on fluids and solids separately.

Determination of Thermal Conductivity of Fluids

Steady State Measurements

Fouriers law can be written in a more general form:

$$q_k = k \, B\Delta T \qquad \text{Eq. 10-14}$$

where ΔT is the temperature difference observed under steady heat flow through the layer of test fluid of geometry B.

There are two common types of thermal conductivity cells, firstly linear heat flow instruments and secondly radial heat flow arrangements. The geometric constant for linear heat flow through a parallel layer of test fluid of area A and thickness L is:

$$B = \frac{A}{L}$$

For radial heat flow:

$$B = 2\pi \frac{h}{\ln D/d}$$ infinite long cylindrical annulus of height h and of thickness D - d

$$B = 2\pi \frac{D \cdot d}{D - d}$$ for a spherical arrangement

$$B = 2\pi \left[\frac{h}{\ln D/d} + \frac{D \cdot d}{D - d}\right]$$ for a combined arrangement cylinder capped with hemispherical ends. (diameter ratio chosen such that logarithmic and hyperbolic temperature profiles are practically identical.

The plane horizontal single layer type apparatus has been used by Schmidt (25) Michels and his co-workers (26, 27) Fritz and Poltz (28) and others. The arrangement is shown principally in Fig. 10-6. The instrument consists of an upper heater plate surrounded by a guard and a lower plate acting as a constant temperature heat sink. The material to be tested is between the two plates. The guard heater can be eliminated (27) by using a hot plate sandwiched between two cold plates with the test fluid in between.

The radial heat flow method consists of measuring the heat dissipation from a wire or cylinder surrounded by an annulus of test fluid and an outer tube acting as a heat sink. The so-called hot wire apparatus was popularized by Schleiermacher (29), the arrangement shown in Fig. 10-7. A fine wire generally made of platinum is axially stretched between the ends of a closed cylinder. The wire serves as heater and also as a resistance thermometer. The heat flow is measured as indicated in the figure by measuring the current and the voltage drop along the measuring section of length h. Coaxial cylinder arrangements have been used extensively by Schmidt and Sellschopp (30), Keyes (31), Ziebland (32), Vodar *et al* (33) and Thodos *et al* (34). In most cases guard heaters have been applied in order to assure radial flow only. Figure 10-8 sketches a representative arrangement of this type of apparatus. Riedel (35) used an spherical arrangement. Schmidt and Leidenfrost (36) introduced an instrument, combining cylinder and sphere arrangements, shown in Fig. 10-9.

The various types of apparatus just discussed are in principle of simple construction. Also the formula (eq. 10-14) applied to determine the thermal conductivity from the quantities measured is simple. But the reader should not be misled by these facts as perfect conditions for which Equation 10-14 is valid rarely exist and many corrections must be applied. In accordance with the statement made in the section on general remarks of this paper it is felt of importance to discuss these corrections in detail.

Investigating q_k first we find:

$$q_k = (E \pm \Delta E)(I \pm \Delta I) - q_r - q_c \pm q_L \pm (q_{osc})_h \qquad \text{Eq. 10-15}$$
$$\pm (q_{osc})_c - (q_{inh})_h - (q_{inh})_c - (q_{inh})_{fl} \pm q_{ch.r} \pm \cdots$$

where the electrical power input (E.I) must be corrected for radiation q_r, free convection q_c, lead-in losses q_L, heat flow due to unsteady state conditions q_{osc} and/or inhomogeneities q_{inh} and for the possible chemical reaction $q_{ch.r}$ of the fluid with the wetted walls, respectively.

Most of these corrections are very difficult, and some even impossible, to apply. Therefore in order to achieve reliable measurements, it is important to select a measurement technique for which the smallest number of corrections are necessary

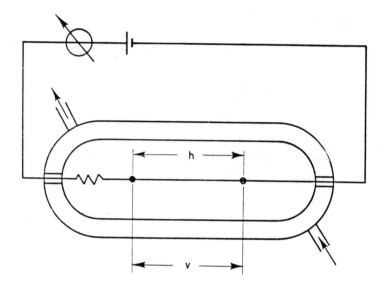

Fig. 10-7   Schleiermacher hot-wire cell

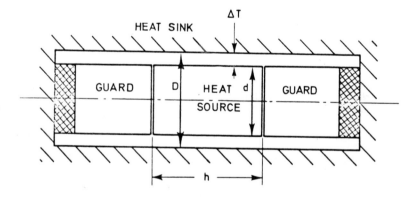

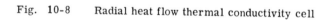

Fig. 10-8   Radial heat flow thermal conductivity cell

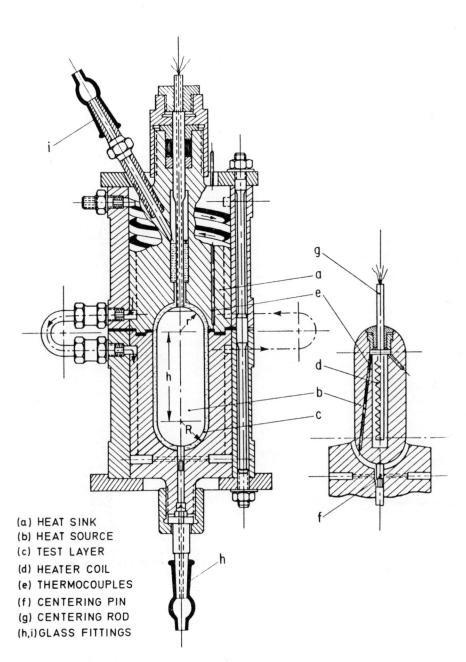

(a) HEAT SINK
(b) HEAT SOURCE
(c) TEST LAYER
(d) HEATER COIL
(e) THERMOCOUPLES
(f) CENTERING PIN
(g) CENTERING ROD
(h,i) GLASS FITTINGS

Fig. 10-9   Thermal conductivity cell

and yet can be properly applied. Corrections for free convection can be avoided by selecting the plane layer type of instrument where the heat is applied from above. Free convection will be presented in all the other cells discussed but can be made negligibly small by providing conditions for which the Ra-number is smaller than its critical value. This can be done in most cases by selecting thin layers of test fluid and by measuring at small ΔT values.

The heat flow due to unsteady state conditions q_{osc} results from temperature fluctuation of the heater or the heat sink and is very difficult to evaluate. The temperature fluctuation in addition influences proper measurements of ΔT. These influences can only be depressed in cells which quickly reach equilibrium, and can .be easily maintained at equilibrium long enough to take the readings. The last two types of instruments mentioned above do not use guard heaters and therefore measuring conditions are more quickly established. But these instruments with the inner body as heater elements require some kind of centering devices, which normally are also used to enclose wires to the electrical heater coil and tempera-ture sensing elements. Thus a path for heat flow is introduced from the hot to the cold body. This type of heat flow, the so called "lead-in loss" is also present in most other instruments, even those with guard heaters, since the temperature of the guard and the heater are not necessarily identical at every location. Lead-in losses can be made zero as proved by Leidenfrost (37) for ideal conditions and can be evaluated for real cases to a high degree of certainty according to Leidenfrost and Tree (38).

Another error influencing the measurements is due to inhomogeneities in the temp-erature field. This field can be disturbed for geometrical reason whenever the geometry of the arrangement deviates from the one described by Equation 10-14 (i.e., misalignment, eccentricity, surface roughness-disturbances at the location where guards join the heater and/or sink and others). All these influences can be properly evaluated as will be demonstrated below.

Disturbances of the temperature field caused by deviation of the surfaces of heater and sink from isothermal conditions cannot be evaluated and every effort must be spent to minimize those effects - also for the reason that they influence the geo-metric constant, B. Deviation from isothermal conditions result from uneven heating or cooling of the heater and/or the sink and from disturbances of the temp-erature field within those bodies caused by temperature sensing elements placed within the walls. Disturbances also might be introduced by uneven heat flow due to radiant heat transfer between surfaces of ununiform optical properties.

The geometric constant B cannot be determined with sufficient accuracy by length measurements alone, but it can be determined easily and accurately by measuring the capacitance of the arrangement (37). This measurement will also account for eccentricity and other inhomogeneities caused by deviation from proper geometry. The geometric constant should be measured electrically for all ranges of temper-ature and, if possible, pressure in order to evaluate the change in geometry and of B with temperature and pressure.

The surface temperature of the walls wetted by the test fluid cannot be measured directly, but must be extrapolated from the temperature drop in the wall that is obtained from sensing elements located in the wall itself. This extrapolation is very difficult to achieve, since the sensing element disturbs the temperature field in the respective bodies as already stated above and discussed by Leidenfrost (39). The more difficult task however is the evaluation of the temperature field and the resulting inhomogeneities and their influence on the geometric constant and the heat flux. Chemical reaction of the test fluid with the walls of the instrument will result a, in a change of the test substance, b in a change of optical properties of walls and c, possibly in the steady or unsteady generation of heat. Since these influences are practically impossible to evaluate the only way to overcome them is to avoid chemical reaction by using contamination free materials in the construction of the instrument.

Assuming that all the corrections discussed so far can be properly applied or can be minimized to a large degree by choosing the most feasible arrangement for the measurement, there are still great difficulties which must be overcome.

The necessity to measure small temperature differences represents by itself quite a task which normally can only be achieved by using most reliable sensing elements. Pt-resistance thermometers and selected thermocouples calibrated within the instrument must be used together with sensitive instrumentation shielded and guarded properly. Radiant heat exchange in addition must be accounted for in all cases of non-opaque test fluids. The most simple case of perfectly transparent media cannot be tested easily, because measurements even under a perfect vacuum will not only yield the radiant heat transfer but also the lead-in losses. Those are a function of apparent thermal conductivity and cannot be subtracted to evaluate the radiant heat exchange.

The situation becomes even more complex in case of test substances able to absorb and emit radiation. The theory for simultaneous radiation and conduction was established by Viskanta and Grosh (40) and applied for correction of thermal conductivity measurements by Leidenfrost (37), and later by Poltz (41) and Kohler (42). Those calculations were based on the gray gas assumption. Furthermore the temperature distribution within the test fluid was assumed to be linear, due only to conduction and not influenced by radiation. Only recently Leidenfrost (43) expanded the evaluation for non-gray conditions and for the true temperature distribution.

In order to correct the thermal conductivity measurements for radiation losses the conservation of energy equation must be solved. However in the case of simultaneous radiation and conduction the energy transfer is governed by a complicated non-linear integro-differential equation. Since the radiation energy flux depends on the test cell configuration the problem was simplified by assuming that the heat transfer takes place between two infinitely large parallel plates. This assumption is permissible for radial heat flow arrangements when the diameter to width ratio of the test layer is large. In order to make the problem soluble additional assumptions were necessary. The walls of the test cell are assumed to be isothermal diffuse absorbers and emitters of thermal radiation, and to have constant radiation properties, except for their variation with wavelength.

Under the two given assumptions the steady-state conservation of energy equation reduces to:

$$\frac{d}{dx} \left(-k \frac{dT}{dx} + q_r \right) = 0 \qquad\qquad \text{Eq. 10-16}$$

clearly the total heat transfer is constant composed only of radiative and conductive contributions.

The computation of the problem is quite involved and can be carried out only with high speed computers. The results proved that radiant heat transfer in an absorbing and emitting gas can influence the accuracy of thermal conductivity measurements by a larger percentage than is normally claimed for thermal conductivity determinations. The percentage increases with temperature and emissivity of the walls. For example, in the case of steam as a test substance, the error due to radiant heat transfer will be of the order of 35% at critical point conditions and black walls. Evaluating radiant heat transfer by approximate methods can yield results still in error by a considerable amount. However, in many instances the correction cannot be performed due to lack of knowledge of the optical properties of the test fluids. Therefore it is of importance to minimize the radiant heat exchange by providing instrument walls with lowest possible emissivity.

The use of fine wires (hot-wire method) and the thin films of test fluid necessary to depress free convection leads to a further complication and deviation from Equation 10-14.

Whenever the measuring conditions are such that the mean free path of the conducting molecules in the fluid becomes comparable with the size of wire or the gap width between heater and sink there is a temperature discontinuity at the surfaces. This is caused by the imperfect interchange of energy between the fluid molecules and the solid surfaces. In case of viscosity we had to apply under similar conditions a slip correction, which accounted for a velocity of the gas at the surface deviating from zero. In case of thermal conductivity there is a 'temperature jump' at the wall. This jump is proportional to the pressure and is a function of the accomodation coefficient, which in turn is dependent on the materials involved. Dickens (44), among others discussed this influence.

The steady state methods discussed so far will produce under normal conditions, accurate data whenever the corrections shown can be applied properly or are not necessary. In most instances lead-in losses, free convection and radiation must be considered, which quite often is very difficult or even impossible. The errors listed will influence all measurements of thermal conductivity and partly also specific heat determination, and are by no means restricted to steady state measurements. Some of the errors might become negligibly small in other measurement techniques but then other influences must be accounted for e.g., in unsteady measurements the observation of time and sometimes location while temperature changes are critical.

Unsteady state devices normally operate so fast that free convective motion has no chance to develop. Furthermore radiant heat transfer seems to be only of very small influence and so is the lead-in loss.

Unsteady Heat Flow Methods

Stalhane and Pyk (45) used a thin straight wire acting as a heat line source surrounded by the infinite homogeneous fluid to be measured. They used this arrangement to determine the thermal conductivity of liquids and also of granular materials. It is also often used for measurements on soil or other materials where steady state instruments fail due to possible moisture change during the long time necessary to establish equilibrium conditions.

The constant rate of heat production in the wire will cause a cylindrical temperature field in the fluid. The rise of temperature in the field dependent upon the thermal properties of the fluid will be an indication of the thermal conductivity. Van der Held and Van Druven (46) showed that the temperature T_1 at time t_1 and temperature T_2 at time t_2 are related as shown below:

$$T_2 - T_1 = \frac{q}{4\pi k} \ln \frac{t_2}{t_1}$$ Eq. 10-17

The equation is valid after a short initial time depending on the size of wire and the properties of the fluid. For a platinum wire of 10 - 30μ diameter the initial time is of 0.1 sec. If the relation between the heat capacity of wire and surrounding liquid is favorable then the initial time may even be shorter than one millisec. Grassmann, Straumann, Widmer and Jobst (47) modified the arrangement in order to overcome the painstaking conversion to a logarithmic time scale by recording the increase of the temperature of the wire immediately as a function of the logarithm of time. This was done by using the increase of the temperature of a second wire immersed in a reference liquid with known thermal conductivity as a logarithmic scale. Both line source wires are branches of two Wheatstone bridges and the resulting voltages are recorded on the axes of a X-Y recorder. The recorder will write a straight line after the initial time has elapsed. The slope of this line will be inversely proportional to the thermal conductivity of the liquid to be measured. Deviation of the recorded curve from a straight line indicates the beginning of free convection. This was observed to start at a Ra-number of 1800. The instrument so modified is a relative one but still produces data of high precision. If the time interval of one measurement is shorter than 10 sec the temperature field is not influenced by the walls of the containing vessel if the distance from the wire is larger than 10 mm. (47).

The application of the line method for measurement of gases was not regarded favorably as the heat capacity of the gas is small compared to that of the wire, increasing therefore the initial time so that free convection might set in too soon. The difficulties were overcome by Briggs, Goldstein and Ibele (48). For conducting liquids the method is not directly applicable and provisions must be made to insulate the wire, which introduces some of the errors discussed for steady state methods. Allen (49) evaluated sources of errors due to finite mass of the line source, temperature variation along the wire, radiation and free convection and also due to deviation from constant power dissipation in the wire.

Cyclic heat flow for measurements of thermal conductivity of fluids also has been used. The penetration of surface temperature fluctuation from a plane slab into the sample can be evaluated by solving the general conduction equation which for this case has the form:

$$\frac{\partial \theta}{\partial t} = a \frac{\partial^2 \theta}{\partial x^2} \qquad \text{Eq. 10-18}$$

where θ is the deviation from the mean temperature at any point at any time. x is the distance measured normal to the surface of the slab.

The penetration of the surface temperature fluctuation into the fluid is given by the well known solution of Equation 10-18:

$$\theta_{(x,t)} = \theta_o \, e^{-x\sqrt{\frac{\omega}{2a}}} \cos\left[\omega t - x\sqrt{\frac{\omega}{2a}}\right] \qquad \text{Eq. 10-19}$$

where ω is the angular velocity and θ_o the amplitude of the signal at $x = 0$. Another relationship for computing thermal diffusivity may be obtained by comparing the amplitude of temperature fluctuation θ_x of the response at distance x with θ_o

$$\frac{\theta_x}{\theta_o} = e^{-x\sqrt{\frac{\omega}{2a}}} \qquad \text{Eq. 10-20}$$

Harrison, Boteler and Spurlock (50) used this method in a cylindrical arrangement.

A new method based upon gas diffusion techniques by Walker and Westenburg (51) has been extended to thermal conductivity measurements by Westenburg *et al* (52). A line source of heat is stretched across a uniform laminar gas flow. The thermal conductivity can be calculated from the peak temperature rise at some known distance downstream and the known input heat rate to the wire. The temperature rise at any point downstream from an infinite source can be expressed by:

$$\Delta T = [q/(4u\,c_p\rho\pi\,kr)^{1/2}]\, e^{[uc_p\rho(x-r)/2k]} \qquad \text{Eq. 10-21}$$

where c_p is the specific heat, ρ the density, q the heat flow, u the velocity of the gas and r the distance from the source and x the distance parallel to flow direction.

Other Methods of Measuring Thermal Conductivity of Fluids

Sengers (53) in a recent article discussed the transport properties of compressed gases pointing out that measurements of thermal conductivity are practically impossible to achieve under critical conditions. At those conditions the Gr-number and therefore the Ra-number become very large and the heat transport is governed by free convection. Under equilibrium conditions $\Delta T = 0$ and Ra has no influence. Measurements under those conditions seem to be possible by optical means.

Sogin and Thompson (54) developed an apparatus to measure transport properties of gases by means of Rayleigh-Jeffereys instability, i.e., by means of free convection. Their system is a linear heat flow cell using a horizontal layer but heated from below. They measure the heat flow under increasing pressure. For all values of Ra $< \mathrm{Ra_{cr}}$ this heat flow will remain constant. When increasing pressure causes Ra $> \mathrm{Ra_{cr}}$ then free convection will suddenly increase the heat flow.

For a single component or a mixture of ideal gases Ra is given as:

$$\mathrm{Ra} = \frac{gL^3 \Delta T c_p p^2}{\mu k\, R^2\, T_m^{\,3}} \qquad\qquad \text{Eq. 10-22}$$

where p $\quad$ = pressure

$\quad$ R $\quad$ = individual gas constant

$\quad$ T_m = mean temperature

The critical value of Ra has been established by many investigators and is known for the parallel layer arrangement with a high degree of certainty. Therefore, when the measurements under increasing pressure cause a sudden increase in heat flux, $\mathrm{Ra_{cr}}$ has been reached and the above relationship, Equation 10-22, can be solved for viscosity or thermal conductivity when all the other quantities are known.

Since viscosity and thermal conductivity of gases are pressure independent to a certain degree and over small ranges, the change of pressure during the measurements has no influence on the properties. In the liquids case $\mathrm{Ra_{cr}}$ must be established by changing ΔT. This influences the measurements as viscosity and thermal conductivity are temperature dependent. The measurements carried out so far by the investigators cited above indicate usefulness of this technique.

Another indirect determination of thermal conductivity is the measurement of the Prandtl - number, introduced by Eckert and Irvine (55). Normally the viscosity and the specific heat are known to a better accuracy than the thermal conductivity and the Pr number can be measured with high precision. Therefore the evaluation of k from direct measurement of Pr has advantages. The method of measurement involves the relation describing the temperature which a flat plate assumes in a high velocity steady two-dimensional gas flow and when the plate exchanges heat only by convection. This recovery temperature T_r is usually described by a recovery factor r:

$$r = \frac{T_r - T_\infty}{T_{ad} - T_\infty} \qquad\qquad \text{Eq. 10-23}$$

where T_{ad} is the stagnation or total temperature, T_∞ the static temperature of the flow.

Busemann proved that for certain ranges of Pr:

$$r = \sqrt{Pr} \qquad\qquad \text{Eq. 10-24}$$

Thus Pr can be measured by temperature measurements and the method has been used successfully since it was established. Smiley (56) and Lauver (57) describe a shock tube technique and Corney, Carnevale and Marshall (58) an ultrasonic method. Both apparatuses are useful especially for high temperature work.

Measurement of the Thermal Conductivity of Solids

The thermal conductivity of solids varies from values as low as those known for gases to values several orders of magnitude higher. The high values of thermal conductivity are observed for metals, especially in metals of high electrical conductivity. This fact makes it understandable that quite different approaches must be used to measure each of these materials and for this reason we shall discuss low conducting and high conducting solids separately.

Steady State Measurements of Thermal Conductivity of Low Conducting Solids

Equation 10-14 is principally applied in linear or radial heat flow devices. For linear heat flow, apparatuses like the one shown in Fig. 10-6 are used or also similar instruments, with single, or multi-layer test substances. The layers can be much thicker because free convection is of no concern. In case of gases and liquids thermal contact with the surfaces of heat source and sink is always achieved and therefore the temperature difference across the test layer is that between surfaces of heater and sink measured by sensing elements placed in the good conducting walls of these bodies.

For low conducting media where contact resistance is of less concern the same measuring techniques for ΔT can be applied. For somewhat better conducting insulators it becomes more important to achieve good contact between the sample and the metallic surfaces of the instrument. This can be done in many instances by means of unevaporating liquids and it might also be necessary to locate the temperature sensing elements inside the sample. But the good contact with the heater or sink still must be assured - otherwise the temperature field is disturbed and Equation 10-14 cannot be applied.

Uniform and low contact resistance normally becomes increasingly difficult to achieve with increasing temperature and for better conducting materials. In those cases it is of advantage to provide poor but uniform contact by means of insulating layers sandwiched between heat source and sink and the test sample. For measurements at high temperatures the insulation can be represented by an air space. This avoids or reduces problems of thermal contact even when the specimen is warped or disturbed by expansion resulting from the temperature gradient established in it during the measurements - or when the surfaces cannot initially be made plane.

An instrument of this kind was originally devised by Dickinson for measurements of standards and has been described in detail by Flynn and Didion (59). The instrument is shown schematically in Fig. 10-10. The apparatus consists of a high temperature furnace, the disk shaped specimen and a steam calorimeter used to measure the heat flow through the sample. The specimen is supported slightly above a circular silicon carbide plate heated by the furnace. The sample receives heat by radiation and conduction through the air gap and looses heat from its upper surface again by radiation and conduction across an air space to the calorimeter. The heat flux through the specimen is determined by the steam calorimeter. This consists of a central metering chamber which is surrounded by a guard chamber operating at the same temperature which prevents edge effects. Boiling water or any other suitable fluid has some advantages over circulating liquid calorimeters with regard to temperature stability and unformity. The temperature drop through

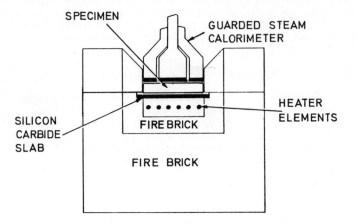

Fig. 10-10   NBS steam calorimeter apparatus for measuring thermal conductivity

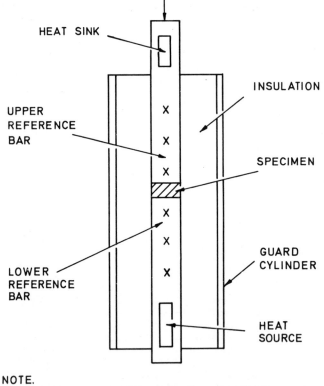

NOTE.

X DENOTES A THERMOCOUPLE POSITION

Fig. 10-11   A schematic cut - bar apparatus

the specimen is measured by means of thermocouples imbedded in its surfaces. This will not cause considerable disturbances of the heat flow pattern since the sample size in this apparatus can be rather large.

Some materials are available only in small samples because of the difficulties of obtaining them with adequate uniformity. In small volume specimens even a small thermocouple may introduce some disturbance and for this reason some investigators prefer to deduce the temperature at the contact surfaces of a specimen by extrapolating temperatures observed in the contacting body. If this is done the difficult problem of the thermal resistance at the contacting interface is encountered.

A so-called cut-bar apparatus for measurements of small specimens is shown in Fig. 10-11 which represents a NBS standard instrument (60). The longitudinal heat flow through the sample is determined from the temperature gradient observed in the reference bars shown in the figure, or it can be measured directly by means of a properly guarded heater located close to the specimen. Radial heat losses are depressed or minimized by guard cylinders surrounding the insulated reference bars and the sample, heated to an identical axial temperature distribution.

Radial heat flow instruments are in most cases of a cylindrical arrangement and spherical only for poor conducting materials (fibers, powders or granulars). A spherical apparatus was described by Black and Glaser (61) and is shown in Fig. 10-12. The instrument consists of an inner sphere and an outer sphere kept at a uniform temperature by means of electrical heaters - or circulating or boiling liquids. The test material is placed between the spheres. The heat flowing through the samples can either be generated electrically in the inner sphere or, as shown in Fig. 10-12, come from the outer sphere and boil off the liquid contained in the inner sphere. The boil-off rate is an indicator of heat flow and is used to calculate the thermal conductivity. One advantage of this type of apparatus is the simplicity of construction. Also, the sample is completely enclosed and can be kept at a constant condition (i.e., moisture free). However, it has the disadvantage that the test material can be filled into the gap only with a certain more or less accidental density and in addition, the heat leak along the neck cannot be easily estimated. Cylindrical arrangements use the test material in the form of long cylinders with small inner bores heated either from the inside or the outside. In the latter case the heat flow is normally measured calorimetrically, by observing the change of temperature of a fluid flowing through the inner bore or by measuring the evaporation rate of a liquid at rest.

Axial heat flow in a solid cylinder cannot be avoided completely and it might be of advantage to introduce axial flow resistance by using rings stacked axially on top of each other. The rings close to the ends of the axial arrangement act as guard to the rings located in the central part. The heat flow generated in this section is measured by observing the voltage drop as indicated in the schematic of Fig. 10-13.

The radial temperature difference is measured by thermocouples (or optically at higher temperature) located in the holes drilled axially at different radii. It is recommended that one of the holes penetrates all the disks so that the longitudinal temperature distribution can be measured.

The size of the holes must be small in order to minimize the disturbance of the temperature field.

Unsteady State Measurements of Thermal Conductivity of Low Conducting Solids

Cyclic heat flow measurements discussed for liquids are also used for solids and the same holds true for the line source arrangement. A typical instrument of the latter kind is shown in Fig. 10-14. Probes are extensively used for porous media

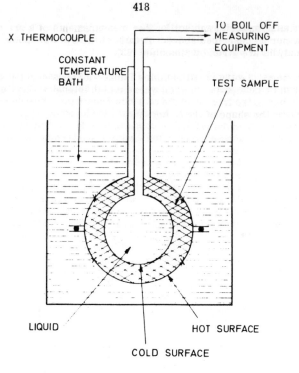

X THERMOCOUPLE

CONSTANT
TEMPERATURE
BATH

TO BOIL OFF
MEASURING
EQUIPMENT

TEST SAMPLE

LIQUID

HOT SURFACE

COLD SURFACE

Fig. 10-12   Thermal conductivity cell with spherical test chamber

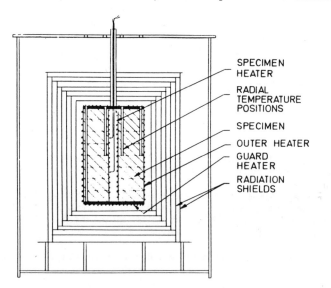

SPECIMEN
HEATER

RADIAL
TEMPERATURE
POSITIONS

SPECIMEN

OUTER HEATER

GUARD
HEATER

RADIATION
SHIELDS

Fig. 10-13   Thermal conductivity cell with disk shaped sample (powder, granular material and soil). The measurements of k are carried out in the same manner as described above. Details of the system shown in Fig. 10-14 and error analysis are given by Messmer (62).

For measurements of very small samples Parker (63) has developed an unsteady (so called flash or heat pulse) method where a high intensity short duration energy pulse is absorbed in the front surface of a thin specimen. The thermal diffusivity is determined by the shape of the temperature versus time curve at the rear surface. Parker solved the general conduction Equation (10-12) which yields, under the assumption of temperature independent properties, the temperature history of the rear surface:

$$\frac{T(L,t)}{T_m} = 1 + 2 \sum_{n=1}^{\infty} (-1)^n \exp(-n^2 \pi^2 at/L^2) \qquad \text{Eq. 10-25}$$

when:

$$T(L,t) = 0.5\, T_m \qquad t = t_{1/2}$$

the simple relationship for the diffusivity results:

$$a = \frac{1.37\, L^2}{\pi^2 t_{1/2}} \qquad \text{Eq. 10-26}$$

where L is the thickness of the specimen, $T(L,t)$ the temperature of the rear surface and T_m its maximum value. The upper limit of the front surface temperature T_f was also derived by Parker. The result is:

$$T_f = \frac{38\, L}{a^{1/2}}\, T_m \qquad \text{Eq. 10-27}$$

which for metals amounts to 10-20° C and for ceramics 50-100° C.

Beck (64) has analyzed the method and extended its application to temperature dependent properties. The heat loss from the sample might become quite high at higher temperatures and can be minimized by using two disks with the rear surfaces facing each other. This technique was applied by Kasper and Zehm (65) but using a periodic flux variation. Another way to minimize the heat loss is to measure in a radial arrangement by heating a cylinder from the outside. Such a method was developed by Nakata (64a). The conduction equation in cylindrical coordinates is:

$$\frac{1}{r}\frac{\partial}{\partial r}\left(r\frac{\partial T}{\partial r}\right) + \frac{1}{r^2}\frac{\partial^2 T}{\partial \phi^2} + \frac{\partial^2 T}{\partial z^2} = \frac{1}{a}\frac{\partial T}{\partial t} \qquad \text{Eq. 10-28}$$

If a circular cylinder whose axis coincides with the axis of z is heated and the initial and boundary conditions are independent of the coordinates ϕ and z the temperature will be a function of r and t only. Equation 10-28 reduces then to:

$$\frac{1}{r}\frac{\partial}{\partial r}\left(r\frac{\partial T}{\partial r}\right) = \frac{1}{a}\frac{\partial T}{\partial t} \qquad \text{Eq. 10-29}$$

In this case the heat flow is radial.

For constant heat input to the cylinder surface the temperature as a function of r and t is:

$$T(r,t) = A_1(r^2 + 4at) + A_2 \qquad \text{Eq. 10-30}$$

where A_1 and A_2 are constants. The thermal diffusivity is obtained by measuring the time $\Delta t = t_2 - t_1$ for the temperature at point r_1 to reach that at point r_2.

Equation 10-30 gives:

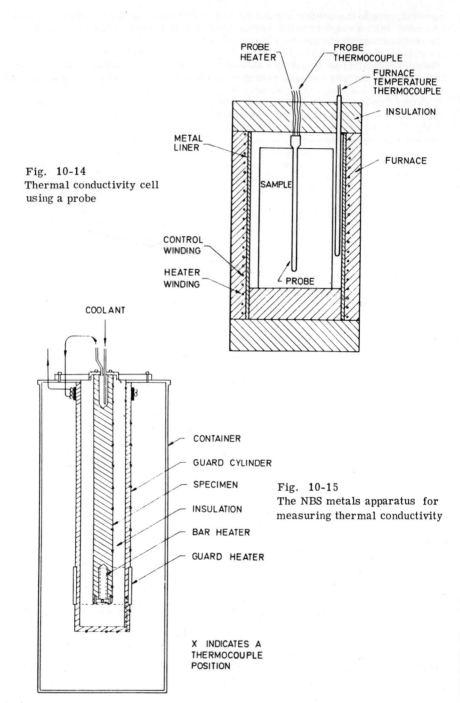

Fig. 10-14
Thermal conductivity cell
using a probe

Fig. 10-15
The NBS metals apparatus for
measuring thermal conductivity

$$a = \frac{r_2{}^2 - r_1{}^2}{4 \Delta t} \qquad \left(\frac{m^2}{s}\right)$$

Eq. 10-31

Many of the instruments and steady and unsteady methods discussed so far for solids can be applied for the determination of the thermal conductivity or diffusivity of metals. For this reason we will discuss here only the arrangements used specifically for metals and/or electrical conductors.

Measurements of Thermal Conductivity of Metallic Solids

The NBS metal apparatus for measuring thermal conductivity is shown in Fig. 10-15. The specimen is supported within an outer container and is drilled at each end. The lower cavity encloses an electrical heater while the upper one is cooled. The guard is cooled in a similar way and heated in order to produce an axial temperature distribution similar to that in the sample. The specimen is rather long and has a rather large temperature difference from end to end. The longitudinal temperature distribution is measured by several thermocouples placed with known distance to each other, therefore enabling the calculation of the thermal conductivity at several temperatures.

The methods discussed so far in most instances applied heat indirectly to the specimens. Metals or other reasonably good electrical conductors can be heated directly by an electrical current. Instruments based on the so called "direct electrical heating method" apply the solution of the general conduction Equation 10-11 expanded by additional terms.

For cylindrical symetrical geometry the equation is:

$$k \left[\frac{\partial^2 T}{\partial x^2} + \frac{\partial^2 T}{\partial r^2} + \frac{1}{r} \frac{\partial T}{\partial r} \right] + \frac{\partial k}{\partial T} \left[\left(\frac{\partial T}{\partial x} \right)^2 + \left(\frac{\partial T}{\partial r} \right)^2 \right]$$

$$+ \lambda \left[\left(\frac{\partial E}{\partial x} \right)^2 + \left(\frac{\partial E}{\partial r} \right)^2 \right] - \mu \frac{I}{A} \frac{\partial T}{\partial x} = c\rho \frac{\partial T}{\partial t} \qquad \text{Eq. 10-32}$$

where λ is the electrical conductivity, E the electrical potential, I the electrical current, A the cross-sectional area of the sample and μ the coefficient of Thompson heat.

The influence of the Thompson heat can be minimized by measuring at small temperature gradients. Using small sizes of the sample allows radial gradients to be neglected and Equation 10-32 becomes for steady state:

$$k \frac{\partial^2 T}{\partial x^2} + \frac{\partial k}{\partial T} \left(\frac{\partial T}{\partial x} \right)^2 + \lambda \left(\frac{\partial E}{\partial x} \right)^2 = 0 \qquad \text{Eq. 10-33}$$

Measuring at small or zero values of $\frac{dT}{dx}$ or assuming $k \neq f(T)$ the second term vanishes and Equation 10-33 becomes:

$$k \frac{\partial^2 T}{\partial x^2} + \lambda \left(\frac{\partial E}{\partial x} \right)^2 = 0 \qquad \text{Eq. 10-34}$$

Kohlrausch (66) applied Equation 10-34 in a simple arrangement where the ends of the cylindrical specimen were kept at some constant temperature and radial heat flow was minimized by insulation. With these provisions a parabolic like axial temperature profile is obtained from which the ratio of thermal and electrical conductivity can be derived. Knowing the electrical conductivity (evaluated by the same measurements) allows one to determine the thermal conductivity.

Neglecting radial heat losses from the sample yields the simple relationship first derived by Kohlrausch:

$$\frac{k}{\lambda} = \frac{1}{2} \frac{(E_1 - E_2)^2}{T_2 - T_1}$$

Eq. 10-35

T_2 is the maximum temperature T_1 a temperature a certain distance away where the electrical potential is E_1. The parabolic temperature profile will be symmetrical when the two ends of the sample are kept at the same temperature.

Bode (67) heated thin wires, the ends of which were kept at the same temperature, and generated within the sample the same amount of heat which was lost radially by radiation to the walls of a thermostated vacuum chamber. The temperature distribution is then uniform along the wire (only small radial temperature distribution) and the assumption made for the Thompson heat in Equation 10-33 is fulfilled. Angel (68) established also a practically uniform temperature distribution at the central region of a very long specimen (kept at lower temperatures at the ends). The thermal conductivity from their measurements can be evaluated from:

$$k = \frac{1}{4\pi} \frac{\Delta E}{L} \frac{I}{\Delta T}$$

Eq. 10-36

where ΔE is the potential drop observed over a length L in the region of uniform temperature distribution and ΔT is the radial temperature difference at the same location.

A similarly simple relationship can be derived for a hollow tube. Samples of this geometry have been used by Powell and Shofield (69) for the measurements of k and λ for carbon and graphite up to 2400° C. Rudkin and Parker (70), Krishnan and Jain (71) and others used more or less similar arrangements in vacuum. A detailed description of all the various instrumental set-ups and the equations derived for the evaluation of the properties would be outside the scope of this paper and the reader is referred to a survey by Powell, Dewitt and Nalbantyan (72). Cezairliyan is conducting unsteady measurements of direct heating by means of capacitance discharge. The work resulted from a study on high speed thermodynamic measurements by Beckett and Cezairliyan (73).

Some Other Methods to Measure Thermal Conductivity of Solids

A very simple instrument able to produce data quickly and cheaply is the thermal comparator by Powell (73) which measures relative thermal conductivity. This method consists in principle of heating two metal spheres of equal size to the same temperature and bringing one sphere into contact with, and the other very close to, a colder specimen. If one assumes that the heat exchange by radiation and gaseous conduction from the two spheres is identical, then the sphere being in contact with the specimen will loose heat in addition by conduction into the specimen across the area of contact. This additional heat flow will result in a more rapid temperature change of this sphere which can be observed by a differential thermocouple placed inside the two spheres.

The radius of the contact with the flat specimen is several orders of magnitude smaller than the sphere and the system can be treated like two semi-infinite large bodies. Under this assumption the system was analyzed by Dahl and Jones (75). The results of the analysis indicated a very short transient period (involving thermal diffusion) but after this transient period the heat flow is by conduction. The instrument therefore virtually is a steady state device. Ginnings (76) analyzed the comparator by including heat transfer by radiation and gaseous conduction from the spheres. This analysis indicated that the sensitivity and accuracy of Powell's comparator are most favorable for measuring materials of moderate conductivity.

Neglecting the transient period the cooling rate observed is related to the thermal conductivities of sample k_2 and sphere k_1 and the heat capacity of the sphere by:

$$\frac{dT}{dt} = \frac{4k_1 k_2 \Delta T_o r_i}{(k_1 + k_2)\rho c_v}$$

Eq. 10-37

where ΔT_o is the excess temperature of the sphere over the sample and r_i is the radius of contact. Observing the cooling rate by measuring samples of different k_2 a calibration curve is established. Powell (77) described in another paper a direct heating form of the thermal comparator. He gives information about material of the probe and minimum size of specimen. The new device records the temperature change at contact location. Kollie and McElroy (78) used the comparator at temperatures up to 400° C and investigated different sphere mountings and tested the reliability of the measured values of thermal conductivity.

Hoch *et al* (79) developed a new method to determine thermal conductivity at high temperatures. A metal cylinder one to two cm in diameter and of approximately same height is heated in a high vacuum by means of high frequency induction to 1000 to 3000° C. At a high current frequency the heating is localized in the skin of the cylindrical surface of the specimen. (Non-metallic samples can be heated by the same means when surrounded by a metal foil). If the heat is uniformly generated in cylindrical surface it will be isothermal. The heat flows into the interior by conduction and is dissipated from the circular end-faces of the specimen by radiation. Under steady state conditions the heat conducted to any point on the end surface must equal the heat radiated from that point.

The describing equation was solved by Hoch and co-workers and the thermal conductivity can be obtained from the relationship (valid for $L/D = 0.18$):

$$k = \frac{\epsilon \sigma T^4}{4 \frac{dT}{dr}} \cdot L$$

Eq. 10-38

where T is the temperature in the center of the circular end face $\frac{dT}{dr}$ the temperature gradient at the center, 'D' the diameter of the specimen, L its half height, σ the Stefan Boltzmann constant and ϵ the emissivity.

Measurements of Specific Heats

Specific heat enters heat transfer processes directly due to enthalpy or internal energy changes of the materials involved and indirectly by means of the thermal diffusivity in all unsteady cases.

The methods described for thermal conductivity and diffusivity in the previous sections of this paper obviously can be applied also for the measurements of specific heat when in addition the density of the material is known. The discussion of the measurements of specific heats will refer in some cases to methods already discussed.

By definition the specific heat is given by:

$$c = \frac{1}{m} \frac{dQ}{dT}$$

Eq. 10-39

and in principle can be evaluated by measuring the heat (dQ) needed to increase the temperature by dT in a mass m of the specimen.

Since the specific heat is temperature dependent the observation must be carried out with small changes of T otherwise the so-called mean specific heat c_m is measured:

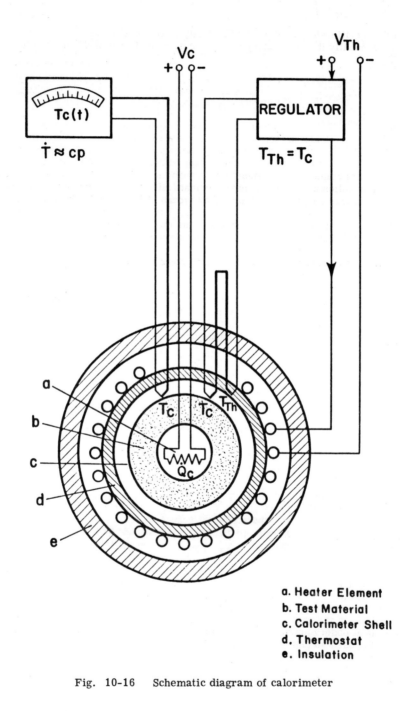

a. Heater Element
b. Test Material
c. Calorimeter Shell
d. Thermostat
e. Insulation

Fig. 10-16   Schematic diagram of calorimeter

$$c_m = \frac{1}{T_1 - T_2} \int_{T_1}^{T_2} c\,dT \qquad\qquad \text{Eq. 10-40}$$

From this relationship c can be obtained only when its temperature dependence is known. Normally it is necessary to observe c_m many times at different values of $T_1 - T_2$.

The change of temperature in the material normally causes a change in volume - this needs additional energy to overcome the intermolecular forces. Measurements under constant pressure therefore will yield a higher value than measurements under constant volume:

$$c_p = c_v + \alpha^2\, \frac{T}{\rho\kappa} \qquad\qquad \text{Eq. 10-41}$$

where α is the volumetric expansion coefficient, ρ the density and κ the compressibility. For solids and liquids, measurements normally are carried out under constant pressure and c_v is determined by means of Equation 10-41.

Equation 10-41 also is used for measurements of gases - those in addition can be determined indirectly by means of thermodynamic relationships or experimentally.

Measurements of the Specific Heat of Solids and Liquids

The methods applied differ from each other mainly by different means of measuring the heat causing the temperature change in the specimen of known mass. The sample might be heated directly electrically (in a few cases by a chemical reaction) or indirectly, by observing the effect on a calorimeter body when brought in heat exchange with the sample. The direct heating methods have been used in many varieties and are most common for adiabatic calorimeters. The adiabatic calorimeter consists of a container with the sample or the sample itself heated by an internal heater and surrounded by a shield heated to the same temperature as the calorimeter. Moser (80) heated the shield to undergo a small linear temperature change and heated the calorimeter to follow the temperature of the shield. Schmidt and Leidenfrost (81), West and Ginnings (82) Stansbury *et al* (83) and others heat the sample and force the shield to follow the temperature change - this approach is simpler in respect to determine the heat generated in the sample.

The instrument developed by Schmidt and Leidenfrost is shown in Fig. 10-16. A small heater sphere is surrounded by the test substance (liquids or solid granulate) in a wide spherical annulus. The outside of the calorimeter is surrounded by a spherical shield which in turn is insulated by radiation shields in a vacuum. These investigators solved the temperature distribution in the test sample undergoing a linear temperature change. They proved that after a certain initial time has elapsed the temperature within the sample will increase at the same rate everywhere. Under those conditions the recorded temperature change with time in the sample is directly proportional to the specific heat:

$$c = \frac{1}{m}\left(\frac{q}{\dot{T}} - w_c\right) \qquad\qquad \text{Eq. 10-42}$$

where $\dot{T}$ is the temperature change with time, q the constant heat input and w_c the heat capacity of the calorimeter body (heater sphere, outer shell and wires). The specific heat observed will be of high accuracy whenever the rate of temperature change is chosen so that the temperature difference within the sample is small enough for the assumption of c = constant, but high enough to detect the temperature change accurately. The spherical arrangement has some advantages for reasons of eliminating end losses which are encountered in cylindrical arrangements and

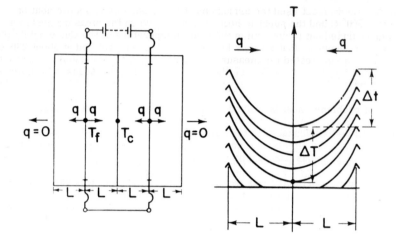

Fig. 10-17   Krischer's instrument for measurements of k and c

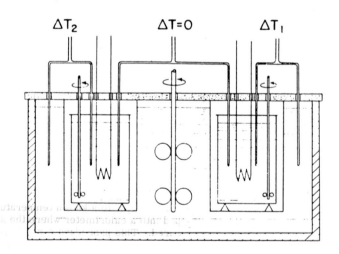

Fig. 10-18   Differential calorimeter

providing for the maximum volume to surface ratio. The latter minimized the potential heat transfer surface relative to the heat supplied to the specimen.

Schmidt and Leidenfrost used the arrangement to measure the specific heat of nickel up to 500° C and the specific heat of liquids. When the measurements on nickel were carried out to determine the exact temperature of the Curie point, the system was so sensitive that another kind of transition was noticed at about 230°C. The system was also tested for measuring simultaneously the thermal conductivity of poor conducting fluids by following the transient technique discussed in the previous sections.

A number of problems must be solved in order to attain precision in adiabatic calorimetry. First, it is difficult to achieve complete adiabacy. Resulting from this there will be heat leakages to the surrounding shield. Lead-in losses also are present and so are the effects of nonuniformity and several other influences already discussed in the previous part and by West (84).

A quasi-adiabatic calorimeter was developed by Krischer (85) especially for the measurements of specific heat of poor conducting solids and for samples of high moisture content. Equally thick layers of the sample are sandwiched together with a foil type heater in between as shown on the left side of Fig. 10-17. If the samples are large enough and unwanted effects are avoided, the uniformly generated heat will cause, after a initial period of time, a quasi-stationary condition within the sample. The conditions are described by equidistant parabolic isotherms shown in the right hand side of the figure. The temperature of the heating foil T_f is measured and that of a center location T_c. Observing the time period Δt necessary for T_c to reach T_f allows one to evaluate the specific heat from equation:

$$c = \frac{q}{\rho L} \frac{\Delta t}{T_f - T_c} \qquad\qquad \text{Eq. 10-43}$$

where L is half thickness of the layer. The equation is valid because every point of the sample undergoes the same temperature change during the time Δt. The arrangement obviously can also be used for thermal conductivity.

Adiabatic calorimeters can produce specific heat data with an accuracy which equals in certain ranges that of the drop-type calorimeter. In other ranges they have in addition the advantage that the specific heat can be evaluated at any temperature covered in one run and that measurements will detect influences of transitions or other changes which might occur within the sample during the test. In the drop-type calorimeter many drops must be performed in order to establish the specific heat values at regions of transition - or the transition might be similarly frozen during the rapid cooling process in the calorimeter.

The drop-type calorimeter technique heats a sample to a known temperature, usually in a furnace, which is then dropped into a calorimeter where the sample cools rapidly and heat it evolves is measured. This procedure essentially measures the enthalpy of the sample at the higher temperature relative to that at the lower temperature. The heat exchanged from the sample to the calorimeter can be measured by observing the temperature change in a liquid or a solid calorimeter body or by determining isothermally the amount of ice melted, or of liquid evaporated or condensed. Of very high precision is the so called "ice calorimeter" a very simple, very accurate, best tested and most commonly applied device.

The calorimeter consists of a inner tube open at the upper end to receive the sample but closed at the bottom. The tube is completely surrounded by a wider vessel. The space between the tube and the vessel is filled with pure, air-free water and some pure mercury at the bottom. Some of the water is frozen. There is only one opening to the outside, by a mercury filled tube connecting the pool of

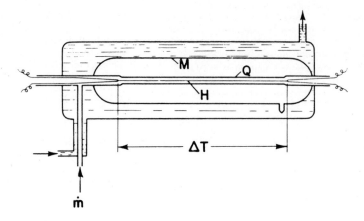

Fig. 10-19   Callandar and Barnes calorimeter

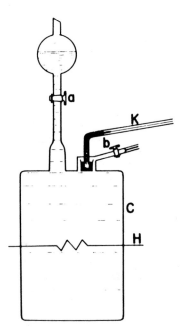

Fig. 10-20   Schlesinger calorimeter

pure mercury to the outside. The heat evolved by the sample when it cools to the ice point melts a corresponding amount of ice which is very precisely measured by the mass of mercury drawn in (from a weighed outside supply) to compensate for the volume shrinkage. A bath of ice water serves as a heat shield making the heat losses of the calorimeter very small and highly constant. A detailed description of the operation and performance of drop-type calorimeter was given by Douglas (86).

Taylor (87) determined specific heat by a pulse-heating method. The small sample in the form of a wire is heated rapidly by the passage of large currents of the order of several thousand amperes and causing heating rates of 10^3 to 10^5 degrees per second. Taylor lists as advantages: heat losses small, no furnace required, chemical interaction and preferential vaporization of specimen is limited, the upper temperature limit is the melting point. The disadvantages are that the sample must be an electrical conductor and the difficulties of measuring the temperature. (Cezairliyan, cited previously, uses tubes and measures temperature by optical and fast recording devices - it appears that he did overcome those difficulties). In Taylor's experiment a dual oscilloscope was used to measure voltage and current simultaneously as a function of time and at discrete time intervals. The specific resistance at each time interval is calculated from the relationship:

$$\rho = \frac{A}{L} \frac{E}{I} \qquad \text{Eq. 10-44}$$

where A is the cross sectional area of the wire, L the distance between voltage probes and E and I the voltage and current respectively.

The specific resistance as a function of time is then determined. The specific heat at any temperature is given by the expression:

$$c_p = \frac{E \cdot I}{m} \frac{\frac{d\rho}{dT}}{\frac{d\rho}{dt}} \qquad \text{Eq. 10-45}$$

where m is the mass of the sample between the voltage probes and $E \cdot I$ the power dissipated in that region. $d\rho/dT$ is the temperature coefficient of the resistance at T and $d\rho/dt$ the time rate of change of the resistivity at T. The accuracy of the specific heat data measured by that method agreed well with those observed in drop-type calorimeters operating with samples heated to the same temperature. The adiabatic and drop-type calorimeter can also be used for liquids by providing suitable containers.

Some other measurement techniques for liquids are shown in the following figures. Figure 10-18 represents a differential calorimeter. One of the calorimeter containers is filled with the test sample the other with a liquid of known specific heat. The specific heat is evaluated from measuring the heat necessary to produce in each calorimeter the same temperature increase, from the masses contained in the calorimeters and the known specific heat. Due to the symmetry of the arrangement it is not necessary to evaluate the heat capacities of the container itself and the heat losses.

Specific heat of liquids quite often is measured by determining the temperature change in a liquid flowing through an insulated tube under constant heat input. A calorimeter of this type is shown in Fig. 10-19 representing a device originally used by Callendar and Barnes (88). H represents the heater wire (normally made of platinum) placed in the center of tube Q which is insulated by a vacuum chamber, M, kept at a constant temperature by a circulating thermostat fluid. The temperature change is measured by two thermocouples or resistance thermometers located at proper places close to the ends of the tube. The heat losses, q_L, in the system can be determined by varying the mass flow rate and heat input under constant ΔT:

$$c = \frac{1}{m}\left(\frac{q}{\Delta T} - q_L\right)$$

Eq. 10-46

Flow calorimeters have been used with success at high pressures and temperatures and also for gases.

Another calorimeter system of interest for reasons of its simplicity and accuracy is that of Schlesinger (89) shown in Fig. 10-20. The calorimeter, C, is filled completely with the test fluid by means of valves (a) and (b) and placed in a thermostat. When equilibrium is established valve (b) is closed and some mercury is forced to enter the capillary (k) by slight increase in pressure through (a) which then is also closed. The liquid is heated (H) by a small amount and for a short time (ΔQ). If the thermal expansion and specific heat can be assumed constant the displacement of the mercury in the capillary immediately will yield the change of volume even when the liquid is heated only in the neighborhood of the heater (H). The liquid next to the walls of (C) remains practically at the temperature of the surroundings and no heat losses are encountered. The specific heat therefore is determined not only quickly but also very accurately.

$$c_p = \frac{\Delta Q}{\Delta V}\,\Delta v$$

Eq. 10-47

where ΔV is the volume change and Δv the specific volume change of one unit of mass of liquid under a temperature change of one degree.

Measurements of the Specific Heat of Gases

The flow type and the mixing calorimeters can be used for gases as well as heating a gas enclosed in a large vessel by an electrical heater of large surface area. The specific heat of gases furthermore can be determined by means of techniques to observe heating values of gas reaction (i.e., $H_2 + \frac{1}{2}O_2$) but adding the gas of unknown specific heat. Measurements also can be carried out by the differential method and many others.

Of more interest are the indirect methods. The adiabatic change of a gas from a state v_o, p_o, T_o to another state v_1, p_1, T_1, is given by the thermodynamic relationship for ideal gases:

$$\frac{p_1}{(p_o)} = \left(\frac{T_1}{T_o}\right)^{\kappa/\kappa-1} \qquad \frac{p_1}{(p_o)} = \left(\frac{v_o}{v_1}\right)^{\kappa}$$

Eq. 10-48

and for real gases:

$$\left(\frac{\partial T}{\partial p}\right)_s = \left(\frac{\partial T}{\partial p}\right)_v{}^{\kappa-1/\kappa}$$

Eq. 10-49

The measurements of two of the related quotients yield $\kappa = c_p/c_v$ and with the molar heats:

$$C_{p_o} - C_{v_o} = R$$

Eq. 10-50

c_p and c_v can be evaluated for ideal gases.

For real gases Equation 10-50 is not valid and an equation of state must be introduced making Equation 10-49 quite complex. However the difficulties can be overcome by special differentiating techniques (90) and with the aid of high speed computers.

κ furthermore can be computed from the velocity of sound. The following process under constant enthalpy yields the Joule-Thompson coefficient

$$\mu = \left(\frac{\partial T}{\partial p}\right)_h = \frac{T\left(\frac{\partial v}{\partial p}\right)_p - v}{c_p} \qquad \text{Eq. 10-51}$$

and c_p can be calculated when $T\left(\frac{\partial v}{\partial p}\right)_p - v$ can be computed from an equation of state.

References

1. **Kestin, J.** 'On the Direct Determination of the Viscosity of Gases at High Pressures and Temperatures, ' Proc. Second Biennial Gas Dynamic Symposium, Ed. A.B. Cambel and J.B. Finn, Northwestern Univ. Press, 1958.

2. **Knudsen, M.,** 'Kinetic Theory of Gases', Methuen, London, 1934.

3. **Schiller, L.,** 'Untersuchung über Laminare und Turbulente Strömung, ' Forschg. Ing., Wes., 248, 1922.

4. **Couette, M.M.,** 'Studies on Viscosity of Liquids, ' Ann.Chem. et. Phys., Vol. 6, 21, pp. 433-509, 1890.

5. **Goldstein, S.,** 'Modern Development in Fluid Dynamics,' Vol. I, Oxford Univ. Press, London, 1938.

6. **Dean, W.R.,** 'The Streamline Motion of a Fluid in Curved Pipe, ' Phil. Mag., Vol. 7, 4, p. 208, 1927 and Vol.5, pp. 673, 1928.

7. **Vasilesco, V.,** 'Récherches Experimentales sur la Viscosité des Gaz aux Températures Elévees, ' Ann. der Phys., 20, pp. 137 and 292, 1945.

8. **Hawkins, G.A., Solberg, H.L., and Potter, A.A.,** 'The Viscosity of Water and Superheated Steam, ' Trans. ASME, 62, p. 677, 1940.

9. **Mayinger, F.,** 'Messung der Viskosität von Wasser und Wasserdampf bis zu 700°C. und 800 atm., ' Int. J. Heat Mass Trans., 5, p. 807, 1962.

10. **Swindels, J.F., Coe, J.R., and Godfrey, T.B.,** 'Absolute Viscosity of Water at 20°C., ' J. Research NBS, 48, p.1, 1952.

11. **Whitelaw, J.H.,** 'Viscosity of Steam at Supercritical Pressures, ' J. of Mech. Eng. Sci., 2, p. 288, 1960.

12. **Flynn, G.P., Hanks, P.R., Lemaire, N.A., and Ross, J.,** 'Viscosity of Nitrogen, Helium, Neon, and Argon from 78.5 to 100°C. below 200 atm., ' J. Chem. Phys., 38, p. 154, 1963.

13. **Rankine, O.A.,** 'On a Method of Determining the Viscosity of Gases Especially those Available only in Small Quantities, ' Proc. Soc. A83, pp. 265 and 516, 1910.

14. **Michels, A., and Gibson, R.O.,** 'The Measurements of the Viscosity of Gases at High Pressures - the Viscosity of Nitrogen to 1000 atms., ' Proc. Roy. Soc., London, 134A, p. 288, 1931.

15. **Ubbelohde, L.,** 'The Simplest and Most Accurate Viscometer and Other Instruments with Suspended Level, ' J. Inst. Petrol. Tech., 19, p.376, 1933.

16. **Cannon, M.R., Manning, R.E., and Bell, J.D.,** 'Viscosity Measurement, the Kinetic Energy Correction and a New Viscometer, ' Analytical Chem., 32, p. 355, 1960.

17. **Gilchrist, L.,** 'An Absolute Determination of the Viscosity of Air, ' Phys. Rev., 1, p. 124, 1913.

18. **Kellström, G.,** 'A New Determination of the Viscosity of Air by the Rotating Cylinder Method, ' Phil. Mag., 23, p. 313, 1937.

19. **Bearden, J.A.,** 'A Precision Determination of the Viscosity of Air, ' Phys. Rev., 56, p. 1023, 1939.

20. **Maxwell, J.D.,** 'On the Viscosity of Internal Friction of Air and Other Gases, ' Phil. Trans. Roy. Soc., London, 156, p. 246, 1866.

21. **Kestin, J., and Leidenfrost, W.,** 'An Absolute Determination of the Viscosity of Eleven Gases Over a Range of Pressure, ' Physica, 25, p. 1033, 1959.

22. **Kestin, J., and Persen, L.N.,** 'Small Oscillations of Bodies of Revolution in a Viscous Flow, ' Proc. of the 9th Int. Congress of Appl. Mech., Brussels, 1956.

23. **Newell, G.F.,** 'Theory of Oscillation Type Viscometers V Disc Oscillating Between Fixed Plates, ' ZAMP, 10, p. 160, 1959.

24. **Kearsley, E.A.,** 'An Analysis of an Absolute Torsional Pendulum Viscometer, ' Trans. Soc. of Rheology, 3, p. 69, 1959.

25. **Schmidt, E.,** 'Uber Trocknungsvorgänge, ' Z. Ges Kälte Ind., Bd. 43, p. 75, 1936.

26. **Michels, A., and Sengers, J.V.,** 'The Thermal Conductivity of Carbon Dioxide in the Critical Region, ' Prog. Int. Research on Thermodynamic and Transport Properties, Second Symp., Academic Press, 1962.

27. **Michels, A., and Botzen, A.,** 'A Method for the Determination of the Thermal Conductivity of Gases at High Pressures, ' Physica, 18, p. 605, 1952.

28. **Fritz, W., and Poltz, H.,** 'Absolutbestimmung der Wärmeleitfähigkeit, von Flüssigkeiten. 1. Kritische Versuche an einerneuen Platten Apparatur, ' Int. J. Heat Mass Transfer, 5, p. 307, 1962.

29. Schleiermacher, Ann Phys., 26, p. 287, 1885.

30. **Schmidt, E., and Sellschopp, W.,** 'Warmeleitfähigkeit des Wassers bei Temperaturen bis 270°C., ' Forsch, Ing. Wes., 2, 165/78 u 213/17, 1931.

31. **Keyes, F.G.,** 'Measurements of Heat Conductivity of Nitrogen - Carbon - Dioxide Mixtures, ' Trans. ASME, 73, p. 597, 1951.

32. Ziebland, H., 'The Thermal Conductivity of Toluene - New Determinations and an Appraisal of Recent Experimental Work,' Int. J. Heat Mass Transfer, 2, p. 273, 1961.

33. Johannin, P., Wilson, M., and Vodar, B., 'Heat Conductivity of Compressed Helium at Elevated Temperatures,' Second Symp. on Thermophysical Properties, ASME, Academic Press, New York, p. 418-433, 1962.

34. Thodos, G., Misic, Dragoslav, 'The Thermal Conductivity of Hydrocarbon Gases at Normal Pressures,' A.J. Ch. E. Journal, 7, p. 264, 1961.

35. Riedel, L., 'New Thermal Conductivity Measurements of Organic Liquids,' Chem. Ing. Techn., 23, 321/324, 1951.

36. Schmidt, E., and Leidenfrost, W., 'Der Einfluss Elektrischer Felder auf den Wärme Transport in Flüssigen Elektrischen Nichtleitern,' Forsch, Ing. Wes., 19, 65/80, 1953.

37. Leidenfrost, W., 'An Attempt to Measure the Thermal Conductivity of Liquids, Gases, and Vapors with a High Degree of Accuracy over Wide Ranges of Temperature (-180°C. to 500°C.) and Pressure (vacuum to 500 atm.),' Int. J. Heat Mass Transfer, 7, 447/478, 1964.

38. Leidenfrost, W., and Tree, D., 'Prediction of Minor Heat Losses in a Thermal Conductivity Cell and Other Calorimeter Type Cells,' Proc. of 7th Conference on Thermal Conductivity, NBS publication, 1967.

39. Leidenfrost, W., 'Theory and Design Considerations in Developing a Multipurpose Instrument for Determination of Twelve Properties,' Int. J. Heat Mass Transfer, to be published, 1966.

40. Viskanta, R., and Grosh, R.J., 'Heat Transfer by Simultaneous Conduction and Radiation in an Absorbing Media,' Trans. ASME, J. Heat Transfer, 84C, 63/72, 1963.

41. Poltz, H., 'Die Wärmeleitfähigkeit von Flüssigkeiten II. Der Strahlungsanteil der Effektiven Wärmekeitfähigkeit,' Int. J. Heat Mass Transfer, 8, p. 515, 1965.

42. Kohler, M., 'Einfluss der Strahlung auf den Wärmetransport durch eine Flüssigkeitsschicht,' Z. Aog. Phys., 18, p. 356, 1965.

43. Leidenfrost, W., 'Critical Analysis of the Experimental Determination of the Thermal Conductivity of Steam,' presented at the 7th Int. Conf. on Properties of Steam, Tokyo, Sept., 1968.

44. Dickens, B.G., 'The Effect of Accomodation on Heat Conduction through Gases,' Proc. of Roy. Soc., A143. p. 577, 1934.

45. Stalhane, B., and Pyk, S., 'Metod for Bestamning av Varmelednings - Coefficienter,' Teknisk Tidskrift, 61, p. 389, 1931.

46. Vander Held, E.F.M., and Van Druven, F.G., 'A Method of Measuring the Thermal Conductivity of Liquids,' Physica, 15, p. 866, 1949.

47. **Grassmann, P., Straumann, W., Widmer, F., and Jobst, W.,** 'Measure-
ments of Thermal Conductivities of Liquids by an Unsteady State Method, '
Prog. in Int. Res. on Thermodynamic and Transport Properties, Second
Symposium on Thermophysical Properties, ASME, Academic Press, p. 447.

48. **Briggs, D.G., Goldstein, R.J., and Ibele, W.E.,** 'Precision Measurements
of the Thermal Conductivity of Gases in a Transient Hot-wire Cell, ' Fourth
Sym. on Thermophysical Properties, ASME, pp. 452, 1968.

49. **Allen, P.H.G.,** 'Fluid Thermal Conductivity by a Transient Method.
Thermodynamic and Transport Properties of Gases, Liquid, and Solids, '
Symp. on Thermal Properties, ASME, McGraw Hill, pp. 350, 1959.

50. **Harrison, W.B., Boteler, W.C., and Spurlock, J.M.,** 'Thermal Diffusivity
of Nitrogen as Determined by the Cyclic Heat Transfer Method, ' Thermodynamic and Transport Properties of Gases, Liquids, and Solids, Symp. on
Thermal Properties, ASME, McGraw Hill, p. 304, 1959.

51. **Westenburg, A.A., and Walker, R.E.,** 'Experiments in the Molecular
Diffusion of Gases at High Temperatures, ' Thermodynamic and Transport
Properties of Gases, Liquids, and Solids, Symp. on Thermal Properties,
ASME, McGraw Hill, p. 314, 1959.

52. **Westenburg, A.A., and deHaas, N.,** 'High Temperature Gas Thermal
Diffusivity Measurements with the Line Source Technique, ' 2nd Symp. on
Thermal Properties, ASME, Academic Press, p. 412, 1962.

53. **Sengers, J.R.,** 'Transport Properties of Compressed Gases, ' Recent
Advances in Engineering Sciences, A.C. Eringen ed. Vol. III, p. 157, 1968.

54. **Sogin, H.H., and Thompson, H.A.,** 'Apparatus to Measure Transport
Properties of Gases by Means of the Rayleigh-Jeffreys Instability, ' Fourth
Symp. on Thermophysical Properties, ASME, p. 416, 1968.

55. **Eckert, E.R.G., and Irvine, Jr., T.F.,** 'A New Method to Measure Prandtl
number and Thermoconductivity of Fluids, ' Appl. Mech., 24, 1, March,
p. 25-28, 1957.

56. **Smiley, E.F.,** 'The Measurements of the Thermal Conductivity of Gases
at High Temperatures with a Shock Tube, ' Ph.D. Thesis, The Catholic
Univ. of America, Washington, 1957.

57. **Kauver, M.R.,** 'Evaluation of Shock Tube Heat Transfer Experiments to
Measure Thermal Conductivity of Argon from 700° to 8600°K', NASA
D-2117, 1964.

58. **Carey, C.A., Carnevale, E.H., and Marshall, T.,** 'Heat Transfer and
Ultrasonic Methods for the Determination of High Temperature Gas
Transport Properties, ' Sixth Conf. on Thermal Conductivity, AFML,
Dayton, Ohio, p. 177, 1966.

59. **Flynn, D.R., and Didion, D.A.,** 'A Steam Calorimeter Apparatus for
Refractories, ' 1st Conf. on Thermal Conductivity, Battelle, p. 81, 1961.

60. **Flynn, D.R.,** 'Thermal Conductivity of Semi-Conductive Solids. Methods
for Steady-state Measurements on Small Disk Reference, ' NBS Report
7367 and 7323.

61. **Black, T.A., Glaser, P.E.,** 'Thermal Conductivity Tests of Cryogenic Insulation,' 2nd Conf. on Thermal Conductivity, p. 111, 1962.

62. **Messmer, J.H.,** 'The Thermal Conductivity of Porous Media IV Sandstone: The Effect of Temperature and Saturation,' 5th Conf. on Thermal Conductivity, Denver Univ. 1, II-E-1, 1965.

63. **Parker, W.J., Jenkins, R.J., Butler, C.P., Abbott, C.L.,** 'Flash Method of Determining Thermal Diffusivity, Heat Capacity, and Thermal Conductivity,' J. Appl. Phys., 32, pp. 1679-84, 1961.

64. **Beck, J.V.,** 'Analytical Determination of Optimum Transient Experiments for Measurements of Thermal Properties,' 3rd Int. Conf. on Heat Transfer Trans., Chicago, 1966.

64a. **Nakata, M.M.,** 'A Radial Heat Flow Technique for Measuring Thermal Diffusitivity,' 2nd Conf. on Thermal Conductivity, Division of Appl. Physics, NRC, Ottawa, 1962.

65. **Kasper, J., and Zehms, E.H.,** 'Thermal Diffusivity Measurements for Very High Temperatures,' 4th Conf. on Thermal Conductivity, U.S. Naval Rad. Def. Laboratory, San Francisco, V-E, 1964.

66. **Kohlrausch, F.,** 'Uber den Stationären Temperatur-zustand eines Elektrisch Geheizten Leiters,' Ann. Physik, 4, 1, 132/158, 1900.

67. **Bode, K.H.,** 'Eine neue Methode zur Messung der Wärmeleitfähigkeit von Metallen bei hohen Temperaturen, 'Allg. Wärmetechnik, 10, 110/120 u 125/142, 1961.

68. **Angell, M.F.,** 'Thermal Conductivity at High Temperatures, 'Physical Review, 33, 421/432, 1911.

69. **Powell, R.W., and Schofield, F.H.,** 'The Thermal and Electrical Conductivities of Carbon and Graphite to High Temperatures,' Proc. Phy. Soc., 51, 153/172, 1939.

70. **Rudkin, R.L., Parker, W.J., and Jenkins, R.J.,** 'Measurements of the Thermal Properties of Metals at Elevated Temperatures,' U.S. Dept. of Commerce Publ., PB 171185hsNRDL-TR-419, pp. 1-24, 1960.

71. **Krishnan, K.S., and Jain, S.C.,** 'Determination of Thermal Conductivities at High Temperatures,' British J. of Appl. Phys. 5, pp. 426-30, 1954.

72. **Powell, R.W., DeWitt, D.P., and Nalbantyan, M.,** 'The Precise Determination of Thermal Conductivity and Electrical Resistivity of Solids at High Temperatures by Direct Electrical Heating Methods,' AFML-TR-67-241.

73. **Beckett, C.W., and Cezairliyan,** 'High Speed Thermodynamic Measurements and Related Techniques,' Experimental Thermodynamics Vol. I Calorimetry of Non-Reacting Systems, Ch. 1, John P. McCullough ed.

74. **Powell, R.W.,** 'Experiments Using a Simple Thermal Comparator for Measurements of Thermal Conductivity, Surface Roughness and Thickness of Foils or of Surface Deposits,' J. Sci. Instrum., 34, p. 485, 1957.

75. **Dahl, A.J., Jones, D.W.,** 'Thermal Conductivity Studies with the Powell Method,' ASME - AIChE Heat Transfer Conf. Buffalo, N.Y./paper 60-HT-30, 1960.

76. **Ginnings, D.C.,** 'Powell Comparator Method for Determining Thermal Conductivities - a discussion,' Conf. on Thermal Conductivity Methods, Battelle, p. 287, 1961.

77. **Powell, R.W.,** 'Thermal Conductivity Measurements by the Thermal Comparator Method,' Black Hills Summer Conf. on Transport Properties, Rapid City, S.D., 1962.

78. **Kollie, T.G., and McLeroy, D.L.,** 'Thermal Comparator Apparatus for Thermal Conductivity Measurements from 40 to 400°C.'Conf. on Thermal Conductivity Methods, Battelle, p. 289, 1961.

79. **Hoch, M., Nitti, D.A., Gottschlich, C.F., and Blackburn, P.E.,** 'New Method for the Determination of Thermal Conductivities between 1000°C. and 3000°C.,'Progress in Int. Res. on Therm. and Transport Prop., ASME Academic Press, 1962.

80. **Moser, H.,** 'Messung der Wahren Spezifischen Wärme von Silber, Nickel, Quarz Kristall und Quarz Glas Zwischen 50 and 700°C.,'Phys. Zeitschrift, 37, p. 512, 1936.

81. **Schmidt, E.O., and Leidenfrost, W.,** 'Optimierung eines Adiabatischen Kalorimeters zur Genauen Messung von Wahren Spezifschen Wärmen Schlecht Wärmeleitender Substanzen,' Int. J. Heat Mass Transfer, 5, p. 267-275, 1962.

82. **West, E.D., and Ginnings, D.C.,** 'An Adiabatic Calorimeter for the Range 30° to 500°C.,' NBS J. of Research, 60, p. 309-316, 1958.

83. **Stansbury, E.E., McLeroy, D.L., Picklesimer, M.L., Elder, G.E., and Pawel, R.E.,** 'Adiabatic Calorimeter for Metals in the Range 50-100°C.,' Rev. of Scientific Inst., 30, p. 121-126, 1959.

84. **West, E.D.,** 'Heat Exchange in Adiabatic Calorimeter,' NBS. of Research, 67A, pp. 331-341, 1963.

85. **Krischer, O.,** 'Über die Bestimmung der Wärmeleitfahigkeit der Wärmekapazität und der Wärmeeindringzahl in einem Kurzzeitverfahren,' Chem. Ing. Techn., 26, p. 42, 1954.

86. **Douglas, T.B.,** 'The Dropping - Type Calorimeter,' 3rd Conf. on Thermal Conductivity, Metals and Ceramics Div. Oak Ridge Nat. Lab. 1962.

87. **Taylor, R.E.,** 'Determining Specific Heat and Other Properties by Pulse Heating,' 3rd Conf. on Thermal Conductivity, Metals and Ceramics Div. Oak Ridge Nat. Lab. 1962.

88. **Calendar, H.L., and Barnes,** 'II - Continuous Calorimetry,' Phil. Trans., 199A, p. 149, 1902.

89. **Schlesinger,** Phys. Z., 10, p. 210, 1909.

90. **Landis, F. and Nilson, E.N.,** The Determination of Thermodynamic Properties by Direct Differentiation Techniques,' Prog. in Int. Res. on Thermodynamic and Transport Properties, Second Symp. on Thermophysical Properties, AMSE Academic Press, p. 218, 1962.

Nomenclature

A	= area
A_1; A_2	= constants
a	= thermal diffusivity
B	= geometric constant
C_p; C_v	= molar heats
c	= specific heat
c_m	= mean specific heat
c_p	= specific heat at constant pressure
c_v	= specific heat at constant volume
D	= outer diameter
d	= inner diameter
E	= electrical potential
E_1; E_2	= electrical potential at locations 1 and 2
ΔE	= potential difference
F	= function
h	= height section of infinitely long cylinder
I	= Electrical current; (eq. 10-7) moment of inertia
k	= thermal conductivity
k_1; k_2	= thermal conductivity of material 1 and 2
k_x; k_y; k_z	= thermal conductivity in x, y and z direction respectively.
L	= thickness and length
M	= viscous torque
M_f	= moment due to viscous forces
m	= mass
$\dot{m}$	= mass flow rate
m_k	= similarity parameter
P_r	= Prandtl number
p	= pressure

p_o; p_1	= pressures at different states
Δp	= pressure drop
Q	= heat
q	= heat flow
q_c	= heat flow by convection
q_k	= heat flow by conduction
q_L	= heat loss
q_{osc}	= heat flow due to unsteady state conditions in steady state devices
q_{inh}	= errors in heat flow due to inhomogenities in a system
$q_{ch.r}$	= heat generation by chemical reaction
q_r	= heat flow by radiation
Ra	= Rayleigh number
R	= gas constant
r	= radial coordinate, recovery factor
r_1; r_2	= radial location
r_i	= radius of a contact area
T	= temperature, (eq. 10-9) period of oscillation
T_{ad}	= stagnation or total temperature
T_c	= temperature in the center of a body
T_f	= front surface temperature, temperature of a heater foil
T_1; T_2	= temperature at location 1 and 2
T_m	= mean temperature (eq. 10-22); maximum temperature (eq. 10-25, 10-27)
T_o	= period of oscillation in vacuum
T_r	= recovery temperature
ΔT	= temperature difference
T_∞	= static temperature
t	= time
t_1; t_2	= time

$t_{1/2}$	= time needed to observe half of the maximum temperature rise at rear surface of a sample when heated by a pulse at the front surface
Δt	= time interval
u	= velocity
V	= volume
$\dot{V}$	= volume flow rate
ΔV	= volume change
v	= specific volume
v_o; v_1	= specific volume at different states 0, 1
Δv	= specific volume change
W	= viscous drag
x	= coordinate
y	= coordinate
z	= coordinate

Greek Symbols

α	= angular motion, volumetric expansion coefficient (eq. 10-41)
α_n	= nth amplitude of a oscillating system
α_{n+1}	= nth + 1 amplitude
δ; Δ	= boundary layer thickness or depth of penetration and damping decrement
ϵ	= emissivity
η	= dimensionless coordinate
θ	= dimensionless frequency (eq. 10-9) temperature fluctuation (eq. 10-18, 10-19, 10-20)
κ	= specific heat ratio
λ	= electrical conductivity
μ	= dynamic viscosity, coefficient of Thompson heat (eq. 10-32), Joule-Thompson coefficient (eq. 10-51)
ν	= kinematic viscosity
ξ	= dimensionless coordinate

ρ	= density and electrical resistivity
σ	= Stefan Boltzmann constant
$\sigma_1; \sigma_2$	= complex roots of a characteristic equation
ϕ	= local angular velocity
ω	= angular velocity
ω_o	= circular frequency in vacuum

11

Transport Property Measurements in the Heat Transfer Laboratory, University of Minnesota

W. IBELE
Dept. of Mechanical Engineering, University of Minnesota.

Summary

Experimental methods are described for measuring properties important for heat transfer calculations; the Prandtl number, a dimensionless quantity which occurs in all convective heat transfer analyses, the coefficient of ordinary diffusion, important in transpiration cooling calculations, and gas thermal conductivity. The methods employed were suggested and perfected because of the scope and intensity of activity in the Heat Transfer Laboratory.

Introduction

There are two reasons why it is scientifically profitable to perform transport property measurements in the environment of a heat transfer laboratory. There is a need for increasingly accurate knowledge of transport properties to complement the increased sophistication and accuracy of various heat transfer analyses. Secondly, the experimental investigations of heat transfer problems on occasion reveal phenomena which may be employed as a basis for measuring transport properties. These stimuli are responsible for the interest in and contributions to the area of thermophysical properties at the Heat Transfer Laboratory.

Prandtl Number of Determinations of Gases and Gas Mixtures by Direct Measurement of the Recovery Factor

The quantity, $\eta C_p/\lambda$, called the Prandtl number Pr is a dimensionless number formed by the viscosity η, the heat capacity at constant pressure C_p, and thermal conductivity, λ. It enters into all convective heat transfer calculations. Nevertheless, the uncertainty that earlier attended the various properties which comprise the dimensionless quantity caused discrepancies to exist even for familiar gases such as air. For example, Irvine [1] shows differences of over six percent between various estimates of air Prandtl number at 711°K.

To remedy this situation a program of measurements was undertaken beginning with the above work in 1956. The analytical model serving as a basis for the measurements is a flat plate, exchanging energy only by convective heat transfer with a high velocity stream at constant pressure. For these conditions the surface of the flat plate, under the competing influences of fluid friction and heat conduction transverse to the flow, assumes a temperature between the static temperature T_S and total temperature T_T of the gas stream called the recovery temperature T_R. This temperature appears in a quantity called the recovery factor, σ, defined as:

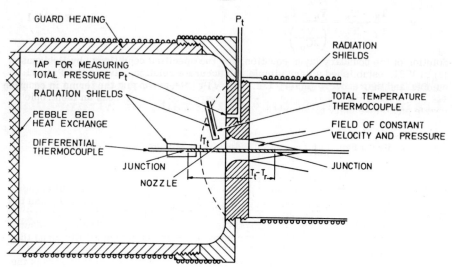

Fig. 11-1   Schematic diagram of Prandtl number measuring device

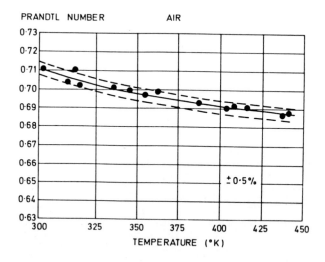

Fig. 11-2   Prandtl number measurements for air at 1 atm pressure

$$\sigma = \frac{T_R - T_S}{T_T - T_S} = \frac{T_R - T_S}{\left(\dfrac{V^2}{2C_p}\right)} \qquad\qquad \text{Eq. 11-1}$$

Solution of the boundary layer equation, for the specified conditions, by Pohlhausen (2) in 1921, established a very simple and accurate relation between the Prandtl number and the recovery factor, i.e., $\sigma = \sqrt{Pr}$. Re-arranging the terms in equation 11-1, and using the relationship between the pressure ratio across an isentropic nozzle and the velocity developed V, gives the equation:

$$\sigma = \sqrt{Pr} = 1 - \frac{T_T - T_R}{T_T\left[1 - \left(\dfrac{P_s}{P_t}\right)^{\frac{\gamma-1}{\gamma}}\right]}$$

Three measurements are necessary to determine Prandtl numbers: the difference between total and recovery temperature $T_T - T_R$, the total temperature T_T and the pressure ratio P_s/P_t. The physical apparatus designed to obtain the necessary measurements prescribed by the analysis is shown in Fig. 11-1. The key measurement is provided by the differential thermocouple which is strung axially along the nozzle axis and serves as the flat plate. The upstream junction senses the total temperature T_T and the downstream junction just beyond the nozzle exit senses the recovery temperature T_R.

Pure Gases

Early results for air in the temperature range 293 to 448°K were obtained with an 0.46 mm diameter manganin, manganin-constantan thermocouple and shown in Fig. 11-2. The Prandtl numbers determined by such measurements are reproducible to ± 0.5 percent, a precision which is attributed to the well defined environment provided by the flat-plate differential thermocouple. This occurs through the use of a blow-down system which provides gas at constant conditions of pressure and temperature to the nozzle for a period of 2 to 3 minutes, an interval adequate for obtaining the required measurements. The test gas may be heated to high temperatures by a pebble-bed heater which provides the apparatus with a temperature capability of room temperature to 670°K. The results obtained for carbon-dioxide, CO_2, a polyatomic gas, are reproducible with the same precision, ± 0.5 percent and are shown in Fig. 11-3.

Helium gas results are interesting since kinetic theory predicts a constant value of the Prandtl number for monatomic gases, yet the values calculated from the 'best' values of viscosity, heat capacity, and thermal conductivity available at the time of the National Bureau of Standards Study in 1954 (4) showed departure from this prediction. The departure is attributed to variation in the helium thermal conductivities then available. The Prandtl number determinations from recovery factor measurements agree with theory as shown in Fig. 11-4. Comparisons are also given with other predictive schemes described in (5) and (6).

Argon, a stable monatomic gas, of medium molecular weight, also has a predicted constant Prandtl number behavior with temperature and is useful as a calibrating gas. Results obtained for argon appear in Fig. 11-5.

Mixtures

The first mixture investigated was the helium-air mixture due to the interest in helium as a transpiration coolant for surfaces exposed to aerodynamic heating. Measurements were conducted using the same apparatus and techniques employed in the previous measurements given for pure gases. Results are shown in Fig. 11-6

PRANDTL NUMBER

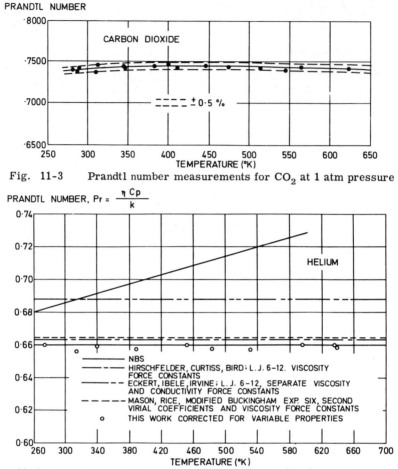

Fig. 11-3   Prandtl number measurements for CO_2 at 1 atm pressure

PRANDTL NUMBER, $Pr = \dfrac{\eta\, Cp}{k}$

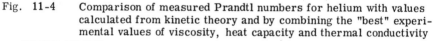

Fig. 11-4   Comparison of measured Prandtl numbers for helium with values
calculated from kinetic theory and by combining the "best" experimental values of viscosity, heat capacity and thermal conductivity

PRANDTL NUMBER

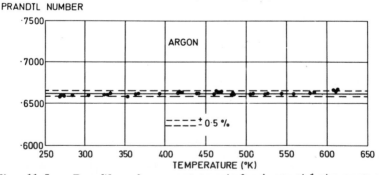

Fig. 11-5   Prandtl number measurements for Argon at 1 atm pressure

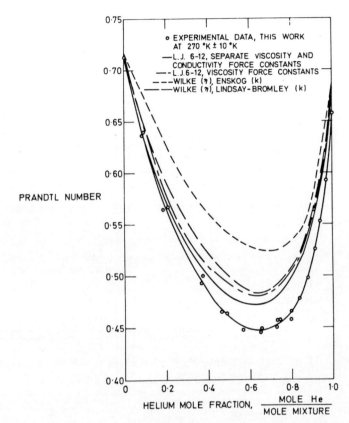

Fig. 11-6   Prandtl numbers measurements for Helium-air mixtures at room
temperature

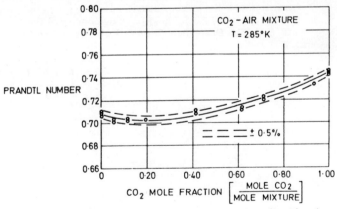

Fig. 11-7   Prandtl number measurements for Carbon dioxide-air mixtures at
room temperature and 1 atm pressure

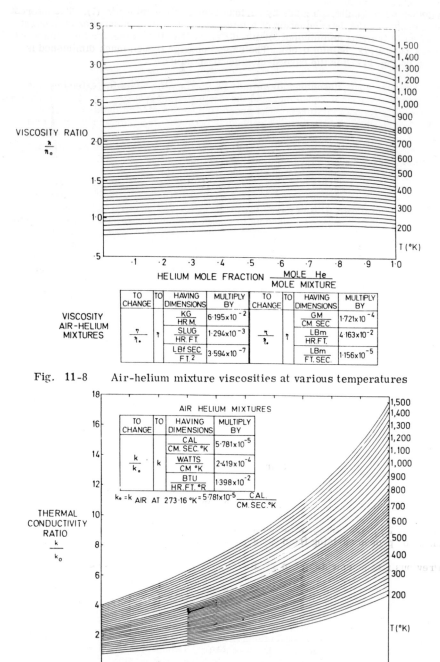

VISCOSITY
AIR-HELIUM
MIXTURES

TO CHANGE	TO	HAVING DIMENSIONS	MULTIPLY BY	TO CHANGE	TO	HAVING DIMENSIONS	MULTIPLY BY
$\frac{\eta}{\eta_o}$	η	$\frac{KG}{HR.M.}$	$6·195 \times 10^{-2}$	$\frac{\eta}{\eta_o}$	η	$\frac{GM}{CM.SEC.}$	$1·721 \times 10^{-4}$
		$\frac{SLUG}{HR.FT.}$	$1·294 \times 10^{-3}$			$\frac{LBm}{HR.FT.}$	$4·163 \times 10^{-2}$
		$\frac{LBf.SEC}{F.T.^2}$	$3·594 \times 10^{-7}$			$\frac{LBm}{FT.SEC.}$	$1·156 \times 10^{-5}$

Fig. 11-8   Air-helium mixture viscosities at various temperatures

Fig. 11-9   Air-helium mixture thermal conductivities at various temperatures

together with predictions made by various schemes described in (7). The interesting result was the determination of a minimum in the Prandtl number (~ 0.45) at 0.65 mole fraction helium appreciably different than the values for the component gases (air, 0.71, helium 0.66). The same behavior though much diminished is given by Fig. 11-7 for the carbon-dioxide-air mixture.

The measurements described above may be used as the basis for extending our knowledge of the Prandtl number and the transport properties, viscosity and thermal conductivity for gas mixtures. The procedure is reported in detail in (7) for helium-air mixtures. Briefly, it recognizes that the superior accuracy of heat capacity C_p data (0.1%), viscosity η data (~ 1%), and the precision of the Prandtl number determinations (~ ± 1.0%) permit the calculation of gas and gas mixture thermal conductivities which generally exceed the accuracy of those determined directly by the various cell methods. The careful selection of an appropriate molecular model to yield the best agreement with measured viscosities and thermal conductivities provides a basis for extrapolating the values of these properties to higher temperatures with reasonable confidence. The properties of the pure components are then combined according to one of a number of mixture rules, the most accurate being given in (5). The solid curve shown in Fig. 11-6 indicates the result of such a procedure in predicting Prandtl numbers for helium-air mixtures at room temperature. The final step of the process develops working charts of viscosity Fig. 11-8, thermal conductivity Fig. 11-9, and Prandtl number Fig. 11-10. Mixtures treated in such a manner are helium-air (7), carbon-dioxide-air (8), nitrogen carbon-dioxide (9), and hydrogen-methane (to be published). Work in progress employs a second Prandtl number apparatus of stainless steel with a temperature capability of 1360°K. Measurements have been performed on air, argon (calibrating gas) and gas mixtures of N_2, O_2, CO_2 and H_2O in proportions representing the combustion products of the fuel $(CH_2)_n$ for stoichiometric, 100 percent, and 200 percent excess air. The results will be published in the near future as a NASA Technical Note.

Coefficient of Ordinary Diffusion - Thermal Diffusion Factor

Recent heat transfer investigations (10), (11), (12), (13), (14) using a low molecular weight gas injected to shield a surface from a high temperature, involved at one stage a situation where diffusion of main stream gas and transpiring gas, though originally at the same temperature, caused large temperature variations on the surface to be observed. This is attributed to the thermal effects associated with the diffusion of unlike gases, i.e., diffusion-thermo effect and the magnitude of the temperature rise (as large as 17°K in some instances) suggested its use in measuring the properties connected with the process: the coefficient of ordinary diffusion D_{12}, for binary diffusion and the thermal diffusion factor, $(\alpha_T)_{12}$ for the diffusion process arising from the generated temperature field.

Previous measurements of binary diffusion have been concerned primarily with the influence of temperature on the ordinary coefficient of diffusion. The method developed here permits measurements of both the temperature and composition dependence of this property, and the thermal diffusion factor as well. The experiment involves a combination of convective and diffusive flow in a test section where the concentration and temperature at a given location are measured simultaneously and both radial and axial distributions of these quantities are obtained with sufficient accuracy to permit the determination of diffusion coefficients and thermal diffusion factors.

The diffusion chamber (25mm dia. by 50mm long) is shown in Fig. 11-11. The gases for which coefficients are to be measured are denoted by 1 and 2, 1 being

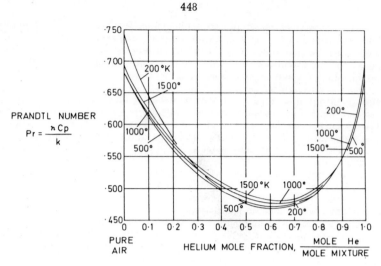

Fig. 11-10   Prandtl   numbers for air-helium mixtures at various temperatures

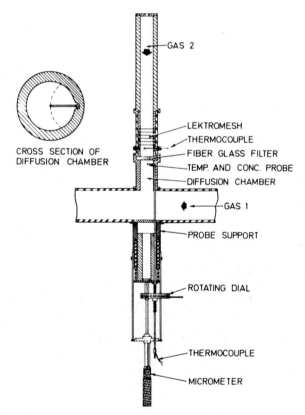

Fig.   11-11   Apparatus for measuring the mass diffusion coefficient and the
thermal diffusion factor

the heavier gas. The vertical tube is divided by a porous section made of layers of filter paper, into two regions. Gas 2 enters at the top of the tube, gas 1 at the same temperature drifts slowly past the tube exit in a direction normal to the tube axis. Both gases flow at velocities so low that the total pressures in both sections of the tube are constant. The presence of gas 1 at the lower end of the test section and gas 2 above the porous section establishes a concentration gradient in the vertical direction and a diffusion mass flow ensues. There follows from this a temperature field due to the diffusion-thermo effect and an additional mass flow occurs in the tube due to the inverse thermal diffusion effect. (Fig. 11-12), (16). Applying the mass conservation law to the mass flux of gas 1 and gas 2 in the vertical tube (y-direction) yields the following expression (15):

$$\dot{m}_2 = D_{12} \frac{M_2}{M} \frac{1}{x_1} \frac{dx_1}{dy} + x_2 (\alpha_T)_{12} \frac{1}{T} \frac{dT}{dy} \qquad \text{Eq. 11-3}$$

where ρ and M are mixture density and molecular weight respectively, M_2 the molecular weight of component 2, x the mole fraction, and T the temperature. The contributions of ordinary diffusion and the coupled diffusion thermo effect are apparent. The assumptions of $\partial P/\partial y = 0$ and $\partial x_1/\partial r = 0$ necessary to generate equation 11-3 were verified experimentally. The temperature-concentration probe is a 0.89mm outer diameter, hollow, stainless steel tube containing a 40 gage iron-constantan thermocouple. Concentration is determined from the gas sampled by a thermal conductivity cell.

For determining diffusion coefficients, the second term of equation 11-3 is neglected since it is approximately two orders of magnitude less than the first, leaving:

$$D_{12} = \frac{RT\dot{m}_2}{M_2 P} \cdot \frac{1}{d(\ln x_1)/dy} \qquad \text{Eq. 11-4}$$

The mass rate of flow of the lighter gas, $\dot{m}_2$, is measured by a carefully calibrated capillary tube submerged in a constant temperature bath.

Results for the gas pair helium-nitrogen at 298°K are given in (16) from which Fig. 11-13 is taken. A dependence of D_{12} upon concentration is clear, as well as the consistency of the results obtained when compared to those of earlier investigations. Also shown are the predictions using two molecular models and two calculation schemes. Similar results were obtained at various temperatures over a range of 200 to 400°K and are given in (16). An analysis of the errors attending the measurement of the mass flow, temperature, pressure and the measurement and analytical representation of the concentration yields an estimated accuracy of 2 percent.

Hot Wire Cell Determination of Gas Thermal Conductivity

Steady-state means of measuring gas thermal conductivities based on Fourier's law of heat conduction each encounter their own special problems. The parallel plate method encounters errors due to end and convective effects and at high temperature, radiation errors. The concentric geometries pose construction problems because of the required symmetry, particularly for the sphere but also for the cylinder, and both encounter radiation errors at high temperature. The line source method introduces a temperature perturbation across a laminar gas stream at known uniform temperature and determines the thermal conductivity from observations of the decay of the perturbation along the flow path (17). The method yields good results but requires a precise measurement of the gas velocity. The Prandtl number method (described earlier) experiences material problems at higher temperatures due to the large regions and number of parts continuously exposed to such an inhospitable environment, with some parts subject to mechanical stress as well.

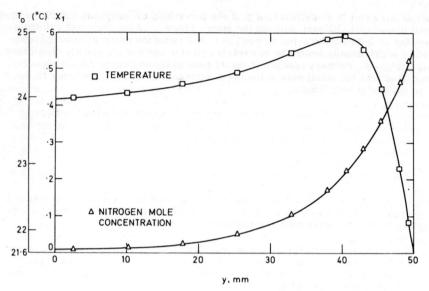

Fig. 11-12   Concentration and temperature profiles along center line for Gas II
(Helium) mass flow rate of 0.00114 kg/s m²

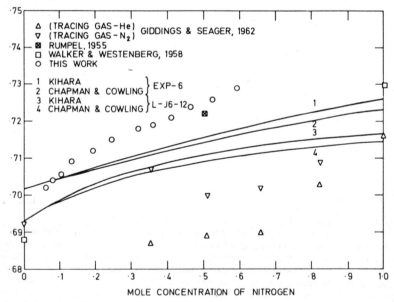

Fig. 11-13   Mass diffusion coefficient for He-N₂ mixture at 298° K and 1 atm

The hot wire cell is an extreme form of the concentric cylinder since it uses a very small diameter (0.025mm) wire as the inner cylinder. When the outer cylinder diameter is 6.35mm the symmetry problem and radiation error at elevated temperature which usually beset the concentric cylinder method are greatly diminished in importance. Primary concern is direct instead to the temperature-jump effect associated with the small size of the inner wire (its diameter is the order of the mean molecular path length).

The test cell is shown in Fig. 11-14 and consists of a center platinum wire, 0.025mm diameter, which serves as the line heat source for the test gas, but is also calibrated as a resistance thermometer. The voltage drop along the 40mm of central wire is measured by means of the 0.0051mm diameter platinum voltage taps connected to 0.051mm diameter platinum leads on either side of the central wire. To measure the cell temperature, a very small current (400 to 600 microamperes) is permitted to flow through the center wire and the voltage drop measured, the temperature calculated and verified by comparing it to readings of three thermocouples (Pt - Pt-10%Rh) attached to the outer wall of the outside cylinder. This establishes the cell and wall T_w temperature.

The current flow in the central wire is increased to 40 to 60 milliamperes, enough to raise the temperature of the center wire T_f 60° to 70°K above the wall temperature. The resistance of the central wire (and therefore its temperature) is determined by measuring the voltage drop again and the current. The current is determined by measuring the voltage drop across a standard resistance in series with the central wire. The wall thermocouples are read again to verify that the wall temperature continues to be that indicated by the initial measurement of the central wire used as a resistance thermometer. The cell chamber of 6.35mm is chosen to eliminate free convection effects by holding the product of Grashof and Prandtl numbers below 1000.

The central wire assembly is installed in the 6.35mm diameter platinum tube of 0.38mm wall thickness, Fig. 11-15, and placed in the tubular chamber of the high temperature furnace, a Lindberg Hevi-Duty Laboratory Furnace of 1770°K capability. Prior measurements of the furnace internal temperatures located a zone which is isothermal (± 0.5°K at 773°K) over the 40mm long test section.

To eliminate the temperature-jump effect and arrive at the true gas thermal conductivity, a succession of measurements are taken at successively lower pressure (1300, 500, 100mm of Hg-pressure) of test gas in the hot wire cell. Readings are taken at each pressure level and an apparent thermal conductivity; λ_{APP}, calculated from:

$$\lambda_{APP} = \frac{Q \ \ln \dfrac{r_w}{r_f}}{2\pi L (T_f - T_w)} \qquad\qquad \text{Eq. 11-5}$$

where Q is the heat flow through the gas sample, obtained from the measured current flow through the central wire and the known resistance between the two voltage taps, r_f is the radius of the central wire, r_w the inner radius of the outer cylinder, L the length of the test section (40mm between voltage taps), T_f the central wire temperature and T_w the outer cylinder wall temperature. Values of $1/\lambda_{APP}$ are plotted against $1/p$ and extrapolated to the zero value of $1/p$. It is known that for the pressure range over which measurements are made, the influence of the pressure on the gas thermal conductivity is insignificant and the departures of λ_{APP} from the true conductivity is due entirely to the temperature-jump effects. The value of $1/\lambda_{APP}$ at $1/p$ equal zero, obtained by the above extrapolation procedure, is the true conductivity value unaffected by temperature-jump effects in accordance with Kennard's (19) representation:

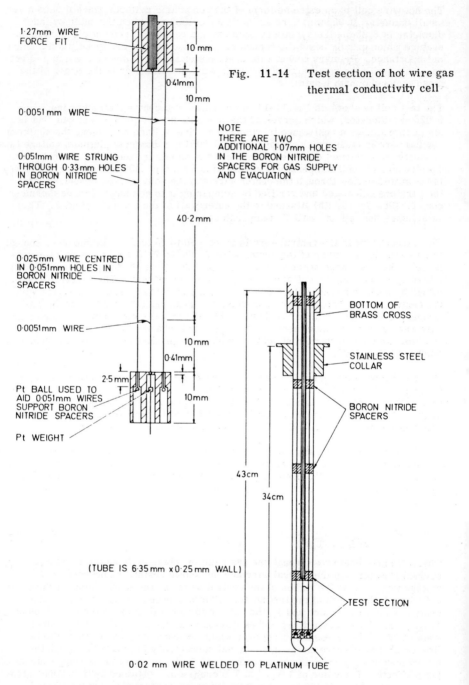

1·27mm WIRE
FORCE FIT

10 mm

0·41mm

10 mm

0·0051mm WIRE

NOTE
THERE ARE TWO
ADDITIONAL 1·07mm HOLES
IN THE BORON NITRIDE
SPACERS FOR GAS SUPPLY
AND EVACUATION

0·051mm WIRE STRUNG
THROUGH 0·33mm HOLES
IN BORON NITRIDE
SPACERS

40·2 mm

0·025mm WIRE CENTRED
IN 0·051mm HOLES IN
BORON NITRIDE
SPACERS

0·0051mm WIRE

10 mm

0·41mm

2·5 mm

10 mm

Pt BALL USED TO
AID 0·051mm WIRES
SUPPORT BORON
NITRIDE SPACERS

Pt WEIGHT

Fig. 11-14   Test section of hot wire gas
thermal conductivity cell

BOTTOM OF
BRASS CROSS

STAINLESS STEEL
COLLAR

BORON NITRIDE
SPACERS

43cm

34cm

TEST SECTION

(TUBE IS 6·35mm x 0·25mm WALL)

0·02 mm WIRE WELDED TO PLATINUM TUBE

Fig. 11-15   Profile of test section enclosed by platinum outer tube

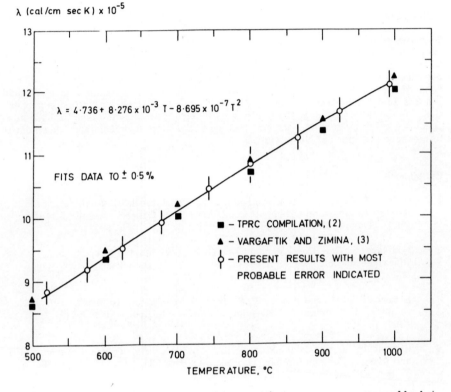

λ (cal/cm sec K) x 10^{-5}

$\lambda = 4 \cdot 736 + 8 \cdot 276 \times 10^{-3}\, T - 8 \cdot 695 \times 10^{-7}\, T^2$

FITS DATA TO $\pm$ 0·5%

■ — TPRC COMPILATION, (2)

▲ — VARGAFTIK AND ZIMINA, (3)

○ — PRESENT RESULTS WITH MOST
PROBABLE ERROR INDICATED

TEMPERATURE, °C

Fig. 11-16   Thermal conductivity of Argon at 1 atm pressure measured by hot
wire cell

$$\lambda = \lambda_{APP} \left(1 + \frac{C}{P}\right)$$

Eq. 11-6

where C is a constant.

Results obtained for argon gas are shown in Fig. 11-16 taken from (18). The references cited are those given in (18) and refer to measurements of other investigators. A careful analysis of the sources of error estimates the most probable error as ± 1.4 percent at 773°K and ± 2.8 percent at 1273°K. Subsequent improvements in measurement circuitry and instrumentation have reduced these errors by a third.

Conclusion

Three measurement schemes for determining quantities important in heat transfer have been presented. The first takes the flat plate boundary layer equation solution for recovery factor as a basis for determining the dimensionless heat transfer quantity Prandtl number, an important factor in all convective heat transfer. The second takes phenomena noted during transpiration heat transfer measurements and designs an optimum test chamber and probe to measure important diffusion properties. In the third instance, the familiar cylindrical geometry is taken to the limit of a very small central wire serving both as heat source and resistance thermometer to measure gas thermal conductivities.

References

1. **Irvine, T.F. Jr.**, 'A New Method for the Experimental Determination of Prandtl Numbers and Thermal Conductivities of Gases'. Results for Air., Ph.D. Thesis, Univ. of Minnesota, 1956.

2. **Pohlhausen, E.**, 'Der Warmeaustausch Zwischen festen Korpern und Flussigkeiten mit Kleiner Riebung und Kleiner Warmleitung,' Zeit. angew. Math. Mech. 1, 115-121, 1921.

3. **Eckert, E.R.G. and Irvine, T.F. Jr.**, 'A New Method to Measure Prandtl Number and Thermal Conductivity of Fluids', J. Appl. Mech., Vol. 24, 1957, p. 25.

4. **Hilsenrath, J. and Touloukian, Y.S.**, 'The Viscosity, Thermal Conductivity, and Prandtl Number for Air, O_2, N_2, NO, H_2, CO, CO_2, H_2O, He, and A,' Trans. ASME, Vol. 76, 1954, pp. 967-983.

5. **Hirschfelder, J.O., Curtiss, C.F. and Bird, R.B.**, 'Molecular Theory of Gases and Liquids,' John Wiley, New York, 1954.

6. **Stroom, P.D., Ibele, W.E., and Irvine, T.F., Jr.** 'Helium Prandtl Number Measurements and Calculated Viscosity and Thermal Conductivity,' Int. Developments in Heat Transfer, Pt. IV, Sect. B, No. 105, Am. Soc. of Mech. Eng., New York, 1961, pp. 870-875.

7. **Eckert, E.R.G., Ibele, W.E., and Irvine, T.F., Jr.**, 'Prandtl Number, Thermal Conductivity and Viscosity of Air-Helium Mixtures,' NASA TN D-533, Washington, D.C., Sept. 1960.

8. **Novotny, J.L. and Irvine, T.F. Jr.**, 'Thermal Conductivity and Prandtl Number of Carbon Dioxide and Carbon Dioxide-Air Mixtures at One Atmosphere,' J. Heat Transfer, Vol. 83, 1961, pp. 125-132.

9. **Ibele, W. E. and Briggs, D. G.**, 'Prandtl Number Measurements and Transport Property Calculations for N_2-CO_2 Mixtures, ' Fourth Symp. on Thermophysical Properties (ASME), Univ. of Maryland, College Park, Md., April, 1968, pp. 392-397.

10. **Tewfik, O. E., Eckert, E. R. G. and Jurewicz, L. S.**, 'Diffusion-Thermo Effects on Heat Transfer from a Cylinder in Cross Flow, ' AIAA Journal, Vol. 1, 1963, p. 1537.

11. **Tewfik, O. E., Eckert, E. R. G. and Shirtliffe, C. J.**, 'Thermal Diffusion Effects on Energy Transfer in a Turbulent Boundary Layer with Helium Injection, ' Proc. of 1962 Heat Transfer and Fluid Mechanics Inst. Stanford Univ. Press, Stanford, Calif., 1962.

12. **Tewfik, O. E. and Yang, J. W.**, 'The Thermodynamic Coupling between Heat and Mass Transfer in Free Convection, ' Int. J. of Heat and Mass Transfer, Vol. 6, 1963, p. 915.

13. **Sparrow, E. M. Minkowycz, W. J., Eckert, E. R. G. and Ibele, W. E.**, 'The Effect of Diffusion Thermo and Thermal Diffusion for Helium Injection into Plane and Axisymmetric Stagnation Flow of Air, ' J. Heat Transfer, Vol. 86, 1964, p. 311.

14. **Sparrow, E. M., Minkowycz, W. J., and Eckert, E. R. G.**, 'Transpiration-induced Buoyancy and Thermal Diffusion-Diffusion Thermo in a Helium-Air Free Convection Boundary Layer, ' J. of Heat Transfer, Vol. 86, 1964, p. 508.

15. **Chapman, S. and Cowling, T. G.**, 'The Mathematical Theory of Non-Uniform Gases, ' Cambridge Univ. Press, London, 1952.

16. **Yang, J. W.**, 'A New Method of Measuring Mass Diffusion Coefficient and Thermal Diffusion in a Binary Gas System, ' Ph. D. Thesis, Univ. of Minnesota, 1966.

17. **Westenberg, A. A. and deHaas.** 'Gas Thermal Conductivity Studies at High Temperature, Line Source Techniques, and Results in N_2, CO_2, and N_2-CO_2 Mixtures, ' Physics of Fluids, Vol. 5, 1962, p. 266.

18. **Desmond, R. M.**, 'Measurement of the Thermal Conductivity of Gases at High Temperature with a Hot Wire Cell, ' Ph. D. Thesis, Univ. of Minnesota, 1968.

19. **Kennard, E. H.**, 'Kinetic Theory of Gases, ' McGraw-Hill, New York, 1939.

Nomenclature

C   Constant

C_p heat capacity at constant pressure

D_{12} binary diffusion coefficient

K   Kelvin temperature

k   thermal conductivity coefficient (also λ)

L   length

M   molecular weight

$\dot{m}$ mass flow rate

p   pressure

p_s static pressure

P_r Prandtl number

p_t total pressure

Q   heat flow

r   radius

r_f wire radius

r_w wall radius

$\bar{R}$ gas constant

T   temperature absolute

T_f wire temperature

T_R recovery temperature

T_T total temperature

T_w wall temperature

V   velocity

x   mole fraction

y   distance

$(\alpha_T)_{12}$ binary thermal diffusion factor

γ adiabatic exponent (C_p/C_v)

λ thermal conductivity coefficient (also k)

λ_{APP} apparent thermal conductivity

η viscosity coefficient

ℓ density

σ recovery factor

Subscripts

1   gas component 1

2   gas component 2

n   integer

Fluid Velocity Measurement from the Doppler Shift of Scattered Laser Radiation

R. J. GOLDSTEIN, D. K. KREID,
University of Minnesota, Minneapolis.

Summary

The basic principles involved in the theory and application of the laser-Doppler system for the measurement of fluid velocity are reviewed. Optimization of the optical system geometry is calculated with respect to signal bandwidth, signal to noise ratio, sensitivity and spatial resolution. Selection of suitable light scattering particles is discussed with respect to scattering efficiency and the extent to which the particles follow the flow. Various alternatives for spectrum analysis of the photomultiplier Doppler current are briefly discussed with regard to the type of velocity information sought. A review is given of the work which has been published in this area and data is presented to illustrate the type of information which can be obtained with the laser-Doppler system.

Introduction

If a source of acoustic or electromagnetic waves of constant frequency ν is put in motion, the frequency of the waves received by a fixed observer will change. This is the well known Doppler effect, which is sometimes called the Fizeau effect when applied to light waves. A similar phenomenon is observed when the source is fixed but the waves are scattered or reflected from a body in motion before being received by the fixed observer. In either case, the apparent change in frequency, or the Doppler shift, ν_D is related to the velocity in the following way:

$$\frac{\nu_D}{\nu} \sim \frac{v_r}{a}$$

where v_r is the speed of the source, (or reflector) relative to the observer, and a is the wave propagation speed.

For acoustic waves, a is the speed of sound and v_r/a is the Mach number. With sound waves, the Doppler shift is often of the same order of magnitude as the source frequency ν. The shift is then usually considerably larger than the source bandwidth and is readily detectable.

For light or electromagnetic radiation, $a = c$, the speed of light and $v_r/c \ll 1$, for all but a few exceptional cases. The change in frequency, relative to the source frequency, is very small and usually difficult to detect. Conventional light sources usually have a bandwidth considerably larger than the Doppler shift (at reasonable velocities) and the Doppler shift cannot easily be measured from the broadened signal. A notable exception is the red shift or apparent recession noted by astronomers in studying the emission spectra of stellar bodies (1). The red shift is the displacement of the spectra of the source toward the red end of the spectrum. This is apparently due to a Doppler shift caused by the relative recession velocity between

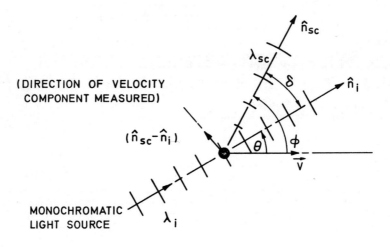

$$\nu_p \;=\; \frac{c - \vec{V} \cdot \hat{n}_i}{\lambda_i} \;=\; \frac{c}{\lambda_i}\left(1 - \frac{\vec{V}}{c} \cdot \hat{n}_i\right)$$

$$\lambda_{sc} \;=\; \frac{c - \vec{V} \cdot \hat{n}_{sc}}{\nu_p} \;=\; \lambda_i\left(\frac{1 - \frac{\vec{V}}{c} \cdot \hat{n}_{sc}}{1 - \frac{\vec{V}}{c} \cdot \hat{n}_i}\right)$$

$$\nu_D \;=\; \nu_{sc} - \nu_i \;=\; \nu_i\left(\frac{\frac{\vec{V}}{c} \cdot (\hat{n}_{sc} - \hat{n}_i)}{1 - \frac{\vec{V}}{c} \cdot \hat{n}_{sc}}\right)$$

$$\left|\vec{V}\right| \ll c$$

$$\nu_D \;\simeq\; \nu_i \,\frac{\vec{V}}{c} \cdot (\hat{n}_{sc} - \hat{n}_i) \;=\; \frac{n\vec{V}}{\lambda_0} \cdot (\hat{n}_{sc} - \hat{n}_i)$$

Fig. 12-1   Frequency shift for light scattered from a moving particle

the stellar source and the earth. An interesting, though perhaps irrelevant, point is that the further the star is from the earth, the greater the frequency shift. This forms the basis of the expanding universe theory of celestial mechanics. Star velocities of the order of 40,000 Km/sec (or, about 0.13 times the velocity of light) at distances of 250 million light years have been detected (2). Velocities of this order of magnitude are rare in non-astronomical systems and thus, for light sources with normal bandwidths, the optical Doppler effect is rarely employed for velocity detection.

It is the introduction of lasers that permits measurement of terrestial values of velocity by optical heterodyne techniques. The laser is a source of essentially coherent radiation of extremely narrow bandwidth. A single axial mode of a He-Ne laser operating at 632.8 mμ ($\nu \sim 5 \times 10^{14}$ Hz) has a bandwidth of about 10 Hz. In comparison, the green mercury line at 546.1 mμ ($\nu \sim 6 \times 10^{14}$ Hz) has a bandwidth of 8×10^8 Hz, which is representative of line widths associated with conventional monochromatic light sources. The Doppler shift of light from a laser source caused by motion of an emitter or reflector moving at moderate speed is still small compared to the source frequency, but it is large compared to the source bandwidth and is thus detectable by heterodyne techniques. Yeh and Cummins (3) (4) first suggested and successfully demonstrated the laser-Doppler technique for measuring fluid velocities in 1964. From the Doppler shift of laser light scattered by particles in flowing water, they measured the laminar velocity profile in a round tube.

The purpose of this paper is to indicate the factors to be considered in the design and application of the laser Doppler system for the measurement of fluid velocity. The advantages, capabilities and limitations of the system are pointed out and analyzed and a bibliography of recent work in this area is included. A limited amount of data from various investigations is presented for the purpose of illustrating the type of information available and specific variations in system design are considered to illustrate design alternatives. The necessary design criteria are specified sufficiently to permit the design of different systems, each best suited for the particular flow to be studied.

Velocity Measurement from Doppler Shift

The Doppler shift is as familiar as the well-known whistle-tooting trainman. The effect for scattered waves is somewhat different than that for emitted ones. A heuristic, nonrelativistic derivation can be made with reference to Fig. 12-1.

Monochromatic radiation of wavelength λ_i, and speed c, emanates from a stationary source. In Fig. 12-1, the radiation passes in the direction defined by the unit vector $\hat{n}_i$ and illuminates a particle having a velocity $\vec{v}$ (where $|\vec{v}| \ll c$).

If the particle were motionless, the number of wave fronts passing - or striking - it per unit time would be c/λ_i (or ν_i). Since, from a nonrelativistic viewpoint, the difference between the velocity of the particle and the illumination is:

$$c - \vec{v} \cdot \hat{n}_i$$

the number of wave fronts incident upon the particle per unit time (or the apparent frequency to the particle) is:

$$\nu_p = (c - \vec{v} \cdot \hat{n}_i)/\lambda_i \qquad \text{Eq. 12-1}$$

This is also the number of wave fronts scattered per unit time by the moving particle.

Consider now a fixed observer toward which a moving particle is emitting - or scattering - radiation in the direction defined by the unit vector $\hat{n}_{sc}$, the number of wave fronts scattered or emitted being ν_p. After the scattering of one wave front, the particle moves toward that wave front with the speed $\vec{v} \cdot \hat{n}_{sc}$. Thus, when the next wave front is scattered after a time interval given by $1/\nu_p$, the first wave front is a distance:

$$(c - \vec{v} \cdot \hat{n}_{sc}) \, \nu_p$$

away from the particle. Thus, to a fixed observer, the apparent wavelength of the scattered radiation is:

$$\lambda_{sc} = \frac{c - \vec{v} \cdot \hat{n}_{sc}}{\nu_p} = \lambda_i \left(\frac{c - \vec{v} \cdot \hat{n}_{sc}}{c - \vec{v} \cdot \hat{n}_i} \right) \qquad \text{Eq. 12-2}$$

The frequency of the scattered radiation to the fixed observer is:

$$\nu_D = \nu_{sc} - \nu_i \qquad \text{Eq. 12-3}$$

The total Doppler shift ν_D is determined from:

$$\nu_{sc} = \frac{c}{\lambda_{sc}} = \frac{c}{\lambda_i} \frac{c - \vec{v} \cdot \hat{n}_i}{c - \vec{v} \cdot \hat{n}_{sc}} = \nu_i \left[\frac{1 - \dfrac{\vec{v} \cdot \hat{n}_i}{c}}{1 - \dfrac{\vec{v} \cdot \hat{n}_{sc}}{c}} \right] \qquad \text{Eq. 12-4}$$

or:

$$\nu_D = \nu_i \left[\frac{1 - \dfrac{\vec{v} \cdot \hat{n}_i}{c}}{1 - \dfrac{\vec{v} \cdot \hat{n}_{sc}}{c}} \right] - \nu_i = \frac{\nu_i}{c} \frac{\vec{v} \cdot (\hat{n}_{sc} - \hat{n}_i)}{\dfrac{\vec{v} \cdot \hat{n}_{sc}}{c}} \qquad \text{Eq. 12-5}$$

It should be noted that even though the foregoing derivation is simplified, the same equation is obtained in the complete relativistic derivation (Eq. 12-5).

Since $|\vec{v}| \ll c$;

$$\nu_D \simeq \frac{n\vec{v}}{\lambda_o} \cdot (\hat{n}_{sc} - \hat{n}_i) \qquad \text{Eq. 12-6}$$

where λ_o is the vacuum wavelength of the incident radiation and n is the index of refraction in the medium surrounding the particle.

Note that, if the directions of the incoming and scattered light beams are fixed (which would be the usual case), the frequency shift gives the component of velocity in the direction given by $(\hat{n}_{sc} - \hat{n}_i)$. This differs from measurements taken with either an impact tube or hot wire anemometer and greatly enhances our techniques for measuring the direction of the velocity.

In practice, the Doppler frequency is determined by an optical heterodyne technique. An optical heterodyne receiver uses a photocathode to mix the scattered (Doppler shifted) beam with a reference beam from the same laser to generate a current whose a.c. component has a frequency equal to the difference frequency. The assumption in this technique is that the probability for the emission of an electron from the photocathode - and thus the photoelectric current - is proportional to the intensity of the light which is incident upon it. However, the intensity of the light is proportional to the square of the total electric field intensity. If two sine waves of different frequency are superimposed on a photocathode, the result is an output signal whose amplitude is modulated by the difference frequency - or Doppler frequency in the present study. Since the photocathode acts as a square law detector, this output signal will vary sinusoidally at the difference frequency.

Consider two monochromatic light beams of slightly different frequency combined on the surface of a photocathode. The two light beams may be represented by:

$$E_1 = E_{10} \sin 2\pi \nu_o t$$

$$E_2 = E_{20} \sin 2\pi (\nu_o + \nu_D) t$$

The output current i is proportional to the square of the total electric field incident on it:

$$i \sim (E_1 + E_2)^2 \qquad \text{Eq. 12-7}$$

Although the photomultiplier is capable of following frequencies up to several hundred megahertz, the frequency of visible light, ν_o, is on the order of 10^8 MHz. Terms in the expansion of i having frequencies of the order of ν_o will result in a d.c. current proportional to the time average of those terms. If ν_D is below the frequency response limit of the photomultiplier, there will also be an a.c. component. For $\nu_D \ll \nu_o$, equation 12-7 reduces to:

$$i \sim \left[\frac{E_{10}{}^2 + E_{20}{}^2}{2} + E_{10} E_{20} \sin 2\pi (\nu_D t + \xi) \right] \qquad \text{Eq. 12-8}$$

where ξ is a phase angle which is constant if the two beams are coherent. The first term is the d.c. current and the second term is the a.c. or Doppler current. To determine the velocity, the spectrum of the photomultiplier current is analyzed and the resulting Doppler frequency is used in equation 12-6.

The velocity at any point in a flowing fluid can be determined by measuring the frequency shift in laser radiation scattered from particles carried with the fluid. The particles used as scattering centers should be very small (sub micron) and neutrally bouyant, and the particle concentration should be quite low. Flow disturbances introduced by the particles can be made negligible in comparison to those produced by conventional velocity probes, and the particles can be assumed to flow at the same velocity as the fluid. All the information concerning the velocity of the fluid at the point observed is contained in the frequency of the scattered light. The apparatus may be set up to measure the velocity component in any desired direction or, with a properly designed system, the full velocity vector may be determined by simultaneously measuring the velocity components in three different directions. The information available, with suitable electronic processing, includes the average or mean velocity, turbulent intensity, scale and power spectrum, Reynolds stresses, etc. In addition, the range of velocities which can be measured is quite extensive.

The basic laser-Doppler technique has been employed in a number of studies. Yeh and Cummins (4) measured the fully developed laminar velocity profile for water flowing in a circular duct. Laminar flow development has been studied in a square duct (6) and in a round duct (7) (8) for water at low Reynolds numbers. Studies have been performed with water (9), (10) (11) and dilute water-polymer solutions (12) covering the range from laminar flow, through transition to full turbulence including measurement of turbulence intensity as well as velocity. Studies of turbulent flow have been made in gases (13), (14), (15), (16), (17) and in rocket and jet exhausts (18), (19).

Lasers have been used in other systems to measure velocities. In one study a short duration high intensity laser pulse generates a line of ionized particles which are used as tracers in a plasma flow to measure the velocity profile (20). Turbulent flow information has been obtained by the crossed beam correlation technique (21) wherein two laser beams are passed though the same point in a flow field and electronically processed to obtain the covariance between the two transmitted beams. Obviously, the Doppler technique can be used to detect the velocity of any body from which laser light may be scattered and observed. Systems have been devised for detection of distance, velocity and acceleration of moving solid bodies (22) and to study clear air turbulence (23), (24). In a somewhat related study, the electron temperature in a plasma has been determined from the Doppler broadening of a laser beam scattered by electrons (25). A bibliography of laser applications of all types (26) has recently been compiled.

Optimization of Scattering Geometry

Intensity of Scattered Light

In the design of a laser-Doppler system for measuring fluid velocities, there are several parameters related to the optical design which must be considered. One matter of concern is the minimum intensity of the scattered light which can be satisfactorily measured. The relative scattered intensity, I_s, is given approximately by (27):

$$\frac{I_s}{I_i} \propto V_{sc} N\sigma \qquad \text{Eq. 12-9}$$

where I_i is the intensity of the incident radiation, V_{sc} is the scattering volume. N is the particle density and σ is the scattering cross section for a particle. Increasing I_i, V_{sc}, N or σ increases the scattered light intensity. For a particular problem, I_i is fixed by the power of the laser available, although focusing of the beam on the scattering volume can significantly increase the intensity ($I_i V_{sc}^{2/3} \sim$ constant). In most applications the scattering volume should be as small as possible to obtain a highly localized measurement. The particle density should not be too large or multiple scattering and particle interactions which disturb the flow may occur. The scattering cross section σ is often a complicated function of angle, wave length and particle size (27), (28) but, in general, for small angles, the scattered intensity falls off rapidly as the scattering angle is increased. Thus, the scattering angle should be as small as possible, as dictated by other design criteria described below.

Magnitude of Frequency Shift

A second parameter which must be considered in optimizing the system geometry is the velocity detection sensitivity, or the magnitude of frequency shift per velocity increment. In many applications, it may be desirable to get the maximum sensitivity to increase accuracy. However, if very large velocities are to be considered, the system sensitivity may have to be decreased to avoid surpassing the frequency range of the detection equipment. The following analysis indicates the optical design to stay within the frequency range of the analyzing equipment for a given velocity range, retaining the highest system sensitivity.

The Doppler shift is given by equation 12-6. Referring to Fig. 12-1 and performing the indicated dot product:

$$\nu_D = \frac{nv}{\lambda_o} (\cos \phi - \cos \theta) \qquad \text{Eq. 12-10}$$

or:

$$\nu_D = 2 \frac{nv}{\lambda_o} \sin \frac{\delta}{2} \sin \left(\theta + \frac{\delta}{2}\right) \qquad \text{Eq. 12-11}$$

The equation is expressed in the latter form to simplify the calculations involved in optimizing the measurement with respect to the scattering angle δ and the incidence angle θ.

It should be noted from equation 12-6 that the maximum velocity detection sensitivity is obtained for direct back scatter (i.e. $\theta = 0$, $\phi = \delta = \pi$ or $\phi = 0$, $\theta = \delta = \pi$). In general for a given value of $\delta < \pi$, maximum sensitivity is obtained when the difference vector $(\hat{n}_{sc} - \hat{n}_i)$ is in the direction of the velocity vector $\vec{v}$ (i.e. $\theta + \frac{\delta}{2} = \frac{\pi}{2}$).

The system is insensitive to the velocity if the difference vector is perpendicular to the velocity vector.

If the frequency limit of the detection apparatus is ν_m and the maximum velocity which is to be measured is v_m, then the limitation on the angles δ and θ can be specified from equation 12-11:

$$\frac{\lambda_o \nu_m}{2 n v_m} \geq \left| \sin \frac{\delta}{2} \sin (\theta + \frac{\delta}{2}) \right| \qquad \text{Eq. 12-12}$$

The inequality equation 12-12 must be satisfied to stay within the frequency range of the detection equipment. In many applications, frequency limitations will not be significant and the optimal configuration for maximum sensitivity will correspond to $(\theta + \frac{\delta}{2}) = \pm \frac{\pi}{2}$. This arrangement has the added advantages of symmetry, which facilitates system alignment, and minimum bandwidth as indicated below.

Signal Bandwidth

The third condition to be considered is that of minimum signal bandwidth. The analysis will be made first on the basis of geometrical optics, neglecting diffraction effects associated with the wave properties of light. Assuming ν_D to be a function of θ and ϕ and taking differentials of equation 12-10, we get:

$$d\nu_D = \frac{nv}{\lambda_o} [\sin\theta \, d\theta - \sin\phi \, d\phi] \qquad \text{Eq. 12-13}$$

The quantity $d\theta$ can be interpreted to be the angular spread in the light incident on the scattering volume due to the focusing lens, defined by $d\theta = (\frac{A}{f})_i$, where A is the aperture (or beam diameter) and f is the focal length. The quantity $d\phi$ may be interpreted to represent the angular spread in light received by the photomultiplier. The calculation of the effective receiver angle $d\phi$ depends on the type of optics employed to limit the region from which scattered light is observed by the photomultiplier. For the present, the definition $d\phi = \Omega$ will be used, where the specific interpretation of this quantity is given in a later section. The general expression for the relative signal bandwidth, $(d\nu_D/\nu_D)$ may be expressed as follows, using equations 12-10, 12-11 and 12-13.

$$\frac{d\nu_D}{\nu_D} = \frac{(\frac{A}{f})_i \sin \theta - \Omega \sin \phi}{\cos \phi - \cos \theta}$$

$$= \frac{1}{2} \left\{ (\frac{A}{f})_i \left[\text{ctn} \frac{\delta}{2} - \text{ctn} (\theta - \frac{\delta}{2}) \right] - \Omega \left[\text{ctn} \frac{\delta}{2} + \text{ctn} (\theta + \frac{\delta}{2}) \right] \right\}$$

Since ϕ and θ are independent, the broadening effect due to each should be cumulative. The relative signal broadening $(d\nu_D/\nu_D)$ is thus:

$$\frac{d\nu_D}{\nu_D} = \frac{1}{2} \left\{ (\frac{A}{f})_i \text{ctn} \frac{\delta}{2} - \text{ctn} (\theta + \frac{\delta}{2}) + \Omega \left[\text{ctn} \frac{\delta}{2} + \text{ctn} (\theta + \frac{\delta}{2}) \right] \right\} \qquad \text{Eq. 12-14}$$

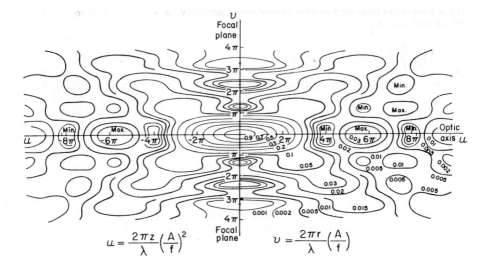

$$u = \frac{2\pi z}{\lambda}\left(\frac{A}{f}\right)^2 \qquad v = \frac{2\pi r}{\lambda}\left(\frac{A}{f}\right)$$

Fig. 12-2   Intensity contours near focus of a converging spherical wave diffracted at a circular aperture (Linfoot and Wolf)

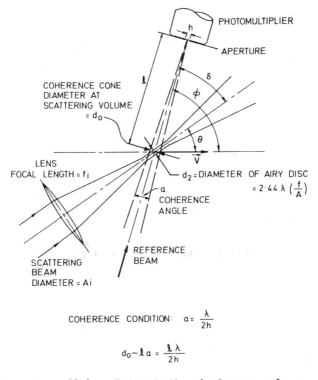

COHERENCE CONDITION: $a = \dfrac{\lambda}{2h}$

$$d_0 \sim \ell\, a = \frac{\ell\,\lambda}{2h}$$

Fig. 12-3   Determination of coherence volume

If the system is designed to give maximum sensitivity, $\theta + \frac{\delta}{2} = \pm \frac{\pi}{2}$ and equation 12-14 reduces to:

$$\left(\frac{d\nu_D}{\nu_D}\right) = \frac{1}{2}\left[\left(\frac{A}{f}\right)_i + \Omega\right] \text{ctn}\, \frac{\delta}{2} \qquad\qquad \text{Eq. 12-15}$$

Equation 12-15 has been experimentally verified for the case where $\Omega \ll \left(\frac{A}{f}\right)_i$ (9).

It should be noted here that the configuration where $(\theta + \frac{\delta}{2}) = \pm \frac{\pi}{2}$ eliminates two terms in equation 12-14 and is thus optimal both for maximum sensitivity and minimum bandwidth (for fixed δ) considerations.

It is interesting to note that equation 12-15 can also be derived by considering the wave properties of light (cf 11) as opposed to the strictly geometric approach employed above. In the volume from which scattered light is observed, a particle is present for only a short time, and thus scatters a wave train of finite length. A finite wave train, of duration Δt, from a monochromatic source has an effective frequency range of the order of the reciprocal of the time Δt. In fact (29):

$$\Delta t\, \Delta\nu \geqslant \frac{1}{4\pi} \qquad\qquad \text{Eq. 12-16}$$

This relation is analogous to the Heisenberg uncertainty principle in quantum mechanics. In many cases of practical application, the inequality may be replaced by an order of magnitude sign.

An intensity profile of the region near the focal point is shown in Fig. 12-2 (30), from which the size of the scattering volume can be visualized. The depth of field or longitudinal dimension is given by (29):

$$d_1 = 4\lambda \left(\frac{f}{A}\right)_i^2 \qquad\qquad \text{Eq. 12-17}$$

and the diameter of the Airy disc is given by (29):

$$d_2 = 2.44\lambda \left(\frac{f}{A}\right)_i \qquad\qquad \text{Eq. 12-18}$$

The time Δt may be approximated by the time in which a particle passes through a cylinder of diameter d_2 and length large compared to d_2 (c.f. Fig. 12-3):

$$\Delta t \simeq \frac{d_2}{v \sin\theta}$$

$$\Delta\nu \sim \frac{1}{4\pi}\, \frac{v \sin\theta}{2.44\lambda \left(\frac{f}{A}\right)_i}$$

Employing equation 12-11 and applying the condition $\theta + \frac{\delta}{2} = \pm \frac{\pi}{2}$, the above reduces to:

$$\frac{\Delta\nu_D}{\nu_D} \sim \left[\frac{1}{2.44\,(4\pi)}\right] \frac{1}{2}\text{ctn}\, \frac{\delta}{2}\, \left(\frac{A}{f}\right)_i \qquad\qquad \text{Eq. 12-19}$$

This result differs from equation 12-15 only by the constant. It represents a lower bound only due to the inequality (Eq. 12 - 16). The important point to note is that the same functional relationship is obtained by both approaches. The concept of angular uncertainty in the focused light in the scattering volume need not be considered in this approach since, by wave theory, the wave fronts are plane and parallel in the focal region. The angular uncertainty due to the acceptance angle at the photomultiplier is significant however and should be included in the broaden-

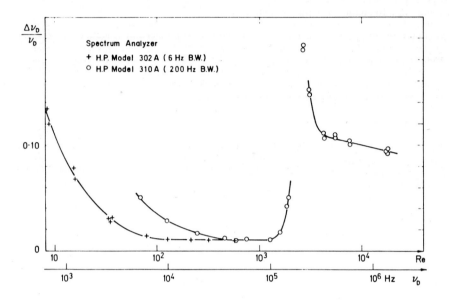

Fig. 12-4   Relative line widths as a function of Reynolds number

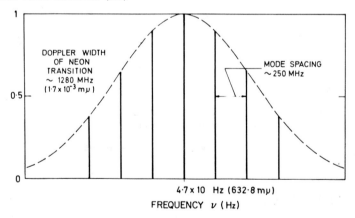

Fig. 12-5   He Ne laser output spectrum, sixty centimeter length seven exited axial modes

ing calculation, as discussed above.

Figure 12-4 is a plot of signal bandwidth, measured at the half power point, vs Reynolds number, for velocity measurements on the centerline of a circular duct. At very low Re (small Doppler frequency, ν_D) the major contribution to signal bandwidth is due to the bandwidth of the spectrum analyzer employed. As the Doppler frequency becomes large compared with the instrument bandwidth, the relative bandwidth, $(\Delta\nu_D/\nu_D)$, approaches a constant value, in laminar flow, as predicted by equation 12-15. The data in Fig. 12-4 was taken employing two spectrum analyzers with bandwidths of 6 and 200 Hz respectively. The data corresponding to the analyzer with the larger bandwidth is considerably broadened at low Doppler frequency but approaches the same value of $(\Delta\nu_D/\nu_D)$ as the data from the small bandwidth analyzer as ν_D gets large. The sudden increase in bandwidth at Re ~ 2300 is due to the transition to turbulent flow.

The net result of the above is that the signal broadening, $(\Delta\nu_D/\nu_D)$, is proportional to the cotangent of the scattering angle δ. Thus, to minimize broadening, δ should be made as large as the particular application will allow. This is in opposition to the requirement that δ be as small as possible to obtain high signal intensity. The actual design of a laser Doppler system depends on the particular application at hand and no generalization can be made which will satisfy all requirements completely.

Another factor that influences the signal width is a velocity gradient in the flow. The magnitude of the broadening due to gradients can be estimated from equation 12-10, from which we get:

$$\frac{\Delta\nu_D}{\nu_D} = \frac{1}{v}\ \frac{\partial v}{\partial y}\ \Delta y \qquad\qquad \text{Eq. 12-20}$$

where Δy can be interpreted as the dimension of the scattering volume perpendicular to the direction of the velocity component measured. The broadening predicted by equation 12-20 must, in general, be added to the result of equation 12-15. If a large velocity gradient is present, equation 12-20 will, in fact, represent the major cause of signal broadening. For slowly varying or uniform flows, gradient broadening may be neglected, as is the case for the data shown in Fig. 12-4.

Signal to Noise Ratio

Another variable which influences the design of the laser-Doppler system is the relative strengths of the scattered and reference beams. The noise current in the photomultiplier tube consists of several components of varying magnitude and importance depending on the application. When used as an optical heterodyne receiver, as in the laser Doppler system, high current levels are usually employed such that noise contributions due to the dark current are negligible. Background noise due to extraneous light from the room is virtually eliminated by using an interference filter, centered at the laser frequency with a very narrow band pass, placed immediately ahead of the phototube. The major source of noise in the tube itself is shot noise, which is roughly proportional to the current level, or equivalently, the total light intensity incident on the photocathode. An additional noise component arises due to noise in the laser. Ideally, if the beam path lengths are exactly the same, laser noise may not be significant but in general it will be present.

An extensive discussion of the parameters effecting the system signal to noise ratio may be found in (31), (32), (33). The important results may be stated as follows. The signal to noise ratio is roughly proportional to the intensity of the scattered beam and is a maximum, for a given scattered beam intensity, when the reference beam is about ten times as intense as the scattered beam. The above

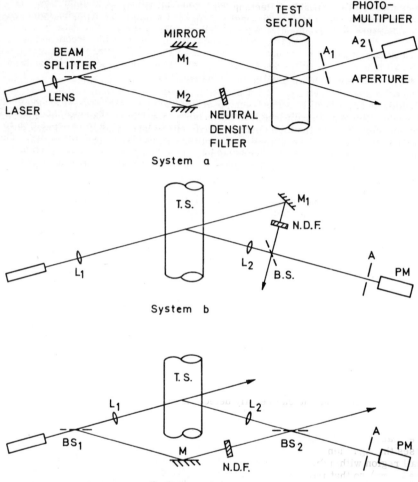

Fig. 12-6   Examples of optical geometry

results have been experimentally verified by several investigators (4), (6), (7), (8). As the signal to noise ratio is proportional to the scattered beam intensity, the requirement that δ should be small to get a high intensity scattered beam is reinforced.

The relative intensity of the two beams is adjusted by placing a neutral density filter in the reference beam. Calibrated sets of reflective and absorbtive filters are commercially available. Rectangular and circular variable filters can be obtained for any range of optical density desired. A polarizer filter could be used as a substitute or in conjunction with a neutral density filter.

Effect of Path Length

Another requirement in mixing the two light beams is that the optical path lengths of the scattered and reference light beams should be the same or differ by integral multiples of 2L, where L is the laser resonator cavity length. However, the allowable difference in path length is much larger for lasers than for non-coherent light sources owing to the high spectral purity of the laser radiation. For a given laser cavity, the allowable difference in path length varies inversely with the number of excited modes in the laser output. For example, employing a sixty centimeter laser with seven excited axial modes (fig. 12-5), a path length difference of ten centimeters results in signal intensity loss of about 20% whereas at forty centimeters the signal is no longer detectable. Curves for relative signal amplitude as a function of path length difference, for lasers with one to twenty-one axial modes are available (34).

Basic Optical Geometry

As mentioned above, Doppler frequency detection by optical heterodyning requires that the Doppler shifted light beam must be made coincident with and parallel to the reference beam at the photocathode. Figure 12-6 illustrates three optical systems which accomplish the beam superposition in slightly different ways. Figure 12-6 is drawn to show only the basic geometry of the alternative systems. Placement of mirrors, filters, lenses, etc. in the figure are representative of particular systems which have been successfully employed, however, the geometry can be varied considerably from that shown.

The design in Fig. 12-6a accomplishes the beam superposition quite simply with the added benefit that one can readily detect visually the point at which the velocity measurement is being made. The laser beam is split into two beams which are focused at the same point in the flow. The photomultiplier is placed in the reference beam behind two apertures which are placed so that the reference beam just passes through them. Only that portion of the scattered light which comes from a small region within the common focal point will fulfill the coherence requirements (see below) so that interference will occur. Aperture A_2 acts as a shield for non-coherent scattered light and background light. Actually this design can be used with only one aperture. The intersection of the two beams is the region at which the velocity is measured and can easily be observed for alignment. To obtain the optimal signal, fine adjustment of the beams can be made while monitoring the photomultiplier signal on an oscilloscope.

The system illustrated in Fig. 12-6b focuses the full laser beam at a point in the flow. Light scattered from the focal region is then recombined with the reference beam which is the transmitted portion of the original beam. The system in Fig. 12-6c does essentially the same thing except that the reference beam is split off before scattering and follows a path outside the test section to be recombined with the scattered light. Both of these systems, 12-6b and 12-6c accomplish the super-

position by directing both the scattered and reference beams at the splitter plate
in such a way that the reflected portion of the reference beam is coincident with
and parallel to the transmitted portion of the scattered beam. This can be very
difficult to accomplish because of the severe alignment criteria which must be met
in combining the two beams. In addition, part of the already weak scattered beam
is reflected and lost giving a loss in signal power. In system 12-6a, the scattered
light goes directly to the photomultiplier and is neither reflected from a mirror nor
transmitted through a splitter plate, thus minimizing losses and distortion. It
should also be noted that systems 12-6a and 12-6c allow for easy adjustment of
beam path length difference for optimal signal as previously discussed. System
12-6b must be set up so that the paths differ by 2jL, where j is an integer, if one
wishes to get the maximum possible signal.

Another laser-Doppler technique, which is not illustrated here, employs a laser
which has partially silvered mirrors at both ends of the resonator cavity (35).
The laser beam from one end is focused at the region of interest and back scattered
light is allowed to re-enter the laser cavity. Beats are set up inside the cavity and
the laser output is modulated as a whole at the Doppler frequency. The output from
the opposite end of the laser is directed at a photomultiplier as in the other systems.
The primary difference in this system is that the laser itself acts not only as the
source but also as the beam mixer and signal amplifier. Difficulties are encountered involving image reflections etc.

Scattering Volume

An important advantage of the Doppler velocity meter technique is the ability to
make highly localized velocity measurements. The size of the scattering volume,
defined as the volume from which scattered radiation is observed, can be estimated
from the geometry of the system used to collect scattered light. When focused
optics are used the diffraction limited spot size at the focal point is given by
equation 12-18 . The size of the scattering volume can be approximated by a
cylinder, whose diameter is the diameter of the Airy disc in the focused incident
beam, d_2, and whose length is determined by the receiver optics.

An important limitation on the length of the scattering volume arises from considering coherence requirements between the scattered and reference beams. If
the two beams arrive at the photocathode differing by a small angle α, an interference pattern will result in which the fringe spacing q is given by:

$$q = \frac{\lambda}{\sin \alpha}$$

$$\simeq \frac{\lambda}{\alpha}$$

When the photomultiplier aperture h(Fig. 12-3) is small compared to q, only a
small portion of one fringe will fall on the photocathode. If the frequencies of the
two wave trains are slightly different, as in the laser-Doppler system, the phase
difference between the two beams at the given point varies sinusoidally as does
the photo-current from the point in question. However, if $h \gg q$ a number of
interference fringes are incident on the photocathode. The sum of the currents
from all points on the photosurface yields a constant d.c. current and the Doppler
current cannot be detected. The criterion for a given misalignment angle α, is
that the diameter of the area illuminated on the photocathode should be less than
one-half fringe width $h < \frac{1}{2}q$, or:

$$\alpha < \frac{\lambda}{2h}$$

For all light waves with angles less than α, the corresponding fringe spacing q is even larger and the coherence requirement is fulfilled.

A more complete analysis will show that the strength of the signal falls to zero for $\alpha h/\lambda = j$, where j is an integer (11), (29), (31). The signal rises to smaller and smaller maximums between each integer value as j increases from unity. If we choose $\alpha = \lambda/2h$ as the maximum value of the difference angle for good mixing, then the diameter of a cone of angle α at the scattering volume will give the diameter of the region from which scattering may effectively be observed. Referring to Fig. 12-3, if the photocathode is a distance ℓ from the scattering volume, the diameter of the coherence cone at the scattering volume, d_o, can be estimated from:

$$\alpha \simeq \frac{d_o}{\ell} = \frac{\lambda}{2h}$$

$$d_o = \frac{\lambda \ell}{2h} \qquad\qquad \text{Eq. 12-21}$$

Thus the diameter of the coherence cone at the scattering volume, d_o, can be adjusted by proper choice of ℓ and h. Scattering occurs from all points in the focal region, but only that portion scattered within the coherence angle and within the field of view of the receiver optics will contribute to the Doppler current. Increasing the size of the region illuminated on the photocathode decreases the size of the coherence volume; however, the total amount of scattered and reference light received will increase, as will the d.c. current and the noise. A smaller scattering volume then, results in a decrease in the signal to noise ratio in addition to the other limitations described below.

The problems of specifying the length dimension of the scattering volume and the angular spread in the scattered beam Ω have arisen several times and will be considered at this time. The first possibility which suggests itself is to use the diameter of the coherence cone at the scattering volume as the length dimension, (Fig.12-3). The angular spread in the scattered light could then be taken as the coherence angle α. However, one also has to consider the diameter of the region from which scattered light can reach the photocathode, as defined by the aperture system or collecting lens used in the receiver optics. If the diameter so defined is smaller than the coherence cone diameter, then this is the dimension which should be used. In this case, Ω can be defined analogous to the definition of the incident angular light spread, $(d\theta = (\frac{A}{f})_i)$ or $\Omega = (\frac{A}{f})_{sc}$, for the case of a collecting lens with aperture A_{sc} and focal length f_{sc}. With a double aperture system, (Fig. 12-6a), Ω is the receiver acceptance angle defined by the two apertures, where $\Omega \sim \frac{A_2 + A_1}{d}$ where d is the distance between the two apertures.

It is possible to adjust the relative magnitude of the coherence angle and the receiver acceptance angle such that either can be the defining factor in determining the scattering volume dimension. The choice must be made on the basis of the specific requirements of the application considered.

To maximize scattered beam intensity and to minimize the scattering volume, the incoming beam has usually been focused on the region of interest within the flow. Care must be taken in focusing a high power laser beam in a fluid, since heating effects in the region of the focal point can be appreciable and could possibly perturb the flow to the extent that the particles might even be deformed or destroyed. Natural convection due to the energy input could also occur. For turbulent flows, in cases where one wishes to study the micro-structure of the turbulence, it would be desirable to keep the scattering volume at least an order of magnitude smaller than the smallest turbulent eddies.

Although the size of the scattering volume can be made quite small, the number of scattering centers in the volume and the intensity of the scattered beam will fall off proportionally. In addition, the scattered light intensity will become intermittent due to the finite numbers of particles entering and leaving the scattering volume. To decrease the diameter of the scattering volume, a lens with a smaller focal length must be used causing increased broadening as predicted by equation 12-15. This is probably the most serious problem in making highly localized measurements if high precision is required. Along with a smaller scattering volume there is also, as indicated in the previous section, a corresponding decrease in the signal to noise ratio. The advantage gained in obtaining a small scattering volume can easily be outweighed by the losses in signal quality.

Velocity and Frequency Limitations

The range of velocities which lie within the capabilities of the laser-Doppler technique is limited by the inherent properties of the laser. The cavity which constitutes the active element of the laser is an optical resonator. Only those frequencies which satisfy the resonance condition, that the resonant cavity length is an integral multiple of one half the wave length, are amplified and thus constitute the output of the laser. The resonance condition is:

$$L = \frac{j\lambda_j}{2}$$

$$\nu_j = \frac{jc}{2L} \qquad\qquad \text{Eq. 12-23}$$

where j is an integer, L is the resonator length and λ_j and ν_j are corresponding possible resonant wave lengths and frequencies respectively. In the case of a He-Ne laser, those frequencies which lie within the Doppler width of the Neon transition at 632.8 mμ and which satisfy the resonance condition (eq. 12-23) are amplified and emitted. The resulting spectrum consists of several discrete peaks or modes centered at 632.8 mμ and separated by, (Fig. 12-5):

$$\Delta\lambda = \frac{\lambda_o^2}{2L} \qquad\qquad \text{Eq. 12-24}$$

Each mode is extremely narrow, the bandwidth being of the order of 10 Hz. Any velocity resulting in a Doppler shift which is less than this would not be easily resolvable. With this as a criterion, the minimum velocity measurable by Doppler velocity technique may be estimated:

$$\nu_D = \frac{n\vec{v}}{\lambda_o} \cdot (\hat{n}_{sc} - \hat{n}_i) \sim \frac{v}{\lambda_o}$$

$$v_{min} \sim 10 \text{ (Hz)} \; 632.8 \times 10^- \;\; (cm)$$

$$v_{min} \sim 10^- \;\; (\frac{cm}{sec})$$

The mode separation given by equation 12-24 gives an effective upper limit for velocities, in that if the velocity is high enough to produce a Doppler shift of the order of the mode separation, inter-modal beats will occur. For a multi-mode He-Ne laser with cavity length of one meter, the upper velocity limit from this criterion is:

$$\Delta\nu_{ms} \sim \frac{c}{2L} \sim 150 \text{ MHz}$$

$$v_{max} \sim \Delta\nu_{ms} \cdot \lambda_o \sim 100 \; \frac{m}{sec}$$

The frequency limit of a good photomultiplier is about the same order of magnitude as the mode separation or slightly greater. By proper choice of scattering angle, as discussed earlier, the upper limit on velocity can be increased to some extent. For measurements very near zero velocity, the reference beam may be frequency shifted by a fixed amount (3), (31). The Doppler shift is then superimposed on the known frequency shift. Similarly for very high frequencies a frequency translator can be used to decrease the Doppler frequency to values which can be handled with available receiving equipment (31).

Signal Detection and Analysis

Photomultiplier

The single most important device in the Doppler velocity meter apparatus, other than the laser, is the photomultiplier which functions as an optical heterodyne receiver and amplifier. A heterodyne receiver is a device which mixes two signals of different frequency and generates a third signal, whose frequency is equal to the difference in the frequencies of the input signals as described earlier. Photomultipliers are available which cover the entire visible spectrum from the ultraviolet to well into the infra-red (31), (32). The type of tube best suited for a particular application depends upon the laser to be used. The He-Ne laser is by far the most widely used at this time although other types of lasers, including those emitting in the infra-red, are now coming into use. The type S-20 tri-alkaline photomultiplier tube is probably best suited for use with He-Ne lasers, but its maximum sensitivity is at about 430 mμ and is about 40% of maximum at 632.8 mμ, the visible laser wavelength. A multi-stage tube should be used since scattered light intensities which are encountered are often low. An amplifier can be used to get further signal amplification, but it cannot compensate for insufficient tube sensitivity. If high velocity measurements are to be made, a tube should be selected which has sufficient frequency response to handle the highest frequencies to be encountered. In addition, a properly designed shielded housing should be used with the tube. Cooling is required only for very low level signals where dark current noise is appreciable.

When it is necessary to amplify the photomultiplier current prior to processing with the spectrum analysis equipment, a variable band, tunable amplifier can be used. In addition to amplification, a considerable amount of the noise can be filtered out by tuning the amplifier to the signal center frequency and narrowing the band as much as desired. No compromise with quality should be made if an amplifier is used, since any distortion introduced will be included and recorded in the final signal analysis. Turbulent measurements could be significantly altered by amplifier distortion.

Spectrum Analysis

The frequency spectrum of the photomultiplier current can be analyzed in several ways depending upon the information sought and the equipment available. A counter can be used to give the mean Doppler frequency directly. Perhaps the simplest technique is to display the voltage across the photomultiplier load resistor directly on an oscilloscope. The Doppler frequency can be determined directly from the oscilloscope screen if the velocity is steady or slowly varying but the accuracies attainable are limited and only the time average velocity at a point can be determined in this way. Even for turbulent flows, the signal can be monitored with an oscilloscope while measurements are made with a more suitable instrument. The oscilloscope is also useful when making fine adjustments in the optics since changes in signal quality are readily observable.

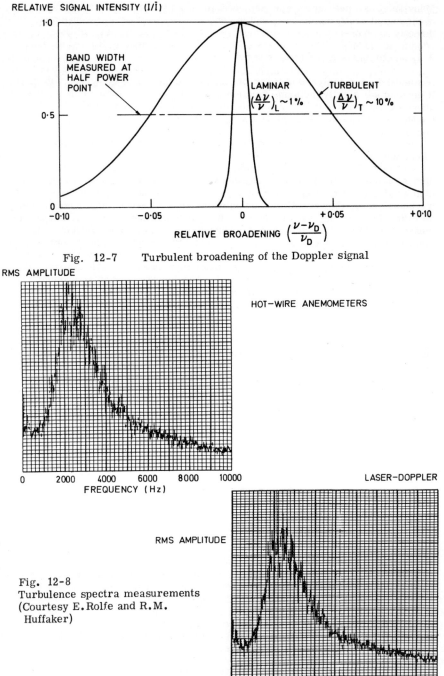

RELATIVE SIGNAL INTENSITY (I/Ī)

BAND WIDTH
MEASURED AT
HALF POWER
POINT

LAMINAR
$\left(\frac{\Delta \nu}{\nu}\right)_L \sim 1\%$

TURBULENT
$\left(\frac{\Delta \nu}{\nu}\right)_T \sim 10\%$

RELATIVE BROADENING $\left(\frac{\nu - \nu_D}{\nu_D}\right)$

Fig. 12-7   Turbulent broadening of the Doppler signal

RMS AMPLITUDE

HOT-WIRE ANEMOMETERS

FREQUENCY (Hz)

LASER-DOPPLER

RMS AMPLITUDE

Fig. 12-8
Turbulence spectra measurements
(Courtesy E. Rolfe and R.M.
  Huffaker)

FREQUENCY (Hz)

Many oscilloscopes accept plug-in spectrum analyzers which allow visual display of the signal spectrum directly on the screen. The time base is converted to read directly in frequency and the ordinate represents signal intensity at the corresponding frequency. The accuracy of this technique is usually limited to about 2-5% due to inherent limitations of the scope.

A standard wave analyzer is a narrow band audio and radio frequency volt meter. It performs basically the same function as the plug-in spectrum analyzer described above except that the tuning mechanism is hand or motor driven and the voltage-frequency display is recorded on a strip chart or x-y recorder.

Figure 12 -7 shows, in simplified form, the type of frequency spectrum obtained where the broadening due to turbulent flow for a particular application (6), (9) is illustrated. The instrument bandwidth is fixed although several bandwidths may be available in some models. Wave analyzers are available in a range of frequencies well up into the mega Hertz range. Due to the hand tuning feature of these wave analyzers, they are slow and applicable only for steady and slowly varying signals. They are however quite accurate and readily calibrated. Even turbulence measurements can be made from the bandwidth of the recorded Doppler signal, since this has been shown to produce the velocity probability function (9).

Another technique employs a scanning plate Fabry-Perot interferometer to measure the Doppler frequency (18), (19). The Fabry-Perot interferometer consists of two partially reflecting mirrors a given distance apart. Light which is transmitted is allowed to interfere with light which is reflected, the degree of interference being governed by the plate spacing and the frequency of the light. By moving one mirror, a variable frequency filter is obtained. By oscillating one mirror, the frequency spectrum of the incident light is scanned and the Doppler shift can be measured. This technique has been used to determine average linear velocity.

An interesting and potentially valuable technique for analyzing the frequency spectrum in the photomultiplier current is that of Rolfe and Huffaker (16). The a.c. component of the photomultiplier current is not a constant frequency a.c. signal but is frequency modulated due to turbulence in the flow, and amplitude modulated due to particle density variations and possibly other effects. The amplitude modulation is first eliminated with an amplitude limiter and the resultant signal is processed with a frequency discriminator which generates an analog voltage that is proportional to frequency. The analog voltage is recorded on magnetic tape to be spectrum analyzed at a convenient time. All the information concerning the fluid velocity is contained in the analog voltage. The recorded tapes are analyzed to obtain mean velocity, turbulent intensity, scale and power spectrum. An example of turbulent power spectra data obtained with such a device is compared with hot wire anemometer data in Fig. 12-8.

As mentioned above, the Doppler current is amplitude modulated and the signal has been observed to go to zero at times. This may be due to the small number of particles in the scattering volume so that at times no particles are present to scatter light to the photomultiplier. Although the frequency of the amplitude modulation is somewhat irregular, an estimate of its magnitude can be made from the oscilloscope trace. The modulation frequency is observed to vary proportionally with the velocity indicating that individual particles are indeed being observed as they pass through the scattering volume. Calculations indicate, however, that for a concentration of 30 ppm by volume of 0.5 micron particles and a spherical scattering volume with a diameter of 100 microns, there should be, on average, about thirty particles in the volume at a given time. The important point to note is that a frequency discriminator requires a constant input to function properly, a condition not satisfied by the a.c. photomultiplier current. The intermittent signal

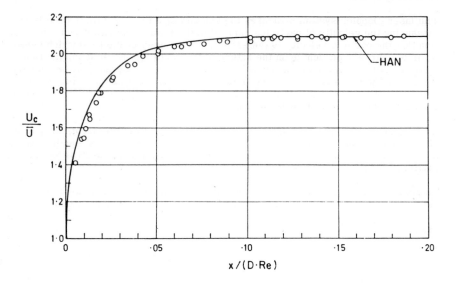

Fig. 12-9   Centerline velocity development

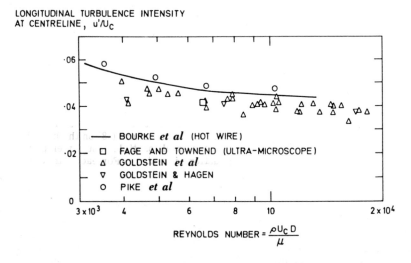

Fig. 12-10   Longitudinal intensity of turbulence measured at center of pipe as a function of centerline Reynolds number

results in high frequency noise in the discriminator output.

Scattering Centers

The laser-Doppler system measures the velocity of a flowing fluid indirectly by measuring the velocity of particles carried in the fluid. The validity of the assumption that the particle velocity is the same as the velocity of the fluid which surrounds it, is of course dependent upon the nature of the particle, the fluid and the flow. In a steady uniform flow a small particle which is neutrally bouyant will be carried along with the same velocity as the fluid. For turbulent flows however, or in other situations where the fluid velocity changes or when there are large velocity gradients, velocity differences can exist.

To minimize the drag force which the fluid must exert on the particle, the particles should be as small as possible. If, however, the particles are too small, Brownian motions will occur and will cause broadening of the frequency spectrum of the scattered light.

To prevent particles from settling, their density should be as near to the fluid density as possible. An estimate of settling velocity can be made by applying Stokes equation for drag on a sphere at low Reynolds number (36). Equating the drag force to the bouyancy force, one obtains:

$$v_s = \frac{(\gamma - 1)\, b^2 g}{18\, \eta} \qquad\qquad \text{Eq. 12-25}$$

where γ is the particle specific gravity (relative to the solvent fluid), and v_s is the settling velocity. With one-half micron polystyrene spheres (specific gravity 1.04) in water, Brownian motion gives rise to Doppler broadening of only 20 Hz (3) and the settling velocity, calculated from equation 12-25 is of the order of 0.2 mm/hr. Particles of this type have been satisfactorily employed by several investigators (3), (4), (6), (7), (8), (10) at concentrations of 10-50 parts per million.

It is more difficult to estimate the effect of turbulence in regard to velocity lag between fluid and particle. The micro-scale of isotropic turbulence is given (37) by:

$$s^2 = 15\, \frac{D\ell_e}{Re\, Tu}$$

where D is the duct diameter, ℓ_e the turbulence macroscale (approximately one half of the duct diameter D), Re is the Reynolds number based on duct diameter and average velocity and Tu is the turbulence intensity so for the conditions D = 1 cm, Re = 10^5 and Tu = 5%; s = 0.04 mm. Thus, the scale of the turbulence is much larger than the particles described above. A study (38) on the behavior of particles in turbulent flow indicates that the small particles usually employed follow satisfactorily the turbulent fluctuations in water. For each particle application similar calculations would have to be done to verify whether the particles involved follow fluid motions closely enough to give information about the turbulent motion of the fluid employed.

Other particles which have been used are naturally occuring dust (7), (10), (13) and milk (11) in water, and smoke combustion products (13), (15) and water mist (17), (19) in air. Research has been done on the detection of clear air turbulence (23), (24) where dust particles and air pollutants act as scatterers. Studies have been performed with large particles in rocket exhausts to measure particle lag (18), (19) but results obtained to date are limited. In such cases a broad range of particle sizes are encountered and problems of the nature described above may be significant.

Sample Results

To illustrate the capabilities of the technique the results of a few investigators are presented in Fig. 12-4, 12-8, 12-9, and 12-10. Figures 12-4 and 12-8 have already been discussed. Figure 12-9 represents the laminar flow development in a square duct obtained from experiments done early in the development of the Doppler technique (6). In this study, considerable pains were taken to establish the degree of accuracy of the system and the reproducibility of data taken with it. The data is compared with the approximate theory for flow development of Han (39), which for fully developed flow, reduces to the exact solution for laminar flow in a square duct. Measurement of the velocity at the center of the duct for fully developed flow gives a standard deviation of the data, and a difference from theory both of about 0.1%.

In addition to the average longitudinal velocity, considerable information is available concerning the turbulent components of the velocity. Since the velocity probability function (modified by the instrument bandwidth) can be obtained (9) much average information on the turbulent flow is available. The results of measurements taken in two investigations (9), (12) using the same apparatus for the longitudinal turbulence intensity on the center line of a circular tube are shown in Fig. 12-10. The experiment was repeated using a very similar apparatus (11) and the excellent agreement of the results can also be observed on the figure. Similar data taken with a hot wire anemometer (40) and with an ultramicroscope (41) are presented for comparison. The data of (11) and (41) had to be converted to Reynolds number based on centerline velocity where the conversion factor $(U_c/\overline{U}) \simeq 1.3$ (12) was used. Other data (10) were also converted in this way and found to agree in magnitude, although their trend is somewhat different.

Conclusion

The Doppler technique is a very recent development and its capabilities and limitations are just beginning to be fully examined and recognized. Research in this area both in application and in variation and improvements of technique is expanding at a rapid pace. The information presented herein is intended to be an outline of the principles involved in the design and operation of the Laser-Doppler system. A representative sample of studies which have been performed in this area is presented to indicate the capabilities of the technique as they have been applied to date.

References

1. **Hubble, E.,** 'A Relation Between Distance and Radial Velocity Among Extra-Galactic Nebulae', Proc. Nat. Sci., Wash., Vol 15, 168, 1929.

2. **Skilling, W. T., and Richardson, R. S.,** 'Astronomy' Rev. Ed. Henry Holt N.Y., 1951, p. 548.

3. **Cummins, H. Z., Knable, N. and Yeh, Y.,** 'Observation of Diffusion Broadening of Rayleigh Scattered Light', Phys. Rev. Letters, Vol 12, 150, 1964.

4. **Yeh, Y., and Cummins, H.,** 'Localized Fluid Flow Measurements With a He Ne Laser Spectrometer', Appl. Phys. Letters, Vol 4, 176, 1964.

5. **Temes, C. L.,** 'Relativistic Consideration of Doppler Shift', IRE Trans. Aero & Navig. Elect., Vol 6, 37, 1959.

6. **Goldstein, R. J., and Kreid, D. K.,** 'Measurement of Laminar Flow Development in a square Duct Using a Laser Doppler Flowmeter', J. Apl. Mech, Vol 34-E, 813, 1967.

7. **Foreman, J. W., Lewis, R. D., Thorton, J. R., and Watson, H. J.,** 'Laser Doppler Velocimeter for Measurement of Localized Flow Velocities in Liquids', Proc. I. E. E. E. Vol 54, 424, 1966.

8. **Berman, N. S., and Santos, V. A.,** 'Laminar Velocity Profiles in Developing Flows Using a Laser Technique', AIChE Journal, 15, 323, 1969.

9. **Goldstein, R. J., and Hagen, W. F.,** 'Turbulent Flow Measurements Utilizing the Doppler shift of Scattered Laser Radiation', Phys. of Fluids, Vol 10, 1349, 1967.

10. **Welch, N. E., and Tomme, W. J.,** 'The Analysis of Turbulence From Data Obtained with a Laser Velocimeter', 5th Aerospace Sciences Meeting AIAA Paper No. 67-179, 1967.

11. **Pike, E. B., Jackson, D. A., Bourke, P. J., and Page, D. I.,** 'Measurement of Turbulent Velocities From the Doppler Shift in Scattered Laser Radiation', J. Sci. Inst., Vol 1, 727, 1968.

12. **Goldstein, R. J., Adrian, R. J., and Kreid, D. K.,** 'Turbulent and Transition Pipe Flow of Dilute Polymer Solutions', to be published. I. & E. C. Fund., 8, 498, 1969.

13. **Foreman, J. W., George, E. W., Jetton, J. L., Lewis, R. D., Thorton, J. R., and Watson, H. J.,** 'Fluid Flow Measurements with a Laser Doppler Velocimeter', I. E. E. E. J. Quantum Elect., Vol 2, 260, 1966.

14. **Lewis, R. D., Foreman, J. W., and Watson, H. J.,** 'Laser Doppler Velocimeter for Measuring Flow Velocity Fluctuations', Phys. of Fluids, Vol 11, 433, 1968.

15. **Foreman, J. W., George, E. W., and Lewis, R. D.,** 'Measurement of Localized Flow Velocities in Gases with a Laser Doppler Flowmeter', Appl. Phys. Letters, Vol 7, 77, 1965.

e

16. **Rolfe, E., and Huffaker, R. M.,** Part I. 'Laser Doppler Velocity Instrumentation For Wind Tunnel Turbulence and Velocity Measurements', Paper Presented at George C. Marshall Sp. Fl. Center Specialist Conf. on Molec. Rad. Applic. to Diagnostic Techniques, 1967.

17. **Bond, R. L.,** 'Measurement of the Intensity of Turbulence', Status Prog. Rep., NASA Res. Gr. No. SC-NGR-04-001-015 N67-40512

18. **James, R. N., Babcock, W. R., and Seifert, H. S.,** 'Application of a Laser-Doppler Technique to the Measurement of Particle Velocity in Gas-Particle Two Phase Flow', Stanford Univ. Dept. of Aeronautics & Astronautics Rep. No. 265, 1966.

19. **James, R. N., Babcock, W. R., and Seifert, H. S.,** 'A Laser-Doppler Technique for the Measurement of Particle Velocity', AIAA J1 Vol 6, 160, 1968.

20. **Chen, C. J.,** 'Velocity Profile Measurement in Plasma Flows Using Tracers Produced by a Laser Beam', J. Appl. Phys., Vol 37, 3092, 1966.

21. **Fisher, M. J., and Krause, F. R.,** 'The Crossed beam Correlation Technique', J. Fl. Mech., Vol 28, 705, 1967.

22. **Watkins, M. C.,** 'Study of Laser Application to Velocity Measuring System', Tech. Sum. Rep. Phase IX. Tech. Rpt MDC-TR-67-136, U. S. A. F. Missile Dev. Center Holloman Base, N. Mexico, 1967.

23. **Bourquin, K. R., and Shigemoto, F. H.,** 'Investigation of Air Flow Velocity By Laser Backscatter', NASA Tech. Note D-4453, 1968.

24. **Zirkle, R. E., Jr.,** 'Study of Techniques for Detection and Measurement of Clear Air Turbulence', Final Rep. AFCRL 1966, p. 66.

25. **Ascoli-Bartoli, U.,** 'Plasma Diagnostic Based on Refractivity', Rapporto Interno LGI 64/17, Laboratorio Gas Ionizzati (Euratom C. N. E. N.) Frascarti, Roma, 1964.

26. **Stickley, C. M., and Gingrande, A.,** 'A Bibliography of Laser Applications', Air Force Cambridge Res. Lab., Rep. No. 67-0223, 1967.

27. **Davies, C. N.,** 'Aerosol Science', Academic Press, N. Y., 1966. pp. 287-355.

28. 'Tables of Scattering Functions for Spherical Particles', Dept. of Com., N. B. S. Math Ser. #4, 1949.

29. **Born, M., and Wolf, E.,** 'Principles of Optics', Second Ed. Permagon Press, Oxford, 1964, pp. 319, 441, 397.

30. **Linfoot, E. H., and Wolfe, E.,** 'Phase Distribution Near Focus in an Aberration Free Diffraction Image', Proc. Phys. Soc., B, Vol 69, 823, 1956.

31 **Ross, M.,** 'Laser Receivers', John Wiley, N. Y., 1966, pp. 98-115, 241.

32. **Siegman, A. E.,** 'The Antenna Properties of Optical Heterodyne Receivers', Proc. I. E. E. E., Vol 54, 1350, 1966.

33. **Stroke, G. W.,** 'An Introduction to Coherent Optics and Holography', Academic Press, N. Y., 1966, pp. 40-69.

34. **Foreman, J. W.,** 'Optical Path Length Difference Effects in Photomixing with Multimode Gas Laser Radiation', Appl. Optics, Vol 6, 821, 1967.

35. **Rudd, M. J.,** 'A Laser Doppler Velocimeter Employing the Laser as a Mixer-Oscillator', J. Sci. Inst., Vol 1, 223, 1968.

36. **Schlichting, H.,** 'Boundary Layer Theory', Fourth Ed., McGraw-Hill, N. Y., 1955, p. 96.

37. **Hinze, J. O.,** 'Turbulence', McGraw-Hill, N. Y., 1959, p. 179.

38. **Hjelmfelt, A. T., and Mockros, L. F.,** 'Motion of Discrete Particles In a Turbulent Fluid', Apl. Sci., Vol 16, 149, 1966.

39. **Han, L. S.,** 'Hydrodynamic Entrance Lengths For Incompressible Flow in Rectangular Ducts', J. Appl. Mech., Vol 27, 403, 1960.

40. **Bourke, P. J., Pulling, D. T., Gill, L. E., and Denton, W. H.,** 'The Measurement of Turbulent Velocity Fluctuations and Turbulent Temperature Fluctuations in the Supercritical Region by a Hot wire Anemometer and a Cold Wire Resistance Thermometer', Symp. on Heat Transfer and Fluid Dynamics of Near Critical Fluids, Paper No. 9, Inst. Mech. Eng. London, 1968.

41. **Fage, A. and Townend, H.,** 'An Examination of Turbulent Flow With an Ultramicroscope', Proc. Roy. Soc., Vol A135, 656, 1932.

Nomenclature

A   aperture diameter

a   wave propagation speed

b   particle diameter

c   speed of light

c_o vacuum speed of light

D   diameter of circular duct and length of side of square duct

d_1 depth of field of a lens

d_2 diffraction limited spot size of a focused beam

d_a distance between apertures A_1 and A_2

d_o diameter of coherence volume

d   distance between apertures A_1 and A_2

E   electric field intensity

f   focal length of lens

g   gravitational constant

h   diameter of region illuminated on photocathode

I_i incident beam intensity

I_{sc} scattered beam intensity

I_r reference beam intensity

i   photomultiplier current

j   an integer

L   length of laser cavity

ℓ_e turbulence macroscale

ℓ distance between photocathode and scattering volume

N   particle number density

n   index of refraction

$\hat{n}_i$ unit vector in direction of incident light

$\hat{n}_{sc}$ unit vector in direction of scattered light

q   fringe spacing

R	signal to noise ratio
Re	Reynolds number based on bulk velocity = $\bar{U}D/\eta$
Re_c	Reynolds number based on centerline velocity = $U_c D/\eta$
s	turbulence microsca/e
t	time
Tu	longitudinal turbulence intensity = u'/U_c
$\bar{U}$	average or bulk velocity
U_c	longitudinal centerline velocity
u	normalized axial coordinate in the focal region (Fig. 12-2)
u'	longitudinal turbulent velocity component
V_{sc}	scattering volume
$\vec{v}$	particle velocity
$\vec{v}_m$	maximum velocity detectable
$\vec{v}_r$	relative particle velocity
v_s	particle settling velocity
v	magnitude of velocity = $|\vec{V}|$
υ	normalized radial coordinate in the focal region (Fig. 12-2)
x	longitudinal distance from duct entrance
Δy	scattering volume dimension perpendicular to the direction of the velocity component measured
α	angle of coherence cone
γ	specific gravity
δ	scattering angle = $\phi - \theta$
η	kinematic viscosity = $\dfrac{\mu}{\rho}$
θ	angle between velocity vector and indicent light beam
λ	wave length
λ_i	wave length of incident light
λ_o	vacuum wave length of laser
λ_j	wave length for which resonance is attained
λ_p	wave length of incident light as seen by the particle
λ_{sc}	wave length of scattered light
μ	dynamic viscosity
ν_p	Doppler frequency
$\bar{\nu}_p$	average value of the Doppler frequency
$\Delta \nu_p$	band width of the Doppler spectrum at the half power points
ν_i	frequency of incident light
ν_j	frequency at which resonance is attained
ν_m	maximum frequency detectable
ν_o	frequency of laser

e*

ν_p frequency of incident light as seen by the particle

ν_{sc} frequency of scattered light

ρ density of fluid

σ scattering cross-section

ξ angle between velocity vector and scattered lightbeam

ϕ phase angle

Ω receiver optics acceptance angle $= d\ \phi$

Subscripts

i   refers to incident beam

j   an index indicating element j of a set

sc   refers to scattered beam

13

Operation and Application of Cooled Film Sensors for Measurements in High Temperature Gases

L. M. FINGERSON and A. M. AHMED

Thermo-Systems Inc. St. Paul, Minnesota and McGill University, Montreal, Canada

Summary

The cooled film sensor is a device permitting measurements in high temperature environments similar to those obtainable at normal temperatures with a hot wire anemometer. The limitations of the technique both in maximum environment conditions and accuracy are discussed. In addition, typical measurements and some special techniques that can be applied are presented. Optimum applications of the cooled film anemometer include environments where transient phenomena are to be measured and where the maximum heat transfer to the sensor (0.15 mm dia. by 1.5 mm long) is less than 10 watts. Up to 20 watts is possible for short term tests.

Introduction

The cooled film sensor is a device for making hot-wire-anemometry-type measurements in a high temperature environment. In the normal hot-wire or hot-film anemometer the temperature of the sensor must be above the environment temperature under conditions where convection dominates the heat transfer. The essential feature of the cooled film is the addition of a heat sink to permit the operation of the sensor below the environment temperature.

Since the introduction of the cooled film sensors (1), additional data has been collected on both operational details and applications. This paper is intended as a review of the work that has been done with cooled probes to date. From this information, a reasonable estimate can be made of the applicability of the cooled film probes to a particular measurement.

The potential of the cooled film sensors for fluid measurements would appear promising. They have many characteristics in common with hot-wire anemometry systems including small sensor size and high frequency response. This permits, ideally, an instantaneous measurement at a point in the fluid stream. In addition, it has the capability of making measurements in temperatures of several thousand degrees where few immersion instruments can survive.

Constant Temperature Anemometry with Wires, Films and Cooled Probes

The electronic control and data reduction technique for cooled film sensors are almost identical to that of the standard constant temperature hot wire or hot film anemometer. Figure 13-1 shows the basic components of a constant temperature anemometer system.

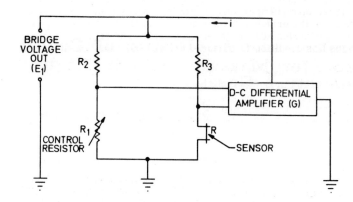

Fig. 13-1   Schematic diagram of constant temperature system

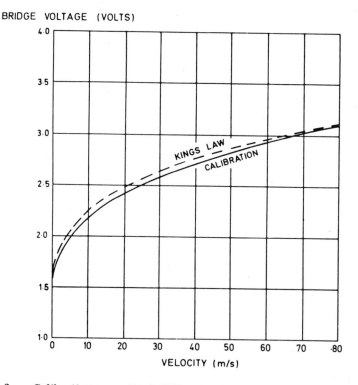

Fig. 13-2   Calibration curve for 0.0038 mm tungsten hot wire and comparison with King's law

The first requirement in the system of Figure 13-1 is that the sensor resistance changes with temperature. For maximum sensitivity, this change of resistance with temperature (temperature coefficient of resistance) should be high. The resistance of the bridge arms are set so that the bridge is in balance with the sensor transferring heat to the environment. The high gain feedback amplifier maintains this condition (a balanced bridge) but adjusting the current through the sensor. For example, as the environment velocity increases, more heat would be transferred between the sensor and its environment. To maintain the sensor temperature, the bridge system increases the current through the sensor. Therefore, the current required by the sensor is a direct measure of the heat transferred between the sensor and its environment. This heat transfer from the sensor (set and maintained at a constant average temperature by the bridge) is therefore the basic measurement.

Heat is transferred from the sensor by convection, radiation, and conduction. Similarly, the rate of heat transfer is affected by any property of the environment that influences heat transfer including temperature, velocity, pressure, composition, etc. In the normal application of anemometry, convection is the dominant mode of heat transfer and velocity is the only environment variable. Hence the term anemometer.

Limiting the heat transfer to convection, the heat transfer between the sensor and environment where velocity is the only variable, can be expressed approximately by what is commonly referred to as King's law (2):

$$P = I^2 R_s = (A + B \ \overline{V}) \quad (T_s - T) \tag{Eq. 13-1}$$

where: A, B = constants

$\quad\quad V$ = environment velocity

$\quad\quad T_s$ = sensor temperature

$\quad\quad T_\infty$ = environment temperature

Figure 13-2 shows a calibration curve of a fine hot-wire and the calculated curve using two calibration points (end points) and King's Law. Many heat transfer relations have been derived which are a significant improvement on King's Law. Still, when discussing hot-wire anemometry the simplicity of the relation in equation 13-1 makes it a useful reference.

Figure 13-3 shows two types of sensors commonly used for work in hot wire anemometry. The fine hot wire is the original type of sensor and still is widely used. The hot film (3), (4) is more recent and has advantages in many applications. It consists of a glass substrate with a thin metallic film on the surface. The glass substrate dominates the physical and thermal characteristics of the sensor while the metal film dominates the electrical characteristics.

Figure 13-4 shows the physical characteristics of a typical cooled film sensor and support and a diagram showing its operation. The entire right hand side of equation 13-1 is simply $- Q_E$ (negative since Q_E is shown as heat transfer to the sensor from the environment) in the Figure. Therefore, for an idealized hot film sensor without cooling:

$$P = - Q_E \tag{Eq. 13-2}$$

and for an idealized hot film sensor with cooling:

$$P = Q_C - Q_E \tag{Eq. 13-3}$$

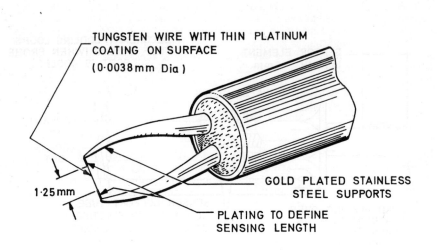

TUNGSTEN WIRE WITH THIN PLATINUM
COATING ON SURFACE
(0·0038mm Dia)

1·25mm

GOLD PLATED STAINLESS
STEEL SUPPORTS

PLATING TO DEFINE
SENSING LENGTH

Fig. 13-3a   Tungsten hot wire sensor and support needles - 0.00015" dia.
(0.0038 mm)

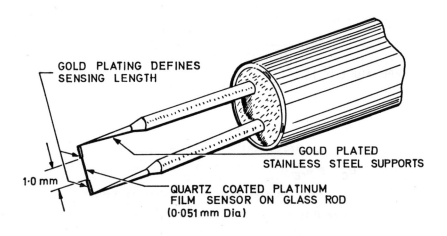

GOLD PLATING DEFINES
SENSING LENGTH

1·0 mm

GOLD PLATED
STAINLESS STEEL SUPPORTS

QUARTZ COATED PLATINUM
FILM SENSOR ON GLASS ROD
(0·051mm Dia)

b   Cylindrical hot film sensor and support needles - 0.002" dia.
(0.051 mm)

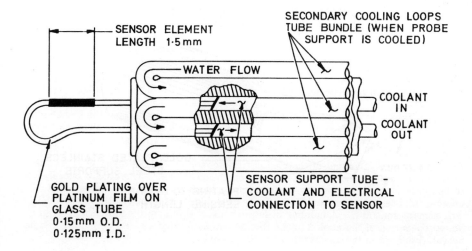

SECONDARY COOLING LOOPS
TUBE BUNDLE (WHEN PROBE
SUPPORT IS COOLED)

SENSOR ELEMENT
LENGTH 1·5mm

WATER FLOW

COOLANT
IN

COOLANT
OUT

GOLD PLATING OVER
PLATINUM FILM ON
GLASS TUBE
0·15mm O.D.
0·125mm I.D.

SENSOR SUPPORT TUBE -
COOLANT AND ELECTRICAL
CONNECTION TO SENSOR

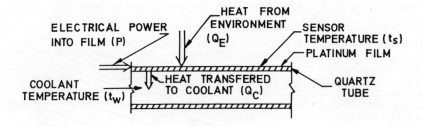

ELECTRICAL POWER
INTO FILM (P)

HEAT FROM
ENVIRONMENT
(Q_E)

SENSOR
TEMPERATURE (t_S)

PLATINUM FILM

COOLANT
TEMPERATURE (t_w)

HEAT TRANSFERED
TO COOLANT (Q_C)

QUARTZ
TUBE

$Q_C = U_C(t_S - t_w) = $ Constant

$U_C = $ Heat Transfer Coefficient, J/S-$^\circ$K

$Q_C = P + Q_E$

$Q_E = $ Heat Transfer From Environment to Sensor

Since P >0

$Q_C > Q_E$ For Proper Operations

Fig. 13-4   Cooled probe and fundamental heat transfer relation

where: P   = electrical power input to the sensor

Q_C = heat transferred from the sensor surface to the cooling fluid

Q_E = heat transferred from the environment to the sensor surface

Equation 13-3 gives the basic information on maximum environment conditions. Since P must be greater than zero, for proper operation:

$$Q_C > Q_E \qquad \text{(Eq. 13-4)}$$

The maximum heat transfer from the environment to the sensor is then equal to the cooling rate. On present sensors the practical upper limit for short term tests is 20 watts with 10 watts being realistic for continuous use in most types of environments. These figures are for the heat transfer rate in watts from the environment to the sensor surface area (0.15 mm dia. by 1.5 mm long). Frequency responses of up to 50 KHz can be attained (-3db point) using cooled film sensors.

An important requirement of the cooled film sensor is that the term Q_c remains constant, independent of external environment conditions. The circuit operates to maintain the average sensor surface temperature constant. If the entering cooling fluid temperature and flow rate is also constant, then ideally the term Q_c will remain constant. A number of factors affect this idealized situation but in actual operation of the cooled probe this assumption must usually be made. Some potential errors in the assumption are discussed later.

In a constant temperature, constant composition environment a calibration curve similar to that shown in Figure 13-2 could be plotted for a cooled probe. The operation and data reduction technique under these conditions are then essentially identical to those for a hot wire of similar diameter operated at constant temperature. The term Q_c can be handled like the free convection term is for a hot-wire.

Perhaps the most important difficulty with the cooled probes is that a high temperature environment seldom, if ever, satisfies the constant temperature condition. In addition composition changes are common due to different constituents, chemical reactions, or even ionization. In this sense measurements with cooled probes resemble more closely measurements in supersonic flows with hot wires. An important difference is that in supersonic flows the hot-wire can usually be operated very close to the environment temperature. This permits quite effective separation of velocity and temperature when two probes are used operating at different surface temperature. In high temperature gases this separation is much more difficult since the sensor cannot be operated close to the environment temperature. Other complexities in cooled probe systems are: the need to water cool the probe, increasing both cost and size; the need for water tight connections with no condensation that can cause electrical shorting; difficulties in inserting the probe in many high temperature environments; and higher power required from control circuitry. These are practical problems that are largely eliminated by proper design and operation of the system.

At high heat fluxes, the cooling fluid in the sensor will be turbulent to maintain the desired cooling rate. This lowers the signal-to-noise ratio of the system when compared with a normal hot wire, since the low frequency signals get transmitted through the tube to the sensitive film. Finally, the cooling also limits over heat ratios because for a given coolant temperature, the heat flux from the surface to the coolant is determined by the sensor operating temperature. Arbitrary selection of a sensor temperature can result in (a) this cooling rate being excessively high, so the cooling water boils or the sensor burns out or (b) the cooling rate,

Q_c, being less than maximum heat transfer from the environment to the sensor, Q_E. Under these conditions the circuit shuts off and no data is obtained until the inequality in equation 13-4 is again satisfied. The result is that it is the maximum expected heat flux, Q_E, that determines sensor operating temperature rather than a selected overheat ratio as in hot-wire anemometer operation.

Heat Transfer Correlation for Cooled Probes

For a cooled-film sensor placed normal to a high temperature fluid stream of low Mach number, the forced convective heat transfer to the film is a function of stream temperature, stream velocity and the fluid transport properties. For a stream composed of a binary mixture, the transport properties of the mixture are functions of the mixture ratio. Thus, a cooled-film anemometer may be calibrated to measure temperature, velocity and percentage composition of a binary mixture flow. Direct calibration is straightforward for measurements in flows where only one of the independent parameters is a variable, as discussed earlier for the common measurement of velocity in low-speed aerodynamics. For measurements in fluid streams where more than one of the independent parameters is a variable, such as in hypersonic wakes, mixing regions of jets of dissimilar fluids and/or of dissimilar temperatures, and diffusion flames, a direct calibration over the entire range of variables is often tedious and time consuming. For such cases interpretation of measured heat flux data by means of a more general, nevertheless accurate, correlation of the appropriate dimensionless groups involved is more appropriate.

In considering the nature of the cooled-film operation and its application for measurements in diffusion flames and hypersonic wakes, one may stipulate that the required heat transfer correlation must be valid for the following cases:

(a)   when the transfer of heat is from the environment to the sensor
       (i.e. $T_\infty > T_s$).

(b)   when the temperature difference between the sensor and the
       environment is large (i.e. $T_\infty/T_s > 2$).

(c)   when the environment is composed of flows of different
       gases and gas mixtures.

(d)   when the Reynolds number (based on sensor diameter)
       of the flow is low, (i.e. Re < 100).

It may be noted that conditions of very low Reynolds numbers, where free and forced convection may interact, also conditions of high Knudsen numbers where free molecular effects may be important, have been left out of the stipulated conditions.

Forced convective heat transfer involving cylinders has been extensively investigated. However none of the investigations, individually or all of them collectively, cover the entire range of conditions mentioned above (5). It must be emphasized that such correlations as that obtained by careful experimentation by Collis and Williams (6) for hot-wire work are not applicable to precise cooled-film work (when $T_s < T_\infty$). This is because of the different nature of dynamical dissimilarity with temperature loading between cases of heating and cooling (5). On the other hand, data obtained for the heating of cooled cylinders such as those by Churchill and Brier (7) are for Reynolds numbers above 300. A detailed discussion of the existing correlations has been presented in (5).

In the present investigation the flow conditions were simulated in a plasma-jet

(jet orifice diameter 12 cm.) The jet conditions were maintained such that at the points of heat transfer measurement (i.e. at the potential core of the jet, where the distribution of velocity, temperature and concentration are uniform) ionization was negligible and recombination was complete. By means of a cooled-film the maximum relative intensity of heat flux fluctuations was found to be less than 3%. If it is considered that the heat flux fluctuations are due only to velocity fluctuations, the error in heat transfer measurement will be less than 2% due to turbulence.

Constant temperature, quartz coated, cooled-films were used as the heat transfer surface. The film is obtained by a deposition of platinum of thickness 1000 - 2000 Å on a loop made on Vycor tube, 0.0152 cm O.D. and 0.0102 cm I.D. The sensitive section of the film is isolated by a heavy gold plating (0.013 - 0.025 mm thick) on the rest of the loop. The length of the sensing film is 0.103 cm and the thickness of its quartz coating is around 5000 Å. Along with the heat transfer measured by the cooled film, velocity and temperature were obtained by means of a carbon tipped pitot probe of orifice diameter 0.103 cm and a Pt - Pt 10% Rh thermocouple of bead diameter .127 cm respectively. Further details of experimental set-up and procedure may be found in (5). The variables and the variable ranges considered in the investigation are as follows:

a. Temperature loading. The range of jet temperature considered was 800°K to 1600°K, and the film temperature was varied in three steps between 350°K to 525°K. From this a temperature loading (T_∞/T_s) range of 1.5 to 4.5 was obtained.

b. Reynolds number. The range of Re based on cylinder diameter was 4 to 80.

c. Flow composition. The plasma-jet was composed of He, N_2 and mixtures of He - N_2, N_2 - CO_2. Two mixture ratios were considered for each mixture.

The true jet temperature was obtained from the thermocouple temperature by applying correction for radiation and conduction errors. Transport property values of the gas species and specie mixtures for data analysis were calculated from the expressions collected in (8).

In the course of data analysis the following points were noted:

a. Consideration of the film temperature $(T_f = \dfrac{T_\infty + T_s}{2})$ for the evaluation of fluid properties in the dimensionless parameters Nusselt number and Reynolds number, was not sufficient to eliminate the temperature loading effect. The residual effect caused a decrease in Nusselt number with increased temperature loading at a particular Re for the present case of heating of cylinders.

b. Replacement of the usual temperature ratio in the temperature loading factor by a kinematic viscosity ratio enabled a unique correlation to be derived for flows composed of gas species whose transport property value variations with temperature are different. This conclusion is supported by arguments presented in (9) for hot wires.

c. The expected slight influence of the small variation of Prandtl number (because of the consideration of different flow species and specie mixtures and also because of variation of temperature), could not be discerned.

d.   The Re_f dependency of Nu_f was found to be different from that according to King's Law.

e.   A discontinuity in the heat transfer curve was noted between Re_f = 40 and Re_f = 55.   Unfortunately, no data were collected between these values of Re_f and no specific investigation was carried out to determine a change in the flow features, (viz. onset of eddy shedding) in this range.   For the present, data collected in the Re_f range below Re_f = 40 was considered for correlation purpose.

In view of the above discussion, the following form of correlation was considered:

$$Nu_f \left(\nu_\infty / \nu_f \right)^n = C + D \, Re_f^{\ m}$$

The constants n, m, C and D evaluated by the least square method were found to be as follows:

Re_f	n	m	C	D
4 - 40	.15	.45	.2068	.4966

Figure 13.5 shows the effectiveness of this relation in correlating the entire body of data below Re_f = 40.   The rms deviation considering this range of data was 0924.

Finally 13-6 compares values of Nu_f calculated from some of the correlations obtained for heat transfer from heated cylinders with values calculated from the present correlation.   The evaluation is for an identical condition of heat transfer to a cooled cylinder with T_s = 400°K, T_∞ = 1200°K and the flow composed of N_2. Even considering the wide discrepancies in values calculated from correlations obtained for heated cylinders only, the error involved in using them to analyse heat transfer to cooled cylinders is quite apparent.

Tests in Severe Environments

The maximum environment capabilities of the cooled film probe have been expressed in terms of heat transfer rates from the environment to the sensor.   To convert this to temperature and velocity requires an accurate heat transfer relation or tests where the conditions are well known.   Although the following data does not completely satisfy either criteria, it does give some indication of the capability of the cooled film sensors.

Figure 13-7 shows a traverse across the tip of an acetylene torch for two distances from the tip.   The inside diameter of the tip is 3.8 mm and maximum heat flux to the sensor is 16 watts.   Referring to Figure 13-7, the traverse was made from left to right.   The sensor did shift in resistance during each traverse, as shown by the failure of the points on the right to approach closer to the abscissa.   A single traverse took approximately five minutes.   The 16 watts represents a heat transfer rate to the 0.15 mm dia. sensor of 2.66 KW/cm^2.

Reference (10) is another application where the cooled film sensors were exposed to a severe environment.   The cooled sensors were used in a combustor that burned ethanol and liquid oxygen at an average chamber pressure of 178 psia. Pressure oscillations of ±15 per cent were sustained at 1190 cps with a siren mounted directly downstream of the exhaust nozzle.   Under test conditions the average environment temperature was calculated to be 1900°K and the maximum velocity (measured from streak photographs) about 110 m/second.   Velocity

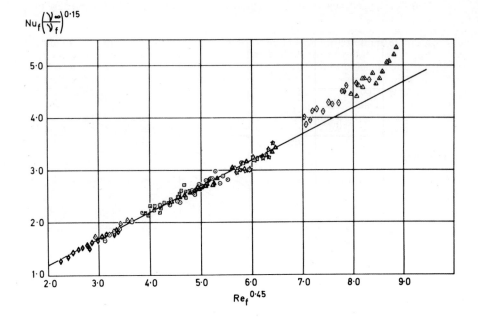

Flow	T K	T_S K	Symbol
Nitrogen	852 -1660	361 -496	▲
Helium	803 - 1360	387 - 532	♦
He 40% by vol. N_2 60% by vol.	900 -1269	361 - 496	⊙
He 77.5% by vol. N_2 22.5% by vol.	900 - 1270	387 - 532	⊡
He 42% by vol. CO_2 58% by vol.	701 -1088	342 -465	◈
He 93.5% by vol. CO_2 6.5% by vol.	702 - 1090	342 - 465	◊
N_2 50% by vol. CO_2 50% by vol.	703 - 1278	367 - 512	♦
N_2 30% by vol. CO_2 70% by vol.	703 - 1277	367 - 512	▲

Fig. 13-5 $Nu_m (\nu_{oo}/\nu_m)^{.15}$ vs $Re_m^{.45}$ showing all heat transfer data for various species and specie Mixtures and for various temperature loadings uniquely correlated by the relation $Nu_m(\nu_{oo}/\nu_m)^{.15} = .2068 + .4966\ Re_m^{.45}$ in the Re_m range of 5 to 40.

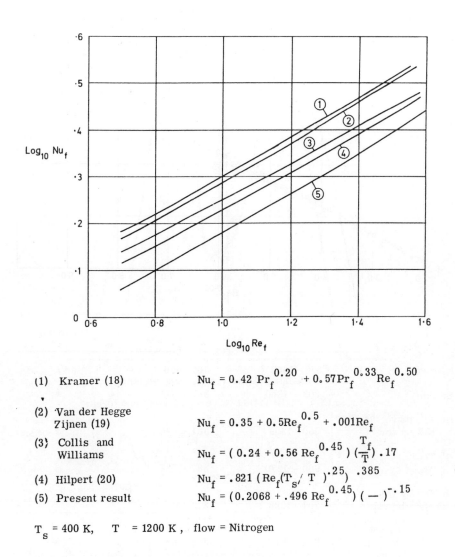

(1) Kramer (18) $\qquad$ $Nu_f = 0.42\,Pr_f^{0.20} + 0.57Pr_f^{0.33}Re_f^{0.50}$

(2) Van der Hegge
     Zijnen (19) $\qquad$ $Nu_f = 0.35 + 0.5Re_f^{0.5} + .001Re_f$

(3) Collis and
     Williams $\qquad$ $Nu_f = (\,0.24 + 0.56\,Re_f^{0.45}\,)\,(\frac{T_f}{T})\,.17$

(4) Hilpert (20) $\qquad$ $Nu_f = .821\,(\,Re_f(T_s/\,T\,)^{.25})\,^{.385}$

(5) Present result $\qquad$ $Nu_f = (0.2068 + .496\,Re_f^{0.45})\,(-\,)^{-.15}$

$T_s = 400\ K,\quad T = 1200\ K,\quad flow = Nitrogen$

Fig. 13-6 $\qquad$ Comparison of present correlation for forced convective heat
transfer to cooled cylinders in heated cross-flow with previous
correlations for heat transfer from heated cylinders in ambient or
near-ambient cross-flow.

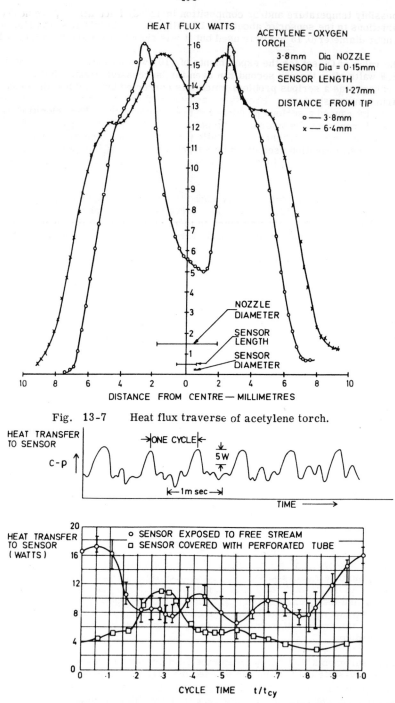

Fig. 13-7   Heat flux traverse of acetylene torch.

Fig. 13-8   Typical heat-flux sensor output and average heat flux for one cycle of oscillation. (reprinted from (10)

(possibly temperature and/or composition included) fluctuations gave heat flux variations to the sensor of about 6 to 17 watts (10). In this case the standard sensor diameter (0.15 mm) was used but it was shorter than standard length 1.0 mm.

The value of Q_c set for the experiments of (10) was 20 watts, which went down to 18.8 watts after the one second run even for 'successful' runs. Initially, sensor breakage was a serious problem which was corrected by shielding the sensor during engine start-up. Even then, as reported in (10), sensor stability and longevity caused a serious problem for the experiments. The velocities calculated from cooled sensor data did not agree with the streak photographs. As pointed out in the reference, no detailed calibration was deemed practical so the heat transfer relation used could be suspect, in addition to other sources of error. The maximum Reynolds number of 580 is well beyond the calibration data of Figure 13-5.

Figure 13-8 shows a typical set of data from the cooled sensor when exposed to the test chamber of (10). The lower curve is for the sensor when shielded on the inlet side. This data was taken to identify the reverse flow point, since a cylindrical sensor cannot differentiate flow direction.

The environment of (10) would seem to be at the upper heat flux limit for useful data from cooled sensors. Since many environments exceed these conditions (e.g. hydrogen oxygen combustors, plasmas, etc.) there is a need to extend the range of cooled sensors to higher temperatures. Some efforts have been made in this direction (11) which led to the present sensor design using Vycor rather than the original Pyrex (1). Although further improvement is always possible, the difficulty of cooling a small tube adequately for survival seems to preclude a significant improvement. Going to larger tubes is not generally desirable since characteristics such as frequency response and spatial resolution would be compromised.

Accuracies With Cooled Probes

Experimental data on the accuracy of the cooled probes is limited. Reference (11) discusses several potential sources of error and gives calculated estimates of the effects while (12) gives details on the error in the two-sensor technique. The consistency of the calibration data in this paper indicates the kind of reproducibility that can be expected for mean measurements.

The primary source of error is in the assumption that the heat transfer from the sensor surface to the cooling fluid, Q_c, is constant during external environment changes. One source of error is the exposed part of the sensor tube between the protective cooling jacket and the 'sensitive' portion of the sensor. In a high temperature environment the water temperature will rise in this passage, while during the tare reading of Q_c there would be no temperature rise. Another cause of error is the re-distribution of sensor surface temperature between the tare reading and the reading in the environment. Some measurements of sensor surface temperature distribution are given in (12). For the calculated conditions in (11), the error estimate for all the above factors was 5.2 per cent on the heat flux reading.

In measurements with hot-wire and hot-film probes, an assumption is made that the steady-state calibration can be used directly to interpret unsteady-state data. This seems valid for the very fine hot wires used near atmospheric temperature and pressure conditions. For the larger cooled films at high Reynolds numbers,

500

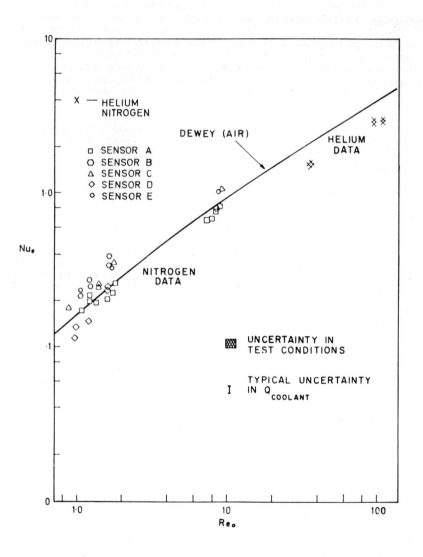

Fig. 13-9   Nusselt-Reynolds number calibration data. (reprinted from (14)

flow separation effects around the sensor could invalidate the assumption. In addition, the complex nature of the cooled film can cause transient errors due to changes in surface temperature distribution both longitudinally and radially under varying flow conditions.

Applications of Cooled Film Sensors

Much of the data given above has been concerned with the problems associated with cooled film sensors. It is important to recognise these problems before undertaking measurements. At the same time, the unique capabilities of the cooled sensors make them not only a valuable tool, but sometimes the only tool that can give the required data in a given situation.

The measurements in a rocket chamber have been discussed as an example of the upper limit of conditions where the cooled films are applicable. Other applications that data are available on are:

a.   Measurements of a hypersonic boundary layer

b.   Measurements in the wake of a hypersonic projectile

Other applications are certainly feasible and in fact have been made, but no published data is available.

Hypersonic boundary layer measurements were made by McCroskey, *et al* (13), (14). Nominal test conditions in the nitrogen tunnel were: $T_{01} = 2000°K$, $P_{01} = 135 - 340$ atm, $M_\infty = 23 - 26$, and Re/cm = 2,950 - 5,900. Tests in Helium were run at $T_{01} = 297°K$, $P_{01} = 15.3$ atm, $M_\infty = 16.5$, and Re/cm = 47,200 (15) with hot wires. Although there is some scatter, most of it is between sensors and the slope for all sensors agrees with Dewey's results.

In this work a pitot probe, a cooled film probe, and the recovery temperature of a hot wire were used to calculate the variables of interest such as velocity, density, and pressure near the leading edge of a sharp flat plate. In the measurements with cooled probes, one of the problems that came up was inadequate resolution. Even though the total temperature of the environment was high, the total heat flux to the probe was 0.1 to 0.5 watts. Therefore, to increase sensitivity and lower dependence on entering coolant temperature, nitrogen was used for cooling rather than water. This increased resolution by permitting a much higher temperature difference between sensor surface and coolant, while keeping the total power dissipation to the coolant low.

An extensive investigation of turbulence characteristics of hypersonic wakes by means of cooled-film anemometers is being carried out at the Canadian Armament Research and Development Establishment at Val Cartier, Quebec (12), (16), (17). Owing to the high temperature encountered in the near wake region of hypersonic projectiles, the application of the cooled-film technique appears appropriate. Further, cooled-films have proved to be sufficiently robust to survive the hypersonic range environment at least for a sufficient length of time to record a signal of several thousand body diameters in duration (15).

The above experiments are performed in the CARDE Hypersonic Range No. 5 which consists of a light gas gun with a 102 mm barrel capable of launching projectiles into a depressurized tank of 122 m length at velocities in excess of 415 m/s (17). Two constant-temperature cooled-film sensors with different sensor surface temperatures, positioned several thousandths' of a centimeter apart are located near the flight axis of the projectile, (16). The cooled film anemometer bridge voltage is recorded by means of oscilloscopes viewed by Wollensak Fastax cameras.

The two cooled film sensors are operated at two different surface temperatures to attempt the separation of environment temperature and velocity. It is important that the temperature difference between sensors be large to optimize the accuracy using this technique (11), (12). At the same time, it is best to have both anemometer circuits operating at about the same power level for nearly equivalent frequency response and sensitivity. One way to satisfy these criteria is to use water as the coolant for the sensor with low surface temperature and an oil (such as Fluorolube FS or Silicon Oil 704) for the sensor with high surface temperature (12). The method of reduction of recorded voltage data in terms of velocity and temperature distribution in the wake, to determine their power spectral density functions has been shown in (12).

Conclusions

From the data presented, some tentative conclusions can be drawn for cooled film sensors presently available:

The maximum heat fluxes from the environment to the sensor are:

a. About 10 watts for good sensor stability and longevity

b. Up to 20 watts maximum with decreasing stability at increasing heat fluxes.

The use of a coolant other than water is often desirable for a given measurement situation.

Accuracies of better than ± five per cent on heat flux are probably not possible unless the calibration covers a range that includes the test conditions exactly.

The heat transfer correlation presented indicates that the cooled sensors can be calibrated in high temperature environments. Of particular interest is the successful use of a transport property (kinematic viscosity) to correlate different compositions.

The cooled film sensor greatly extends the temperature range of the hot-wire or hot-film anemometer. It retains many of the important features such as small size, high frequency response, and high resolution which make the hot-wire anemometer a valuable tool in fluid mechanics research. Also, like the hot wire, it has definite limitations in both accuracy and environment conditions which must be recognized before measurements are attempted.

References

1. Fingerson, L. M., 'A Heat Flux Probe for Measurements in High Temperature Gases,' Ph. D. Thesis, Univ. of Minnesota, 1961.

2. King, L. V., 'On the Convection of Heat from Small Cylinders in a Stream of Fluid: Determination of the Convective Constants of Small Platinum Wires with Applications to Hot-Wire Anemometry,' Proc. Roy. Soc. (London), Vol., 214A, No. 14, 1914, p. 373.

3. Ling, S. L., and Hubbard, P. G., 'The Hot-Film Anemometer A New
    Device for Fluid Mechanics Research,' Jour. Aero. Sci., Vol. 23, 1956,
    p. 890.

4. Lowell, Herman H., 'Response of Two-Material Laminated Cylinders to
    Simple Harmonic Environment Temperature Change,' Jour. Appl. Phys.
    Vol. 24, No. 12, 1953, p. 1473.

5. Ahmed, A. M., 'Forced Convective Heat Transfer to Cooled Cylinders at
    Low Reynolds Numbers and With Large Temperature Difference,' McGill
    MERL. T. N. 67-5.

6. Collis, D. C., Williams, M. J., 'Two Dimensional Convection from Heated
    Wires at Low Reynolds Numbers,' J. of Fluid Mech. Vol. 6, 1959, p. 357.

7. Churchill, S. W., Brier, J. C., 'Convective Heat Transfer from a Gas
    Stream at High Temperature to a Circular Cylinder Normal to the Flow,'
    Chem. Eng. Progr. Symposium Series, No. 17, 51, 57, 1955.

8. Brokaw, R. S., 'Alignment Charts for Transport Properties Viscosity,
    Thermal Conductivity and Diffusion Coefficients for Nonpolar Gases and
    Gas Mixtures at Low Density,' NASA TR-R81.

9. Davies, P. O. A. L., and Fisher, M. J., 'Heat Transfer from Electrically
    Heated Cylinders,' Proc. of the Royal Society, A, Vol. 280, 1964, pp. 486-527.

10. Povinelli, Frederick P., and Ingebo, Robert D., 'Evaluation of a Thin-Film,
    Heat-Flux Probe for Measuring Gas Velocities in an Unstable Rocket Com-
    bustor,' NASA Tech. Mem. TM X-1333, Feb., 1967.

11. Fingerson, L. M., 'Research on the Development and Evaluation of a Two-
    Sensor Enthalpy Probe,' Aerospace Res. Lab. Rep. ARL 64-161, Oct., 1964.

12. Ellington, D., and Trottier, G., 'Some Observations on the Application of
    Cooled-Film Anemometry to the Study of the Turbulent Characteristics of
    Hypersonic Wakes,' Canadian Armament Research and Development Estab-
    lishment Report CARDE T. N. 1773/67, Sept. 1967.

13. McCroskey, W. J., Bogdonoff, S. M., and McDougall, J. G., 'An Experi-
    mental Model for the Leading Edge of a Sharp Flat Plate in Rarefied Hyper-
    sonic Flow,' AIAA Paper 66-31, 1966.

14. McCroskey, W. J., 'A new Probe for Hot-Wire Anemometry at High Temp-
    erature,' Princeton Gas Dynamics Lab. Int. Mem. 7, Aug. 1965.

15. Dewey, C. F., 'Hot Wire Measurements in Low Reynolds Number Hyper-
    sonic Flows,' J. ARS, Vol. 31, No. 12, Dec. 1961, p. 1709.

16. Trottier, G., Ahmed, A. M., Ellington, D., 'Cooled-Film Anemometer
    Measurements in the Hypersonic Wake,' CARDE TN 1720/66, May, 1966.

17. Staff of Aerophysics Wing - Compiled by D. Heckman, 'Re-Entry Physics
    Research Program on Turbulent Wakes,' CARDE TN 1741/67, Jan. 1967.

18. Kramer, H., Physics, Vol. 12, no. 2-3, 61, 1946.

19. Van der Hegge Zijnen, B. G., Appl. Sci. Research A, Vol. 6, 129, 1956.

20. **Hilpert, R.**, Forsch, Gebiete Ingenieurw., 4, 215, 1933.

Nomenclature

A, B, C, D	=	constants
d	=	sensor diameter
I	=	current in sensor
M	=	Mach number
m, n	=	constants
P	=	electrical power input to sensor
Q_c	=	heat transferred from sensor surface to cooling fluid
Q_E	=	heat transferred from environment to sensor surface
Re	=	Reynolds number (Vd/ν)
R_s	=	sensor operating resistance
t	=	temperature
T	=	absolute temperature
V	=	environment velocity
ν	=	kinematic viscosity

Subscripts:

s	=	sensor surface
f	=	arithmetic mean (when referring to fluid properties, signifies they are evaluated at the arithmetic mean temperature (e.g. $T_f = \dfrac{T_\infty + T_s}{2}$
∞	=	free stream

Index

g*